CURRENT TOPICS IN

DEVELOPMENTAL BIOLOGY

VOLUME 15

NEURAL DEVELOPMENT
PART I

Emergence of Specificity in Neural Histogenesis

CONTRIBUTORS

MARTIN BERRY

IRA B. BLACK

MARIANNE E. BRONNER-FRASER

J. A. CAMPOS-ORTEGA

ALAN M. COHEN

KEVIN CONWAY

JONATHAN COOKE

W. M. COWAN

KATHARINE FEIOCK

CHRISTINE GALL

MARGARET HOLLYDAY

R. KEVIN HUNT

K. KISHI

GARY LYNCH

E. R. MACAGNO

PATRICIA McCONNELL

JACQUES MALLET

PAUL H. PATTERSON

LAURI SAXÉN

JOBST SIEVERS

B. B. STANFIELD

CURRENT TOPICS IN
DEVELOPMENTAL BIOLOGY

EDITED BY

A. A. MOSCONA

DEPARTMENTS OF BIOLOGY AND PATHOLOGY
THE UNIVERSITY OF CHICAGO
CHICAGO, ILLINOIS

ALBERTO MONROY

STAZIONE ZOOLOGICA
NAPLES, ITALY

VOLUME 15
NEURAL DEVELOPMENT
PART I

Emergence of Specificity in Neural Histogenesis

VOLUME EDITOR

R. KEVIN HUNT

THOMAS C. JENKINS DEPARTMENT OF BIOPHYSICS
THE JOHNS HOPKINS UNIVERSITY
BALTIMORE, MARYLAND

1980

ACADEMIC PRESS

A Subsidiary of Harcourt Brace Jovanovich, Publishers

New York   London   Toronto   Sydney   San Francisco

ACADEMIC PRESS, INC.
111 Fifth Avenue, New York, New York 10003

United Kingdom Edition published by
ACADEMIC PRESS, INC. (LONDON) LTD.
24/28 Oval Road, London NW1 7DX

LIBRARY OF CONGRESS CATALOG CARD NUMBER: 66–28604

ISBN 0–12–153115–5

PRINTED IN THE UNITED STATES OF AMERICA

80 81 82 83   9 8 7 6 5 4 3 2 1

CONTENTS

List of Contributors   ix
Preface   xi

CHAPTER 1.   The Neural Crest: What Can It Tell Us about Cell Migration
and Determination?
MARIANNE E. BRONNER-FRASER AND ALAN M. COHEN

I.   Introduction   1
II.   Control of Neural Crest Migration and Localization   4
III.   Neural Crest Differentiation   15
IV.   Conclusion   21
References   23

CHAPTER 2.   Developmental Regulation of Neurotransmitter Phenotype
IRA B. BLACK AND PAUL H. PATTERSON

I.   Introduction   27
II.   The Neural Crest   28
III.   Neural Crest Migration   29
IV.   Initial Phenotypic Expression   31
V.   Change in Phenotype during Development   33
VI.   Postnatal Development and Transsynaptic Regulation   36
References   38

CHAPTER 3.   Biochemistry and Immunology of Neurological Mutants
in the Mouse
JACQUES MALLET

I.   Introduction   41
II.   The Cerebellum and Some of Its Mutants   42
III.   Neurotransmission   45
IV.   Attempts to Identify Components Characteristic of
Neuronal Cell Types   52
V.   Conclusions   61
References   62

CHAPTER 4.   Dendritic Growth and the Control of Neuronal Form
             MARTIN BERRY, PATRICIA MCCONNELL, AND
             JOBST SIEVERS

    I.   Introduction   67
   II.   Dendritic Growth Cones and Filopodia   68
  III.   Possible Forms of Interaction between Axons and Dendrites
         during Development   71
   IV.   Quantitative Analysis of Dendritic Growth   75
    V.   Purkinje Cell Dendritic Growth   77
   VI.   Influence of Functional Activity on Dendritic Growth...................   91
  VII.   Remodeling of the Mature Dendritic Tree   93
 VIII.   Conclusion   95
         References   96

CHAPTER 5.   The Development of the Dentate Gyrus
             W. M. COWAN, B. B. STANFIELD, AND K. KISHI

    I.   Introduction   103
   II.   The Morphology of the Dentate Gyrus in the Rat and Mouse   104
  III.   The Development of the Dentate Gyrus   115
   IV.   Conclusions and Future Perspectives.................................   152
         References   154

CHAPTER 6.   The Regulation of Fiber Growth and Synaptogenesis in the
             Developing Hippocampus
             CHRISTINE GALL AND GARY LYNCH

    I.   Introduction   159
   II.   Regulation of the Size of a Developing Afferent Field   160
  III.   Regulation of Synaptogenesis within the Target Region   169
   IV.   The Later Stages of Development   171
         References   179

CHAPTER 7.   Motoneuron Histogenesis and the Development of
             Limb Innervation
             MARGARET HOLLYDAY

    I.   Introduction   181
   II.   Spinal Motoneurons and the Muscles of the Limbs   182
  III.   Development of the Lateral Motor Column   189
   IV.   Development of Limb Innervation   194
    V.   Experimental Manipulations of Developing Limb Innervation   200
   VI.   Developmental Mechanisms to Account for
         Experimental Observations   209
         References   212

CHAPTER 8.   Polyclones and Patterns in Growing *Xenopus* Eye
             KEVIN CONWAY, KATHARINE FEIOCK, AND
             R. KEVIN HUNT

    I.   Introduction 217
   II.   Polyclone Patterns in Pigment Retinal Epithelium 245
  III.   Iris, Choroid, and Neural Retina 264
   IV.   Retinotectal Patterns 273
    V.   Some Unanticipated Results 300
   VI.   Conclusion 307
         References 313

CHAPTER 9.   Genetic Approaches to Invertebrate Neurogenesis
             E. R. MACAGNO

    I.   Introduction 319
   II.   Review of Genetic Approaches 321
  III.   Constancy and Variability of Neuronal Phenotype in
         Isogenic Organisms 324
   IV.   Developmental Interactions between the Compound Eye
         and Optic Lobes 332
    V.   The Formation of Sensory Nerve Projections in Homeotic Mutants 336
   VI.   Summary and Conclusions 342
         References 343

CHAPTER 10.   On Compound Eye Development in *Drosophila melanogaster*
              J. A. CAMPOS-ORTEGA

    I.   Introduction 347
   II.   The Morphology of the Compound Eye 349
  III.   The Embryonic and Larval Development of the Compound Eye 350
   IV.   Pattern of Mitosis in Compound Eye Development 353
    V.   Early Cell Lineages 358
   VI.   Late Cell Lineages 360
  VII.   Genetic Analysis of Compound Eye Morphogenesis 363
 VIII.   Concluding Remarks 369
         References 370

CHAPTER 11.   Early Organization of the Central Nervous System:
              Form and Pattern
              JONATHAN COOKE

    I.   Introduction 373
   II.   The Spatial Pattern of Brain Parts: Field Properties in the
         Plane of the Primitive Neuroepithelium/Inducing Mesoderm 376
  III.   The Radial (Ependymal → Pial) Structure within Brain Parts:
         Cell Birthday and Organization over the Primitive Epithelium 392

IV. Fiber Tracts: The Plan of Connectivity between Centers 399
    References 404

CHAPTER 12.   Neural Induction: Past, Present, and Future
               LAURI SAXÉN

  I. Past: Biological Framework for Induction 409
 II. Present: Chemical Nature and Mode of Transmission of the
     Signal Substances 413
III. Future: Toward Molecular Mechanisms 415
     References 417

Index 419
Contents of Previous Volumes 423

LIST OF CONTRIBUTORS

Numbers in parentheses indicate the pages on which the authors' contributions begin.

MARTIN BERRY, *Department of Anatomy, Medical School, University of Birmingham, Birmingham B15 2TJ, England* (67)

IRA B. BLACK, *Laboratory of Developmental Neurology, Department of Neurology, Cornell University Medical College, New York, New York 10021* (27)

MARIANNE E. BRONNER-FRASER,* *Thomas C. Jenkins Department of Biophysics, The Johns Hopkins University, Baltimore, Maryland 21218* (1)

J. A. CAMPOS-ORTEGA, *Institut für Biologie III, Albert Ludwigs-Universität, 7800 Freiburg im Breisgau, Federal Republic of Germany* (347)

ALAN M. COHEN,† *Department of Cell Biology and Anatomy, The Johns Hopkins University School of Medicine, Baltimore, Maryland 21205* (1)

KEVIN CONWAY, *Thomas C. Jenkins Department of Biophysics, The Johns Hopkins University, Baltimore, Maryland 21218* (217)

JONATHAN COOKE, *Division of Developmental Biology, National Institute for Medical Research, Mill Hill, London NW7 1AA, England* (373)

W. M. COWAN,‡ *Department of Anatomy and Neurobiology, Washington University School of Medicine, St. Louis, Missouri 63110* (103)

KATHARINE FEIOCK, *Thomas C. Jenkins Department of Biophysics, The Johns Hopkins University, Baltimore, Maryland 21218* (217)

* Present address: Department of Physiology, California College of Medicine, University of California, Irvine, California 91719.

† Present address: Department of Anatomy and Neurobiology, Washington University School of Medicine, St. Louis, Missouri 63110.

‡ Present address: The Salk Institute for Biological Studies, P.O. Box 85800, San Diego, California 92138.

CHRISTINE GALL,* *Department of Psychobiology, University of California, Irvine, California 91717* (159)

MARGARET HOLLYDAY, *Department of Pharmacological and Physiological Sciences, The University of Chicago, Chicago, Illinois 60637* (181)

R. KEVIN HUNT, *Thomas C. Jenkins Department of Biophysics, The Johns Hopkins University, Baltimore, Maryland 21218* (217)

K. KISHI, *Department of Anatomy and Neurobiology, Washington University School of Medicine, St. Louis, Missouri 63110* (103)

GARY LYNCH, *Department of Psychobiology, University of California, Irvine, California 91717* (159)

E. R. MACAGNO, *Department of Biological Sciences, Columbia University, New York, New York 10027* (319)

PATRICIA McCONNELL, *Netherlands Institute for Brain Research, Ijdijk 28, Amsterdam, The Netherlands* (67)

JACQUES MALLET, *Service de Neurobiologie, Département de Biologie Moléculaire, Institut Pasteur, 28 Rue du Docteur Roux, 75724, Paris Cedex 15, France* (41)

PAUL H. PATTERSON, *Department of Neurobiology, Harvard Medical School, Boston, Massachusetts 02115* (27)

LAURI SAXÉN, *Department of Pathology, University of Helsinki, Helsinki, Finland* (409)

JOBST SIEVERS, *Department of Neuroanatomy, University of Hamburg, D-2000 Hamburg 20, Federal Republic of Germany* (67)

B. B. STANFIELD,† *Department of Anatomy and Neurobiology, Washington University School of Medicine, St. Louis, Missouri 63110* (103)

* Present address: Department of Neurology, School of Medicine, State University of New York at Stony Brook, Long Island, New York 11794

† Present address: The Salk Institute for Biological Studies, P.O. Box 85800, San Diego, California 92138.

PREFACE

In the summer of 1977, the Editors of *Current Topics in Developmental Biology* suggested a special project on neural development. The hope was for a series of essays that would both evolve naturally from the past traditions of *Current Topics in Developmental Biology* and also would stand as a self-contained set of volumes offering a broad overview of neurogenesis. In the years of planning and production, the project has grown to three volumes. The present collection, "Emergence of Specificity in Neural Histogenesis," is the first of these three books. Yet, while the project has grown in scope and a number of additional contributors have been added to keep abreast of recent developments, the principal reasons for the volumes have not changed.

Developmental neurobiology has grown in leaps and bounds over the past decade. Findings from the developing nervous system have begun to inform on general issues of embryonic development and ought to be shared with the general community of developmental biologists. At the same time, as neuroscience has grown into a large interdisciplinary area of scholarship, the need of developmental neurobiologists for a continuing dialog with other members of the embryological community is equally great. Finally, although a number of timely textbooks have appeared in the area, no broad collection of essays on neural development was then available.

Our aim in these volumes has been to present a broad panoramic view of neural development, from the earliest stages of neural induction through the latest stages of physiological maturation. We have tried, as well, to represent a broad range of viewpoints. Inevitably, some topics have been slighted. If any overt prejudice has crept into the organization of these volumes, it is the belief that most of the major questions of neural development will ultimately be answered on the molecular level; but those molecular answers will only be forthcoming in studies that respect the cellular organization of the nervous system and that yoke molecular approaches with careful anatomical and physiological characterizations.

We are deeply indebted to the staff of Academic Press for their flexibility in scheduling the production of these volumes. The willingness of Academic Press to bend to meet the busy schedules of our contributors, and to make adjustments for chapters on areas that grew in prominence during the period of production, made my task much more enjoyable. Finally, I would like to thank the contributors themselves, who rose to the occasion and who have given the volumes what enduring value they have.

More than 30 years ago, in a classic article, "Differentiation and Growth of Nerve Cells and Fibers," Professor Jean Piatt observed that if the study of neural development was to have a future, that future lay in drawing together workers from areas as diverse as biophysics, neurophysiology, neuroanatomy, and experimental embryology. If the present volume makes any single statement, it is surely that Professor Piatt's vision of the future has been realized.

R. Kevin Hunt

CURRENT TOPICS IN

DEVELOPMENTAL BIOLOGY

VOLUME 15

NEURAL DEVELOPMENT
PART I

Emergence of Specificity in Neural Histogenesis

CHAPTER 1

THE NEURAL CREST: WHAT CAN IT TELL US ABOUT CELL MIGRATION AND DETERMINATION?

*Marianne E. Bronner-Fraser**

THOMAS C. JENKINS DEPARTMENT OF BIOPHYSICS
THE JOHNS HOPKINS UNIVERSITY
BALTIMORE, MARYLAND

and Alan M. Cohen†

DEPARTMENT OF CELL BIOLOGY AND ANATOMY
THE JOHNS HOPKINS UNIVERSITY SCHOOL OF MEDICINE
BALTIMORE, MARYLAND

I.	Introduction	1
II.	Control of Neural Crest Migration and Localization	4
III.	Neural Crest Differentiation	15
IV.	Conclusion	21
	References	23

I. Introduction

Of all vertebrate structures, the nervous system has perhaps the greatest cellular diversification and complexity of organization. The study of developmental neurobiology, therefore, sharply probes the central issue of embryogenesis; i.e., how does a complex system arise from a single cell? During development, ectodermal tissue becomes determined along neuronal lines via contact or "primary induction" from the roof of the archenteron (Mangold, 1933; Spemann, 1938). A major problem is how the morphologically indistinguishable stem cells of the neuroectoderm become progressively determined along divergent developmental lines such that they give rise to a myriad of cell types in the mature nervous system. Another question posed by this system is how the cells migrate to their final locations and become organized in precise spatial arrays. Once the pattern is composed, what mechanisms govern the establishment of the proper con-

---

* Present address: Department of Physiology, California College of Medicine, University of California at Irvine, Irvine, California.

† Present address: Department of Anatomy and Neurobiology, Washington University School of Medicine, St. Louis, Missouri.

*CURRENT TOPICS IN
DEVELOPMENTAL BIOLOGY, Vol. 15*

nections between neurons and other neurons, as well as between neurons and their target organs?

The vertebrate neural crest, which is the anlage of the peripheral nervous system, has become a popular subset of neural development for the analysis of these problems. The neural crest arises from the neuroectoderm and migrates extensively along well-defined pathways. The crest gives rise to diverse and numerous derivatives including sensory and autonomic ganglia, Schwann sheath cells, chromaffin cells, melanocytes, cranial cartilage, and many others (Weston, 1970). Unlike most of the central nervous system, the neural crest is readily accessible to surgical and biochemical manipulations during both initial and certain later stages in its development. Because of the temporally and spatially patterned movements which characterize neural crest migration and the diversity of crest derivatives, this population of cells affords a unique opportunity for the study of morphogenesis and cytodifferentiation.

Like stem cells of the neuroectoderm, neural crest cells appear morphologically similar at the onset of migration. In the trunk of the avian embryo, the crest arises on the dorsal side of the embryo as the neural folds close to form the neural tube. Shortly after formation, the crest cells migrate away from the neural tube in two directions: either dorsolaterally just under the ectoderm or ventrally along side the neural tube (see Fig. 1). The dorsolateral stream is composed primarily

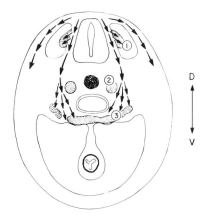

FIG. 1. Diagram illustrating the normal routes of neural crest migration in the trunk region of the avian embryo. Cells choosing the ventral (V) pathway localize in three main areas: (1) the sensory ganglia; (2) the primary sympathetic chain; and (3) the adrenal gland, aortic plexuses, and some cells of the metanephric mesenchyme. Crest cells following the dorsolateral (D) pathway migrate under the ectoderm and become skin melanocytes. From Bronner and Cohen (1979).

of presumptive melanocytes. The cells of the ventral stream migrate between the neural tube and the somites, contributing to the sensory ganglia, sympathetic ganglia, adrenal medulla, aortic plexus, and some cells of the metanephric mesenchyme.

What then causes this outwardly homogeneous population of cells to migrate extensively and give rise to cell types as divergent as neurons and melanocytes? The neural crest cells may, in fact, be determined prior to migration and undergo "directed" movements to appropriate final sites. Alternatively, the neural crest could be pluripotent at the onset of migration, migrate in response to environmental cues, and differentiate according to interactions experienced during or at the conclusion of migration. Many mechanisms have been suggested to play a role in crest migration; these include contact guidance and contact inhibition, specific cell recognition, differential adhesion, and chemotaxis. Which of these possible mechanisms influences the distribution and localization of crest cells remains unclear. These are questions which may be answered using experimental embryological and cell culture techniques.

We are studying questions of neural crest migration and determination using a combination of tissue culture and embryological methods on avian embryos. When neural tubes are explanted *in vitro*, crest cells migrate from the dorsal aspect of the neural tube similar to the crest emigration *in vivo*. Cohen and Konigsberg (1975) took advantage of the natural tendency of crest cells to migrate and developed a technique for isolating and cloning neural crest cells. After crest cells have migrated from the neural tube, the tube is scraped away, leaving a monolayer of mesenchymal crest cells. The cells, after a period of growth, are replated at low densities to establish clones; that is, populations of sister cells derived from a single precursor. Three types of clones arise under these conditions: all pigmented cells, all unpigmented cells, and mixed pigmented and unpigmented cells. To examine the migration and developmental potential of these cells we have developed a method for injecting neural crest clones and other cell types back into chick embryos (Bronner and Cohen, 1979). The injected cells are derived from quail embryos and therefore can be distinguished from those of the chick hosts (see Section II). We find that cloned pigment cells and unpigmented crest cells migrate along the ventral neural crest pathway when injected in this manner. These clones undergo melanotic and adrenergic differentiation *in vitro* (Sieber-Blum and Cohen, 1979) and *in vivo* (Bronner-Fraser *et al.*, 1980). The following discussion reviews recent data from our laboratory and others relating to migration and determination of the avian neural crest.

II. Control of Neural Crest Migration and Localization

Migration of the neural crest is both a temporally and spatially ordered phenomenon. Initiation of migration begins in the anterior regions of the embryo and moves as a progressively posterior wave. Therefore a continuum of stages of crest migration exists in a single embryo (Fig. 2). Though initiation of migration appears similar along most of the neural axis, crest migration and the range of derivatives vary for different regions of the neural axis. For example, the cranial crest (emerging from the axial levels above the otic vesicles; see Fig. 3) gives rise to much different derivatives than does the trunk crest (somites 8–28) described in Section I. Cranial crest gives rise to cranial cartilage, bones, muscles, connective tissue, and parasympathetic and sensory ganglia of the head. The trunk crest, on the other hand, does not give rise to cartilage or parasympathetic ganglia but does contribute to sympathetic and sensory ganglia among other derivatives. The migratory routes taken by cranial crest cells also are different from the pathways in the trunk region. For example, mesencephalic crest cells migrate laterally and ventrally between the presumptive epidermis and the mesodermal mesenchyme (Johnston, 1966; Noden, 1975). Vagal crest (somites 1–7) and lumbosacral crest (behind the twenty-eighth somite) contribute to the enteric ganglia and Remak's ganglion of the gut (LeDouarin and Teillet, 1973) and display migratory patterns different from those of both trunk and cranial crest.

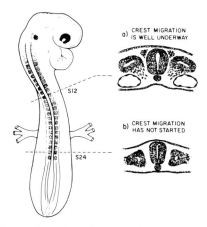

Fɪɢ. 2. Diagram illustrating selected stages of migration of neural crest cells in a stage 14–15 embryo. At anterior levels (somite 12) of the neural axis, crest migration is well under way while at posterior levels (somite 24) crest migration has not yet started. From Bronner-Fraser and Cohen (1980).

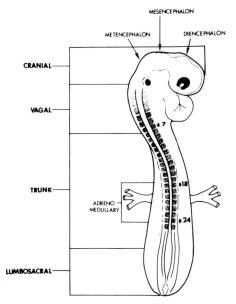

FIG. 3. Diagram illustrating regions along the neural axis which differ in their range of neural crest derivatives and in crest migratory routes. The cranial crest emerges from levels of the neural tube above the otic vesicles. The vagal crest arises from the neural tube between somitic levels 1 and 7. The trunk crest emerges from axial levels between somites 8 and 28, with those crest cells which contribute to the adrenal gland arising from somitic levels 18 to 24. The lumbosacral crest emerges from axial levels beyond somite 28.

The mechanisms that account for crest migration must explain: (1) the initiation of migration; (2) the precise nature of the migratory route; and (3) the cessation of migration and precise localization of the cells. Understanding control of crest migration, therefore, is dependent on defining the role of each component of the embryonic environment composing the migratory route and the effects of these components upon the crest population. Equally important is defining the response of the crest cells themselves to environmental factors. Examination of these issues is complicated by the fact that neural crest cells are indistinguishable from the cells of surrounding tissues through which they migrate. Therefore, various cell-marking techniques have been used to follow the normal migration of crest cells. The most successful methods for the analysis of the migratory patterns of neural crest populations in the avian embryo have been accomplished by transplantation experiments used in combination with cell labeling (Weston, 1963; Weston and Butler, 1966; Johnston, 1966; LeDouarin, 1973; Noden, 1975).

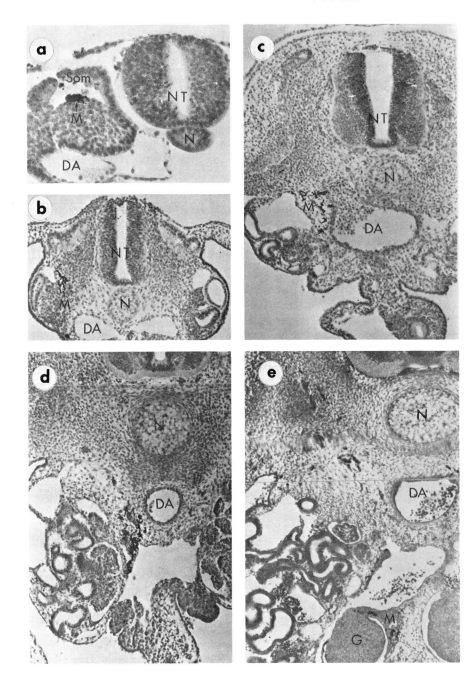

Neural tubes and associated neural crest cells are marked either by using tritiated thymidine or by using neural tubes from the Japanese quail. These are then implanted into unlabeled chick embryos in place of an appropriate length of host neural tube. In the former case, the isotopically labeled cells are followed autoradiographically. In the latter, cells are distinguished from host chick cells by the nucleolus-associated heterochromatin unique to the quail cells (LeDouarin, 1973). This marker is stable through cell division and therefore allows long-term identification of implanted cells. The transplantation technique involves excision of the neural tube from a host embryo and its replacement with a marked donor neural tube. This operation is traumatic and causes a delay in the onset of crest migration (Weston, 1963). Such transplantation can most successfully be performed on early developmental stages prior to extensive vascularization. At later stages, hemorrhaging following the operation leads to death or abnormal development (Weston and Butler, 1966).

To circumvent some of the problems associated with the transplantation experiments, we have described a new technique for implanting marked crest cells (Bronner and Cohen, 1979). Here, clones of neural crest cells from the Japanese quail are injected into chick embryos. Using this approach, the migration and differentiation of a homogeneous population of cells derived from a single neural crest precursor have been monitored. The injection technique provides several advantages over previous methods for introducing marked neural crest cells into host embryos. Cells can be implanted in this manner causing little trauma or perturbation to the host environment. The injection technique requires insertion of the cells directly into the somitic lumen via a fine glass micropipet. The cells are initially contained within the somitic cavity (Fig. 4a), but after the somite disperses the cloned crest cells are released onto the ventral pathway of neural crest migration.

FIG. 4. Light photomicrographs of transverse sections demonstrating the ventral migration of cloned quail melanocytes (M) injected into the newly formed somites (Som) of 2.5-day chick embryos and fixed at progressively older stages of development. (a) Immediately after injection, melanocytes are restricted to the somitic cavity ($\times$158); (b) one day after injection, melanocytes have migrated to the region of the sensory ganglion. Note the single melanocyte adjacent to the dorsal aorta ($\times$100); (c) two days after injection, melanocytes are found further ventrally in the region of the sympathetic ganglia and lateral to the dorsal aorta ($\times$84); (d) three days after injection melanocytes have migrated beyond the dorsal aorta and are seen next to the developing adrenal gland, metanephric mesenchyme, and aortic plexuses ($\times$90); (e) four days after injection, melanocytes are present further ventrally in the vicinity of the gonads (G) ($\times$90); neural tube (NT), notochord (N), and dorsal aorta (DA).

When injected into somites, cloned quail melanocytes (Bronner and Cohen, 1979) and unpigmented neural crest cells (Bronner-Fraser *et al.*, 1980) migrate along the ventral pathway with a time course similar to that of endogenous crest cells. Pigmented clones localize near the adrenal gland, aortic plexus, metanephric mesenchyme, gonads, and gut. Unpigmented quail crest cells contribute to sympathetic ganglia, the adrenal medulla, and cells of the aortic plexuses.

The injection technique has proved important in examining several problems regarding crest migration and localization. One question is what regulates the distribution of crest cells along the ventral pathway. In the trunk, crest cells come to reside in three distinct sites and differentiate into sensory ganglia, sympathetic ganglia, and cells of the adrenal gland (see Fig. 1). A possible explanation for this differential localization is that the environment changes in its capacity to support migration of crest cells. Consequently, the cells are restricted to several sites on the ventral pathway. Recently, we tested this supposition using the injection technique. Cloned quail melanocytes, injected into the somites in regions where crest migration is just beginning, migrate ventrally and localize around the adrenal gland, metanephric mesenchyme, gonads, or gut (Fig. 4d and e). However, when melanocytes are injected into somites at levels of the neural axis where crest migration is well under way, the degree of ventral migration is restricted (Bronner-Fraser and Cohen, 1980; Fig. 5b). Pigment cells derived from a single clone were split into two groups and injected into older (anterior) and younger (posterior) somites in the same embryo (Fig. 2). Those cells injected into older sites do not migrate as far as those melanocytes injected into young sites. Therefore, sister pigment cells localize in different sites according to the degree of development in the host. We conclude that changes in the environment occurring as a consequence of developmental age restrict the migration of crest cells. The nature of the environmental restrictions remains to be identified.

Another possible explanation for the differential localization of crest cells is that the crest is in fact a heterogeneous population of cells specifically determined to migrate to particular sites even before the cells leave the neural tube. This idea was tested by Weston and Butler (1966) who isolated older neural tubes from which many crest cells had already migrated. These older neural tubes were labeled with tritiated thymidine and transplanted into younger levels of the trunk neural axis where few if any crest cells had migrated into neighboring tissues. The crest cells emerging from the older grafted neural tubes migrated as extensively as crest cells from endogenous younger levels would have migrated. These results indicate either that: (1) crest cell popula-

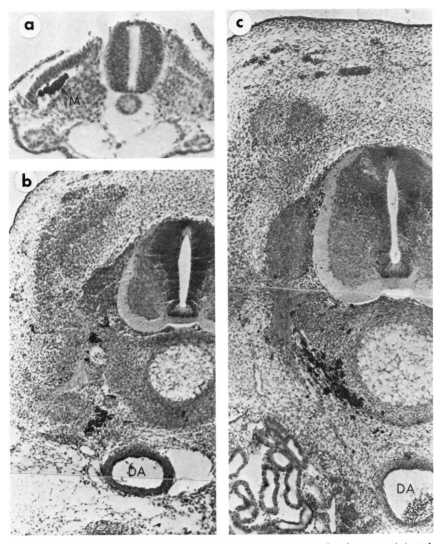

Fig. 5. Transverse sections illustrating restricted migration of melanocytes injected into somites at developmentally older axial levels. (a) Injected melanocytes (M) are contained within the older somite (cf. Fig. 4a) (×174); (b) four days after quail melanocytes were injected into an anterior level (somite 15) of a 25-somite embryo, the melanocytes migrated no further than the dorsal aorta (DA) (×97); (c) four days after quail melanocytes were injected into posterior levels (somite 21) of a 32-somite embryo, the melanocytes migrated no further than the dorsal aorta (DA) (×97). See Fig. 4e for extent of ventral migration of melanocytes injected into posterior somites of developmentally earlier stage. From Bronner-Fraser and Cohen (1980).

tions are pluripotent at the onset of migration and their pattern of migration and subsequent differentiation is under environmental control; or (2) crest cells are developmentally restricted but leave the neural tube in a random order. To distinguish between these alternatives, Weston and Butler performed the reciprocal experiment in which neural tubes from younger levels were transplanted into developmentally older regions where crest migration was already well under way. The distal migration of crest cells from younger levels was limited in the older environment. Weston and Butler concluded that crest cells are pluripotent at the onset of migration and localize as a consequence of developmental changes in the environment. As described, the migration of injected melanocytes is also affected by the developmental age of the region into which the cells are injected (Bronner-Fraser and Cohen, 1980).

Work from a number of laboratories has demonstrated that the environment provided by the tissues along the migratory route plays a key role in guiding neural crest migration. LeDouarin and Teillet (1974) transplanted neural tubes from adrenomedullary levels (somites 18–24) into vagal (somite 1–7) levels of the neural axis. The grafted crest cells, which *in situ* would migrate only as far ventrally as the adrenal gland, migrate in accordance with their new environment and localize adjacent to the gut to form enteric parasympathetic ganglia. Noden (1975, 1978a,b) also showed that the environment affects migration and distribution of cranial crest cells. When he exchanged crest cells from mesencephalic, metencephalic, and diencephalic levels, he found that the cells migrated appropriately for their implantation site regardless of their original location. Thus, in heterotopic transplantation, the crest cells follow the routes expected for the level of implantation rather than the pathways expected for the level of origin of the cells. These experiments indicate the importance of environment on neural crest migration.

However, some donor cells in the transplantation experiments find their way to their original target areas in the host. When crest cells from vagal levels, for example, are grafted into host adrenomedullary levels, the vagal cells migrate as would adrenomedullary crest to sensory, sympathetic, and adrenomedullary locations. But some vagal crest cells in these experiments also invade the mesentery of the intestines and contribute to the enteric ganglia (LeDouarin and Teillet, 1974). These locations are not normally reached by endogenous adrenomedullary crest cells. The donor-specific migration of some vagal crest cells in these exchange experiments indicates that some cells may be predetermined to find their original target. Twitty also reported that melanoblasts undergo a type of self-directed migration. When he performed neural tube transplantations between amphibian species characterized by different pigmentation patterns, the pigmentation pattern in the area of the transplant was characteristic of the *donor* species (Twitty, 1944). Thus, some cells migrate in a manner inappropriate to their site of implantation, but appropriate to their original embryonic location. Although the migratory route itself can influence crest movements, some cells may be predetermined to find their original target. This raises the possibility that subsets exist among the crest population which differ in their migratory potential.

The environment itself appears to have strong effects on the initiation and restriction of migration. This is indicated by recent experiments in which melanocytes which have ceased migrating *in vitro* are injected back into embryonic regions of active crest migration (Bronner and Cohen, 1979). The melanocytes reinitiate migration and follow the ventral pathway. The ventral migration of injected cells is restricted with developmental age of the host since melanocytes injected into embryonic regions 10 to 12 hours older than those described earlier do not migrate as far ventrally (Bronner-Fraser and Cohen, 1980). LeDouarin *et al.* (1978) observed a similar return of motility to previously nonmotile cells. They implanted quail parasympathetic ganglia, containing cells undergoing cytodifferentiation, back into young chicken embryos. The parasympathetic quail cells migrate along the ventral pathway and participate in normal sympathetic and adrenomedullary cell formation. Thus, a critical embryonic period seems to exist during which the environment promotes migration even in nonmotile cells.

One possible explanation for this phenomenon is via a contact inhibition mechanism (Abercrombie, 1970). This model, based on analysis of fibroblast movements *in vitro*, proposes that the distribution of cells is affected by cell–cell contacts. When active migration brings the leading edge of one migratory cell in contact with the surface of another cell, the first cell stops moving, forms a new leading edge, and moves in a different direction. Thus, contact inhibition of movement would result in migration of cells away from an area of high density (e.g., the neural tube) to regions with sparse densities (e.g., the extracellular space between the neural tube and the somite, or between the somite and the ectoderm). Thus crest cells which had stopped migrating might again initiate migration under proper environmental conditions. Neural crest cells explanted *in vitro* do in fact move away from the neural tube and away from one another in the early stages of migration (Cohen and Konigsberg, 1975). Amphibian melanophores in culture exhibit a mutual replusion (Twitty, 1949; Twitty and Niu, 1948, 1954), though this is probably chemically mediated. An example of contact inhibition *in vivo* is the regulation that occurs after a short region of the neural crest is ablated. Crest cells emigrating from sites adjacent to the gap invade the unoccupied regions. After a time, however, crest cells both *in vivo* and in tissue culture again reestablish close contacts with other cells. Thus, contact inhibition may account for some of the early events in crest migration; but, clearly, there are other mechanisms involved.

In later stages of migration, differential cellular affinities may play a role in control of crest migration. Adhesive and repulsive forces between cells have been implicated in various aspects of morphogenesis for quite some time (Holtfreter, 1939). Townes and Holtfreter (1955) proposed that many morphogenetic events could be accounted for by a combination of differential cellular affinities and chemotaxis. Steinberg (1963) was able to explain cell-sorting phenomena by differential adhesion alone. The differential adhesion hypothesis, briefly stated, explains cell sorting by assuming that: (1) cells have affinities for similar cells that are stronger than the affinities between dissimilar cells; and (2) cells will sort to attain the most thermodynamically stable configuration, such that their free energies are minimized. The differential adhesion model can account for many *in vitro* cell-sorting events (Steinberg 1962a, 1963, 1964, 1970) and has recently been extended to the development of the visual system (Fraser, 1980; Fraser and Hunt 1980). Recent studies strongly implicate a role for differential adhesion in somite formation and the migration of pronephric duct cells in *Ambystoma* embryos (Poole and Steinberg, 1980). It is possible that this type of cell sorting also plays a role in neural crest migration. Bronner-Fraser and Cohen (1980) find that melanocytes, as well as unpigmented crest cells (Bronner *et al.*, 1980), migrate and localize in areas appropriate for crest cells. When quail somite cells are injected in an identical manner as melanocytes, the somite cells remain dorsally, associated with the chick somitic mesenchyme; melanocytes, coinjected with the somitic cells, however, migrate ventrally. Similarly, injected fibroblasts derived from quail skin and present as single cells migrate under the ectoderm. Clumps of fibroblast cells, however, migrate ventrally (Fig. 6). The fact that neural crest-derived cells, somite cells, and fibroblasts (when present as single cells) all populate regions occupied by "like" cells is strongly reminiscent of a cell-type specific sorting described by the differential adhesion model. That aggregates of fibroblasts migrate ventrally might reflect that the energy required for such a large group of cells to reach their most thermodynamically stable configuration is prohibitive. Their ventral migration, therefore, could be a consequence of the clumps settling in a secondary minimum. These ideas are supported by *in vitro* studies which show that elongating nerve fibers (Letourneau, 1975) and migrating cells (Carter, 1965; Gail and Boone, 1972; Harris, 1973) orient toward and migrate on substrata which permit contacts of greatest adhesiveness.

It is possible that the neural tube itself and the extracellular matrix through which the crest migrates may be substrata which provide the necessary adhesive sites to support migration but do not provide the directing influence (Weiss, 1961; Hay, 1968). The environment at the onset of crest migration is permissive for cell migration. The synthesis of hyaluronic acid and the formation of a cell-free space frequently occur prior to or concomitant with cell migrations in vertebrate development. If hyaluronidase is administered to the cell-free space through which cranial crest cells migrate, neural crest emigration is prevented (Pratt *et al.*, 1976). Characteristic glycosaminoglycans demonstrated by Alcian Blue staining are seen in regions of active neural crest cell migration in avian (Pintar, 1978) and mouse (Derby, 1978) embryos. Extracellular matrix in the trunk is rich in hyaluronic acid at the onset of migration. In later stages of migration, the extracellular matrix is characterized by different glycosaminoglycan concentrations. Weston (1963) suggests that crest cell migration is promoted within the somitic mesenchyme and limited in the intersomitic regions. This in part accounts for the metameric nature of the spinal ganglia (Detwiler, 1934). The mucopolysaccharide composition of the somitic matrix may be responsible for promoting early migration of crest cells across the somitic milieu, while at later stages, alterations in composition of the matrix might cause cessation of migration and even condensation of crest cells to form dorsal root and sympathetic ganglia.

Morphogenetic phenomena may be mediated by cell surface components of migrating crest cells interacting with the extracellular matrix. Changes in the cell surface as assayed by lectin binding occur during differentiation of neural crest cells *in vitro* (Sieber-Blum and Cohen, 1978). Morphologically undifferentiated crest cells are homogeneous with respect to lectin binding, but after cytodifferentiation into melanocytes and adrenergic cells the binding changes markedly. These *in vitro* observations may correlate with cell surface changes in the embryo. *In vivo*, fucosyltransferase activity is high in the neural tube, cranial crest, and skin ectoderm of stage-10 chick embryos. However, by stage 17, no fucosyltransferase activity is detected (Shur, 1977). It seems likely, therefore, that changes in cell-surface carbohydrates play some role in crest migration and localization.

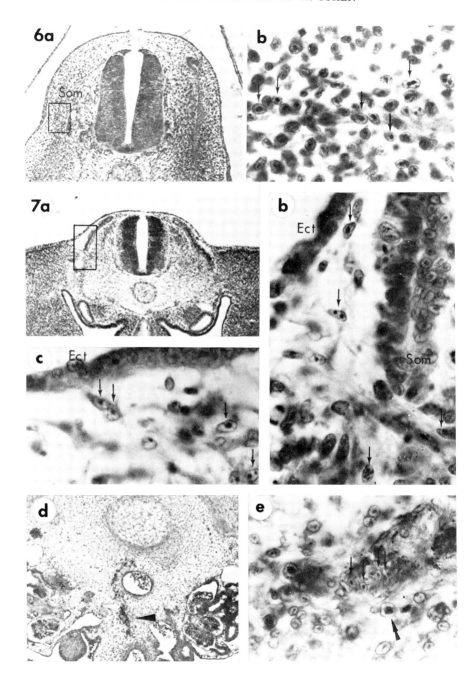

Chemotaxis is another mechanism implicated in guiding the distribution of neural crest cells. LeDouarin and Teillet (1974) propose that vagal crest cells are selectively attracted to the gut, since the cells migrate to the intestines even when transplanted into adrenomedullary levels. Endogenous crest cells from this region normally migrate only as far ventrally as the adrenal gland. Cloned quail melanocytes injected into early somites at adrenomedullary levels also migrate beyond the adrenal gland and to the gut (Bronner and Cohen, 1979). It is important to note that unpigmented crest cells injected similarly migrate only as far as the adrenal gland (Bronner-Fraser et al., 1980). Further evidence for some chemotactic influence by the environment comes from tissue culture experiments in which nerve outgrowth is promoted by the presence of explanted target organs (Chamley et al., 1973; Chamley and Dowel, 1975; Coughlin, 1975; Pollack and Liebeg, 1977).

III. Neural Crest Differentiation

A central issue in studying neural crest development is identifying those events which control cytodifferentiation and divergence. At some point in the developmental history of the cell, the phenotypic potential of each neural crest cell becomes restricted. This may occur either prior to or concomitant with biochemical and cytological expression of the differentiated state. Perhaps prior to migration, the population is a mosaic of determined cells which preferentially migrate to appropriate final locations and differentiate there according to their fate. Restriction of developmental potential, on the other hand, may occur during

---

FIG. 6. Light photomicrographs of a transverse section through a chick embryo fixed 2 days after quail somite cells were injected into the posterior somites. The quail somite cells remain associated with the somitic mesenchyme (Som). At higher magnification (b, inset) the quail cells are identified by a Feulgen-positive nucleolar mass. Arrows indicate cells in which the quail marker is most visible. (a) ×89; (b) ×628. From Bronner and Cohen (1979).

FIG. 7. Transverse sections through chick embryos injected with quail fibroblast cells into the posterior somites. Arrows indicate cells in which the quail intranuclear marker is most visible. (a) Embryo 1 day after injection has quail fibroblasts at the base of the somite and under the ectoderm (×74); (b) higher magnification of (a) inset (×736) shows quail cells at the base of the somite (Som) and between the somite and the ectoderm (Ect); (c) embryo with quail fibroblast cells under the ectoderm but located closer to the neural tube, 1 day after injection (×736); (d) two days after injection, a clump (arrowhead) of quail fibroblast cells is seen ventral to the notochord (N) and dorsal aorta (DA) (×79); (e) at a higher magnification of (d) (×628), quail fibroblasts are detected in the clump. Cells with the large condensed nuclei are chick erythrocytes (double arrowheads). From Bronner-Fraser and Cohen (1980).

the migratory period in response to interactions with the environment. Or, the neural crest cells may remain pluripotent during their migration and differentiate at their terminal locations in response to cues from the local environment. Any one or some combination of these general alternatives might account for determination and cytodifferentiation in the crest populations.

Are there differences in the developmental potential of neural crest cells prior to migration? Yntema and Hammond (1945) and Hammond (1949) concluded from extirpation experiments that the crest cells first leaving the neural tube may possess different developmental potentials than those cells migrating later. For example, ablations of the crest performed prior to migration yield complete depletion of crest-derived structures while ablations performed during migration or after crest migration has ceased cause a lesser degree of depletion or none at all. Detwiler (1937) suggested that the most ventral portion of migrating crest cells gives rise to sympathetic rudiments, whereas the dorsal portion provides the cells of the sensory ganglia. Weston and Butler (1966) found that the first cells to leave the neural tube do in fact migrate the farthest. The extensive ventral migration of the first crest cells to leave the neural tube does not, however, reflect differences in developmental potential between these and late migrating crest cells. Weston and Butler demonstrated that the later migrating cells have the same range of developmental potentials as do early migrating cells. The differential localization is caused, rather, by changes in the environment through which the crest cells move (see Section II). In tissue culture, as well, the later migrating cells seem to be similar to the early migrating cells in appearance and developmental potential (unpublished observation). Therefore, the population of crest cells in the trunk region seems to be pluripotent prior to migration, but the cells localize and differentiate in response to environmental cues. Neural crest cells both *in vivo* (Bancroft and Bellairs, 1976) and *in vitro* (Cohen and Konigsberg, 1975; Cohen, 1977) appear to be morphologically similar, indicating that they may in fact be homogeneous. Some trunk crest cells, however, appear distinct when observed by scanning electron microscopy (Tosney, 1978); these cells are coated with a basal lamina-like material. This could be either a secretion product or extracellular matrix material accumulated during migration.

There is some evidence that populations of neural crest cells may be restricted in their developmental potential at early stages. This is most clearly seen in the head crest that is induced to form cartilage in response to pharyngeal endoderm (Horstadius, 1950). Trunk crest, on the other hand, is unable to respond to the endodermal signals when exchanged for head crest. Chibon (1966) showed that the transplanted amphibian trunk neural crest is capable of migrating into visceral arches but does not form bone or cartilage. LeDouarin and Teillet (1974) found this to be true in avian embryos as well. Clearly, the neural crest cells are not equipotential for all axial levels.

The expression of certain phenotypes seems to be dependent upon interactions between crest cells and the environment. One example is the induction of cartilage from head crest previously mentioned. Another example of this type of induction occurs in the formation of the sclera; the cranial crest mesenchyme is induced by retinal pigmented epithelium cells to condense and chondrify adjacent to the eye (Newsome, 1972, 1975; Stewart and McCallion, 1975). A third example is the requirement of crest cells for nerve processes in order to differentiate into Schwann cells (Peterson and Murray, 1955). In addition, contact with connective tissue matrix may be required for the normal interaction of Schwann cells and nerve fibers since cultured Schwann cells are abnormal in appearance and decreased in number in the absence of collagen matrix (Bunge and Bunge, 1978).

In the trunk region of avian embryos, interactions of migrating crest cells with their environment appear to promote adrenergic differentiation. Cohen (1972) and Norr (1973) cultured trunk crest cells either on the chorioallantoic membrane or *in vitro* along with various axial structures encountered by crest cells during migration. Their results indicate that adrenergic neuroblast formation is dependent upon interactions between migrating crest cells and tissues along the ventral pathway, namely, the somitic mesenchyme and the ventral neural tube. In earlier studies, crest cells cultured isolated *in vitro,* differentiated only into melanocytes (Dorris, 1936; Weston, 1970). This was taken as further evidence that tissue interactions are in fact vital for differentiation of crest cells into phenotypes other than melanocytes.

However, trunk crest cells grown *in vitro* on collagen-coated petri plates and fed medium containing embryo extract differentiate into a variety of cell types in the absence of heterotypic tissue influences (Cohen, 1977). These include melanocytes, sympathetic neuroblasts, small intensely fluorescent cells, cholinergic neuroblasts (Kahn and Cohen, 1979), and possibly others. Cultures of cranial crest cells also develop pigmented and cholinergic traits (Greenberg and Schrier, 1977). The differentiation of these cell types in the absence of heterotypic interactions raises a question regarding determination of their fate. Premigratory crest cells may be restricted in their developmental fate and capable of autonomous differentiation under the proper environmental circumstances. Alternatively, premigratory crest cells may be multipotent with a finite probability of developing along a number of different lines under permissive conditions.

Determination is not a single step event in the neural crest system. For example, some crest cells first appear to become determined along neuronal lines; the choice of transmitter synthesis, however, seems to be determined at a later time in development (Patterson, 1978; Bunge *et al.*, 1978). There is good evidence that the transmitter decision is reversible for a certain critical period even in postmitotic cells. Rat superior cervical ganglia cultured *in vitro* under appropriate conditions produce catecholamines (Mains and Patterson, 1973). When identical cultures are grown in the presence of nonneural cells, the cultures produce acetylcholine in amounts as much as 1000-fold higher than in control cultures, with a concomitant reduction in catecholamine synthesis (Patteron and Chun, 1974). These neurons also make functional cholinergic synapses (O'Lague *et al.*, 1974, 1975; Nurse and O'Lague, 1975; Furshpan *et al.*, 1976). Medium which has been conditioned by appropriate nonneural cells is also capable of eliciting the adrenergic to-cholinergic transition. Thus, functional contact is not a prerequisit for transmitter changes. Since the same results are seen in single cell experiments (Reichardt *et al.*, 1976), transmitter determination in these neural populations may occur postmitotically within single cells.

Environmental factors also influence the choice of transmitter synthesis in avian embryos. This has been demonstrated in experiments using chick–quail chimeras to examine determination and migration of crest cells (see Section II). When quail neural crest cells from adrenomedullary levels are transplanted to vagal (somites 1–7) levels in chick hosts, quail crest cells populate the enteric ganglia of the host (LeDouarin *et al.*, 1975). These implanted cells, *in situ*, would normally produce adrenergic neurons, but in their new (enteric) site, become cholinergic neurons. In the reciprocal transplant, presumptive cholinergic quail cells extirpated from vagal regions participate in adrenergic ganglion formation when transplanted to adrenomedullary levels (LeDouarin and Teillet, 1974). In addition, quail parasympathetic cells from the ciliary and Remak's ganglia which are not motile and are already synthesizing acetylcholine will reinitiate migration, populate the developing sympathetic ganglia and adrenal gland, and synthesize catecholamines when placed back into young embryos (LeDouarin *et al.*, 1978). Thus, in the proper environment, neurons or stem cells which would normally synthesize one type of transmitter can be induced to produce another.

An important question is whether the inductive events effecting neurotransmitter synthesis occur during migration or only after migration terminates. This was tested by Smith *et al.* (1977) who transplanted premigratory vagal or adrenomedullary neural crest directly into aneural chick gut and cultured the chimeric tissue on the chorioallantoic membrane of chick embryos. In this way, presumptive adrenergic or cholinergic crest populations are placed directly in association with the target tissue where cholinergic enteric ganglia develop, eliminating the possibility of migratory influences. Both crest populations give rise to cholinergic neurons, but no adrenergic neurons form. Migration is not, therefore, a prerequisite for differentiation.

These experiments do not rule out the possibility that in the premigratory crest populations of cells may exist, determined along neurogenic lines but unspecified, prior to migration, as to which transmitter to synthesize. Noden (1978a,b) addressed this question by means of heterotopic transplantation experiments using quail and chick cranial crest. Diencephalic crest cells, when implanted in place of metencephalic crest cells, develop into sensory and autonomic neurons, accessory cells, and Schwann cells. Cells from the diencephalic level do not normally form *any* neurons. His results suggest two possibilities: (1) that neural crest cells are pluripotent and able to develop according to environmental cues; or (2) that there exists a subpopulation of cells determined along neurogenic lines, but in some region (e.g., the diencephalon) these cells do not develop and degenerate. Although the latter cannot be ruled out, the former possibility seems most plausible.

The question of neural crest potentiality has been examined most recently by cloning trunk neural crest cells in tissue culture. Clonal techniques were first applied to the study of crest determination by Cohen and Konigsberg (1975). They took advantage of the natural tendency of neural crest cells to migrate away from the neural tube *in vitro,* similar to the *in vivo* emigration. By isolating the crest cells which had migrated away from the neural tube and replating these at sparse densities, clones of cells derived from a single neural crest cell were obtained. Under clonal conditions, three types of clones arise: all pigmented, nonpigmented, or mixed clones containing both pigmented and unpigmented cells. That pigmented and unpigmented cells arise in the same clone, from a single neural crest precursor, was verified by screening the cells and growing them in isolation. Recently, Sieber-Blum and Cohen (1979) showed that such single crest cells give rise to both pigmented and adrenergic cells in the same clone when cultured under appropriate conditions. Bronner-Fraser *et al.* (1980) have injected quail neural crest clones back into chick embryos (see Section II) and found that unpigmented crest cells migrate ventrally and participate in forming paraaortic and adrenomedullary cell bodies

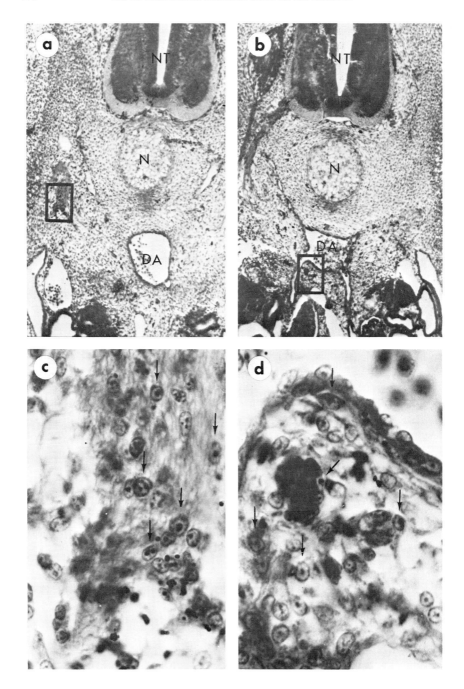

and sympathetic ganglia (Fig. 8). A mixed clone, consisting of both pigmented cells and undifferentiated neural crest cells, will give rise to adrenergic neurons as well as pigment cells after injection into chick embryos (Figs. 9 and 10). The cells of such mixed clones are the progeny of a single neural crest cell which was isolated in tissue culture, allowed to proliferate, and subsequently injected *in vivo*. These experiments are the first definitive proof that the descendants of a single neural crest cell can differentiate into multiple phenotypes. Thus, we have unequivocally proved that at least a population of the premigratory neural crest in the trunk region is bipotential and probably pluripotential.

IV. Conclusion

The results presented in this chapter indicate that cells of the premigratory neural crest are multipotent and become determined in accordance with interactions with other crest cells and cells of the environment. The crest, therefore, probably is not a mosaic of predetermined cells. Along the length of the neural axis, however, crest populations do apparently differ in both migratory and developmental potential. The migratory route and the final cytodifferentiation of crest cells are largely determined by environmental factors, but the crest is capable of autonomous differentiation in the absence of heterotypic tissue interactions.

The mechanisms whereby neural crest morphogenesis and cytodifferentiation occur are not completely understood. There is good evidence that contact inhibition and differential adhesion are key mechanisms, although a role for chemotaxis cannot be ruled out. Characterization of environmental influences on the crest is just beginning and perhaps, with studies at the microenvironmental level and by further clonal analysis, we will come to better understand components of the

---

FIG. 8. Light photomicrographs of transverse sections demonstrating the ventral migration and localization of unpigmented quail neural crest cells derived from mixed clones and injected into the newly formed somites of 2.5-day chick hosts. (c) Three days after injection, some quail cells are present in the sympathetic ganglia (×90); (b) higher magnification of (a) inset shows many quail cells within the sympathetic ganglion; (b) another embryo 3 days after injection in which quail neural crest cells have migrated to the level of the adrenal gland (×883); (d) higher magnification of (b) inset shows the quail nucleolar marker within adrenal structures (×883). NT, Neural tube; N, notochord; DA, dorsal aorta. Arrows indicate cells in which the quail marker is most visible. From Bronner-Fraser *et al.* (1980).

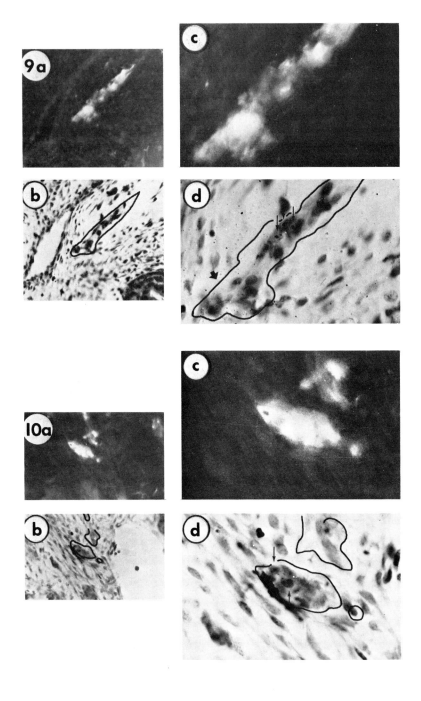

crest migratory environment and the response these evoke in crest cells.

ACKNOWLEDGMENTS

We express our gratitude to Ms. Susan Jaffe for her expert technical assistance. The research was supported by U.S. Public Health Service Grant HD-07389 and a Basic Research Grant from the National Foundation-March of Dimes.

REFERENCES

Abercrombie, M. (1970). *In Vitro* **6**, 128–142.
Bancroft, M., and Bellaris, R. (1976). *Zoon* **4**, 73–85.
Bronner, M. E., and Cohen, A. M. (1979). *Proc. Natl. Acad. Sci. U.S.A.* **76**, 1843–1848.
Bronner-Fraser, M. E., and Cohen, A. M. (1980). *Dev. Biol.* **76**, 296–307.
Bronner-Fraser, M. E., Sieber-Blum, M., and Cohen, A. M. (1980). *J. Comp. Neurol.* (in press).
Bunge, R. P., and Bunge, M. B. (1978). *J. Cell Biol.* **78**, 943–950.
Bunge, R., Johnston, M., and Ross, C. D. (1978). *Science* **199**, 1409–1416.
Carter, S. B. (1965). *Nature (London)* **108**, 1183–1187.
Chamley, J. H., and Dowel, J. J. (1975). *Exp. Cell Res.* **90**, 1–7.
Chamley, J. H., Galler, I, and Burnstock, G. (1973). *Dev. Biol.* **31**, 362–379.
Chibon, P. (1966). *Mem. Soc. Zool., France,* **36**, 4–117.
Cohen, A. M. (1972). *J. Exp. Zool.* **179**, 167–182.
Cohen, A. M. (1977). *Proc. Natl. Acad. Sci. U.S.A.* **74**, 2899–2903.
Cohen, A. M., and Konigsberg, I. R. (1975). *Dev. Biol.* **46**, 262–280.
Coughlin, M. D. (1975). *Dev. Biol.* **43**, 140–158.
Derby, M. A. (1978). *Dev. Biol.* **66**, 321–336.
Detwiler, S. R. (1934). *J. Gen. Physiol.* **67**, 395–441.
Detwiler, S. R. (1937). *Am. J. Anat.* **61**, 63–94.
Dorris, F. (1936). *Proc. Soc. Exp. Biol. Med.* **34**, 448–449.
Fraser, S. E. (1980). *Dev. Biol.* (in press).
Fraser, S. E., and Hunt, R. K. (1980). *Annu. Rev. Neurosci.* **3**, 319–352.

FIGS. 9 and 10. Light and fluorescence photomicrographs of transverse sections demonstrating catecholamine histofluorescence in quail neural crest cells 3 days after injection of mixed clones into chick embryos.

FIG. 9. (a) Embryo with catecholamine fluorescence in a group of quail cells (×267); (b) light photomicrograph of the same section with the fluorescent area outlined around quail cells adjacent to the dorsal aorta (×267); (c) histofluorescence at higher power (×808) of the same section; (d) light photomicrograph of (c) (×808) demonstrates that the injected quail cells contain catecholamines; small arrowheads indicate cells in which the quail marker is visible; the larger arrowhead indicates quail cells in which the heterochromatin marker is out of the plane of focus.

FIG. 10. (a) Another embryo with catecholamine fluorescence in a more ventral site (×267); (b) light photomicrograph of same section as (a) (×267) with the fluorescent area outlined around the group of fluorescent cells lateral to the inferior vena cava; (c) histofluorescence of the same section at higher power (×808); (d) light photomicrograph of (c) (×808) shows that the injected quail cells are positive for catecholamines; small arrowheads indicate cells in which the quail heterochromatin marker is visible; note the quail melanocyte adjacent to the fluorescent cluster of cells.

Furschpan, E. J., MacLeish, P. R., O'Lague, P. H., and Potter, D. D. (1976). *Proc. Natl. Acad. Sci. U.S.A.* **73,** 4225–4229.
Gail, M. H., and Boone, C. W. (1972). *Exp. Cell Res.* **70,** 33–40.
Greenberg, J. H., and Schrier, B. K. (1977). *Dev. Biol.* **61,** 86–93.
Hammond, W. S. (1949). *J. Comp. Neurol.* **86,** 237–266.
Harris, A. (1973). *Exp. Cell Res.* **77,** 285–297.
Hay, E. D. (1968). *In* "Epithelial–Mesenchymal Interactions" (R. Fleischmajer and R. E. Billingham, eds.), pp. 31–55. Williams & Wilkins, Baltimore, Maryland.
Holtfreter, J. (1939). *Arch. Exp. Zellforsch.* **23,** 169–209.
Horstadius, S. (1950). "The Neural Crest." Oxford Univ. Press, London and New York.
Johnston, M. C. (1966). *Anat. Rec.* **156,** 143–156.
Kahn, C. R., and Cohen, A. M. (1979). *J. Cell Biol.* **83,** 31a *(Abstract).*
LeDouarin, N. M. (1973). *Dev. Biol.* **30,** 217–222.
LeDouarin, N. M., and Teillet, M. A. (1973). *J. Embryol. Exp. Morphol.* **30,** 31–48.
LeDouarin, N. M. and Teillet, M. A. (1974). *Dev. Biol.* **41,** 162–184.
LeDouarin, N. M., Renaud, D., Teillet, M. A., and LeDouarin, G. (1975). *Proc. Natl. Acad. Sci. U.S.A.* **72,** 728–732.
LeDouarin, N. M., Teillet, M. A., Ziller, C., and Smith, J. (1978). *Proc. Natl. Acad. Sci. U.S.A.* **75,** 2030–2034.
Letourneau, P. C. (1975). *Dev. Biol.* **44,** 92–101.
Mains, R. E., and Patterson, P. H. (1973). *J. Cell Biol.* **59,** 329–345.
Mangold, O. (1933). *Naturwissenschaften* **21,** 394–397.
Newsome, D. A. (1972). *Dev. Biol.* **27,** 575–579.
Newsome, D. A. (1975). *Dev. Biol.* **49,** 496–507.
Noden, D. M. (1975). *Dev. Biol.* **42,** 106–130.
Noden, D. M. (1978a). *Dev. Biol.* **67,** 296–312.
Noden, D. M. (1978b). *Dev. Biol.* **67,** 313–329.
Norr, S. C. (1973). *Dev. Biol.* **34,** 16–18.
Nurse, C. A., and O'Lague, P. H. (1975). *Proc. Natl. Acad. Sci. U.S.A.* **72,** 1955–1959.
O'Lague, P. H., Obata, K., Claude, P., Furschpan, E. J., and Potter, D. D. (1974). *Proc. Natl. Acad. Sci. U.S.A.* **71,** 3602–3606.
O'Lague, P. H., MacLeish, P. R., Nurse, C. A., Claude, P., Furschpan, E. J., and Potter, D. D. (1975). *Cold Spring Harbor Symp. Quant. Biol.* **40,** 399–407.
Patterson, P. H. (1978). *Annu. Rev. Neurosci.* **1,** 1–17.
Patterson, P. H., and Chun, L. L. Y. (1974). *Proc. Natl. Acad. Sci. U.S.A.* **71,** 3607–3610.
Peterson, E. R., and Murray, M. R. (1955). *Am. J. Anat.* **96,** 319–355.
Pintar, J. E. (1978). *Dev. Biol.* **67,** 444–464.
Pollack, E. D., and Liebeg, V. (1977). *Science* **197,** 899–900.
Poole, T. J., and Steinberg, M. S. (1979). Submitted.
Pratt, R. M., Morriss, G., and Johnston, M. C. (1976). *J. Gen. Physiol.* **68,** 15a.
Reichardt, L. F., Patterson, P. H., and Chun, L. L. Y. (1976). *Ann. Soc. Neurosci., 6th, Abstr.* **327,** 197.
Shur, B. D. (1977). *Dev. Biol.* **58,** 23–39.
Sieber-Blum, M., and Cohen, A. M. (1978). *J. Cell Biol.* **76,** 628–638.
Sieber-Blum, M., and Cohen, A. M. (1979). *J. Cell Biol.* **83,** 23a *(Abstract).*
Smith, J., Cochard, P., and LeDouarin, N. M. (1977). *Cell Diff.* **6,** 199–216.
Spemann, H. (1938). "Embryonic Development and Induction." Yale Univ. Press, New Haven, Connecticut.
Steinberg, M. S. (1962a). *Proc. Natl. Acad. Sci. U.S.A.* **48,** 1577–1582.
Steinberg, M. S. (1962b). *Proc. Natl. Acad. Sci. U.S.A.* **48,** 1769–1776.

Steinberg, M. S. (1963). *Science* **141**, 401–408.
Steinberg, M. S. (1964). *In* "Cellular Membranes in Development" (M. Locke, ed.), pp. 321–366. Academic Press, New York.
Steinberg, M. S. (1970). *J. Exp. Zool.* **73**, 395–434.
Stewart, P. A., and McCallion, D. J. (1975). *Dev. Biol.* **46**, 383–389.
Tosney, K. T. (1978). *Dev. Biol.* **62**, 317–333.
Townes, P. L., and Holtfreter, J. (1955). *J. Exp. Zool.* **128**, 53–120.
Twitty, V. C. (1944). *J. Exp. Zool.* **95**, 259–290.
Twitty, V. C. (1949). *Growth* **13** (Suppl. 9), 133–161.
Twitty, V. C., and Niu, M. C. (1948). *J. Exp. Zool.* **108**, 405–437.
Twitty, V. C., and Niu, M. C. (1954). *J. Exp. Zool.* **125**, 541–574.
Weiss, P. A. (1961). *Exp. Cell Res.* (Suppl. 8), 260–281.
Weston, J. A. (1963). *Dev. Biol.* **6**, 279–310.
Weston, J. A. (1970). *Adv. Morph.* **8**, 41–114.
Weston, J. A., and Butler, S. L. (1966). *Dev. Biol.* **14**, 246–266.
Yntema, C. L., and Hammond, W. S. (1945). *J. Exp. Zool.* **100**, 237–263.

CHAPTER 2

DEVELOPMENTAL REGULATION OF NEUROTRANSMITTER PHENOTYPE

Ira B. Black

LABORATORY OF DEVELOPMENTAL NEUROLOGY
DEPARTMENT OF NEUROLOGY
CORNELL UNIVERSITY MEDICAL COLLEGE
NEW YORK, NEW YORK

and Paul H. Patterson

DEPARTMENT OF NEUROBIOLOGY
HARVARD MEDICAL SCHOOL
BOSTON, MASSACHUSETTS

I. Introduction 27
II. The Neural Crest 28
III. Neural Crest Migration 29
IV. Initial Phenotypic Expression 31
V. Change in Phenotype during Development 33
VI. Postnatal Development and Transsynaptic Regulation 36
References 38

I. Introduction

The extraordinary scope of neuronal plasticity has been appreciated only recently. The neuron is capable not only of altering structure and function quantitatively, but also of undergoing phenotypic transformation under appropriate circumstances. It is now well established from *in vivo* and *in vitro* studies that neurons may change transmitters, and thus phenotypes, during a relatively prolonged period of life. This, of course, has raised the possibility that neurons can change a variety of functions and capabilities, and that, for example, recovery after illness or regeneration after injury may be induced by appropriate treatments. In turn, a central issue in understanding the regulation of phenotypic expression in neurons, as well as other systems, concerns the relationship of intrinsic cellular information to environmental factors.

Is the developmental fate of the neuroblast completely determined extremely early in embryonic life? Alternatively, is the primitive neuron pluripotent, possessing a variety of potentials, any of which can be expressed depending on environmental conditons? Recent studies of

27

autonomic neuronal development have begun to address these, and related, questions. A number of experiments have clearly established that environmental signals play a critical role in the regulation of neurotransmitter choice. Moreover, the embryonic microenvironment may elicit phenotypic transformation in some autonomic neuroblasts as a normal stage in development. On the other hand, increasing evidence suggests that, in some sense, the neural crest and its derivatives are heterogeneous, expressing different phenotypic characters in response to seemingly similar environmental stimuli. This apparent paradox is examined in this chapter.

We describe autonomic development in sequence, from embryonic neural crest induction to transsynaptic regulation in postnatal ganglia, to illustrate the variety of influences affecting transmitter phenotypic expression. *In vivo*, tissue culture, and cell culture experiments are reviewed to analyze the manner in which heterogeneous cell populations interact with the environmental signals to define transmitter phenotypes. A number of recent reviews dealing with this subject are recommended (Black, 1978; Patterson, 1978; Varon and Bunge, 1978).

II. The Neural Crest

The peripheral autonomic system arises from the neural crest, a transient embryonic structure which develops from the neural plate, neural folds, and neural tube (Detwiler, 1937). The mechanisms underlying the derivation of neural crest from neural tube are unknown, although it has been suggested that lateral sectors of the archenteron roof induce crest formation (Raven and Kloos, 1945). All of the ectoderm of the neural plate–neural tube region may constitute presumptive neural crest (Raven, 1931), differentiation of which is dependent on appropriate signals from cells of the archenteron roof. However, the cells involved have not been clearly defined, the signals themselves remain unknown, and the precise intracellular events which comprise differentiation into crest are uncharacterized.

Are there, in fact, a set of characters which, in aggregate, constitute a unique neural crest phenotype? The evidence is incomplete. Recent work has suggested that crest cells may possess some unique properties prior to migration. Treatment of pregnant mice with L-dihydroxyphenylalanine (L-DOPA) is associated with the appearance of catecholamine (CA) histofluorescence in crest cells of intrauterine 7–8 somite embryos (Pearse and Polak, 1971). Apparently, crest cells possess the ability either to concentrate and decarboxylate L-DOPA, or to concentrate dopamine, norepinephrine, and/or epinephrine formed from L-DOPA and released by other embryonic cells. In either case, it is unclear whether the crest uptake process involves a stereospecific, energy-requiring, saturable, high-affinity uptake mechanism (Iversen, 1967), which could be regarded as a specific phenotypic trait. Moreover, the presence of DOPA-decarboxylase (L-aromatic amino acid decarboxylase) in crest cells cannot be regarded as phenotypically specific, since this enzyme is widely distributed in the organism (Sourkes, 1966). It would be of great interest, and experimentally very useful, to define those phenotypic traits, if any, which are uniquely expressed by neural crest cells prior to migration and further differentiation.

III. Neural Crest Migration

From the dorsal midline position adjacent to the neural tube, crest cells migrate throughout the embryo, giving rise not only to neurons, but also to chromatophores, nonneuronal cells of the peripheral nervous system, chromaffin cells, calcitonin-producing cells, and mesenchymal derivatives of the cephalic region (Coulombre et al., 1974). Cellular fate in general and neuronal fate in particular are influenced by the microenvironment encountered en route and at the definitive site. In turn, migration itself is dependent on environmental signals: grafting of newly condensed crest into progressively older hosts results in progressive attenuation of migration, which suggests that the embryonic microenvironment may be critical in regulating migration patterns (Weston and Butler, 1966). The mechanisms by which the environment regulates crest cell migration remain to be defined. This topic is discussed in more detail elsewhere (Le Douarin, this series, Volume 16).

The major pathways of neuronal differentiation of crest lead to development of sensory (Tennyson, 1965) and autonomic neurons (Pick, 1963). In turn, autonomic neurons may utilize a variety of transmitters, including acetylcholine and norepinephrine. Increasing evidence indicates that cellular interactions play a pivotal role in transmitter choice. In the chick embryo, appearance of catecholamine histofluorescence in presumptive sympathoblasts is influenced by interactions with somitic mesenchyme and, therefore, may require ventral crest migration (Cohen, 1972, 1973). In addition, ablation of ventral neural tube, including the notochord area, reduces the quantity of nervous tissue formed, which suggests that neural tube, notochord, somitic mesenchyme, and sympathoblasts undergo determinative interactions (Cohen, 1972, 1973). This contention is supported by in vitro studies of chick neural crest that demonstrate that for catecholamine differentiation crest cells must be contiguous with the somite (Cohen, 1973). Ventral neural tube may act across a millipore filter to induce appropriate changes in the somite (Cohen, 1973). In addition, the continued presence of ventral neural tube is required for survival of the differentiating sympathetic neurons. Ventral neural tube may be replaced by nerve growth factor (NGF) in assuring survival of the differentiating sympathetic neurons (Cohen, 1973). These observations suggest that ventral neural tube induces changes in somitic mesenchyme, which then promotes sympathoblast differentiation. In summary, ventral neural tube and somitic mesenchyme may elaborate diffusible factor(s) which directly or indirectly influence crest transmitter choice and survival.

Le Douarin and colleagues have analyzed migration and differentiation in avian systems (Le Douarin and Teillet, 1973, 1974; Le Douarin et al., 1975, 1977; Smith et al., 1977). Normally, the neural crest in the trunk region gives rise to CA-containing cells of sympathetic ganglia and adrenal medulla, whereas the "vagal" region (somites 1–7) gives rise to enteric ganglion cells, some of which are cholinergic. However, if trunk (sympathoadrenal) crest is grafted to the "vagal" region, the gut is colonized by enteric ganglion cells, some of which exhibit cholinergic functions. If, on the other hand, cephalic crest is transplanted to the "adrenomedullary level" in the trunk region, some of the cells exhibit adrenergic adrenomedullary chromaffin properties. It may be concluded that preferential migratory pathways are located at precise levels of the crest in the embryo and lead cells to their definitive sites. Moreover, the expression of a given phenotype may be regulated by the environment of the definitive site and/or by cells encountered en route.

These studies have not defined the manner in which the microenvironment influences transmitter choice in crest populations. Exogenous signals may *instruct* the neutral or unbiased crest cell to choose a specific transmitter. Alternatively, the environment may *select* one of several predetermined populations for survival. In this instance exogenous signals would not, of course, affect gene expression directly. It is extremely difficult to distinguish experimentally between these alternatives *in vivo*. However, as discussed below, experiments performed on sympathetic neurons in culture strongly suggest that the microenvironment can regulate, and even change, transmitter expression in single cells. It is possible, consequently, that the microenvironment exerts instructive, rather than selective influences.

In contrast to the foregoing observations on the regulation of phenotype by environmental cues, other studies have indicated that a portion of transplanted cephalic neural crest still differentiates into mesenchymal derivatives even when transplanted to the trunk area (Le Douarin and Teillet, 1974). Consequently, the phenotypic fate of certain crest derivatives may be defined early during development, may be relatively immutable, and may govern the pattern of migration. In fact, more recent work has indicated that phenotypic fate may be defined prior to migration in some crest populations. Neural crest cells removed from Japanese quail, and grown *in vitro* without other embryonic tissues, develop endogenous CA histochemical fluorescence and characteristic norepinephrine storage vesicles (Cohen, 1977). Although these observations suggest that transmitter fate can be defined before migration, it is possible that cell–cell interactions in culture resulted in the appearance of the noradrenergic phenotype. To examine this question, crest cell differentiation in culture has been examined at clonal density (Sieber-Blum and Cohen, 1978). Some cells did, in fact, develop catecholaminergic or melanotic characteristics under clonal conditions, suggesting that interaction with somite, neural tube, or other crest cells is not an absolute requirement for differentiation. However, it is also possible that the culture medium or the substratum contained developmental signals normally provided by embryonic tissues. Perhaps the most interesting result of the clonal study was that different cells within a clone developed catecholaminergic or melanotic characteristics, even though derived from a single cell and exposed to identical culture conditions (A. M. Cohen, personal communication). Conceivably, the culture environment contained a variety of developmental cues and the crest cell reacted in a stochastic fashion.

These observations complement other studies which indicate that the neural crest consists of a heterogeneous population. For example, as previously discussed, different cells in a crest transplant follow different migratory routes in the new embryonic environment. It is also clear that the crest follows a rostrocaudal developmental gradient, reflected by migration times, ganglion aggregation times, etc. (see the following). Consequently, different crest populations are at different developmental stages at any one time, and this variable alone could alter, or bias, a cell's response to its environment. Exposure to external signals may increase the probability of expression of a given phenotype in cells with different intrinsic biases.

IV. Initial Phenotypic Expression

The interaction of external signals and intrinsic neuronal biases may be better understood by characterizing sequential phenotypic expression in the developing neuroblast *in vivo*. This is a complex task, since mature transmitter function is dependent on the appearance of

32   IRA B. BLACK AND PAUL H. PATTERSON

biosynthetic enzymes, storage mechanisms, physiologic transmitter release, high-affinity re-uptake processes, and degradative enzymes.
Nevertheless, recent work has begun to define the initial expression of
noradrenergic characters in crest cells of the rat embryo. The ontogeny
of tyrosine hydroxylase (T-OH), the rate-limiting enzyme in
catecholamine biosynthesis (Levitt *et al.*, 1965), dopamine-β-
hydroxylase (DBH), which converts dopamine to norepinephrine, and
phenylethanolamine-N-methyltransferase (PNMT), which converts
norepinephrine to epinephrine, has been defined using an im-
munocytochemical approach (Cochard *et al.*, 1978a,b). The appearance
of the CA transmitters themselves has been documented by his-
tofluorescent methods (Cochard *et al.*, 1978a,b). In summary, this work
has indicated that a number of noradrenergic characters appear synchronously in the sympathetic ganglion primordia, and transiently appear in a population of neuroblasts within the embryonic gut. Tyrosine
hydroxylase, DBH, and CA simultaneously appear and disappear
within the gut neuroblasts over the course of 3 days. In contrast,
PNMT is not detectable in either neuroblast population during the
period of study (Cochard *et al.*, 1978b).

Tyrosine hydroxylase and DBH, as well as the CA transmitters, are
undetectable in the neural crest itself, the migrating crest cells, or any
other embryonic structures (Cochard *et al.*, 1978a,b). Tyrosine hydroxylase, DBH, and CA initially, and simultaneously, appear at 11.5
days of gestation (27–30 somites) in neuroblasts within the sympathetic primordia and those within the gut. In the ganglion *anlage,* the
noradrenergic phenotype appears in a rostrocaudal direction, re-
capitulating the sequence of crest migration and primitive ganglion
condensation (Cochard *et al.*, 1978b). The presence of intense CA histofluorescence in the neuroblasts suggests that storage mechanisms
and high-affinity re-uptake processes may also be present at this time,
although this remains to be demonstrated. Regardless, these observations indicate that, as a minimum, T-OH, DBH, DOPA decarboxylase
(which converts L-DOPA to dopamine), and CA are present in the
neuroblast at 11.5 days of gestation. On the other hand, in avian embryos, indirect biochemical and pharmacologic studies have suggested
that noradrenergic enzyme *activities* appear sequentially over a period
of days (Burack and Badger, 1964; Ignarro and Shideman, 1968).
Whole chick embryos converted [^{3}H]tyrosine to L-DOPA on the first day
of incubation, to dopamine on day 2 and to norepinephrine on day 4
(Ignarro and Shideman, 1968). However, since these studies were performed in whole embryos, and since recent work suggests that chick
embryo notochord can synthesize and store CA (Kirby and Gilmore,

1972; Lawrence and Burden, 1973; Allan and Newgreen, 1977; Strudel
et al., 1977), cellular localization is unclear. On the basis of the studies
in rat embryos, however, it is likely that a number of noradrenergic
characters appear synchronously within a given population of cells.

Expression of the adrenergic phenotype is regulated differently from
the noradrenergic phenotype, since PNMT is not detectable in developing neuroblasts or adrenal medullary cells when T-OH and DBH are
present. It is well documented that the development of PNMT in the
adrenal medulla phylogenetically (Coupland, 1953), and in sympathetic ganglia ontogenetically (Ciaranello et al., 1973), is stimulated by
glucocorticoids. It is not improbable then, that development of PNMT
requires a glucocorticoid stimulus, and would be apparent at a later
stage of maturation with the association of autonomic chromaffino-
blasts and adrenal cortex. In fact, this has recently been demonstrated
independently by two laboratories (Teitelman et al., 1978; Verhofstad
et al., 1980).

V. Change in Phenotype during Development

The gut neuroblasts may provide several clues to understanding
mechanisms governing phenotypic expression. As previously indicated,
T-OH, DBH, and CA appear in gut neuroblasts at 11.5 days of gestation. Cells exhibiting these characters increase in numbers over the
ensuing 24 hours, but by 14 days of gestation have virtually completely
disappeared.

To define the fate of the gut neuroblasts further, the high-affinity
uptake of norepinephrine was examined (Jonakait et al., 1979). Guts
were incubated with low concentrations of norepinephrine, and the
appearance of formaldehyde-induced histofluorescence due to CA was
defined. At 12.5 days of gestation, when the gut cells contain T-OH,
DBH, and endogenous CA, they also possess a high-affinity norepinephrine (NE) uptake system. Following incubation with NE, there is no
apparent increase in the number of fluorescent cells; rather, the uptake
and retention of CA by previously identified noradrenergic cells simply
enhance fluorescence of their nerve terminals (Jonakait et al., 1980). It
appears, consequently, that the gut neuroblasts which contain T-OH,
DBH, and CA also possess a highaffinity uptake system for NE.

By 13.5 days the cells have lost their characteristic transmitter
enzyme gene products and no longer exhibit endogenous CA
fluorescence. However, exposure to exogenous NE at this later stage
restores CA fluorescence, revealing a population of neuroblasts which
apparently retains the high-affinity uptake system for NE (Jonakait et
al., 1979). These observations strongly suggest, therefore, that the

same neuroblasts which lose T-OH, DBH, and endogenous CA retain the NE uptake mechanism for a period thereafter.

What is the fate of these neuroblasts? First, they may migrate out of the gut. This is unlikely because noradrenergic cells have not been observed in other locations, and the gut cells have already elaborated long cytoplasmic processes, rendering future migration improbable (Cochard et al., 1978a,b). Second, the gut neuroblasts may be destined to die. Last, the noradrenergic gut neuroblasts may constitute the progenitors of myenteric plexus neurons, which ultimately use other neurotransmitters. Consequently, the disappearance of noradrenergic characters may reflect conversion from norepinephrine to another transmitter. Previous work, performed both in vivo and in vitro, tends to favor the last alternative.

As previously discussed, in avian embryos, transplantation of presumptive noradrenergic neuroblast populations results in colonization of the gut and emergence of cholinergic enteric ganglion cells of donor origin. However, it is difficult to determine whether this change in the fate of the population is due to selective cell death, or change of the developmental fate of single cells. The most compelling evidence for the alteration of transmitter choice in individual neurons by environmental factors derives from studies on neonatal rat sympathetic neurons grown in dissociated cell culture. These neurons initially develop catecholaminergic properties, as indicated by morphological (Johnson et al., 1976) and biochemical (Mains and Patterson, 1973b) criteria. This is not surprising since, as previously discussed, these properties are expressed in the superior cervical ganglion (SCG) very soon after its formation (Coughlin et al., 1977; Cochard et al., 1978b), and even while the neuroblasts are still dividing (Cohen, 1973; Rothman et al., 1978). Under appropriate conditions, the cultured neurons continue to develop catecholaminergic properties, qualitatively paralleling ontogeny in vivo (Mains and Patterson, 1973b; Rees and Bunge, 1974; Patterson et al., 1975; Burton and Bunge, 1975; Patterson and Chun, 1977b). Under these circumstances, the development of cholinergic properties is minimal (Mains and Patterson, 1973a; Landis, 1976; Patterson and Chun, 1977b).

On the other hand, growth under certain conditions reverses the early catecholaminergic development, and cholinergic differentiation occurs instead. The neurons synthesize and store acetylcholine (ACh) (Patterson and Chun, 1974; Johnson et al., 1976; Patterson and Chun, 1977b) and form functional cholinergic synapses (O'Lague et al., 1974, 1978; Johnson et al., 1976; Ko et al., 1976), with appropriate cholinergic morphologic junctions (Johnson et al., 1976; Landis, 1976). It is possible to obtain sister cultures in which 100% of the neurons produce CA, or in which more than 90% produce ACh (Reichardt and Patterson, 1977), without significantly altering neuronal survival or growth (Patterson and Chun, 1977a). Thus individual sympathetic neurons have the capacity to become noradrenergic or cholinergic and this decision can be regulated by exogenous cues. In fact the neurons can reverse the initial catecholaminergic choice even after beginning to express that phenotype. The transition from catecholaminergic to cholinergic differentiation is largely reciprocal; most of the former CA properties are lost (Landis, 1976; Patterson and Chun, 1977a; Reichardt and Patterson, 1977). However, the mechanism for high-affinity uptake of CA does persist in the cholinergic neurons for some time (Landis, 1976; Reichardt and Patterson, 1977; Wakshull et al., 1978a). These observations in culture are entirely comparable to those previously discussed, in which the CA uptake mechanism persists in gut neuroblasts which have lost other noradrenergic characters. Moreover, the results obtained in vitro support the contention that the gut neuroblasts are converting to another transmitter phenotype in vivo.

If virtually all of the cultured neurons are noradrenergic at the outset, but then develop cholinergic functions, it might be possible to identify neurons which express both transmitter properties simultaneously. Such "dual-function" neurons have, in fact, been identified in microcultures containing single sympathetic neurons grown on islands of heart cells (Furshpan et al., 1976; Landis, 1976). These neurons can release both CA and ACh at functional synapses with cardiac myocytes. The frequency of occurrence and the duration of this dual function stage remain to be determined.

What is the nature of the environmental stimulus that causes the sympathetic neurons to become cholinergic? Such signals can be produced by certain types of nonneuronal cells and are found in a freely diffusible form in the culture medium (Patterson et al., 1975; Patterson and Chun, 1977a) and bound to the membranes of the nonneuronal cells (E. Hawrot, unpublished). In both cases the active factors have protein-like properties, and the diffusible factor has an apparent molecular weight of about 50,000 (M. Weber, unpublished). The particular types of cells that produce the factor(s) are of interest: there is a correlation between the degree of cholinergic innervation a tissue normally receives and its ability to produce this factor in culture (Patterson and Chun, 1977a). However, since fibroblasts also produce the factor, the importance of this correlation is not clear (Patterson, 1978).

It is useful to contrast the functional role of the diffusible cholinergic factor and NGF. The former is not necessary for the survival of sympathetic neurons, does not stimulate growth, but does regulate transmitter choice and synapse type. These effects are clearly different from those of NGF. Nerve growth factor is necessary for the survival of these neurons and does stimulate growth (Chun and Patterson, 1977a,b). However, NGF does not influence choice of transmitter; increasing concentrations of NGF in culture promote the differentiation of both catecholaminergic and cholinergic properties. In fact, in cultures producing both CA and ACh, NGF stimulates the production of both transmitters to the same extent (Chun and Patterson, 1977c). This permissive, as opposed to instructive role for NGF is consistent with the early observation that NGF is also necessary for the survival of a certain population of sensory neurons, which appear to produce neither CA nor ACh.

Recent work performed with rat embryos *in vivo* is consistent with these contentions. Treatment of rat embryos *in utero* with NGF results in increased numbers of the aforementioned noradrenergic neuroblasts in the gut, and persistence of these cells for a longer period (Kessler *et al.*, 1979). Although subject to a number of interpretations, these observations are consistent with the contention that NGF regulates survival and growth of neuroblasts already expressing the noradrenergic phenotype.

Clearly, phenotypic expression remains mutable long after neuroblast migration has terminated and mitosis has ceased. The culture experiments just described utilized ganglia from neonatal rats. Similar findings have recently been obtained in embryological studies *in vivo*. Transplantation of the cholinergic ciliary or Remak ganglia to the trunk neural crest level of younger avian embryos leads to migration of donor neurons. Migration to sympathetic ganglia or the adrenal gland results in the acquisition of CA histofluorescence (Le Douarin *et al.*, 1978). Conversely, localization to the gut wall results in differentiation into nonfluorescent, silver-staining ganglion cells. Furthermore, sympathetic neurons removed from *adult* rat ganglia can also express a measure of cholinergic function in culture (Johnson, 1978; Wakshull *et al.*, 1978b). However, evidence suggests that such plasticity is quantitatively less extensive as the neuron matures (Hill and Hendry, 1977; Patterson and Chun, 1977b; Ross *et al.*, 1977).

VI. Postnatal Development and Transsynaptic Regulation

Orthograde transsynaptic regulation in sympathetic ganglia is critical for quantitative aspects of noradrenergic expression during the postnatal period. Although the sympathetic neuron expresses noradrenergic characters prior to afferent innervation (see Section V), development of the normal complement of transmitter enzyme molecules is dependent on transsynaptic influences.

Transection of the preganglionic cholinergic trunk in neonatal mice or rats prevents the normal postnatal 6- to 10-fold increase in postsynaptic T-OH activity (Black et al., 1971, 1972). The effects of ganglion decentralization are reproduced by ganglionic blocking agents, which compete with acetylcholine for postsynaptic nicotinic receptor sites (Black and Geen, 1973, 1974). However, atropine, a muscarinic antagonist, has no effect on postsynaptic maturation (Black and Geen, 1974). These observations suggest that presynaptic terminals, through the mediation of the nicotinic properties of transsynaptic acetylcholine, regulate postsynaptic ontogeny. Although acetylcholine may be necessary for transsynaptic regulation, it may not be sufficient, since acetylcholine or its agonists cannot replace presynaptic terminals in this regulation (Black et al., 1972). Consequently, other transsynaptic factors may also be involved, as has been suggested for the neurotrophic regulation of striated muscle (Smith and Kreutzberg, 1976).

The developmental increase of T-OH activity could be due to the activation of preexistent enzyme molecules or the synthesis of new enzyme protein. Immunotitration with a specific antiserum to T-OH was used to distinguish between these alternatives (Black et al., 1974). The ontogenetic increase in T-OH activity in mouse and rat SCG is entirely attributable to accumulation of increased numbers of molecules per noradrenergic neuron (Black et al., 1974). The kinetics of the developmental rise in T-OH suggest that increased synthesis, and not decreased degradation, is responsible for neonatal development of the enzyme (Black et al., 1974). These immunochemical studies, and other physicochemical experiments (Black et al., 1974), suggest that there is no alteration in the species of T-OH synthesized during development. Rather, maturation appears to consist of accumulation of the same species of enzyme present in the neonate, in contrast to a number of nonneuronal systems in which cellular ontogeny progresses through sequential appearance and disappearance of different species of enzyme molecules (Paigen, 1971). Orthograde transsynaptic transmission may also play a role in transmitter choice. Chronic depolarization of sympathetic neurons in culture with elevated K^+ or veratridine leads to dramatic changes in the ratio of ACh to CA produced by these cells (Walicke et al., 1977). With depolarization, the neurons retain their initial noradrenergic character and become resistant to the cholinergic signal from nonneuronal cells. Such effects also occur if the neurons are simply stimulated electrically with action potentials at the physiological frequency of one per second. Thus, normal electrical activity can influence the choice of transmitter in these cells. Experiments with Ca^{2+} antagonists suggest that the effect of depolarization may be mediated by Ca^{2+} entry during electrical activity (Walicke et al., 1977). These observations raise the possibility that the majority of sympathetic neurons are preserved in their prenatal noradrenergic state in vivo, due to depolarization by the developing preganglionic innervation from the spinal cord. As a corollary, those few neurons destined to become cholinergic (and innervate certain blood vessels and sweat glands) may acquire preganglionic input only after being influenced by nonneuronal cells in the ganglion. Consequently, the selective formation of synapses between specific preganglionic axons and particular ganglionic neurons (Walicke et al., 1977) may not only determine circuitry, but may also influence the phenotypic expression.

REFERENCES

Allan, I. J., and Newgreen, D. F. (1977). Am. J. Anat. 149, 413–429.
Black, I. B. (1978). Annu. Rev. Neurosci. 1, 183–214.
Black, I. B., and Geen, S. C. (1973). Brain Res. 63, 291–302.
Black, I. B., and Geen, S. C. (1974). J. Neurochem. 22, 301–306.
Black, I. B., Hendry, I. A., and Iversen, L. L. (1971). Brain Res. 34, 229–240.
Black, I. B., Hendry, I. A., and Iversen, L. L. (1972). J. Neurochem. 19, 1367–1377.
Black, I. B., Joh, T. H., and Reis, D. J. (1974). Brain Res. 75, 133–144.
Burack, W. R., and Badger, A. (1964). Fed. Proc. 23, 561.
Burton, H., and Bunge, R. P. (1975). Brain Res. 97, 157–162.
Chun, L. L. Y., and Patterson, P. H. (1977a). J. Cell Biol. 75, 694–704.
Chun, L. L. Y., and Patterson, P. H. (1977b). J. Cell Biol. 75, 705–711.
Chun, L. L. Y., and Patterson, P. H. (1977c). J. Cell Biol. 75, 712–718.
Ciaranello, R. D., Jacobowitz, D., and Axelrod, J. (1973). J. Neurochem. 20, 799–805.
Cochard, P., Goldstein, M., and Black, I. B. (1978a). Proc. Natl. Acad. Sci. U.S.A. 75, 2986–2990.
Cochard, P., Goldstein, M., and Black, I. B. (1978b). Dev. Biol. 71, 100–114.
Cohen, A. L. (1972). J. Exp. Zool. 179, 167–192.
Cohen, A. M. (1973). In "Dynamics of Degeneration and Growth in Neurons" (K. Fuxe, L. Olson, and Y. Zotterman, eds.), pp. 359–370. Pergamon, New York.
Cohen, A. M. (1977). Proc. Natl. Acad. Sci. U.S.A. 74, 2899–2903.
Coughlin, M. D., Boyer, D. M., and Black, I. B. (1977). Proc. Natl. Acad. Sci. U.S.A. 74, 3438–3442.
Coulombre, A. J., Johnston, M. C., and Weston, J. A. (1974). Dev. Biol. 36, f15.
Coupland, R. E. (1953). J. Endocrinol. 9, 194–203.
Detwiler, S. R. (1937). Am. J. Anat. 61, 63–94.
Furshpan, E. J., MacLeish, P. R., O'Lague, P. H., and Potter, D. D. (1976). Proc. Natl. Acad. Sci. U.S.A. 73, 4225–4229.
Hill, C. E., and Hendry, I. A. (1977). Neuroscience 2, 741–749.
Ignarro, L. J., and Shideman, F. E. (1968). J. Pharmacol. Exp. Ther. 159, 38–48.
Iversen, L. L. (1967). In "The Uptake and Storage of Noradrenaline in Sympathetic Nerves," pp. 108–139. Cambridge Univ. Press, London and New York.

Johnson, M. (1978). *Soc. Neurosci. Abstr.* **4**, 343.

Johnson, M., Ross, D., Meyers, M., Rees, R., Bunge, R., Wakshull, E., and Burton, H. (1976). *Nature (London)* **262**, 308–310.

Jonakait, G. M., Wolf, J., Cochard, P., Goldstein, M., and Black, I. B. (1979). Submitted.

Kessler, J. A., Cochard, P., and Black, I. B. (1979). *Nature (London)* **280**, 141–142.

Kirby, M. L., and Gilmore, S. A. (1972). *Anat. Rec.* **173**, 469–478.

Ko, C. P., Burton, H., Johnson, M. I., and Bunge, R. P. (1976). *Brain Res.* **117**, 461–485.

Landis, S. C. (1976). *Proc. Natl. Acad. Sci. U.S.A.* **73**, 4220–4224.

Landis, S. C., MacLeish, P. R., Potter, D. D., Furshpan, E. J., and Patterson, P. H. (1976). *Soc. Neurosci. Abstr.* **2**, 197.

Lawrence, I. E., and Burden, H. W. (1973). *Am. J. Anat.* **137**, 199–208.

Le Douarin, N. M., and Teillet, M. A. (1973). *J. Embryol. Exp. Morphol.* **30**, 31–48.

Le Douarin, N. M., and Teillet, M. A. (1974). *Dev. Biol.* **41**, 162–184.

Le Douarin, N. M., Renaud, D., Teillet, M. A., and Le Douarin, G. H. (1975). *Proc. Natl. Acad. Sci. U.S.A.* **72**, 728–732.

Le Douarin, N. M., Teillet, M. A. M., and Le Lievre, C. (1977). *In* "Cell and Tissue Interactions" (J. Lash and M. Burger, eds.), pp. 11–27. Raven, New York.

Le Douarin, N. M., Teillet, M., Ziller, C., and Smith, J. (1978). *Proc. Natl. Acad. Sci. U.S.A.* **75**, 2030–2034.

Levitt, M., Spector, S., Sjoerdsma, A., and Udenfriend, S. (1965). *J. Pharmacol. Exp. Ther.* **148**, 1–8.

Mains, R. E., and Patterson, P. H., (1973a). *J. Cell Biol.* **59**, 329–345.

Mains, R. E., and Patterson, P. H. (1973b). *J. Cell Biol.* **59**, 361–366.

O'Lague, P. H., Obata, K., Calude, P., Furshpan, E. J., Potter, D. D. (1974). *Proc. Natl. Acad. Sci. U.S.A.* **71**, 3602–3606.

O'Lague, P. H., Potter, D. D., and Furshpan, E. J. (1978). *Dev. Biol.* **67**, 384–443.

Paigen, K. (1971). *In* "Enzyme Synthesis and Degradation in Mammalian Systems" (M. Rechcigl, Jr., ed.), pp. 1–46. Univ. Park Press, Baltimore, Maryland.

Patterson, P. H. (1978). *Annu. Rev. Neurosci.* **1**, 1–17.

Patterson, P. H., and Chun, L. L. Y. (1974). *Proc. Natl. Acad. Sci. U.S.A.* **71**, 3607–3610.

Patterson, P. H., and Chun, L. L. Y. (1977a). *Dev. Biol.* **56**, 263–280.

Patterson, P. H., and Chun, L. L. Y. (1977b). *Dev. Biol.* **60**, 473–481.

Patterson, P. H., Reichardt, L. F., and Chun, L. L. Y. (1975). *Cold Spring Harbor Symp. Quant. Biol.* **40**, 389–397.

Pearse, A. G. E., and Polak, J. M. C. (1971). *Gut* **12**, 783–788.

Pick, J. (1963). *J. Comp. Neurol.* **124**, 267–317.

Raven, C. P. (1931). *Roux Arch. Entwicklungs mech.* **125**, 210–292.

Rees, R., and Bunge, R. P. (1974). *J. Comp. Neurol.* **157**, 1–11.

Reichardt, L. F., and Patterson, P. H. (1977). *Nature (London)* **270**, 147–151.

Ross, D., Johnson, M., and Bunge, R. (1977). *Nature (London)* **267**, 536–539.

Rothman, T. P., Gershon, M. D., and Holtzer, H. (1978). *Dev. Biol.* **65**, 322–341.

Sieber-Blum, M., and Cohen, A. M. (1978). *J. Cell Biol.* **79**, 31a.

Smith, B. H., and Kreutzberg, G. W., eds. (1976). "Neurosciences Research Program Bulletin: Neuron-Target Cell Interactions," Vol. 14.

Smith, J., Cochard, P., and Le Douarin, N. M. (1977). *Cell Differ.* **6**, 199–216.

Sourkes, T. L. (1966). *Pharmacol. Rev.* **18**, 53–60.

Strudel, G., Recasens, M., and Mandel, P. (1977). *C. R. Acad. Sci. Ser. D* **284**, 967–969.

Teitelman, G., Baker, H., Joh, T. H., and Reis, D. J. (1978). *Soc. Neurosci.* **4**, 128.

Tennyson, V. (1965). *J. Comp. Neurol.* **124**, 267–317.

Varon, S. S., and Bunge, R. P. (1978). *Annu. Rev. Neurosci.* **1,** 327–361.
Verhofstad, A. A. J., Hökfelt, T., Goldstein, M., Steinbusch, H. W. M., and Joosten, H. W. J. (1980). *Cell and Tissue Res.* (in press).
Wakshull, E., Johnson, M., and Burton, H. (1978a). *J. Cell Biol.* **79,** 121–131.
Wakshull, E., Johnson, M., and Burton, H. (1978b). *Soc. Neurosci. Abstr.,* p. 1878.
Walicke, P. A., Campenot, R. B., and Patterson, P. H. (1977). *Proc. Natl. Acad. Sci. U.S.A.* **74,** 5767–5771.
Weston, J. A., and Butler, S. I. (1966). *Dev. Biol.* **14,** 246–266.

CHAPTER 3

BIOCHEMISTRY AND IMMUNOLOGY OF NEUROLOGICAL MUTANTS IN THE MOUSE

Jacques Mallet

SERVICE DE NEUROBIOLOGIE
DÉPARTEMENT DE BIOLOGIE MOLÉCULAIRE
INSTITUT PASTEUR
PARIS, FRANCE

I.	Introduction	41
II.	The Cerebellum and Some of Its Mutants	42
III.	Neurotransmission	45
	A. Neurotransmitters	45
	B. Receptors	47
	C. Cyclic Nucleotides	50
IV.	Attempts to Identify Components Characteristic of Neuronal Cell Types	52
	A. Cell Surface Carbohydrates	52
	B. Immunological Study of Purkinje Cells	54
	C. The P_{400} Protein	59
V.	Conclusions	61
	References	62

I. Introduction

How nerve circuits work and how these circuits come to be properly connected during development are two central questions in neurobiology. A powerful way to gain insight into these phenomena is to perturb the system in a controlled fashion and analyze the consequences of the perturbation. Afferences to a given cell can be destroyed, or proliferating cells can be selectively killed by X-ray irradiation or virus. Developmental flaws can also result from mutations, and those mutations which lead to well-characterized anatomical manifestations represent valuable tools for unraveling the complexity of the nervous system.

In mice more than a hundred mutations are known to affect the nervous system. Most of them have been classified by Sidman and his colleagues, and several represent good models for human heredodegenerative diseases (Sidman *et al.*, 1965; Sidman and Green, 1970). These mutations have fostered many genetic, anatomical, and electrophysiological studies. Biochemical and immunological analyses are, on the other hand, fewer in number. Demyelination mutants have

CURRENT TOPICS IN
DEVELOPMENTAL BIOLOGY, Vol. 15

been well analyzed, anatomically and biochemically, and most of this work has recently been reviewed by Hogan (1977). The present chapter will focus attention on mutants in the cerebellum. Many have been identified because their associated behavior is easily recognized. In addition, they represent modifications of a rather simple system and so are more likely to give straightforward answers.

Instead of presenting the accumulated data on each mutant investigated separately, I have chosen to discuss several topics which are presently the focus of greatest interest, in each case giving minimum background to the problem and emphasizing the information that has been gained from the use of mutants. In some instances, the investigation of mutants has not provided new information on a given problem but has helped in analyzing the extent of the mutation.

As an introduction to the discussion, a schematized description of the cerebellum and some of its neuropathological mutants is presented first.

II. The Cerebellum and Some of Its Mutants

Morphologically, five distinct types of neurons have been identified in the cerebellar cortex (Ramón y Cajal, 1911; Palay and Chan-Palay, 1974). This system receives two major excitatory afferences. One of them, the climbing fiber system, contacts Purkinje cells directly on proximal dendritic spines. The other is provided by the mossy fibers which contact the granule cells, by far the most numerous cell type on the cerebellum. The T-shaped axons of the latter form the parallel fibers which in turn make synapses on tertiary dendritic spines of Purkinje cells. Three other types of interneurons have been identified, viz. stellate, basket, and Golgi cells. Recently, a small number of noradrenergic inhibitory afferents from the locus coeruleus have been demonstrated that synapse with the Purkinje cell (Hökfelt and Fuxe, 1969; Bloom et al., 1971). In addition, some serotonergic fibers arising from the raphe nucleus have been found scattered throughout the molecular layer or ending as mossy fibers (Hökfelt and Fuxe, 1969; Bloom et al., 1972b; Palay, 1975).

The axons of the Purkinje cells constitute the only efference of the system and modulate muscle coordination during motion by controlling neuronal activity in deep cerebellar nuclei.

In mice, more than 10 mutations have been identified that lead to morphological changes in the cerebellum. We will first present two mutations in which the Purkinje cells seem to degenerate selectively, although to a certain extent: nervous (nr) and Purkinje cell degeneration (pcd). Then we will discuss three mutations in which granule cell degeneration predominantly occurs: weaver (*wv*), staggerer (*sg*), and reeler (*rl*).

Nervous (*nr*). In nervous (*nr*) recessive autosomal mutation (Sidman and Green, 1970), the Purkinje cells show abnormal mitochondria at about postnatal day 9, and start dying about day 15 (Landis, 1973a). By 2 months only 10% of the Purkinje cell population has survived in the cerebellar hemispheres and about 50% in the vermis; few changes occur thereafter.

In addition to the Purkinje cell loss, the nervous mutation leads to a slow degeneration of photoreceptor cells in the retina, starting in the second postnatal week and slowly progressing for at least a year (Mullen and Lavail, 1975).

Purkinje cell degeneration (*pcd*). Like nervous, *pcd* is an autosomal recessive mutation affecting Purkinje cells (Mullen et al., 1976); however, the time course of the disease process is much more rapid. Degeneration starts around day 15 and results in virtually complete loss of Purkinje cells 2 weeks later. In addition, Mullen (1977) has shown that the *pcd* locus exerts its primary effect within the Purkinje cells.

As do nervous mice, *pcd* mutants display a slow progressive retinal degeneration. In addition, the *pcd* mutation leads to a slow initial cell degeneration in the olfactory bulb and to sperm abnormalities in adult males.

Weaver (*wv*). Weaver (*wv*) is an autosomal, incompletely dominant mutation leading in homozygotes to massive degeneration of cerebellar granule cells. Death of the granule cells has been assigned to a failure of migration caused by an earlier abnormality of Bergman glia fibers (Rakic and Sidman, 1973), although this interpretation has been challenged (Bignami and Dahl, 1974; Sotelo and Changeux, 1974b).

In weaver, the Purkinje cells are never contacted by the parallel fibers. They nevertheless autonomously develop spines with morphologically normal postsynaptic specialization (Hirano and Dembitzer, 1974; Rakic, 1976; Sotelo, 1975). The large majority of the synaptic contacts have kept their specificity and can be classified as homologous synapses. However, heterologous synapse formation has also been observed in weaver (Sotelo, 1975).

Staggerer (*sg*). At an early age, all normal classes of synaptic connections, except for the parallel fiber Purkinje spine synapses, are present in mice carrying this autosomal recessive mutation (Sidman et al., 1962; Landis and Sidman, 1978). By postnatal day 14 granule cells undergo degeneration which could result from their failure to establish a normal synaptic connection (Sotelo and Changeux, 1974a) or could be due to a pleiotropic effect of the staggerer gene (Yoon, 1976). Around day 33, most of the granule cells have disappeared (Sidman, 1972, 1974; Sotelo, 1975). The staggerer is also characterized by an increased accumulation of a brain-filament-like protein (Lee et al., 1977). Why do most granule cells survive in nervous and pcd although their specific targets degenerate? A possible explanation is that in the nervous and pcd the Purkinje cells degenerate after synapses with granule cells have been established, and it is possible that these synaptic contacts, once formed, provide for the subsequent survival of granule cells.

Reeler (rl). Reeler (rl) autosomal recessive mutation causes extensive perturbation in the development of the cerebellum but also affects the cerebral cortex and hippocampal formation (see reviews by Caviness, 1977; Mariani et al., 1977). The mutation leads to a relative malposition of different neuronal classes in many laminated structures and, in particular, of the Purkinje cells in the cerebellum. The granular layer is also greatly reduced in this mutant. It is not known whether the reeler mutation has a pleiotropic effect simultaneously and independently altering both the proliferation of the granule cells and the position of the Purkinje cells or whether the hypoplasia of the granule cells is secondary to the mispositioning of the Purkinje cells.

The wet weight of the cerebella of agranular mutants is much reduced compared to their normal counterparts (see Table I). These decreases reflect the loss of granule cells, which represent the major popu-

TABLE I

WET WEIGHTS, DNA CONTENT, AND DNA OVER PROTEIN RATIO IN THE CEREBELLA FROM
WILD-TYPE AND HOMOZYGOUS WEAVER, STAGGERER, REELER, NERVOUS, AND pcd MICE[a]

Strain	Wet weight (mg per cerebellum)	DNA (gm per cerebellum)	DNA/protein (gm/gm)
B6/CBA/51 (+/+) 22 days	44.5 ± 2.7 (10)	226 ± 53 (5)	0.056 ± 0.014
B6/CBA/51 (wv/wv) 20 days	13.5 ± 0.5 (10)	33 ± 5 (7)	0.030 ± 0.019
C57BL (dse+/dse+) 20 days	42.2 ± 2.7 (4)	238 ± 53 (3)	0.059
C57BL (++sg/++sg) 19 days	7.85 ± 1.3 (4)	25 ± 2 (4)	0.038 ± 0.006
C3HcB/5 (+/+) 71 ± 6 days	59.2 (2)	248 (2)	0.037
C2HcB/5 (nr/nr) 71 ± 6 days	34.9 (2)	201 (2)	0.047
C57BL/C (+/+) 20 days	39.1 (4)	281 (4)	0.070
C57BL/C (rl/rl) 2 days	13.8 (3)	35 (3)	0.030
C57BL/6 (+/+) 35 days	49.85 (2)	293 (2)	
C57BL/6 (pcd/pcd) 35 days	33.75 (2)	259 (2)	

[a] The numbers of cerebella used in each case are given in parentheses. Adapted from Mallet et al. (1976), Mariani et al. (1977), and Mikoshiba et al. (1979).

lation of cerebellar cells (Palay and Chan-Palay, 1974). Also, granule cells contain a large heterochromatic nucleus surrounded by very little cytoplasm. This characteristic property was used to confirm that the hypoplasia of these mutants affects granule cells in particular. First, nuclear proteins such as histones and more particularly histone F_1 were barely visible on sodium dodecyl sulfate (SDS) polyacrylamide gels (Mallet et al., 1974, 1976; Beckingham, 1976; Mariani et al., 1977). Also, in weaver, staggerer, and reeler, the DNA content was reduced more than was their wet weight and the DNA-to-protein ratio was found to be decreased relative to controls (Table I).

In the nervous, the loss of DNA (Table I) is only 10–20%. This decrease reflects the loss of Purkinje cells which is accompanied by that of some other neurons (granule cells in particular (Landis, 1973b). Because of the extremely low DNA-to-cytoplasm ratio of the Purkinje cells (according to Sidman, 1974, the volume of the axons plus dendrites is 16 times that of the soma), the disappearance of the Purkinje cells and of their processes might cause a significant increase in the DNA-to-protein ratio of the cerebellum. Indeed, contrary to what was observed with the agranular mutant, the DNA-to-protein ratio increases as a consequence of the nervous mutation. In pcd mutants, only a small decrease of the DNA content was observed with respect to controls (Table I).

III. Neurotransmission

A. NEUROTRANSMITTERS

The choice of a given neurotransmitter is the most characteristic of the differentiated properties of a neuron. Little is known of the neurotransmitters of the cerebellum, although it is a relatively simple system. So far, only the GABAergic nature of the Purkinje cells has been firmly established (Fonnum et al., 1970; McLaughin et al., 1974; Obata and Takeda, 1969; Otsuka et al., 1971; Storm-Mathisen, 1975).

The mutants given in Section II represent a unique opportunity to correlate cerebellar development with neurotransmitter biochemistry. It is most important to establish a correlation between the decrease of a given neurotransmitter or its synthetic enzymes and the lack or paucity of a specific cell type and then infer the nature of the neurotransmitter that this cell type utilizes.

The level of many putative neurotransmitters has been measured in the cerebellum and other brain areas of cerebellar mutant mice. The most interesting finding is a decrease of about 70% of the content of glutamate in the cerebella of weaver, staggerer, and reeler mutants with respect to control animals (Hudson *et al.*, 1976; McBride *et al.*, 1976; Roffler-Tarlov and Sidman, 1978). These mutants are characterized by an almost complete absence of granule cells and the most logical interpretation of the decreased content of glutamate in their cerebella is that the concentration of glutamate is higher in granule cells than in other cells in the cerebellum. This may be a reflection of a transmitter role for this amino acid. A number of studies have demonstrated that glutamate is excitatory when iontophoretically applied to cerebellar Purkinje cells (Kawamura and Provini, 1970; Woodward *et al.*, 1971, 1974; Geller and Woodward, 1974). In addition Young *et al.* (1974) reported that a selective depletion of glutamic acid was associated with a viral-induced loss of granule cells in the hamster cerebellum. They also found that the high-affinity uptake of glutamate was reduced by 70%. Thus the data are consistent with the interpretation that glutamate may be functioning as an excitatory transmitter released from the granule cells in the cerebellar cortex. Nevertheless, a rigorous interpretation of these data is not possible.

Although the decrease in the content of glutamate in the weaver and staggerer mutants might reflect a high concentration of glutamate in granule cells, it could also reflect changes in the metabolism of existing cells and/or possible loss of supportive glial cells. The inherent difficulties of interpretation are emphasized by the finding (Roffler-Tarlov and Sidman, 1978) that a similar loss of glutamate occurs in the isolated deep cerebellar nuclei of the weaver and staggerer mice. These results do not discount the possibility that glutamate is the neurotransmitter of the granule cells but call for another explanation as far as the deep nuclei are concerned, particularly for weaver where the deep nuclei have a normal weight.

Still more evidence is needed before glutamate is firmly established as a neurotransmitter of the granule cells. Experiments to compare specific calcium-dependent release of glutamate from normal and granuloprival cerebellar cortex and deep nuclei may further help to define its role. In any case, the granuloprival mutants represent the best model available for identifying a neurotransmitter, because the granule cells represent numerically the most abundant neuronal type in the cerebellum.

As for the Purkinje cells, for example, although GABA is well established as their transmitter, whole cerebellar extracts from nervous mice show no change in GABA concentration (McBride *et al.*, 1976). Loss of GABA in cerebellar cortex after death of Purkinje cells is either too slight to be recognized in a region rich in other GABA-containing fractions or offset by an increased net GABA content of these other cells.

Analysis of the levels of the neurotransmitters or of their enzymes can also be a means to assess the extent of the mutation within the cerebellum. Beart and Lee (1977) have analyzed the transmitter enzymes glutamate decarboxylase, GABA transaminase, choline acetylase, and tyrosine hydroxylase in the cerebella of weaver and staggerer mice and their controls. In all cases, they observed a reduction in the total enzyme activity in the cerebella of the mutant mice. A possible explanation is that the number of GABAergic, cholinergic, and noradrenergic neurons is reduced in staggerer and weaver. Alternatively, the existing neurons may be modified such that they contain fewer enzyme molecules, or both changes may occur.

Biochemical analysis also allows us to determine whether the mutations are confined to the cerebella.

For example, gross changes were not observed in the size or weight of the cerebrum of staggerer, weaver, and nervous, and in fact McBride *et al.* (1976) found very few changes in levels of the putative amino acid neurotransmitters in brain stems or cerebra of these three mutants. In contrast, when Black (1976a,b) studied the catecholamine enzymes in locus coeruleus neurons of the weaver which are deprived of a normal field of innervation, he found that activity of tyrosine hydroxylase (T-OH) and dopamine-β-hydroxylase (DBH) was increased by a factor of two. This alteration in enzyme activity appeared to be specific for the locus coeruleus. The increase may be due to factors intrinsic to the locus coeruleus neurons or may be secondary to influences external to the adrenergic cell such as faulty locus cerebellar connections.

Lane *et al.* (1977) found that the abnormalities on the weaver extend to the forebrain, in which there is a 52% decrease in the level of dopamine, a 18% increase in the level of serotonin, and a 16% increase in the level of norepinephrine with respect to control values. In contrast, in the staggerer and nervous mutants, the levels of these three biogenic monoamines show no significant differences from their respective controls.

Clearly, these results show that in the weaver, the mutation is not confined exclusively to the cerebellum and primary or secondary effects occur elsewhere.

B. Receptors

1. β-Adrenoreceptors

I have indicated that noradrenergic axons form inhibitory synapses with Purkinje cells. Recently, Atlas and Levitzki (1977) have synthesized a high-affinity fluorescent β-blocker (9-aminoacridine propranolol; 9-AAP) which allows the localization of β-adrenoreceptors *in situ*. This method was used by Melamed *et al.* (1976) to investigate the localization of the β-adrenoreceptors in the cerebellum and they, indeed, found the fluorescence of the 9-AAP in the Purkinje cell layer. However, this study did not eliminate the possibility that labeling of presynaptic receptor or uptake sites of the propranolol-like compound into noradrenergic terminals had occurred. These possibilities were eliminated following the observation that, after selective degeneration of adrenergic axon, the fluorescence of the Purkinje cell layers remains (Atlas *et al.*, 1977). The fluorescence was even increased implying supersensitivity at the central noradrenergic synapses.

Final proof that the 9-AAP fluorescence is indeed associated with Purkinje cells was obtained from studies on the nervous mutant (Atlas *et al.*, 1977). In this case no fluorescence was observed at the interface between the molecular and granular layers. Only in some regions were fluorescence rings occasionally observed which most certainly corresponded to residual Purkinje cells which had not degenerated.

The fluorescent mapping of the β-adrenoreceptor has been used in several other instances. Nevertheless a word of caution was very recently sounded by Hess (1979) who claimed that the fluorescence that is attributed to 9-AAP might, in some cases, be due only to autofluorescent granules.

2. GABA Receptors

Cerebellum has been found to contain the highest density of GABA binding sites in the brain (Zukin *et al.*, 1974; Enna and Snyder, 1975; Olsen *et al.*, 1978). Golgi, basket, stellate, and Purkinje cells are inhibitory and probably utilize GABA as neurotransmitter. To analyze the density of GABA receptors associated with various cell types Simantov *et al.* (1976) studied the Na^+-independent [^{3}H]GABA binding in hamster cerebella which had suffered a viral-induced granule cell loss. Their results suggest that over 50% of GABA receptor binding sites in the cerebellum are associated with granule cells. Recently, Olsen and Mikoshiba (1978) analyzed the Na^+-independent [^{3}H]GABA binding in several mutants and controls. They found that the binding of GABA, per milligram of protein, is four times lower in weaver, staggerer, and reeler mutants than their respective controls. In contrast, no difference could be found between nervous and its control. These findings substantiated those of Simantov *et al.* (1976) and seem to indicate the presence of considerable amounts of GABA binding sites on granule cells.

It should be noted that, surprisingly, even between control strains, the numbers of GABA binding sites may vary by a factor of 4 (Olsen and Mikoshiba, 1978). It is perhaps unfortunate that these workers did not determine whether this fluctuation reflected methodological problems or was the result of the different ages of the animals.

3. Benzodiazepine Receptors

High-affinity benzodiazepine binding sites that are both stereospecific and saturable have recently been characterized in the mammalian central nervous system (Squires and Braestrup, 1977; Möhler and Okada, 1977a,b; Williamson et al., 1978). The good correlation obtained between the binding affinities of a series of benzodiazepines and their potencies as anticonvulsants, anxiolytics, and muscle relaxants strongly suggests that these sites may function as pharmacological receptors for benzodiazepines (Squires and Braestrup, 1977; Möhler and Okada, 1977b).

In cerebellum the Purkinje cells have been shown to be sensitive to benzodiazepine both neurochemically (Costa et al., 1975) and electrophysiologically (Pieri and Haefely, 1976; Mariani and Delhaye-Bouchaud, 1978). To determine if the benzodiazepine receptors are present on Purkinje cells, different groups have compared the binding of [³H]diazepam in cerebella of nervous mice with that of controls. At an age of 60–70 days, Lippa et al. (1978) found that the binding in mutant mice was reduced to 17% of normal littermate values. Scatchard analysis revealed a marked reduction in the maximum number of benzodiazepine binding sites in nervous with no apparent alteration in receptor affinity for [³H]diazepam. In control experiments performed with 15- to 21-day nervous mice, no difference was observed. These results demonstrate an age-related loss of benzodiazepine receptors in the cerebellum of mutant mice, parallel to that observed for the degeneration of cerebellar Purkinje cells. Similar studies were carried out by Skolnick et al. (1979) who found that the [³H]diazepam binding in 70- to 80-day nervous mice was reduced to 79% of that in normal mice. The different results might reflect the use of different membrane fractions in these two sets of experiments. Skolnick et al. used a total tissue homogenate for their binding assay while Lippa et al. used a "P₂" membrane fraction. Clearly, these results suggest that the Purkinje cells possess a large number and high density of diazepam receptors. In contrast, no reduction has been found in weaver mice (cited in Skolnick et al., 1979), suggesting that the granule cells do not carry benzodiazepine receptors.

It should be noted that the data on GABA and benzodiazepine high-affinity binding presented suggest that distribution of the two classes of binding site is not similar in the cerebellum, indicating that they are not always closely associated.

C. CYCLIC NUCLEOTIDES

High levels of cyclic nucleotides have been found in the brain, and their possible role in mediating the postsynaptic action of neurotransmitters has been stressed (Greengard, 1976; Daly, 1977). Cerebellar mutants offer interesting material for identifying the cell types in which cyclic AMP or cyclic GMP may intervene to regulate neuronal transmission.

1. Cyclic AMP

Cyclic AMP (cAMP) is present in large amounts in the brain, and its distribution in the cerebellum is rather homogeneous (Bloom et al., 1972a). Biochemical studies on brain slices (Kakiuchi and Rall, 1968; Palmer et al., 1969) or homogenates (Klainer et al., 1962; Weiss and Costa, 1968; Weiss and Kidman, 1969) show that certain neurotransmitters including norepinephrine (Rall, 1971) can regulate the level of cAMP, which suggests that this nucleotide plays a role in central adrenergic neurotransmission.

Adrenergic terminals exist throughout the cerebellum (Battenberg and Bloom, 1975; Rubin et al., 1976), but in view of the existence of a noradrenergic pathway from the locus coeruleus to the Purkinje cells, the question arose as to whether an adenylate cyclase activity was associated with Purkinje cells. First, using an immunofluorescent histochemical technique for cAMP localization, Siggins et al. (1973) found that iontophoretic application of epinephrine or stimulation of the norepinephrine-containing afferent from the locus coeruleus led to a striking increase in the number of Purkinje cells with strong cyclic adenosine monophosphate reactivity. Other putative inhibitory neurotransmitters had no significant effect on staining of Purkinje cells.

To confirm this observation and obtain more quantitative data, Schmidt and Nadi (1977) compared the content of cAMP in slices of cerebella from nervous mice and their normal littermates. The basal levels of cAMP per milligram protein were quite similar, which confirmed the staining experiments of Siggins et al. (1973) showing that cAMP was present in both granule and Purkinje cells. However, upon addition of 10^{-4} M norepinephrine, the level of cAMP increased about 25-fold in the normal mice and 38-fold in the nervous mutants. This result can be explained either by the existence of a considerable number of noradrenergic synapses impinging on neurons other than Purkinje cells or by a supersensitivity of the noradrenergic receptors of the remaining 10% of Purkinje cells. In this respect it would be interesting to carry out the experiment on slices of the *pcd* mutant, which retains only 1% of its Purkinje cell population.

2. Cyclic GMP

Investigations into the identification of cerebellar cells containing cyclic GMP (cGMP) was first prompted by the observation that this tissue contains the highest level of cGMP of any tissue.

Most of the cGMP was thought to be associated with the Purkinje cells. It was clearly shown that the cGMP levels were dependent upon the activity of the climbing fibers. Excitation of these fibers by harmaline, which induces tremors, elicited a severalfold increase in the level of cGMP in the cerebellar cortex (Mao *et al.* 1975a). Also, after chemical destruction of these fiber by 3-acetylpyridine (Guidotti *et al.*, 1975), the tremorogenic effect of harmaline disappeared and there was no increase in cerebellar cortex cGMP.

Further, an increase in cGMP was observed after administration of drugs that reduce or block the function of the GABAergic system. In particular, much attention has been devoted to the antiepileptic drug diazepam, which has been reported (Mao *et al.*, 1975a) to lower levels of cGMP in the cerebellum *in vivo*, and antagonized the tremors and accumulation of cGMP produced by harmaline. To ascertain that a sizable pool of the cGMP occurs in the Purkinje cells, Mao *et al.* (1975b) compared the content of cGMP in normal and nervous mice and found that the nervous contained 80% less cGMP than the normal counterparts. They also observed that diazepam reduces the concentration of cGMP in normal mice to values similar to those observed in nervous mice and has no effect on the cGMP concentration in nervous mice. These observations suggest that a large cGMP pool resides in Purkinje cells and that excitatory and inhibitory influences on Purkinje cells have an important regulatory effect on the size of this pool. It should be noted in passing that these results corroborate data described which indicated that receptors for benzodiazepines on Purkinje cells exist.

The pool of cGMP seems also to be controlled by the parallel fibers. Biggio and Guidotti (1976) showed that in rats treated with 3-acetylpyridine, which leads to a degeneration of the climbing fibers and leaves intact all other cerebellar elements, glutamate, a putative neurotransmitter for the parallel fibers, increased the cGMP level to the same extent as in control rats. It was tempting to conclude that the cGMP pool residing in the Purkinje cells is also affected by glutamate.

In this regard Schmidt *et al.* (1977) reported that kainic acid, a conformationally restricted cyclic analog of glutamic acid, was a potent stimulant of cAMP and cGMP synthesis in slices of rat and mouse cerebella. They suggested that this glutamate-like compound might be acting selectively on Purkinje cells. To test this hypothesis, Schmidt and Nadi (1977) examined *in vitro* the effect of kainic acid on nervous mice. When low doses of kainic acid were used ($10^{-4} M$), the synthesis of cGMP was reduced in nervous compared to controls, supporting the hypothesis that kainic acid stimulates the Purkinje cells to synthesize cGMP.

However, when high concentrations ($10^{-3} M$) of kainic acid (Schmidt and Nadi, 1977) or agents that cause cellular depolarization (Nadi and McBride, 1976) are used, the difference in the elevation of cGMP levels between nervous and normal mice disappears. This observation suggests the existence in the cerebellum of another pool of cGMP that has not yet been localized.

Finally, Bandle and Guidotti (1978) studied the localization of cGMP monophosphate-dependent protein kinase in normal and nervous mice and could conclude that this enzyme was mostly associated with the Purkinje cells.

IV. Attempts to Identify Components Characteristic of Neuronal Cell Types

During the development of the nervous system, various cell types are positioned and connected in an orderly manner, and it is commonly believed that characteristic molecules of the cell surface play a role in determining this organization. Various approaches have been used to identify such molecules.

A. CELL SURFACE CARBOHYDRATES

The cell surface carbohydrates which are prominent constituents of the external faces of plasma membrane are thought to play an important role during histogenesis (Roseman, 1974; Burger *et al.*, 1975). The first few days after birth represent an important period in the development of the mouse cerebellum and it has been shown that this period is associated with changes in cell surface carbohydrates (Trenker and Sarkar, 1977; Hatten and Sidman, 1978).

It was of interest to analyze and to compare the carbohydrate composition of the surface of cerebellar cells from normal and mutant mice. More particularly, the staggerer, in which synapses between the parallel fiber axons of the granule cells and the dendrites of Purkinje cell neurons fail to form, appeared suitable for such an analysis.

Hatten and Messer (1978) investigated the cell surface of staggerer cerebellar cells with lectins. Cerebellar cells were dissociated with trypsin and allowed to recover from this treatment, and the agglutination of cells was measured in the presence of concanavalin A (Con A) and wheat germ agglutinin (WGA).

The experiments were performed before and after birth on normal mice and on the seventh and tenth day after birth (P7, P10) on the staggerer (P7 being the earliest age when staggerer animals can be identified). The results are summarized in Table II and clearly show that cell surface properties necessary for WGA-induced agglutination are abnormal in the mutant cerebellar cell population whereas those necessary for Con A-induced agglutination are not.

TABLE II

AGGLUTINATION OF STAGGERER AND WILD-TYPE CELLS WITH CON A AND WGA[a]

Genotype	Age	WGA	Con A
Wild type C57BL/6J	E13	50	200
	P0	450	800
	P3	>500	>1000
	P7	>500	>1000
	P10	>500	>1000
Wild type +dse/+dse	P7	>500	>1000
	P10	>500	>1000
Staggerer sg++/sg++	P7	55	>1000
	P10	48	>1000

[a] Values for C57BL/6J embryonic animals are taken from Hatten and Sidman (1978). Values for postnatal wild-type and staggerer animals are given as lectin concentration (micrograms per milliliter) required for half maximum agglutination (75%). From Hatten and Messer (1978).

Trenkner (1979) used antibodies specifically directed against microbial polysaccharides as carbohydrate probes for developing cerebellar cell populations, *in vitro*. Cerebellar cells were maintained in culture in microwells and the number of fiber cables formed between cell aggregates was determined as a quantitative assay for antibody reactivity.

Antimeningococcus type-B polysaccharide antibodies (anti-B) (antigenic determinant neuraminic acid) were shown to react preferentially with pre- and neonatal cerebellar cells of C57BL/6J mice, but did not react with 7-day-old (P7) cells. Anti-α-1,6-mannan antibodies, on

TABLE III

FIBER OUTGROWTH IN MICROWELL CULTURES OF 7-DAY-OLD sg/sg AND +/+ CEREBELLUM
IN THE PRESENCE OF ANTICARBOHYDRATE ANTIBODIES[a]

| | | | Number of fibers in six microwells | | | |
Experiment	Antibody	Dilution	+/+	Inhibition (%)	sg/sg	Inhibition (%)
1	Rabbit serum	1:50	180		193	
2			178		169	
3			222		176	
1	Anti-B	1:200	162	10	16	92
2			148	17	12	93
3			195	12	38	78
1	Anti-α-1,6-mannan	1:300	14	92	129	33
2			2	99	118	30
3			8	96	108	39

[a] A single-cell suspension (1×10^7 cells/ml) of 7-day-old +/+ and sg/sg cerebellum, respectively, was plated at 5 μl per microwell and 5 μl of antibody dilution in medium then added. Fiber formation was scored in six microwells after 2 days *in vitro* using a phase contrast light microscope. The variation among cultures was determined as = 20%. The data represent the total number of fibers in six microwells obtained in three different experiments. The number of fibers obtained in cultures containing rabbit serum was used as standard for 100% fiber formation per experiment. From Trenkner (1979).

the other hand, react with both prenatal and postnatal cerebellar cells (Table III).

These results are compatible with those of Hatten and Messer (1978) in showing the persistence of characteristic features of the embryonic cerebellar cell surface in the staggerer.

Further studies are required to elucidate the significance of the expression of immature and/or altered cell-surface molecules in the sg/sg mutation. The cell types which are abnormal should be identified as a first step in determining the role of cell surface carbohydrates in the abnormal cerebellar development of sg/sg.

B. IMMUNOLOGICAL STUDY OF PURKINJE CELLS

The specificity and the sensibility of the immune system is well suited to reveal and characterize the antigens, if any, which are specific to a given tissue or cell type. Mallet et al. (1979) have analyzed the antibodies raised against an enriched population of Purkinje cells. In the course of the work the use of the mutant *pcd* has been instrumental in firmly establishing the existence in the serum of antibodies directed specifically against Purkinje cells.

The Purkinje cells account for only a small percentage of the total cell number in the cerebellum. It was thus imperative to immunize with an enriched cell population. Absorption of the sera on various tissues was required to purify cell-specific antibodies.

Purkinje cells were purified following the method of Sellinger *et al.* (1974). Unlike other methods this purification does not include a trypsinization step, which is known to alter surface antigens to a large extent. Only 5–10×10^5 cells were injected in rabbits. Nevertheless, by the Ouchterlony diffusion test, the best serum gave several precipitation lines against cerebellar membranes solubilized by nondenaturing detergents.

Quantitative information on the strength and specificity of the anti-Purkinje cell serum was obtained by a direct binding assay. Increasing amounts of cerebellar membranes were added to a fixed amount of ^{125}I-labeled IgG. The ^{125}I-labeled IgG which binds to cerebellar membranes was then estimated by Millipore filtration.

This method, combined with absorption experiments, allowed Mallet *et al.* to test quantitatively the specificity of the IgG with respect to various tissues. About 2% of the antibodies bound to an excess of cerebellar membranes. Of those 7% were not absorbed by liver, heart, and cerebrum membranes and were specifically directed against cerebellar antigens (Fig. 1).

The specificity of the anti-Purkinje cell serum toward the Purkinje cell was analyzed by making use of the *pcd* mutant. The binding curves with cerebellar membranes from normal and *pcd/pcd* mice with unabsorbed and absorbed ^{125}I-labeled anti-Purkinje cell antibodies are compared in Fig. 3. Before absorption (Fig. 2A) a small difference between the two curves was already apparent. After absorption on liver and heart membranes, the difference became more significant. About 17% of the antibodies did not bind to *pcd/pcd* cerebellar membranes (Fig. 2B). Finally, after absorption on cerebrum, this fraction increased up to 75% (Fig. 2C). The binding to *pcd/pcd* cerebellar membranes was nevertheless still significant compared to the nonspecific binding which was identical with membranes prepared from normal and mutant cerebella.

The differences observed between *pcd* and normal mice cerebella unambiguously show that the anti-Purkinje cell serum contains antibodies directed against antigens which are specific to the Purkinje cell. However, about 25% of the cerebellum-specific antibodies are as-

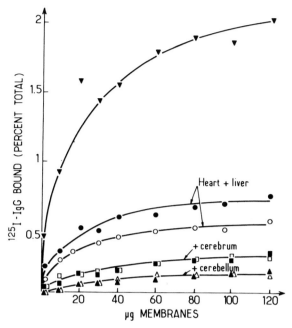

FIG. 1. Binding of ^{125}I-labeled anti-Purkinje cell IgG on rat cerebellar membranes after successive absorptions. Absorptions and binding assays were performed as described by Mallet *et al.* (1979). Unabsorbed serum (▼), serum absorbed once (●) and twice (○) with liver and heart membranes, then once (■) and twice (□) with cerebrum membranes, and finally once (▲) and twice (△) with cerebellum membranes. From Mallet *et al.* (1979).

sumed to correspond to antigens present in other categories of cells in the cerebellum.

Indirect immunofluorescent staining of cerebellar tissue slices confirmed that the cerebrum-absorbed serum contained antibodies directed against the Purkinje cells (Fig. 3). No staining could be detected in the granular layer. However, not surprisingly, analysis of other brain regions revealed that the antiserum also stained large cerebellar nuclei and brain stem cells. This finding corroborated and extended the results gained from the comparative binding assays performed with *pcd/pcd* membranes (Woodhams *et al.*, 1979).

Interestingly, a further absorption of the serum with brain stem membranes removed the staining not only of the large cells of the brain stem, but also of the deep nuclei while the Purkinje cells were still positive. The specificity of staining vis-à-vis large neurons from the deep nuclei is interesting in view of the fact that these neurons and the

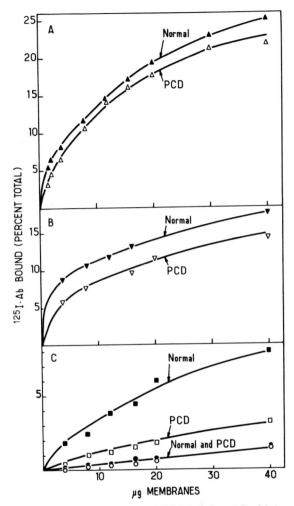

FIG. 2. Comparative binding of enriched ¹²⁵I-labeled anti-Purkinje cell antibodies to normal and *pcd/pcd* mouse cerebellar membranes. Anti-Purkinje cell antibodies were enriched by selective adsorption and subsequent elution from cerebellar membranes. (A) Unabsorbed antibodies. (B) Antibodies were absorbed on heart and liver membranes. (C) Antibodies were further absorbed with cerebrum membranes (■ and □) and, finally, in order to determine the nonspecific binding, antibodies were absorbed with cerebellum membranes (● and ○). From Mallet *et al.* (1979).

Purkinje cells have a common origin and are generated in development at a similar time (Altman and Bayer, 1978).

The immunohistochemical approach has proved very useful because it allows the site of reaction of the antibody to be localized not only to a

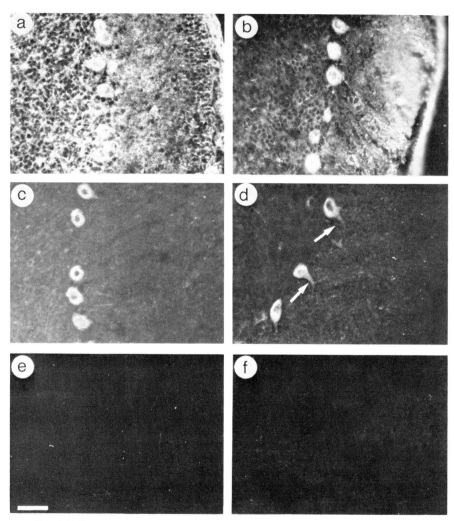

FIG. 3. Indirect immunofluorescence staining of transverse sections of 14-day-old rat cerebella. (a) Note the bright fluorescence of the internal granular layer with unabsorbed serum. Progressive absorptions on membranes from heart and liver (b), forebrain (c), brain stem (d), and cerebellum (e). Purkinje cell dendrites are clearly visible in (a) (arrows). Control incubation with preimmune serum is shown in (f). Scale bar = 50 μm. From Woodhams et al. (1979).

particular region of the brain but also within the organ in question. However, the specificity of an antibody for a given tissue or cell type cannot be ascertained if only this technique is used. Antigens present in lower amount in some cells than in others may escape detection.

The antigens corresponding to the cerebellum and Purkinje cell-specific antibodies have not yet been identified. The Purkinje cell-specific antibodies can be of use as cell markers in cultures of explants or dissociated cells and allow one to map the appearance and development of those cells during embryogenesis. It remains to establish the subcellular localization of the cerebellum-specific antigens, and particularly to see if they are surface antigens.

The immunological approach with a view to obtaining cell-specific antisera has been used in many instances (see references in Mallet *et al.*, 1979; Stallcup and Cohn, 1979). While each of these studies has provided useful information, none of the antisera that have been analyzed have been shown to be specific for a particular type of cell. This, for the most part, is due to the fact that heterogeneous tissues have been used for immunization because most cell types cannot be purified to homogeneity in sufficient amount. Several workers have circumvented this hurdle by immunizing with cloned cell lines. However, cloned cell lines suffer from the drawback that the cells may differ in several respects from their normal counterparts.

The need to immunize with a purified cell population has now become less stringent with the advent of the "hybridoma" technique. Clones can be isolated which produce monospecific antibodies in unlimited quantities. This method no longer requires the performance of tedious sequential absorptions. However, statistically, many clones will have to be tested before a specific antibody can be obtained.

C. THE P_{400} PROTEIN

An SDS–gel electrophoresis analysis of the membrane protein pattern of the nervous mouse and its control revealed after Coomassie blue staining that a protein of apparent molecular weight 400,000 (P_{400}) failed to appear in this mutant (Fig. 4) (Mallet *et al.*, 1975, 1976). The P_{400} was present in purified Purkinje cells but was not detected in cerebrum. These first results suggested that P_{400} is characteristic of the Purkinje cell. Interestingly, this protein was also not detected in membranes from the cerebellum of the staggerer, which lacks synapses between Purkinje cells and parallel fibers (Mallet *et al.*, 1975, 1976). This last finding corroborated electrophysiological data by Crepel and Mariani (1975) which revealed an abnormality of the Purkinje cells. As for the agranular mutants weaver and reeler, the content of P_{400} per milligram of protein increases in the cerebellum.

The P_{400} protein was found to be a glycoprotein. It has been purified by preparative SDS–gel electrophoresis and its sugar composition has been analyzed. About 43% of its weight is made up of sugars and

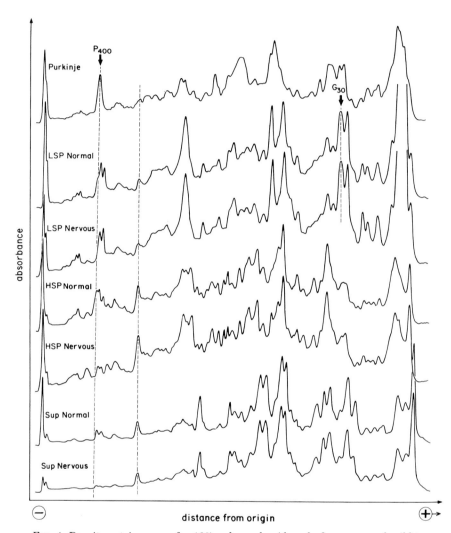

FIG. 4. Densitometric scans of a 10% polyacrylamide gel of nervous and wild-type cerebellar proteins. Three different subcellular fractions were submitted to gel electrophoresis in SDS: a low-speed pellet (LSP) which contains nuclei, mitochondria, and various cell debris, a high-speed pellet (HSP) where the microsomes are abundant, and the resulting supernatant (S) which contains all the soluble proteins. The gel was stained with Coomassie blue. Reproduced with permission from Mallet *et al.* (1976).

among these mannose is preponderant (J. P. Zametta, personal communication).

Mikoshiba *et al.* (1979) took advantage of the high amount of mannose in P_{400} to improve its detection on SDS gels by using ^{125}I-labeled

Con A as described by Burridge (1976), Tanner and Anstee (1976), and Robinson *et al.* (1975).

This very sensitive technique indicated that a small amount of P_{400} was indeed present in nervous and staggerer as was expected. At least 10% of the Purkinje cells remain in nervous. Also, some residual functional (Crepel and Mariani, 1975) and anatomical (Sotelo, 1975) synapses between parallel fibers and Purkinje cells have recently been observed on the main dendritic branches of the Purkinje cells of staggerer mice. However, no P_{400} was found in pcd/pcd mice in which less than 1% of the Purkinje cells remain.

Finally, the ^{125}I-labeled Con A method did not reveal any P_{400} in other tissues such as skeletal muscle, liver, heart muscle, kidney, or cerebrum.

Antibodies have been raised against the P_{400} purified from preparative SDS gels (Mikoshiba *et al.*, 1979). The indirect fluorescence technique performed on tissue sections showed that the anti-P_{400} antibodies were associated only with the Purkinje cells and their dendritic arborizations. No staining was observed in other large cells of the deep nuclei or of the olfactory bulb. The staining persisted after thorough absorption of the serum on cerebrum membranes, confirming the high specificity of the antibodies. To ascertain fully the specificity of the antibodies quantitative assays with ^{125}I-labeled anti-P_{400} antibodies remain to be performed on cerebellar membranes from pcd/pcd mice and their controls, as was described in Section IV,B for the case of anti-Purkinje cell serum. It should also be of interest to test whether the anti-Purkinje cell serum contains antibody against the P_{400}.

The anti-P_{400} serum should allow the localization of the P_{400} protein at the ultrastructural level. Although it is clear that this protein is associated with membranes, it is not yet possible to infer whether it is a plasma membrane protein, an intracytoplasmic element, or a component of the glycocalyx. The antibodies may help to elucidate the function of this highly specific protein.

V. Conclusions

Little is known about the biochemistry of the cerebellum even though it is a relatively simple system. The use of mutants has provided useful information on the biochemistry of the neurotransmission of specific cell types by establishing correlations between the decrease in cyclic nucleotides and putative neurotransmitters or receptors and the lack or the paucity of a given cell type. In particular, this approach has lent strong support for the role of glutamate as a neurotransmitter of the granule cells, confirmed the presence of a high density of

diazepam and β-adrenergic receptors on Purkinje cells, and established
that a large amount of cyclic GMP in the cerebellum is associated with
the Purkinje cells. Nevertheless this method can only be one element of
a multiple approach. The effects of the mutations are manifold either
because they are pleiotropic or because of *en cascade* events and the
correlations are often difficult to establish. Also the decrease of particular molecules associated with the lack of a cell type can be offset by
their increased synthesis in other cells.

These drawbacks do not apply to attempts to identify molecules
that are characteristic of a cell type. The use of the mutants *pcd* and
nervous has been instrumental in demonstrating the existence of antigens specific to the Purkinje cell and more particularly in the identification of the P_{400} protein. It remains to be established whether these
molecules intervene in the setting out of the neuronal network.

ACKNOWLEDGMENTS

I would like to thank my colleagues who have participated in the preparation of this
review: Pierre Benoit, Jean-Pierre Changeux, Christopher Henderson, Manfred
Karobath, Jean Mariani, Ariane Monneron, Hoang Oanh Nghiem, and Alain Privat for
their helpful discussions and readings of the manuscript; and Dominique Vitalyos for her
help with the preparation of the manuscript.

REFERENCES

Altman, J., and Bayer, S. A. (1978). *J. Comp. Neurol.* **179**, 23–48.
Atlas, D., and Levitski, A. (1977). *Proc. Natl. Acad. Sci. U.S.A.* **74**, 5290–5294.
Atlas, D., Teichberg, V. I., and Changeux, J. P. (1977). *Brain Res.* **128**, 532–536.
Bandle, E., and Guidotti, A. (1978). *Brain Res.* **156**, 412–416.
Battenberg, E. L. F., and Bloom, F. E. (1975). *Psychopharmacol. Commun.* **1**, 1–13.
Beart, P. M., and Lee, V. (1977). *Brain Res.* **124**, 171–177.
Beckingham Smith, K. (1976). *Biochem. Biophys. Res. Commun.* **69**, 868–877.
Biggio, G., and Guidotti, A. (1976). *Brain Res.* **107**, 365–373.
Bignami, A., and Dahl, D. (1974). *J. Comp. Neurol.* **155**, 219–230.
Black, I. B. (1976a). *Brain Res.* **105**, 602–605.
Black, I. B. (1976b). *Brain Res.* **110**, 635–637.
Bloom, F. E., Hoffer, B. J., and Siggins, G. R. (1971). *Brain Res.* **25**, 501–521.
Bloom, F. E., Hoffer, B. J., Battenberg, E. R., Siggins, G. R., Steiner, A. L., Parker, C. W.,
    and Wedner, H. J. (1972a). *Science* **177**, 436–438.
Bloom, F. E., Hoffer, B. J., Siggins, G. R., Barker, J. L., and Nicoll, R. A. (1972b). *Fed.
    Proc.* **31**, 97–106.
Burger, M. M., Turner, R., Kuhus, W. J., and Weinbaum, G. (1975). *Philos. Trans. R. Soc.
    London B* **271**, 379–393.
Burridge, K. (1976). *Proc. Natl. Acad. Sci. U.S.A.* **73**, 4457–4461.
Caviness, U. S. (1977). *In* "Neuroscience Symposia," Vol. II. Society for Neuroscience,
    Bethesda, Maryland.
Costa, E., Guidotti, A., and Mao, C. C. (1975). *In* "Mechanism of Action of Ben-
    zodiazepines" (E. Costa and E. Greengard, eds.), pp. 113–130. Raven, New York.
Crepel, F., and Mariani, J. (1975). *Brain Res.* **98**, 135–147.

Daly, J. (1977). "Cyclic Nucleotides in the Nervous System." Plenum, New York.

Enna, S. J., and Snyder, S. H. (1975). *Brain Res.* **100**, 81–97.

Fonnum, F. I., Storm-Mathisen, J., and Walberg, F. (1970). *Brain Res.* **20**, 259–275.

Geller, H. M., and Woodward, D. J. (1974). *Brain Res.* **74**, 67–80.

Guidotti, A., Biggio, G., and Costa, E. (1975). *Brain Res.* **96**, 201–205.

Greengard, P. (1976). *Nature (London)* **260**, 101–108.

Hatten, M. E., and Messer, A. (1978). *Nature (London)* **276**, 504–506.

Hatten, M. E., and Sidman, R. L. (1978). *Exp. Cell Res.* **113**, 111–125.

Hess, A. (1979). *Brain Res.* **160**, 533–538.

Hirano, A., and Dembitzer, H. M. (1974). *J. Neuropathol. Exp. Neurol.* **33**, 354–364.

Hirano, A., and Dembitzer, H. M. (1975). *Exp. Neurol.* **34**, 1–11.

Hogan, E. L. (1977). *In* "Myelin" (P. Morell, ed.), pp. 489–520. Plenum, New York.

Hökfelt, T., and Fuxe, K. (1969). *Exp. Brain Res.* **9**, 63–72.

Hudson, D. B., Valcana, T., Bean, G., and Timiras, P. S. (1976). *Neurochem. Res.* **1**, 73–81.

Kakiuchi, S., and Rall, T. W. (1968). *Mol. Pharmacol.* **4**, 367–378.

Kawamura, H., and Provini, L. (1970). *Brain Res.* **24**, 293–304.

Klainer, L. M., Chi, Y. M., Freidberg, S. L., Rall, T. W., and Sutherland, E. W. (1962). *J. Biol. Chem.* **237**, 1239–1243.

Landis, S. (1973a). *J. Cell Biol.* **57**, 782–797.

Landis, S. (1973b). *Brain Res.* **61**, 175–189.

Landis, D. M. D., and Sidman, R. L. (1978). *J. Comp. Neurol.* **179**, 831–863.

Lane, J. D., Nadi, N. S., McBride, W. J., Aprison, M. H., and Kusano, K. (1977). *J. Neurochem.* **29**, 349–350.

Lee, V., Yen, S. H., and Shelanski, M. L. (1977). *Brain Res.* **128**, 389–392.

Lippa, A. S., Sano, M. C., Coupet, J., Klepner, C. A., and Beer, B. (1978). *Life Sci.* **23**, 2213–2218.

McBride, W. J., Aprison, M. H., and Kusano, K. (1976). *J. Neurochem.* **14**, 465–472.

McLaughlin, B., Wood, J., Saito, K., Barber, R., Vaughn, J., Robert, E., and Wu, J. Y. (1974). *Brain Res.* **76**, 377–391.

Mallet, J., Huchet, M., Shelanski, M., and Changeux, J. P. (1974). *FEBS Lett.* **46**, 243–246.

Mallet, M., Huchet, M., Pougeois, R., and Changeux, J. P. (1975). *FEBS Lett.* **52**, 216–220.

Mallet, J., Huchet, M., Pougeois, R., and Changeux, J. P. (1976). *Brain Res.* **103**, 291–312.

Mallet, J., Christen, R., and Changeux, J. P. (1979). *Dev. Biol.* **72**, 308–319.

Mao, C. C., Guidotti, A., and Costa, E. (1975a). *Brain Res.* **83**, 516–519.

Mao, C. C., Guidotti, A., and Landis, S. (1975b). *Brain Res.* **90**, 335–339.

Mariani, J., and Delhaye-Bouchaud, N. (1978). *Neuropharmacology* **17**, 45–51.

Mariani, J., Crepel, F., Mikoshiba, K., Changeux, J. P., and Sotelo, C. (1977). *Philos. Trans. R. Soc. London B* **281**, 1–28.

Melamed, E., Lehav, M., and Atlas, D. (1976). *Nature (London)* **261**, 420–422.

Mikoshiba, K., Huchet, M., and Changeux, J. P. (1980). *Dev. Neurosci.* **2**, 254–275.

Möhler, H., and Okada, T. (1977a). *Life Sci.* **20**, 2101–2110.

Möhler, H., and Okada, T. (1977b). *Science* **198**, 849–851.

Mullen, R. J. (1977). *Nature (London)* **270**, 245–247.

Mullen, R. J., and Lavail, M. M. (1975). *Nature (London)* **258**, 528–530.

Mullen, R. J., Eicher, E. M., and Sidman, R. L. (1976). *Proc. Natl. Acad. Sci. U.S.A.* **73**, 208–212.

Nadi, N. S., and McBride, W. J. (1976). *Neuroscience* **2**, 164 (Abstr.).

Olsen, R. W., and Mikoshiba, K. (1978). *J. Neurochem.* **30**, 1633–1636.

Obata, K., and Takeda, K. (1969). *J. Neurochem.* **16**, 1043–1047.

Olsen, R. W., Greenlee, D., Van Ness, P., and Ticku, M. K. (1978). *In* "Amino Acids as Chemical Transmitters" (F. Fonnum, ed.), pp. 467–486. Plenum, New York.

Otsuka, M., Obata, K., Miyata, and Tanayka, Y. (1971). *J. Neurochem.* **18**, 287–295.

Palay, S. L. (1975). *Anat. Embryol.* **148**, 235–265.

Palay, S. L., and Chan-Palay, V. (1974). "Cerebellar Cortex, Cytology and Organization." Springer Verlag, Berlin and New York.

Palmer, E. C., Sulser, F., and Robinson, G. A. (1969). *Pharmacologist* **11**, 157–162.

Pieri, L., and Haefely, W. (1976). *Arch. Pharmacol* **296**, 1–4.

Rakic, P. (1976). *Cold Spring Harbor Symp. Quant. Biol.* **40**, 333–346.

Rakic, P., and Sidman, R. L. (1973). *Proc. Natl. Acad. Sci. U.S.A.* **70**, 240–244.

Rall, T. W. (1971). *Ann. N.Y. Acad. Sci.* **185**, 520–530.

Ramón y Cajal (1911). "Histologie du Système Nerveux de l'Homme et des Vertébrés." Maloine, Paris.

Robinson, P. J., Bull, F. G., Anderton, B. H., and Roitt, J. M. (1975). *FEBS Lett.* **58**, 330–333.

Roffler-Tarlov, S., and Sidman, R. L. (1978). *Brain Res.* **142**, 269–283.

Roseman, S. (1974). *In* "The Cell Surface in Development" (A. A. Moscona, ed.), pp. 255–291. Wiley, New York.

Rubin, E. H., McDougal, D. B., Jr., and Ferrendelli, J. (1976). *Proc. Fed. Am. Soc. Exp. Biol.* **35**, 583.

Schmidt, M. J., and Nadi, N. S. (1977). *J. Neurochem.* **29**, 87–90.

Schmidt, M. J., Thornberry, J. F., and Molloy, B. B. (1977). *Brain Res.* **121**, 182–189.

Sellinger, O. Z., Legrand, J., Clos, J., and Ohlsson, W. G. (1974). *J. Neurochem.* **23**, 1137–1144.

Sidman, R. L. (1972). *In* "Cell Interactions." Proceedings of the Third Lepetit Colloquium (L. G. Silvestri, ed.) pp. 1–13. North-Holland, Amsterdam.

Sidman, R. L. (1974). *In* "The Cell Surface in Development" (A. A. Moscona, ed.), pp. 221–253. Wiley, New York.

Sidman, R. L., and Green, M. C. (1970). *In* "Les mutants pathologiques chez l'animal. Leur intérêt dans la recherche biomédicale" (M. Sabourdy, ed.), pp. 69–79. C.N.R.S., Paris.

Sidman, R. L., Lane, P., and Dickie, M. (1962). *Science* **137**, 610–612.

Sidman, R. L., Green, M. C., and Appel, S. H. (1965). "Catalog of the Neurological Mutants of the Mouse." Harvard Univ. Press, Cambridge, Massachusetts.

Siggins, G. R., Battenberg, E. F., Hoffler, B. J., Bloom, F. E., and Steiner, A. L. (1973). *Science* **179**, 585–588.

Simantov, R., Oster-Granite, M. L., Herndon, R. M., and Snyder, S. H. (1976). *Brain Res.* **105**, 365–371.

Skolnick, P., Syapin, P., Paugh, B., and Paul, S. (1979). *Nature (London)* **277**, 397–398.

Sotelo, C. (1975). *In* "Advances in Neurology" (G. W. Kreutzberg, ed.), Vol. XII, pp. 335–351. Raven, New York.

Sotelo, C., and Changeux, J. P. (1974a). *Brain Res.* **67**, 519–526.

Sotelo, C., and Changeux, J. P. (1974b). *Brain Res.* **77**, 484–491.

Squires, R. F., and Braestrup, C. (1977). *Nature (London)* **266**, 732–734.

Stallcup, W. B., and Cohn, M. (1979). *TINS* **2**, 20–23.

Storm-Mathisen, J. (1975). *Brain Res.* **84**, 409–427.

Tanner, M. J. A., and Anstee, D. J. (1976). *Biochem. J.* **153**, 265–270.

Trenkner, E. (1979). *Nature (London)* **277**, 566–567.

Trenkner, E., and Sarkar, S. (1977). *J. Supramol. Struct.* **6**, 465–472.
Weiss, B., and Costa, E. (1968). *Biochem. Pharmacol.* **17**, 2107–2116.
Weiss, B., and Kidman, A. D. (1969). *Adv. Biochem. Psychopharmacol.* **1**, 131–164.
Williamson, M. J., Paul, S. M., and Skolnick, P. (1978). *Nature (London)* **275**, 551–553.
Woodhams, P. L., Mallet, J., Changeux, J. P., and Balazs, R. (1979). *Dev. Biol.* **72**, 320–326.
Woodward, D. J., Hoffer, B. J., Siggins, G. R., and Bloom, F. E. (1971). *Brain Res.* **34**, 73–97.
Woodward, D. J., Hoffer, B. J., and Altman, J. (1974). *J. Neurobiol.* **5**, 283–304.
Yvon, C. H. (1976). *Brain Res.* **109**, 206–215.
Young, A. B., Oster-Granite, M. L., Herndon, R. M., and Snyder, S. H. (1974). *Brain Res.* **73**, 1–13.
Zukin, S. R., Young, A. B., and Snyder, S. H. (1974). *Proc. Natl. Acad. Sci. U.S.A.* **71**, 4802–4807.

CHAPTER 4

DENDRITIC GROWTH AND THE CONTROL OF NEURONAL FORM

Martin Berry

DEPARTMENT OF ANATOMY, MEDICAL SCHOOL
UNIVERSITY OF BIRMINGHAM
BIRMINGHAM, ENGLAND

Patricia McConnell

NETHERLANDS INSTITUTE FOR BRAIN RESEARCH
AMSTERDAM, THE NETHERLANDS

Jobst Sievers

DEPARTMENT OF NEUROANATOMY
UNIVERSITY OF HAMBURG
HAMBURG, FEDERAL REPUBLIC OF GERMANY

I. Introduction 67
II. Dendritic Growth Cones and Filopodia 68
III. Possible Forms of Interaction between Axons and Dendrites
    during Development 71
IV. Quantitative Analysis of Dendritic Growth 75
    A. Metrical Analysis 75
    B. Topological Analysis 75
V. Purkinje Cell Dendritic Growth 77
    A. Cerebellar Development in the Rat 79
    B. The Role of Afferent Fibers in the Control of Purkinje
       Cell Dendritic Growth 85
VI. Influence of Functional Activity on Dendritic Growth 91
VII. Remodeling of the Mature Dendritic Tree 93
VIII. Conclusion 95
    References 96

I. Introduction

The geometry of dendritic trees often characterizes the morphology of neurons into sets (Scheibel and Scheibel, 1970). This stereotyping ostensibly suggests that genetic factors largely control dendritic growth. But, since the arborizations of cells in the same set have similar synaptology, and are exposed to the same environmental influences during ontogeny, epigenetic factors could be the major architect. At-

CURRENT TOPICS IN
DEVELOPMENTAL BIOLOGY, Vol. 15

tempts to discover the relative contributions of nature and nurture to the development of the central nervous system are especially difficult because it is impossible to follow events continuously *in vivo*. Our knowledge of growth is obtained second-hand, extrapolated from the analysis of a chronological series of static pictures or gleaned from the results of experimental testing of hypotheses about how ontogeny might occur. Nevertheless, some progress has been made recently in defining the factors which control dendritic growth and organization. These advances spring from a series of classical rapid Golgi studies performed by Morest in the late 1960s (Morest, 1968, 1969a,b). Although this work inevitably recapitulated some of the earlier observations of Ramón y Cajal (1960), it gave impetus to the present wave of research by emphasizing that dendritic growth cones and filopodia are involved in the dynamics of the growth of trees and that ingrowing axons might be capable of influencing development by an effect on filopodial/growth cone mechanisms. Since then, research efforts have better defined the morphology of dendritic growth cones and their interaction with axons in the developing neuropil. Manipulation of the environment and the use of cerebellar mutants are helping to clarify the role of genes in development while the introduction of new quantitative morphometric techniques for dendritic fields has improved the definition of tree structure and increased our understanding of how branching patterns are generated.

II. Dendritic Growth Cones and Filopodia

Growth cones were first described by Ramón y Cajal in 1909 as "flattened expansions whose edges bristled with short processes or lamellar appendages" at the ends of growing nerve fibers in the spinal cord of chick embryos. Ramón y Cajal (1909, p. 599) predicted that the very fine processes or pseudopodia display amoeboid activity, and this was confirmed by the tissue culture studies of Harrison (1910) and, more recently, the importance of terminal growth cones in the growth of nerve fibers has been confirmed in time-lapse films of neurites in culture (Pomerat *et al.*, 1967; Bray, 1973). However, as developing axons cannot readily be distinguished from developing dendrites in short-term culture, these latter studies could not determine whether the fibers were axonal or dendritic in character.

The positive identification of growth cones on dendritic processes relied upon *in vivo* observations. Morest (1969a,b) and Scheibel and Scheibel (1971), in light microscopic studies of neurons from a variety of brain regions, identified growth cones and filopodia at the tip, along the shaft, and at the base of growing dendrites. Bodian (1966) and del

Cerro and Snider (1968) were the first to demonstrate the fine structure of dendritic growth cones in electron microscopic studies of the motoneuron neuropil of the developing monkey spinal cord and rat cerebellum, respectively.

These early accounts of the fine structure of dendritic growth cones described protoplasmic enlargements about 0.5 μm in diameter, containing large numbers of agranular vesicles but lacking mitochondria and other ultrastructural components. These observations were later confirmed by Kawana et al. (1971) who also noted the presence of filopodia projecting from the cones. However, these results differ markedly from other more recent descriptions of neuritic growth cones in vitro (Yamada et al., 1970, 1971; Bunge, 1973; Privat et al., 1973) and of positively identified axonal (Tennyson, 1970; Skoff and Hamburger, 1974; Vaughn and Sims, 1978) and dendritic growth cones (Hinds and Hinds, 1972; Skoff and Hamburger, 1974; Vaughn et al., 1974) in vivo. The general picture which emerges from these latter studies is that of bulbous or club-shaped enlargements, 1–5 μm in length, from which several filopodia project and which contain a characteristic set of organelles. Immediately underlying the plasma membrane, and filling the filopodia, is a network of microfilaments, thought to be the structural basis of growth cone motility (Yamada et al., 1970, 1971). Deep below this, the body of the growth cone contains randomly distributed, smooth-surfaced vesicles of various shapes and sizes, together with occasional mitochondria and clusters of ribosomes, and with microtubules and neurofilaments reaching into the more proximal parts of the cone. Axonal and dendritic growth cones are similar in general structure, although several differences in their detailed arrangement have been noted (Skoff and Hamburger, 1974).

A number of ideas have been put forward in an attempt to explain the differences between the more recent observations of growth cone morphology and those of the earlier studies of Bodian (1966) and del Cerro and Snider (1968). It has been suggested that the vesicle-containing protrusions observed in the earlier work may have been immature growth cones (Tennyson, 1970), artifacts of fixation (Morest, 1969b; Bunge, 1973; Privat et al., 1973), areas of pathological change (Privat et al., 1973), or regions of pinocytosis (Bunge, 1973). However, similar vesicle-filled mounds have recently been shown to be characteristic features of the terminal growth cones of neurites in culture (Pfenninger and Bunge, 1973; Pfenninger et al., 1974; Pfenninger and Rees, 1976), and it has been suggested that these structures may have been mistaken for whole cones in the earlier studies.

Although conclusive evidence is lacking, Pfenninger and Bunge

(1973) and Pfenninger *et al.* (1974) have proposed the hypothesis that vesicle-containing mounds are the sites at which new membrane is inserted into the plasmalemma of the growing nerve fiber. Their studies on the uptake of external tracer substances show that the vesicles are not derived from the plasma membrane, and experiments labeling the growing cell surface suggest that the membrane of the vesicles actually becomes incorporated into the plasmalemma. This view is in agreement with the earlier observations of Hughes (1953) and Bray (1970, 1973) that the growth of nerve fibers occurs by the addition of new membrane in the region of the growing tip. Membrane of similar composition to that seen in the vesicles has been observed in the Golgi apparatus of developing cells (Pfenninger and Bunge, 1973; Pfenninger *et al.*, 1974), and occasionally vesicles have been found in continuity with the Golgi membrane and along the neurite. Hence, it has been suggested by these workers that the vesicles are derived from the Golgi apparatus in the cell body and pass along the neurites to the peripheral mounds where they are inserted into the plasmalemma by fusion.

The tissue culture evidence indicating that nerve fibers grow (Hughes, 1953; Bray, 1970, 1973) and branch (Bray, 1973) at their terminals receives support from the analysis of the branching patterns of pyramidal and Purkinje cell dendrites growing *in vivo* (Hollingworth and Berry, 1975; Smit *et al.*, 1972). The results of these studies suggest that terminal branching predominates during the development of the basal dendrites of cortical pyramidal cells, the side branches of their apical dendrites, and the dendrites of Purkinje cells. However, although terminal growth may be the general rule (Berry and Bradley, 1976a), there is much circumstantial evidence to support the suggestion made by Morest (1969a,b) that growth and branching can also occur at sites along the shafts of growing dendrites. A number of authors have noted the occurrence of vesicle-filled mounds along the shafts of nerve fibers (del Cerro and Snider, 1968; Grainger and James, 1970; Bunge, 1973), while others have observed filopodia projecting from segmental growth cones (Morest, 1969a,b) or directly from the trunks of neurites, proximal to the terminal growth cone (Morest, 1969a,b; Bray, 1970, 1973; Yamada *et al.*, 1971; Pfenninger and Bunge, 1974; Skoff and Hamburger, 1974; Privat, 1975; Roberts, 1976).

More direct evidence that interstitial membrane insertion may occur is provided by Valverde's (1971) studies on the genesis of dendritic spines on existing dendrites and by the quantitative work of Berry and Bradley (1976b) on growing Purkinje cell dendritic trees and of McConnell and Berry (1978a,b) on the effects of refeeding after postnatal starvation. Evidence of segmental branching, albeit transitory, comes from Hollingworth and Berry's (1975) study of dendritic branching patterns of neocortical pyramidal cells. They found that although the branches of apical dendrites grow terminally, the collaterals stemming from the apical shaft appear to form by segmental branching. The observation that the established bifurcation ratio (Berry and Bradley, 1976a; Berry, 1976) in both Purkinje and pyramidal cell trees exceeds 3.0 also indicates that some segmental branching occurs although terminal growth predominates. Similarly, Speidel's (1942) observations on growing cutaneous nerves of amphibian tadpoles indicate that a limited degree of segmental branching does occur during normal development.

III. Possible Forms of Interaction between Axons and Dendrites during Development

The fundamental mechanisms governing the formation of neural connections have long been a subject of debate among neurobiologists. Ideas have ranged from empiricist views (Ramón y Cajal, 1909, p. 615; von der Malsburg, 1973) suggesting that neuronal connectivity is specified largely by afferent activity, to strict preformist ideas suggesting that genes program much of development (Sperry, 1943, 1944; Hubel and Wiesel, 1963). Recent evidence tends to favor a compromise between these two extremes, and the hypothesis *en vogue* proposes that the genome directs the interactions between major classes of neurons but that the number of connections and the precise morphology of dendritic networks may be subject to extrinsic influences of either a structural or functional nature (Rakic, 1975; Changeux and Danchin, 1976; Berry *et al.*, 1978).

Morest (1969b) proposed that "the differentiation of dendritic branches coincides in time and place with the differentiation of the afferent axonal end branches that form synaptic contacts with the dendrites" and suggested (1969a,b) that afferent axons may actually influence or induce the formation of dendritic branches. The observation that the outgrowth of Purkinje cell dendrites is able to proceed in agranular cerebellar explants (Privat, 1975; Privat and Drian, 1976; Calvet *et al.*, 1976) indicates that the presence of afferents is not essential for dendritic growth per se. However, there is much evidence, from a number of regions of the central nervous system (CNS), to suggest that afferent connections regulate the normal development of dendritic networks (Shofer *et al.*, 1964; Valverde, 1968; Rakic and Sidman, 1973a,b; Rakic, 1974; Smith, 1974; Herndon and Oster-Granit, 1975; Sotelo, 1975a; Altman, 1976a; Bradley and Berry, 1976a,b, 1978a,b; Berry and Bradley, 1976c; Borges and Berry, 1976, 1978). Morest

(1969b), in fact, proposed a mechanism whereby such effects could be mediated. Modifying an original suggestion by Ramón y Cajal (1909, p. 615, 1911, p. 87), Morest proposed that the growth of dendrites is associated with the formation of contacts between their growth cone filopodia and the appropriate afferent axons.

There was little definitive evidence in support of this hypothesis until fairly recently, when a number of workers (Skoff and Hamburger, 1974; Vaughn *et al.*, 1974; Hinds and Hinds, 1976) identified synaptic profiles on dendritic growth cones and filopodia, noting that the most immature synapses are found closest to the free end of the growing dendrite (Skoff and Hamburger, 1974; Hinds and Hinds, 1976). This observation, together with the finding that during development of the mouse spinal cord there is a decrease in the proportion of synapses on growth cones relative to synapses on dendritic shafts, led Vaughn and his co-workers to formulate the filopodial synaptogenic hypothesis of dendritic growth (Fig. 1). This hypothesis proposed that presynaptic terminals form their initial contacts on dendritic filopodia, which are thus stabilized. The remaining filopodia are retracted and dendritic growth occurs by the movement of protoplasm from the growth cone

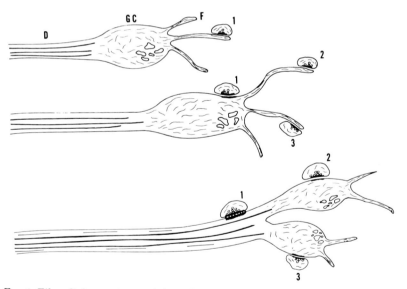

FIG. 1. Filopodial synaptogenetic hypothesis of dendritic growth (from Vaughn *et al.*, 1974). D, Dendritic shaft; GC, growth cone; F, filopodium. A single filopodium attaches to axon terminal 1. This contact is then translocated onto the growth cone and dendritic shaft as the growth cone advances. Where filopodia contact axons 2 and 3 simultaneously, the growth cone divides and a branch point is established.

into the contacted filopodium. This expands to form a new cone distal to the synapse, while the original growth cone develops the characteristics of a mature dendrite. Thus synapses are translocated from the filopodium where they initially form to the growth cone and from there to the dendritic shaft. As shown in Fig. 1 the mechanism can account for both the growth and branching of dendrites, a branch being formed when two filopodia are contacted simultaneously.

This hypothesis, renamed the filopodial attachment hypothesis, in view of evidence that the contacts between axons and dendritic filopodia are not exclusively synaptic (Berry et al., 1978), has been further elaborated by Berry and Bradley (1976a). Extending the ideas to take account of segment growth and the formation of trichotomous and other higher order nodes (Fig. 2), they were able to make a number of predictions about the formation of dendritic trees: (a) terminal branching will predominate, as growth cones are always translocated to the tip of a stabilized filopodium, (b) dendritic growth will be directed into areas in which the density of growing axons is maximal, (c) segment lengths will be inversely related, while (d) the number of segments and (e) the frequency of different orders of branching (dichotomous, trichotomous, etc.) will be directly related to the density of axons in the neuropil around the developing dendritic tree, providing that the properties of the growing terminals remain constant (Fig. 2).

To date, these predictions have all been borne out by quantitative studies of Purkinje and pyramidal cell dendritic trees in normal rats (Hollingworth and Berry, 1975; Berry and Bradley, 1976b), Purkinje cell trees in normal mice (Bradley and Berry, 1978a), weaver and staggerer mutant mice (Bradley and Berry, 1978a), and rats rendered agranular by irradiation of the neonatal cerebellum (Bradley and Berry, 1976a; Berry and Bradley, 1976c) or by the administration of methylazoxymethanol acetate (Bradley and Berry, 1978b). Thus, at the present time, the filopodial attachment hypothesis can provide an acceptable working model of the way in which the size, orientation, and topology of a dendritic network may be influenced by the surrounding axon field.

There is, however, one observation which suggests that the hypothesis should be further modified. The results obtained from the studies of Purkinje cells from abnormal cerebella, together with the observation that Purkinje cells are able to form a rudimentary dendritic tree in vitro, in the absence of afferent connections, suggest that dendritic growth occurs in two phases and that the hypothesis may be applied only to the second of these (Berry et al., 1978).

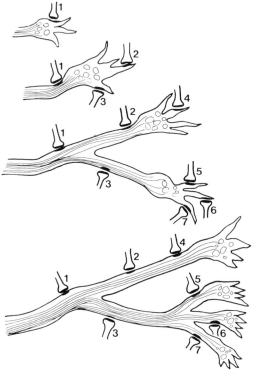

FIG. 2. Schematic representation of the natural history of the growth of a single dendritic process according to the filopodial adhesive hypothesis. The dendrite is growing at a constant rate from left to right and its branching history is related to the number of axonal adhesive sites which growth cone filopodia contact. The adhesion of axon 1 to a filopodium prevents this structure from retracting into the growth cone; all noncontacted filopodia collapse into the cone. Axon 1 becomes translocated onto the dendritic shaft as the growth cone advances into the anchored filopodium. The direction of growth is thus that of the orientation of this anchored process. As growth proceeds two filopodia become contacted and anchored by axons 2 and 3. A dichotomous branch is produced as a part of the original cone passes into the two anchored filopodia. The angle of branching is the angle of divergence of the contacted filopodia. A filopodium on the growth cone of one segment is contacted by axon 4 while three filopodia on the cone of the other segment are contacted by axons 5, 6, and 7. In the former growth proceeds in the direction of the contacted filopodium; in the latter a trichotomous branch is produced and growth diverges according to the orientation of the three anchored processes. From this diagram it can be seen that during the growth of dendritic trees the magnitude of segment lengths is inversely proportional, and the order of branching and the number of branches and segments produced directly proportional to the frequency of adhesive sites about growth cones. Growth will be directed into areas of neuropil where the frequency of adhesive sites is greatest. Since growth cones are largely located terminally branching patterns will be those generated by terminal dichotomy. The fate of adhesive sites on dendritic shafts is unknown.

IV. Quantitative Analysis of Dendritic Growth

The quantitative methods applied to the analysis of dendritic fields often fail to distinguish adequately between topological and metrical parameters. However, in a few recent studies (Smit et al., 1972; Berry et al., 1975; Hollingworth and Berry, 1975; Smit and Uylings, 1975; Uylings and Smit, 1975; Berry and Bradley, 1976a), the separate analysis of data relating to the spatial configuration of networks and the measurements of segment lengths and branching angle has provided a more complete description of the extent, morphology, and mode of growth of dendritic trees.

A. METRICAL ANALYSIS

With the exception of gross parameters of dendritic morphology such as total dendritic length or dendritic density, the quantitation of dendritic branching involves the application of an ordering method which ideally groups together those segments with similar structural or functional characteristics. Such methods can be classified into two groups: the centripetal systems, in which order numbering starts at the terminal segments of the tree and increases progressively toward the stem; and the centrifugal systems, which start order numbering at the stem and number outward toward the periphery.

The relative merits of these methodologies have been discussed by Berry et al. (1975) and by Uylings et al. (1975) who conclude that the choice of the most appropriate method depends on the nature of the investigation. For example, it is suggested that centrifugal ordering methods provide the most appropriate means of studying dendritic outgrowth. The centrifugal order of established segments is unchanged by the addition of new terminal segments, while centripetal methods require that the network be reordered each time a new segment is added. On the other hand, centripetal systems are thought to be better suited for characterizing large, asymmetrically branching networks such as those of Purkinje cells, in which the number of orders produced by the centrifugal method would be too large to allow meaningful statistical analysis.

B. TOPOLOGICAL ANALYSIS

The application of ordering techniques not only facilitates the definition of the metrical properties of a dendritic network, it also provides a means of quantifying dendritic connectivity. A network may be defined in terms of the frequencies of branches of various orders, and their interrelationships. In practice, the relationship between orders can be expressed in terms of a single parameter, the *bifurcation ratio*, which is the ratio between the frequencies of branches of adjacent orders (Berry *et al.*, 1975; Berry, 1976; Berry and Bradley, 1976a). It is found that for networks of a given maximum order, the ratio between branches of any two adjacent orders begins to stabilize as the number of branches in the network increases (Berry *et al.*, 1975). Using the Strahler method of ordering (Berry, 1976), this "established bifurcation ratio" is attained initially between first and second Strahler orders, at the periphery of the tree, with the ratios between the more proximal, higher orders progressively becoming established as the number of branches increases further.

The actual value of the established ratio depends on the mode of growth of the system. A ratio of 2 is found in systems grown by symmetrical, dichotomous branching on terminal segments and the value increases with the incidence of collateral branching on proximal segments. Thus, comparison of the established bifurcation ratio for a given network, with the established ratios for model networks generated according to various growth hypotheses (*vide infra*) may give some indication of the mode of growth. However, this distinction between different patterns of growth in terms of the established bifurcation ratio is not absolute; different modes of growth may generate networks with the same, or very similar ratios while others achieve an established ratio only in very large networks (Berry *et al.*, 1975). Hence, it is propitious to combine ordering studies of connectivity with a more precise topological analysis in order to define the mode of growth of a dendritic network with more confidence.

For a given hypothesis of growth, the frequency distribution of the distinct topological types with a specified number of terminals is unique (Berry *et al.*, 1975; Berry and Bradley, 1976a). These distributions may be calculated using computer-generated model networks, in which branching patterns are constructed for different hypotheses of growth from a single segment. The initial stages of this calculation are shown in Fig. 3 and 4 for networks generated by branching on random terminal segments or branching on any segment in the tree. Figures 5 and 6 show the final distributions of topological types obtained by Berry and Bradley (1976a) for systems grown according to these two hypotheses.

Comparison of the observed distribution of topological patterns in a dendritic network with these expected distributions for networks generated in a specified manner can thus provide insight into the way in which the network has developed. However, such indirect studies of dendritic development can obviously never conclusively specify the mode of growth.

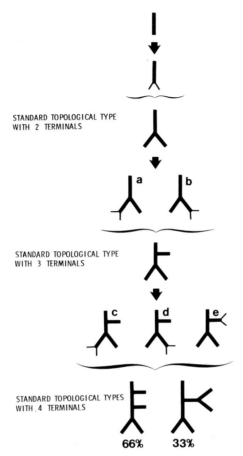

STANDARD TOPOLOGICAL TYPE
WITH 2 TERMINALS

STANDARD TOPOLOGICAL TYPE
WITH 3 TERMINALS

STANDARD TOPOLOGICAL TYPES
WITH 4 TERMINALS

66%   33%

FIG. 3. Topological branching patterns formed by dichotomous branching on random terminals. The root point of each pattern is uppermost. Beginning with a single dendrite the addition of a dichotomous branch produces a single topological type with two terminals. The further addition of a dichotomous branch to either of these terminals produces types a and b, which may be resolved into a single standard type with three terminals. Addition of a dichotomous branch to any one of these terminals produces types c, d, and e, each with four terminals. These may be resolved into two standard types. If the addition of dichotomous branches to the terminals of dendrites with three terminals occurs randomly, then the two standard topological types with four terminals will be distributed in the ratio 2:1.

V. Purkinje Cell Dendritic Growth

The Purkinje cell (PC) dendritic tree is very well suited to dendritic field analysis. The arborizations are all planar, lying at right angles to the long axis of folia, and thus the analysis of sections cut in the plane of the tree will not be fraught with the errors of projection artifact and

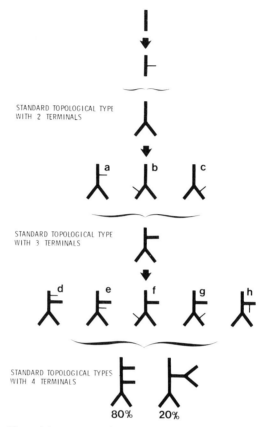

FIG. 4. Topological branching patterns formed by segmental branching. The root point of each pattern is uppermost. Beginning with a single dendrite the addition of a single segmental branch produces a topological type with two terminals. The addition of a branch singly to any of the three segments of this pattern produces types a, b, and c which are resolvable into a single topological type with three terminals. The addition of a single branch to any of the five segments of this pattern produces types d, e, f, g, and h with four terminals. These may be resolved into two standard topological types. If the addition of branches to the segments of the pattern with three terminals occurs randomly then the two types with four terminals will be distributed in the ratio 4:1.

sectioning losses (Berry *et al.*, 1972a). Moreover, the tree is innervated by well-defined fiber systems which converge on different parts of the network. Climbing fibers (CFs) from the inferior olivary nucleus innervate the "smooth" proximal branches, parallel fibers (PFs) engage spines on the distal branches, and monoaminergic fibers ramify about the soma and proximal dendrites (Palay and Chan-Palay, 1974).

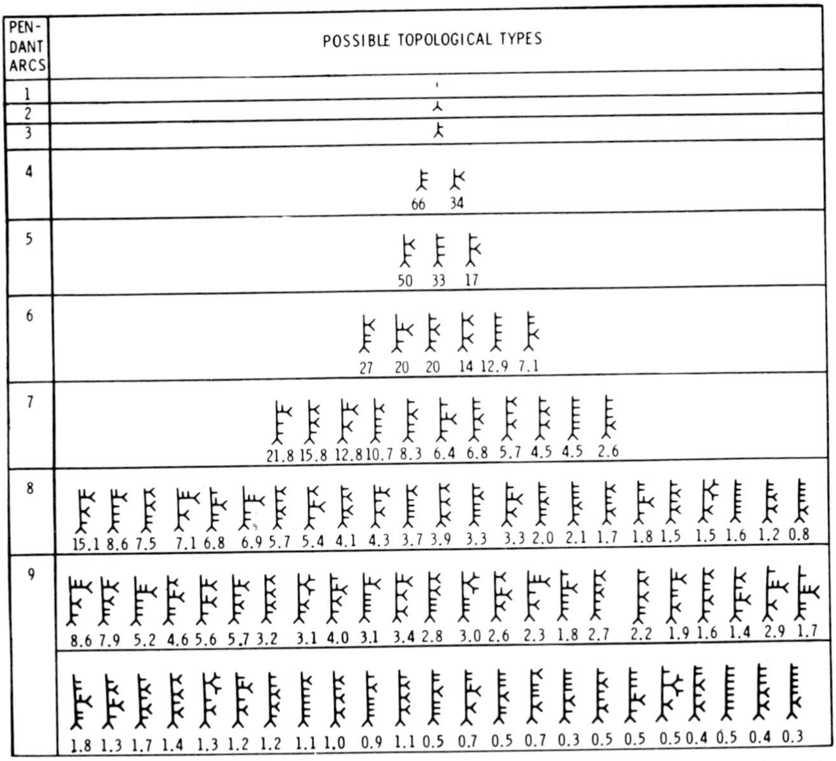

FIG. 5. Frequencies of topological branching patterns with up to nine terminals in networks generated by dichotomous branching on random terminals. From Berry and Bradley (1976a).

A. CEREBELLAR DEVELOPMENT IN THE RAT

Most PCs originate in the cerebellar anlage on E15 (Das and Nornes, 1972; Schultze *et al.*, 1974; Altman and Bayer, 1978). They migrate through the deep nuclear neuropil and, at birth, accumulate in a layer 6–12 cells deep below the external granular layer (Altman and Bayer, 1978; Altman, 1972b). By 3–4 days postpartum (pp) PCs have assembled into a monolayer (Altman and Winfree, 1977).

Cells begin to emerge from the external granular layer at about 5 days pp (Altman, 1969). Basket cells migrate in the first week and stellate and granule cells are produced in postnatal weeks 2 and 3. PFs are thus laid down at this time and probably become functional in the second week as mossy fiber synaptogenesis gets underway (Addison, 1911; Altman, 1969, 1972c, 1973). CFs are functional by 3 days pp

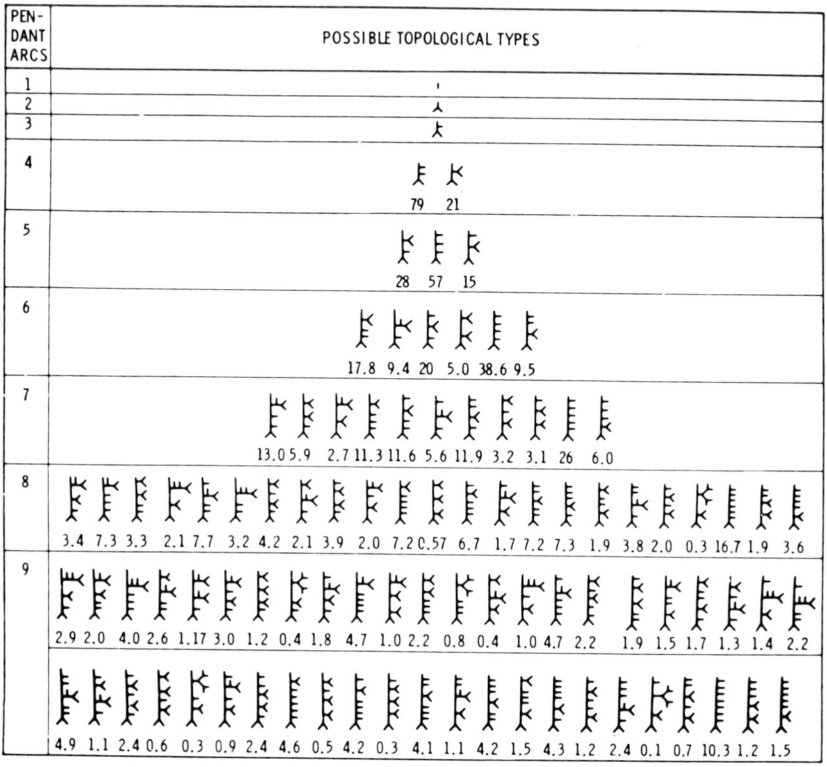

PEN-DANT ARCS	POSSIBLE TOPOLOGICAL TYPES
1	
2	
3	
4	79 21
5	28 57 15
6	17.8 9.4 20 5.0 38.6 9.5
7	13.0 5.9 2.7 11.3 11.6 5.6 11.9 3.2 3.1 26 6.0
8	3.4 7.3 3.3 2.1 7.7 3.2 4.2 2.1 3.9 2.0 7.2 0.57 6.7 1.7 7.2 7.3 1.9 3.8 2.0 0.3 16.7 1.9 3.6
9	2.9 2.0 4.0 2.6 1.17 3.0 1.2 0.4 1.8 4.7 1.0 2.2 0.8 0.4 1.0 4.7 2.2 1.9 1.5 1.7 1.3 1.4 2.2
	4.9 1.1 2.4 0.6 0.3 0.9 2.4 4.6 0.5 4.2 0.3 4.1 1.1 4.2 1.5 4.3 1.2 2.4 0.1 0.7 10.3 1.2 1.5

FIG. 6. Frequencies of topological branching patterns with up to nine terminals in networks generated by branching on random segments. From Berry and Bradley (1976a).

(Crépel, 1971) and engage many PCs at this time (Crépel *et al.*, 1976), but by 15 days the adult one-to-one relationship is achieved. Monoaminergic fibers have been demonstrated in the anlage of the rat cerebellar cortex on E17 (Seiger and Olson, 1973), and at birth they are seen to ramify within the internal granular and PC layer, but very few are seen in the external granular layer (Sievers *et al.*, 1980a).

The distribution of NA fibers in the adult cerebellum is diffuse to the internal granular and molecular layer with a concentration of fibers about PC somata and proximal dendrites (Hölkfelt and Fuxe, 1969; Olson and Fuxe, 1971; Bloom *et al.*, 1971; Landis and Bloom, 1975). Presumed NA presynaptic elements are seen apposed to PC main stem dendrites and to spines. In many cases true synaptic appositions are not seen in association with the vesicle-filled varicosities and terminals of the NA system. Nonetheless, β-receptor distribution appears to mirror that of NA varicosities (Melamed *et al.*, 1976; Atlas *et al.*, 1977). Thus, although NA fibers may act at specific synaptic sites to modulate PC function (Freedman *et al.*, 1977), NA varicosities might release mediator into interstitial spaces which then functions as a local neurohumor (Bloom, 1974).

The 5-HT system is composed of specific afferents which synapse as mossy fibers in the granular layer or run into the molecular layer, bifurcate, and run along the long axes of folia with PFs, synapsing with Purkinje and stellate cell dendrites. A diffuse system is also present whose axons ramify throughout all layers. This system has few specialized synaptic junctions and, like the diffuse NA fibers, could be part of a neurohumoral system releasing transmitter into the surrounding milieu. The cell bodies of 5-HT axons innervating the cerebellum lie in the raphe nuclei (Chan-Palay, 1977).

Purkinje cell dendritic development is summarized in Fig. 7. At first the cells are multipolar, but by the time they have formed a monolayer most of the perisomatic processes have been absorbed and polarity is achieved as the primordial tree begins to sprout from the pole of the cell which faces the external granular layer, a process thought to be associated with the formation of basket cell axosomatic synapses (Altman, 1976b). Growth is very rapid. At first the tree establishes its lateral domain and then grows in height. Most segments of the tree are formed during the period of migration of granule cells, but some growth occurs up to about 50 days pp. Segments also lengthen after they are established. Proximal segments grow longer than distal segments (Berry and Bradley, 1976b). This interstitial growth is supported by membrane insertion between nodes perhaps at the sites of vesicle-filled mounds or by the absorption of spines.

It has been suggested that the development of the PC dendritic tree is controlled by two inductive stimuli (Berry *et al.*, 1978). Primary induction, possibly by monoaminergic fibers, occurs in the prenatal or immediate postnatal period and organizes the initial phases of dendritic growth. Dendritic growth is maintained for a period up until a few apical branches appear, but if growth is to proceed beyond this point secondary induction is mandatory. This latter stimulus is delivered specifically by a finite number of PF contacts as granule cell migration gets underway. Secondary induction seems capable of switching normal growth on for a period of time of precise duration. Dendrites advance through the neuropil at a constant rate and form the same mean path lengths independent of their branching history. The frequency of PFs about growing dendritic terminals determines the number of branches formed by adhesive interaction with dendritic growth cone

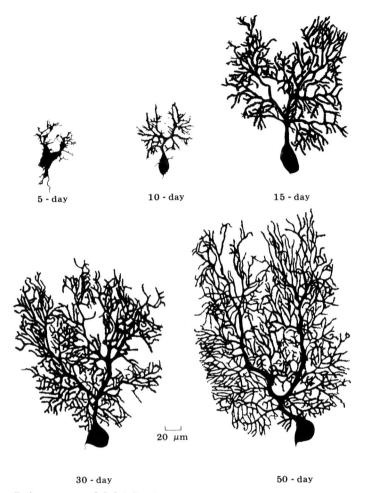

FIG. 7. Appearance of Golgi-Cox-impregnated PCs in the cerebellum of the rat at various ages after birth. From Berry *et al.* (1972b).

filopodia (Berry and Bradley, 1976b; McConnell and Berry, 1978a,b; Hollingworth and Berry, 1975; Bradley and Berry, 1976b, 1978a). This is well illustrated in the quantitative study by McConnell and Berry (1980) which shows that, in the development of the normal rat cerebellum, the deposition of PFs (as measured by granule cell counts) exactly correlates with the formation of PC dendritic segments (Fig. 8). In starved animals the deposition of PFs is retarded and so is the generation of segments by PCs, but the correlation of number of PC dendritic segments formed with number of PFs deposited is maintained (Fig. 8).

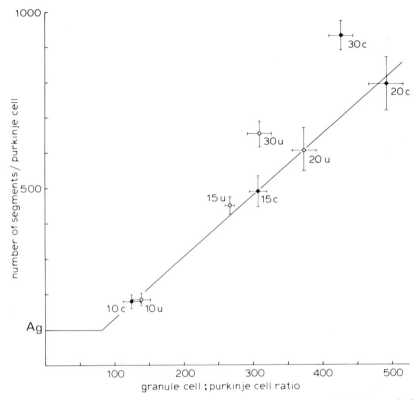

Fig. 8. Relationship between the number of segments generated by PCs and the number of parallel fibers deposited, as measured by the granule cell/PC ratio on day 10, 15, 20, and 30 postpartum in normal (N) and starved (S) rats. The point labeled Ag on the graph represents the number of segments produced by PCs in almost completely agranular cortex (Berry and Bradley, 1976c). Since secondary induction occurs in these latter animals it is assumed that the small number of granule cells present are capable of mediating induction. No granule cell counts were performed in the study by Berry and Bradley (1976c), but by projection through the value for the number of segments generated, onto the line defining the relationship between the frequency of dendritic segments and number of parallel fibers deposited, the minimal value for the granule cell/PC ratio necessary for induction can be extrapolated, i.e., approximately 80 granule cells/PC cells are necessary for induction and approximately 100 segments can be formed by PCs before secondary induction occurs. The points on the graph for 30-day-old normal and starved rats do not lie on a line calculated from the values from younger animals because granule cells are no longer formed after 20 days and granule cell death occurs in the 20- to 30-day period reducing the granule cell/PC ratio. Some segments are produced over this period because parallel fibers increase in length.

The growth of the tree continues after PF formation has ceased on about 22–23 days pp (Altman, 1972a) and is probably associated with growth in length of PFs (Lauder, 1978). As expected, the correlation between the number of PFs and PC dendritic segment frequency is lost after 22–23 days pp (Fig. 8).

Topological analysis of branching during development of the normal rat indicates that nonrandom terminal growth occurs before 15 days pp and this is probably associated with changes in the direction of

TERMINALS	OBSERVA-TIONS	PROPERTY		TOPOLOGICAL TYPES						x^2	p
4	196	TOPOLOGICAL TYPES								df = 1	
		DISTRIBUTION	A - TERMINAL GROWTH	2	1						
			B - SEGMENTAL GROWTH	4	1						
		OBSERVED FREQUENCIES		126	70						
		EXPECTED FREQUENCIES	DISTRIBUTION A	130.6	65.3					0.239	0.8 - 0.9
			DISTRIBUTION B	156.8	39.2					12.04	<0.001
5	132	TOPOLOGICAL TYPES								df = 2	
		DISTRIBUTION	A - TERMINAL GROWTH	3	2	1					
			B - SEGMENTAL GROWTH	2	4	1					
		OBSERVED FREQUENCIES		66	52	14					
		EXPECTED FREQUENCIES	DISTRIBUTION A	66	44	22				2.44	0.7 - 0.5
			DISTRIBUTION B	37.6	75.2	18.8				12.71	0.01-0.001
6	96	TOPOLOGICAL TYPES								df = 5	
		DISTRIBUTION	A - TERMINAL GROWTH	4	3	3	2	2	1		
			B - SEGMENTAL GROWTH	4	2	4	8	1	2		
		OBSERVED FREQUENCIES		20	17	18	16	18	7		
		EXPECTED FREQUENCIES	DISTRIBUTION A	25.6	19.2	19.2	12.8	12.8	6.4	2.104	>0.9
			DISTRIBUTION B	18.3	9.1	18.3	36.7	4.6	9.1	18.75	0.01-0.001

Fig. 9. An example of the results of a topological analysis of normal Purkinje cell dendritic trees from 30-day-old rats (from Bradley and Berry, 1976a). Thus, for example, there are 196 samples of dendrites with four terminals in the 10 cells studied. There are two distinct topological types for trees with four terminals (see Figs. 3 and 4) and these were distributed as 126 of one type and 70 of the other. If the system had grown by random segmental branching as in Fig. 4, the distribution would have been 157 of the former and 39 of the latter and if grown by random terminal branching 131 and 65. The latter hypothesis thus provides the best fit to the observed data. The matching of expected frequencies according to the random terminal model, with the observed data, is as good for dendrites with five and six terminals (see Figs. 5 and 6). The random terminal growth of the PC dendritic trees is probably brought about because PFs are deposited in a uniformly dense field about growing PC dendrites in the molecular layer of the cerebellum.

growth of the field (Berry and Bradley, 1976b). Thereafter growth appears to establish branching patterns by random terminal dichotomy in the rat and mouse (Fig. 9). (Hollingworth and Berry, 1975; Bradley and Berry, 1976a, 1978a; Berry and Bradley, 1976b; McConnell and Berry, 1978a,b; Price and Berry, 1979).

B. THE ROLE OF AFFERENT FIBERS IN THE CONTROL OF PURKINJE CELL DENDRITIC GROWTH

1. Parallel Fibers

a. Complete Absence of Parallel Fiber Contacts. i. Homozygous weaver mutant mouse. Very few PFs are formed in the weaver mouse because granule cells fail to migrate and die in the external granular layer before the elaboration of PFs (Rakic and Sidman, 1973a,b; Sidman et al., 1965; Sidman, 1968). Basket and stellate cells are, however, formed successfully (Rakic and Sidman, 1973a,b) and their axons contact PCs with inhibitory synapses (Puro and Woodward, 1977). Dendritic spines develop in the absence of PFs and remain unattached indefinitely. CFs make contact with PC somata and dendrites (Landis, 1973) and there is multiple innervation of PCs by CFs (Puro and Woodward, 1977; Crépel and Mariani, 1976) and a corresponding increased density of CF varicosities in the cortex (Sotelo, 1975b). The distribution of catecholamine fibers in the weaver cerebellar cortex is normal but their density is increased (Sidman, 1968, 1972, 1974; Landis et al., 1975; Landis and Bloom, 1975; Siggins et al., 1976).

The dendritic trees of PCs in weaver mice are randomly oriented and they do not form a monolayer (Fig. 10). Most PCs are unipolar and a few are bipolar as in the normal mouse. Only some 12% of the total number of segments is elaborated and path lengths are significantly reduced (Bradley and Berry, 1978a). Both metrical and topological analyses of weaver trees show that growth is arrested at about 7 days pp at a time when, in normal mice, PF deposition begins (Fugita, 1967). Bradley and Berry (1978a) concluded that the weaver mutant demonstrates primary but not secondary induction.

Disorientation of PCs may be attributable to the absence of PFs but could also be correlated with a defect in Bergmann glia in this mutant (Rakic and Sidman, 1973a,b,c; Sotelo and Changeux, 1974a), although the spatial organization and extent of the radial meshwork of Bergmann glia has been found to be relatively normal in weaver mice (Bignami and Dahl, 1974).

ii. Homozygous staggerer mutant mouse. In the staggerer mutant PFs form only rudimentary contacts with PC dendrites (Sotelo, 1973,

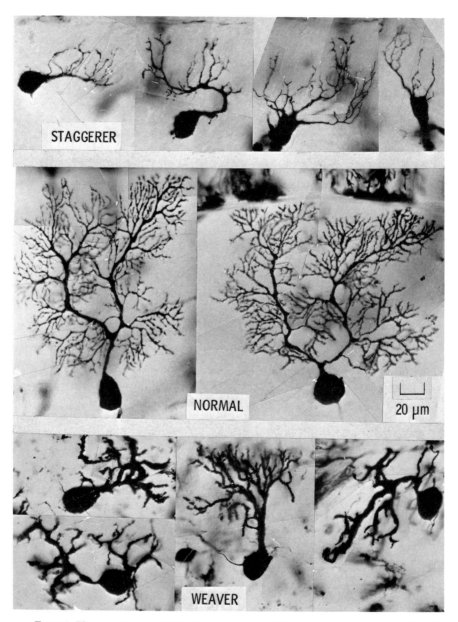

Fig. 10. Photomontages of Golgi-Cox specimens of four staggerer, two normal, and four weaver PCs taken from mice aged 20 days pp. Note the florid growth of the normal cells and stunted growth of the mutants. It is assumed that in both mutants and normal

1975a). Spines do not develop (Sidman, 1968, 1972; Sotelo, 1975a; Yoon, 1976). Although PF activation of PCs occurs (Crépel and Mariani, 1975), this is of low efficiency. In fact most PFs degenerate, possibly because normal axospinous synapses cannot be established (Sidman, 1974; Sotelo and Changeux, 1974b).

Climbing fiber density is reduced (Sotelo, 1975a). The PC response to CF activation is atypical and only 40% of PCs respond (Crépel and Mariani, 1975). The density of monoaminergic fibers is increased as in the weaver mutant (Landis and Bloom, 1975).

The growth of the PC dendritic tree of the staggerer, like that of the weaver, is arrested at about 7 days pp and similarly only 12% of the mature number of segments is produced (Fig. 10). Presumed secondary induction may not occur in this mutant since mediation through a finite number of mature PF/PC axospinous synapses is impossible. The dendritic tree of the staggerer differs from that of the weaver in several aspects. It is nonspiny, multipolar, and normally oriented. Normal orientation may reflect the normality of the Bergmann glial population (Bignami and Dahl, 1974), but the failure to polarize could be attributable to some deficit in basket cell synaptogenesis (Altman, 1976b).

b. *Partially Agranular Cerebellum.* The administration of X-rays (Shofer *et al.*, 1964; Altman and Anderson, 1972; Berry and Bradley, 1976c; Crépel *et al.*, 1976), methylazoxymethanol acetate (MAM) (Hirano *et al.*, 1972; Woodward *et al.*, 1975; Bradley and Berry, 1978b), or virus infections (Herndon *et al.*, 1971; Llinás *et al.*, 1973) in the neonatal period reduces the number of granule cells and thus the number of PFs in the molecular layer. After prolonged irradiation very few granule cells survive (Altman and Anderson, 1972; Berry and Bradley, 1976c; Crépel *et al.*, 1976), and PC trees develop a small number of very long dendrites (Fig. 11). This result implies that sufficient granule cells have survived for their PFs to mediate secondary induction through axospinous synapses. Growth is accordingly switched on and dendrites proceed to advance through the neuropil. Since PC dendrites meet few, if any, PFs, adhesive interaction is infrequent and branching is a correspondingly rare event. Since path lengths are normal in such animals (Berry and Bradley, 1976c), it is assumed that growth occurs for the same duration as normal and thus the off-switch for growth (whatever it may be) is normally functional. The signal for cessation of growth in

cells primary induction has occurred but that in the mutants secondary induction has failed to occur because PFs do not make axospinous contact with these trees. Both mutants therefore demonstrate the limits of growth under the influence of primary induction only. From Bradley and Berry (1978a).

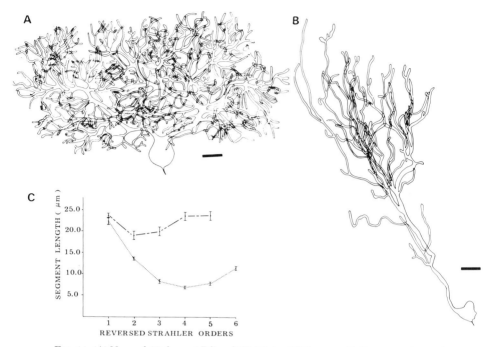

FIG. 11. (A) Normal 30-day rat PC and (B) 30-day PC from partially agranular cortex. Note that in contrast to the mutant cells in Fig. 10, PCs in partially agranular cortex have received a secondary inductive stimulus and dendrites proceed to advance through the cerebellar neuropil. However, because there are much fewer PFs deposited than in the normal rat, few branches are formed and segments are much longer (C). Bars = 20 μm. From Berry and Bradley (1976a).

agranular animals cannot be the saturation of a finite number of post-synaptic sites (Benes *et al.*, 1977; Liu and Liu, 1971) by PFs because PFs are absent and spines unattached (see Berry and Bradley, 1976c for references). Although Berry and Bradley (1976c) did not perform granule cell counts it is possible to extrapolate from Fig. 8 that the minimal number of PFs per PC required for secondary induction is approximately 80. This work also shows that presumed primary induction is capable of stimulating the growth of about 100 segments in both rats and mice (see Sections V,B,1,i and ii).

Severe degranulation also causes a failure in the formation of a PC monolayer; PCs are often multipolar and disoriented. Multiple innervation of PCs by CFs is also commonly found (Hámori, 1969; Woodward *et al.*, 1974; Crépel *et al.*, 1976) as in the weaver and staggerer mutants and this phenomenon probably represents, in all cases, a persistence of the early postnatal organization of CFs. As already mentioned, the presence of multipolar PCs could indicate a failure of contact by basket cell axons which may normally organize the resorption of perisomatic PC processes (Altman, 1976b). Furthermore, disorientation could result from disorganization and hypoplasia of the Bergmann glial population since mitotic arrest occurs after all degranulating procedures and would thus affect neuroglia actively dividing at this time in the internal granular layer (Lewis et al., 1977).

When larger numbers of granule cells survive as, for example, after milder schedules of irradiation (Bradley and Berry, 1976), or after a single injection of MAM (Bradley and Berry, 1978a), the effects on the dendritic tree are also predictable according to the dendritic filopodia adhesive hypothesis of growth. Thus, fewer but longer segments are generated and trichotomous branches are less frequent than normal.

2. Climbing Fibers

Climbing fibers (CFs) make transient contact with the perisomatic processes of PCs during the formation of a monolayer in the first few days postpartum (Mugnaini, 1969, 1970; Larramendi, 1969; Larramendi and Victor, 1967; Altman, 1972b). As polarity is attained CFs invade the proximal dendrites pari-passu with basket cell axosomatic synaptogenesis and the absorption of perisomatic processes. It has been suggested that as CFs ultimately cap the terminals of apical dendrites they could induce dendritic growth (Kornguth et al., 1968; Kornguth and Scott, 1972). As dendritic growth proceeds CFs invade the more proximal spiny branches and effect spine resorption converting these segments to smooth branches (Larramendi and Victor, 1966; Berry and Bradley, 1976b). The incorporation of spine membrane into the dendritic shaft could cause elongation by a concertina affect. When CFs are absent, as after neonatal ablation (Kawaguchi et al., 1975; Bradley and Berry, 1976a; Sotelo and Arsenio-Nunes, 1976), or in rat cerebellum isolated from the inferior olive in organ culture (Calvet et al., 1976; Privat et al., 1973, 1974), spines persist on distal branches but are not resorbed from proximal branches. Moreover, when CFs are destroyed in adult animals, spines reappear over previously smooth branches and persist on distal spiny branchlets (Sotelo et al., 1975; Bradley and Berry, 1976b). These findings clearly refute the proposition that spines are "heterotopically" induced by CFs (Hámori, 1973); on the contrary, they suggest that CFs are in some way actively responsible for resorption of spines in selective competition for postsynaptic space with PFs (Sotelo et al., 1975).

In summary, CFs do not appear to have any inductive influence on growth since after neonatal CF ablation PC trees are normally polarized and oriented and branching patterns are normal. CFs do, however, appear to have a trophic influence since, in their absence, dendritic fields are uniformly smaller than normal (Bradley and Berry, 1976a; Kawaguchi *et al.*, 1975; Sotelo and Arsenio-Nunes, 1976).

3. Monoaminergic Fibers

The 5-HT and NA fibers are the first axons to invade the cerebellum. Their early arrival on E17 (Seiger and Olson, 1973), long before the cerebellum is functional, makes monoaminergic fibers strong contenders for the mediation of presumed primary induction of PC dendritic growth, particularly since NA and 5-HT are capable of initiating and maintaining differentiation by mobilizing intracellular cAMP (Bloom, 1974).

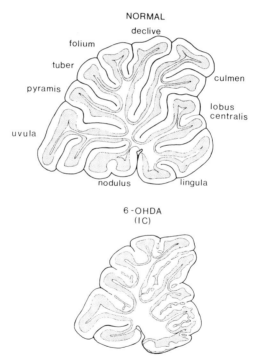

FIG. 12. Diagram of sagittal vermal sections from 30-day-old normal rats and rats treated with intracisternal (IC) 6-hydroxydopamine (6-OHDA) at birth. The hatched area shows the positions of granule cells. In the normal animal the granule cells lie in the internal granule layer of all folia. In the treated rats foliation is primitive, although all folia are present, and fissuration is rudimentary except between the nodulus and uvula. There are large islands of granule cells which have failed to migrate. These ectopic granule cell nests are most prevalent in the posterior fissures and rarely seen in the nodulus or uvula. Thus the phylogenetically old folia largely escape these gross effects while the newer folia are progressively more grossly deformed.

Cerebellar NA fibers can be destroyed by treatment with the false transmitter 6-hydroxydopamine (6-OHDA). After such treatment on day 1 pp in the rat, cerebellar development is very abnormal (Sievers *et al.*, 1980b). The cerebellum is greatly reduced in size, fissuration is arrested, and foliation is primitive. Granule cell migration is impaired and large areas containing ectopic granule cells are seen. These effects are greatest in the anterior vermal folia while the uvula and nodulus are largely spared (Fig. 12). Despite these abnormalities PC morphology does not appear to be directly altered by the absence of NA terminals. Thus, although dendritic trees are disorganized within the molecular layer and have fewer, longer segments than normal (Fig. 13), such changes are consistent with the effects of a reduction in PF number caused by granule cell hypoplasia and ectopia. Accordingly, these results strongly suggest that if NA fibers have a primary inductive influence on dendritic growth then they must be exerting this effect prenatally since the absence of monoaminergic fibers after birth does not influence polarity, orientation, or the overall characteristics of the growth of the tree directly.

VI. Influence of Functional Activity on Dendritic Growth

There is growing evidence that the quality and quantity of unit activity converging on dendritic trees can influence growth but the

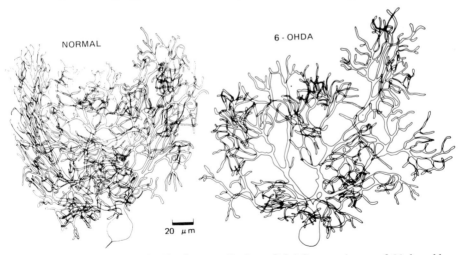

FIG. 13. Two camera lucida drawn cells from Golgi-Cox specimens of 30-day-old normal and 6-OHDA specimens, both from the base of the primary fissure. Note that the main differences between the two cells are a reduction in segment number and an increase in segment length in the fields of PCs from 6-OHDA-treated rats. It is clear that despite the gross disorganization caused by 6-OHDA treatment, presumed secondary induction has occurred.

mechanisms by which this is achieved are unclear. In the neocortex, for example, deafferentation retards the development of pyramidal cell dendritic trees (Valverde, 1968; Berry and Hollingworth, 1973; Globus and Scheibel, 1976a,b; Coleman and Riesen, 1968) while rearing in enriched environments (Holloway, 1966; Volkmar and Greenough, 1972; Greenough and Volkmar, 1973; Greenough et al., 1973) increases the size of networks. With respect to stellate cells in the neocortex, Valverde (1968) observed a reorganization of trees in layer IV of the visual cortex in mice enucleated at birth and Borges and Berry (1976, 1978) recorded similar changes in field orientation of visual cortical stellate cells in dark reared rats. Such environmental influences on the extent and direction of growth of dendritic fields could be explained in terms of the filopodial adhesive hypothesis if the traffic of unit activity in the *axons,* converging on trees, controlled the degree of arborization in the terminal axonal fields. This would lead to a dendritic reaction according to the above hypothesis, because it is the number of adhesive sites offered by axons and their disposition in space which determines the branching frequency and direction of growth of dendrites.

It is the quality of the environment and the duration of exposure to it which, to a large extent, determine firing patterns in projection systems and there is some evidence from studies on the visual system that different levels of exposure to the environment are directly correlated with the size of terminal axonal arbors of the geniculostriate projection. Thus, Cronly-Dillon and Perry (1976) demonstrated a surge in the production of neural processes, as measured by tubulin synthesis, immediately after eye opening in the rat visual cortex and Thorpe and Blakemore (1975), using HRP injection into the visual cortex, demonstrated reduced uptake in the deprived lateral geniculate laminae of monocular cats. These latter workers argued that reduced uptake of HRP in the cortex is directly due to a dramatic reduction in the density of axon terminals caused by reduced activity in fibers connected with the deprived eye. Although, it has since been shown that the incorporation of HRP into axonal terminals is dependent on nerve activity (Singer et al., 1977), it has also been demonstrated, using orthograde HRP techniques, that axon fields in the eye dominance columns of the primary visual cortex are able to retract and expand according to the level of activity passing through the system when one eye is closed and then reopened within the sensitive period (Hubel et al., 1977). These changes are correlated with shrinkage and enlargement of cell bodies in the lateral geniculate body (Guillery, 1972) suggesting that protein synthetic mechanisms supporting growth are being modulated by activity (Hydén, 1973). The monocular visual deprivation paradigm is, however, complicated by the possibility that centripetal activity may influence LGB growth (Guillery, 1972) and that the monoaminergic system might control the plastic responsiveness of cells to environmental manipulation (Kasamatsu and Pettigrew, 1976; Pettigrew and Kasamatsu, 1978).

VII. Remodeling of the Mature Dendritic Tree

Uylings et al. (1978) have recently shown that cells in the cerebral cortex of adult rats produce new dendritic branches when the animals are maintained under conditions of environmental enrichment, while Rutledge et al. (1974) observed dendritic outgrowth in the cortex of adult cats after long-term electrical stimulation. Several electron microscopic studies (Hashimoto and Palay, 1965; Angaut and Sotelo, 1973; Chan-Palay, 1973) have found evidence of altered axon terminals in a variety of brain regions from apparently normal adult animals, and it has been suggested (Hashimoto and Palay, 1965; Sotelo and Palay, 1971) that these represent the degenerative phase of a continuous process of synaptic remodeling. A recent study of the dendritic networks of murine PCs (Weiss and Pysh, 1978) provides more specific evidence of dendritic plasticity. These workers observed that the elongation of dendritic segments occurring during late postnatal development was accompanied, from 20 days pp, by a decline in segment number, thus leading to the remodeling of the network. McConnell and Berry (1978a,b) have also found evidence for dendritic remodeling in their topological analysis of PC trees in normal rats between 30 and 80 days despite there being no increase in segment number during this period. Thus, it appears that the networks undergo some form of remodeling, remaining capable of new segment production although no longer actually expanding.

Evidence that PC dendritic growth cones remain functional during the 30- to 80-day period is provided by an analysis of dendritic fields in animals starved for 30 days and then fed ad libitum until 80 days. Networks from these animals, although showing no significant increase in segment number between 30 and 80 days, did show an increase in segment length such that the deficits in distal segment length seen after starvation were wholly, or partially, restored by 80 days (Fig. 14). Both terminal and nonterminal segments underwent elongation during this period, suggesting that terminal and segmental growth cones are functional in these animals. Topological analysis of the PC dendritic trees of these treated rats at 30 and 80 days also shows remodeling.

To what extent dendritic remodeling is dependent on a lability of

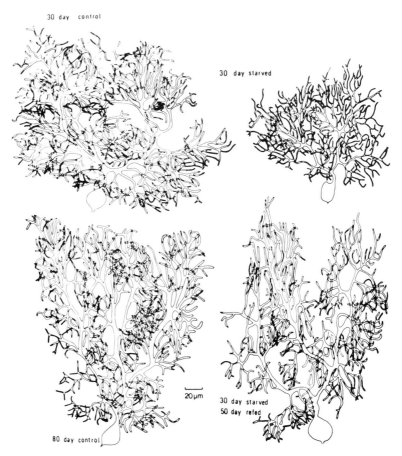

FIG. 14. Camera lucida drawings of PC dendritic fields from 30-day-old normal and starved rats and normal 80-day-old rats and animals starved to 30 days and then fed *ad libitum* to 80 days. Note the increase in segment lengths of the refed rat. In both 80-day animals topological analysis detected branching patterns different from those in trees at 30 days of age indicating remodeling. From McConnell and Berry (1978c).

axodendritic contacts or on vagaries in the pattern of input to PCs is unknown. But since the PC/granule cell ratio declines from 20 days pp in the rat remodeling could be associated with parallel fiber loss (McConnell and Berry, 1980). Loss of dendrites has however been seen after deafferentation in the adult olfactory bulb (Matthews and Powell, 1962), spinal cord (Gelfan *et al.*, 1972), nucleus laminaris (Benes *et al.*, 1977), and prepyriform cortex (Jones and Thomas, 1962) suggesting that normal patterned input may be important for the maintenance of normal dendritic topology.

In the cerebellum attempts to test this hypothesis have produced conflicting results: Herndon (1968) could not find any fine structural evidence for changes in PC dendritic geometry in the adult rat after the administration of thiophene, a potent degranulating agent. On the other hand Bradley and Berry (1979), also using thiophene, were able to detect (both qualitatively and quantitatively), nonrandom loss of dendritic segments. Moreover, Mouren-Mathieu and Colonnier (1969) observed similar changes in PC dendritic fields after sagittal incision through the folia of the cerebellum in adult cats. Bradley and Berry (1979) argued that in their thiophene-treated animals it was the distal segments which disappeared after PF deafferentation. Similarly, Coleman and Riesen (1968), Volkmar and Greenough (1972), Diamond et al. (1976), and Uylings et al. (1978) concluded that the terminal branches of neocortical cells exhibit the greatest potential for plasticity in stimulus deprivation and enhancement studies.

Attempts to change the quality and quantity of input through PF/PC spinous synapses have been performed by Anwar and Berry (1980). In these experiments rats were subjected to bilateral hemispherectomy at birth, a procedure which greatly reduces pontine mossy fiber input through PFs. At 30 days pp a quantitative analysis of the cerebellum of these animals showed that granule cell and PC numbers were normal. The PC dendritic segments were of normal length, but topologies were abnormal and segment frequency reduced by some 15%. These results are thought to demonstrate remodeling contingent upon abnormal PF input and not to a primary effect of altered input on the genesis of branching patterns. This conclusion stems from the observation that PFs mature before granule cell dendrites become functional (Altman, 1972a) and thus PC branching patterns are normally established by interaction with a deafferented axon system. Remodeling normally occurs after 30 days in response to a loss of (?redundant) parallel fibers and to the changing functional demands made on the cerebellum as the animal grows. Remodeling may be accelerated after hemispherectomy when the demands for functional adaption, caused by an imbalance of mossy fiber input, may appear much earlier than in the normal animal.

VIII. Conclusion

We conclude that, in the developing cerebellum, the form of the PC is largely under the control of the "environment." Genes may specify the positions and biophysical properties of adhesive sites and postsynaptic thickenings. The spatial interaction of these specialized areas of membrane with particular groups of axons ramifying about the growing tree may be sufficient to shape the characteristic geometry of the PC.

Environmental effects may be divided into two major influences. The first induces PCs to form primitive perisomatic branches. Although this could be an autonomous property of PCs (if not of all neurons) it also seems possible that this primary inductive stimulus could be mediated, in the prenatal period, by monoaminergic fibers which are the only extrinsic fibers associated with PCs at this early time. The cell soon achieves polarity as thick dendrites stem from the pole of the cell facing the external granular layer and resorption of perisomatic processes occurs, possibly under the influence of basket cell axosomatic synaptogenesis. Orientation may be achieved by contact with the radial processes of Bergmann glia. Growth appears to cease soon after this stage (as seen in weaver and staggerer mutant mice) unless a small but finite number of PF axospinous synapses are formed on the shafts of the primordial tree. This secondary inductive stimulus triggers the PC to insert membrane in the tips of its dendrites at a constant rate. Thus, after secondary induction, dendrites advance through the neuropil of the molecular layer at a constant speed. The number of branches they produce is related to the number of PF adhesive sites the dendritic filopodia contact. In fact, there is good evidence that this latter type of interaction determines not only the frequency and order of branching, but also both the magnitude of segment lengths and the direction of growth. The planar organization of the tree and the boundaries of the lateral domains appear to be defined by interaction between adjacent PC dendritic fields and a possible periodic refractoriness in the reactivity of PFs with PC dendritic filopodia (see Berry and Bradley, 1976c, and Berry et al., 1978 for references).

The growth spurt which follows secondary induction establishes a tree whose character is determined by the above physical constraints. Functional activity plays a minor role at this stage because mossy fiber granule cell contacts have not matured. The tree does however become refined and remodeled as the system becomes functional and this coincides with some granule cell death and increases in parallel fiber length. Functional refinement of dendritic fields may be organized presynaptically, by dendritic filopodial adhesive interaction with axons, if the pattern of unit activity passing through projection systems controls the metabolic events supporting terminal axonal arborizations.

REFERENCES

Addison, W. H. F. (1911). J. Comp. Neurol. 21, 459–488.
Altman, J. (1969). J. Comp. Neurol. 136, 269–294.
Altman, J. (1972a). J. Comp. Neurol. 145, 353–398.

Altman, J. (1972b). *J. Comp. Neurol.* **145**, 399–464.
Altman, J. (1972c). *J. Comp. Neurol.* **145**, 465–514.
Altman, J. (1973). *J. Comp. Neurol.* **149**, 153–180.
Altman, J. (1976a). *J. Comp. Neurol.* **165**, 65–76.
Altman, J. (1976b). *J. Comp. Neurol.* **165**, 31–48.
Altman, J., and Anderson, W. J. (1972). *J. Comp. Neurol.* **146**, 355–406.
Altman, J., and Bayer, S. A. (1978). *J. Comp. Neurol.* **179**, 23–48.
Altman, J., and Winfree, A. T. (1977). *J. Comp. Neurol.* **171**, 1–16.
Angaut, D., and Sotelo, C. (1973). *Exp. Brain Res.* **16**, 431–454.
Anwar, A., and Berry, M. (1980). *Neurosci. Lett.* Submitted.
Atlas, D., Teichberg, I. V., and Changeux, J. P. (1977). *Brain Res.* **128**, 532–536.
Benes, F. M., Parks, T. N., and Rubel, E. W. (1977). *Brain Res.* **122**, 1–13.
Berry, M. (1976). *In* "Proceedings 4th International Congress of Sterology" (E. E. Underwood, ed.), pp. 49–54. National Bureau of Standards Special Publications No. 431. U.S. Government Printing Office, Washington, D. C.
Berry, M., and Bradley, P. (1976a). *Brain Res.* **109**, 111–132.
Berry, M., and Bradley, P. (1976b). *Brain Res.* **112**, 1–35.
Berry, M., and Bradley, P. (1976c). *Brain Res.* **116**, 361–387.
Berry, M., and Bradley, P. (1976d). *J. Anat.* **122**, 709–710.
Berry, M., Hollingworth, T. (1973). *Experientia* **29**, 204–207.
Berry, M., Hollingworth, T., Flinn, R. M., and Anderson, E. M. (1972a). *TIT J. Life Sci.* **2**, 129–140.
Berry, M., Hollingworth, T., Flinn, R. M., and Anderson, E. M. (1972b). *J. Anat.* **111**, 491–493.
Berry, M., Hollingworth, T., Anderson, E. M., and Flinn, R. M. (1975). *In* "Advances in Neurology (G. W. Kreutzberg, ed.), Vol. 12, pp. 217–245. Raven, New York.
Berry, M., Bradley, P., and Borges, S. (1978). *In* "Maturation of the Nervous System, Progress in Brain Research" (M. A. Corner *et al.*, eds.), Vol. 48, pp. 133–146. Elsevier, Amsterdam.
Bignami, A., and Dahl, D. (1974). *J. Comp. Neurol.* **155**, 219–230.
Bloom, F. E. (1974). *Rev. Physiol. Biochem. Pharmacol.* **74**, 1–103.
Bloom, F. E., Hoffer, B. J., and Siggins, G. R. (1971). *Brain Res.* **25**, 501–521.
Bodian, D. (1966). *Bull. Johns Hopkins Hosp.* **119**, 129–149.
Borges, S., and Berry, M. (1976). *Brain Res.* **112**, 141–147.
Borges, S., and Berry, M. (1978). *J. Comp. Neurol.* **180**, 277–300.
Bradley, P., and Berry, M. (1976a). *Brain Res.* **109**, 133–151.
Bradley, P., and Berry, M. (1976b). *Brain Res.* **112**, 133–140.
Bradley, P., and Berry, M. (1978a). *Brain Res.* **142**, 135–141.
Bradley, P., and Berry, M. (1978b). *Brain Res.* **143**, 499–511.
Bradley, P., and Berry, M. (1979). *Neuropathol. Appl. Neurobiol.* **5**, 9–16.
Bray, D. (1970). *Proc. Natl. Acad. Sci. U.S.A.* **65**, 905–910.
Bray, D. (1973). *J. Cell Biol.* **56**, 702–712.
Bunge, M. B. (1973). *J. Cell Biol.* **56**, 713–735.
Calvet, M. C., LePault, A. M., and Calvet, J. (1976). *Brain Res.* **111**, 399–406.
Cerro, M. P., del, and Snider, R. S. (1968). *J. Comp. Neurol.* **133**, 341–362.
Changeux, J. P., and Dauchin, A. (1976). *Nature (London)* **264**, 705–712.
Chan-Palay, V. (1973). *Z. Anat. Entwicklungsg.* **142**, 23–35.
Chan-Palay, V. (1977). "Cerebellar Dentate Nucleus: Organization, Cytology and Transmitters." Springer-Verlag, Berlin and New York.
Coleman, P. D., and Riesen, A. H. (1968). *J. Anat.* **102**, 363–374.

Crépel, F. (1971). *Brain Res.* **35,** 272–276.

Crépel, F., and Mariani, J. (1975). *Brain Res.* **98,** 135–147.

Crépel, F., and Mariani, J. (1976). *J. Neurobiol.* **7,** 579–582.

Crépel, F. Delhaye-Bouchaud, N., and LeGrand, J. (1976). *Arch. Ital. Biol.* **114,** 49–74.

Cronly-Dillon, J. R., and Perry, G. W. (1976). *Nature (London)* **261,** 581–583.

Das, G., and Nornes, H. O. (1972). *Z. Anat. Entwicklungsg.* **138,** 155–166.

Diamond, M. C., Ingham, C. A., Johnson, R. E., Bennett, E. L., and Rosenzweig, M. R. (1976). *J. Neurobiol.* **7,** 75–86.

Freedman, R., Hoffer, B. J., Woodward, D. J., and Puro, D. (1977). *Exp. Neurol.* **55,** 269–288.

Fujita, S. (1967). *J. Cell Biol.* **32,** 354–364.

Fujita, S., Shimada, M., and Nakamura, T. (1966). *J. Comp. Neurol.* **128,** 191–208.

Gelfan, S., Kao, G., and Ling, H. (1972). *J. Comp. Neurol.* **123,** 73–96.

Globus, A., and Scheibel, A. B. (1967a). *Exp. Neurol.* **18,** 116–131.

Globus, A., and Scheibel, A. B. (1967b). *Exp. Neurol.* **19,** 331–345.

Grainger, F., and James, D. W. (1970). *Z. Zellforsch.* **108,** 93–104.

Greenough, W. T., and Volkmar, F. (1973). *Exp. Neurol.* **40,** 491–504.

Greenough, W. T., Volkmar, F., and Juraska, J. M. (1973). *Exp. Neurol.* **41,** 371–378.

Guillery, R. W. (1972). *J. Comp. Neurol.* **144,** 117–127.

Hámori, J. (1969). *In* "Neurobiology of Cerebellar Evolution and Development" (R. Llinás, ed.), pp. 845–858. American Medical Assoc. Chicago, Illinois.

Hámori, J. (1973). *Brain Res.* **62,** 337–344.

Hashimoto, P. H., and Palay, S. C. (1965). *Anat. Rec.* **151,** 454–455.

Harrison, R. G. (1910). *J. Exp. Zool.* **9,** 787–846.

Herndon, R. M. (1968). *Exp. Brain Res.* **6,** 49–68.

Herndon, R. M., and Oster-Granit, M. L. (1975). *In* "Advances in Neurology," Vol. 12: Physiology and Pathology of Dendrites (G. W. Kreutzberg, ed.), pp. 361–371. Raven, New York.

Herndon, R. M., Margolis, G., and Kilham, L. (1971). *J. Neuropathol. Exp. Neurol.* **30,** 557–569.

Hinds, J. W., and Hinds, P. L. (1972). *J. Neurocytol.* **1,** 169–187.

Hinds, J. W., and Hinds, P. L. (1976). *J. Comp. Neurol.* **169,** 41–62.

Hirano, A., Dembitzer, H. M., and Jones, M. (1972). *J. Neuropathol. Exp. Neurol.* **31,** 113–125.

Hölkfelt, T. and Fuxe, K. (1969). *Exp. Brain Res.* **9,** 63–72.

Hollingworth, T., and Berry, M. (1975). *Phil. Trans. R. Soc. B* **270,** 227–264.

Holloway, J. R., Jr. (1966). *Brain Res.* **2,** 393–396.

Hubel, D. H., and Wiesel, T. N. (1963). *J. Neurophysiol.* **26,** 994–1002.

Hubel, D. H., Wiesel, T. N., and Levay, S. (1977). *Phil. Trans. R. B* **278,** 377–409.

Hughes, A. (1953). *J. Anat.* **87,** 150–162.

Hydén, H. (1973). *In* "Macromolecules and Behaviour" (G. B. Ansell and P. B. Bradley, eds.), pp. 51–57. Macmillan, London.

Jones, W. H., and Thomas, D. B. (1962). *J. Anat.* **96,** 375–381.

Kasamatsu, T., and Pettigrew, J.-D. (1976). *Science* **194,** 206–209.

Kawaguchi, S., Yamamota, T., Mizuno, N., and Iwahori, N. (1975). *Neurosci. Lett.* **1,** 301–304.

Kawana, E., Sandri, C., and Akert, K. (1971). *Z. Zellforsch.* **115,** 284–298.

Kornguth, S. E., and Scott, G. (1972). *J. Comp. Neurol.* **146,** 61–82.

Kornguth, S. E., Anderson, J. W., and Scott, G. (1968). *J. Comp. Neurol.* **132,** 531–546.

Landis, S. C. (1973). *Brain Res.* **61,** 175–189.
Landis, S. C., and Bloom, F. E. (1975). *Brain Res.* **96,** 299–305.
Landis, S. C., Shoemaker, W. J., Schlumpe, M., and Bloom, F. E. (1975). *Brain Res.* **93,** 253–266.
Larramendi, L. M. H. (1969). *In* "Neurobiology of Cerebellar Evolution and Development" (R. Llinás, ed.), pp. 803–843. American Medical Assoc. Chicago, Illinois.
Larramendi, L. M. H., and Victor, T. (1966). *Anat. Rec.* **154,** 373.
Larramendi, L. M. H., and Victor, T. (1967). *Brain Res.* **5,** 15–30.
Lauder, J. M. (1978). *Brain Res.* **142,** 25–40.
Lewis, P. D., Fülöp, Z., Hajós, F., Balázs, R., and Woodhams, P. C. (1977). *Neuropathol. Appl. Neurobiol.* **3,** 183–190.
Liu, C. N., and Liu, C. Y. (1971). *Anat. Rec.* **169,** 369.
Llinás, R., Hillman, D. E., and Precht, W. (1973). *J. Neurobiol.* **4,** 69–74.
McConnell, P., and Berry, M. (1978a). *J. Comp. Neurol.* **177,** 159–172.
McConnell, P., and Berry, M. (1978b). *J. Comp. Neurol.* **178,** 759–772.
McConnell, P., and Berry, M. (1978c). *J. Anat.* **127,** 423–425.
McConnell, P., and Berry, M. (1980). *J. Comp. Neurol.* Submitted.
Malsburg, von der, C. (1973). *Kybernetik* **14,** 85–100.
Matthews, M. R., and Powell, T. P. S. (1962). *J. Anat.* **96,** 89–102.
Melamed, E., Lahav, M., and Atlas, D. (1976). *Nature (London)* **261,** 420–421.
Morest, D. K. (1968). *Z. Anat. Entwicklungsg.* **127,** 201–220.
Morest, D. K. (1969a). *Z. Anat. Entwicklungsg.* **128,** 271–289.
Morest, D. K. (1969b). *Z. Anat. Entwicklungsg.* **128,** 290–317.
Mouren-Mathieu, A., and Colonnier, M. (1969). *Brain Res.* **16,** 307–316.
Mugnaini, E. (1969). *In* "Neurobiology of Cerebellar Evolution and Development" (R. Llinás, ed.), pp. 749–782. American Medical Assoc. Chicago, Illinois.
Mugnaini, E. (1970). *Brain Res.* **17,** 169–179.
Olson, L., and Fuxe, K. (1971). *Brain Res.* **28,** 165–171.
Palay, S. L., and Chan-Palay, V. (1974). "Cerebellar Cortex: Cytology and Organisation." Springer Publ., New York.
Pettigrew, J. D., and Kasamatsu, T. (1978). *Nature (London)* **271,** 761–763.
Pfenninger, K. H., and Bunge, M. A. (1973). *J. Cell Biol.* **59,** 264a.
Pfenninger, K. H., and Rees, R. P. (1976). *In* "Neuronal Recognition" (S. H. Barondes, ed.), pp. 131–178. Chapman & Hall, London.
Pfenninger, K. H., Bunge, M. B., and Bunge, R. P. (1974). *In* "Proc. 8th Int. Cong. Electronmicroscopy, Canberra," Vol. II, pp. 234–235. Australian Academy of Science, Canberra.
Pomerat, C. M., Hendelman, W. J., Raibom, C. W., and Massey, M. H. (1967). *In* "The Neuron" (H. Hydén, ed.), pp. 119–178. Elsevier, Amsterdam.
Price, S., and Berry, M. (1979). In preparation.
Privat, A. (1975). *In* "Advances in Neurology," Vol. 12: Physiology and Pathology of Dendrites (G. W. Kreutzberg, ed.), pp. 201–216. Raven, New York.
Privat., A., and Drian, M. J. (1976). *J. Comp. Neurol.* **166,** 201–244.
Privat, A., Drian, M. J., and Mandon, P. (1973). *Z. Zellforsch.* **146,** 45–67.
Privat, A., Drian, M. J., and Mandon, P. (1974). *J. Comp. Neurol.* **153,** 291–308.
Puro, D. G., and Woodward, D. J. (1977). *Brain Res.* **129,** 141–146.
Rakic, P. (1974). *In* "Frontiers in Neurology and Neuroscience Research" (P. Seeman and G. M. Brown, eds.), pp. 112–132. Univ. of Toronto Press, Toronto, Canada.
Rakic, P. (1975). *In* "Advances in Neurology," Vol. 12: Physiology and Pathology of Dendrites (G. W. Kreutzberg, ed.), pp. 117–134. Raven, New York.

Rakic, P., and Sidman, R. L. (1973a). *J. Comp. Neurol.* **152**, 103–132.
Rakic, P., and Sidman, R. L. (1973b). *J. Comp. Neurol.* **152**, 133–162.
Rakic, P., and Sidman, R. L. (1973c). *Proc. Natl. Acad. Sci. U.S.A.* **70**, 240–244.
Ramón y Cajal, S. (1909). "Histologie du système nerveux de l'homme et des vertébrés Vol. I" (L. Azoulay, trans.). Reprinted by Instituto Ramón y Cajal del C.S.I.C. Madrid, 1952–1955.
Ramón y Cajal, S. (1960). "Studies on Vertebrate Neurogenesis" (L. Guth, trans.). Thomas, Springfield, Illinois.
Roberts, A. (1976). *Brain Res.* **118**, 526–530.
Rutledge, L. T., Wright, C., and Duncan, J. (1974). *Exp. Neurol.* **44**, 209–228.
Scheibel, M. E., and Scheibel, A. B. (1970). *Int. Rev. Neurobiol.* **13**, 1–25.
Scheibel, M. E., and Scheibel, A. B. (1971). *In* "Brain Development and Behaviour" (M. B. Sterman, D. J. McGinty and A. M. Adinolfi, eds.), pp. 1–21. Academic Press, New York.
Schultze, B., Nowak, B., and Maurer, W. (1974). *J. Comp. Neurol.* **158**, 207–218.
Seiger, A., and Olson, L. (1973). *Z. Anat. Entwicklungsg.* **140**, 281–318.
Shofer, R. J., Pappas, G. D., and Purpura, D. P. (1964). *In* "Response of the Nervous System to Ionising Radiation" (J. J. Haley and R. S. Snider, eds.), pp. 476–508. Little, Brown, New York.
Sidman, R. L. (1968). *In* "Physiological and Biochemical Aspects of Integration" (F. D. Carlson, ed.), pp. 163–193. Prentice-Hall, New York.
Sidman, R. L. (1972). *In* "Cell Interactions, Proceedings of the Third Lepetit Colloqium" (L. G. Silvestri, ed.), pp. 1–13. North Holland, Amsterdam.
Sidman, R. L. (1974). *In* "The Cell Surface in Development" (A. A. Moscona, ed.), pp. 221–255. Wiley, New York.
Sidman, R. L., Green, M. C., and Appel, S. H. (1965). "Catalog of the Neurological Mutants of the Mouse." Harvard Univ. Press, Cambridge, Massachusetts.
Sievers, J., Anwar, A., Baumgarten, J. and Berry, M. (1979). *Nature (London)* (in press).
Sievers, J., Sievers, H., and Klemm, H. P. (1980a). *Verh. Anat. Ges.* **74** (in press).
Sievers, J., Klemm, H. P., Jenner, S., Baumgarten, H. G., and Berry, M. (1980b). *J. Neurochem.* **34**, 765–771.
Siggins, G. R., Henriksen, S. J., and Landis, S. C. (1976). *Brain Res.* **114**, 53–70.
Singer, W., Hollander, H., and Vanegas, H. (1977). *Brain Res.* **120**, 133–137.
Skoff, R. P., and Hamburger, V. (1974). *J. Comp. Neurol.* **153**, 107–148.
Smit, G. J., and Uylings, H. B. M. (1975). *Brain Res.* **87**, 41–53.
Smit, G. J., Uylings, H. B. M., and Veldmaat-Wansink, L. (1972). *Acta Morphol. Neerl.-Scand.* **9**, 253–274.
Smith, D. E. (1974). *Brain Res.* **74**, 119–130.
Sotelo, C. (1973). *Brain Res.* **62**, 345–351.
Sotelo, C. (1975a). *In* "Advances in Neurology," Vol. 12: Physiology and Pathology of Dendrites (G. W. Kreutzberg, ed.), pp. 335–351. Raven, New York.
Sotelo, C. (1975b). *Brain Res.* **94**, 19–44.
Sotelo, C., and Arsenio-Nunes, M. L. (1976). *Brain Res.* **111**, 389–395.
Sotelo, C., and Changeux, J. P. (1974a). *Brain Res.* **77**, 484–491.
Sotelo, C., and Changeux, J. P. (1974b). *Brain Res.* **67**, 519–526.
Sotelo, C., and Palay, S. L. (1971). *Lab. Invest.* **25**, 653–671.
Sotelo, C., Hillman, D. E., Zamora, A. K., and Llinás, R. (1975). *Brain Res.* **98**, 574–581.
Speidel, C. C. (1942). *J. Comp. Neurol.* **76**, 57–73.
Sperry, R. W. (1943). *J. Comp. Neurol.* **79**, 33–55.
Sperry, R. W. (1944). *J. Neurophysiol.* **7**, 57–69.

Tennyson, V. M. (1970). *J. Cell Biol.* **44,** 62–79.

Thorpe, P. A., and Blakemore, C. (1975). *Neurosci. Lett.* **1,** 271–276.

Uylings, H. B. M., and Smit, G. J. (1975). *Brain Res.* **87,** 55–60.

Uylings, H. B. M., Smit, G. J., and Veltman, W. A. M. (1975). *In* "Advances in Neurology," Vol. 12: Physiology and Pathology of Dendrites (G. W. Kreutzberg, ed.), pp. 247–254. Raven, New York.

Uylings, H. B. M., Kuypers, K., and Veltman, W. A. M. (1978). *Progr. Brain Res.* **48,** 261–274.

Valverde, F. (1968). *Exp. Brain Res.* **5,** 274–292.

Valverde, F. (1971). *Brain Res.* **33,** 1–11.

Vaughn, J. E., and Sims, T. (1978). *J. Neurocytol.* **7,** 337–363.

Vaughn, J. E., Henriksen, C. K., and Grieshaber, J. A. (1974). *J. Cell Biol.* **60,** 664–672.

Volkmar, F. N., and Greenough, W. T. (1972). *Science* **176,** 1445–1447.

Weiss, G. M., and Pysh, J. J. (1978). *Brain Res.* **154,** 219–230.

Woodward, D. J., Hoffer, B. J., and Altman, J. (1974). *J. Neurobiol.* **5,** 253–304.

Woodward, D. J., Bickett, D., and Chanda, R. (1975). *Brain Res.* **97,** 195–214.

Yamada, K. M., Spooner, B. S., and Wessells, N. K. (1970). *Proc. Natl. Acad. Sci. U.S.A.* **66,** 1206–1212.

Yamada, K. M., Spooner, B. S., and Wessells, N. K. (1971). *J. Cell Biol.* **49,** 614–635.

Yoon, C. H. (1976). *Brain Res.* **109,** 206–215.

CHAPTER 5

THE DEVELOPMENT OF THE DENTATE GYRUS*

W. M. Cowan,† B. B. Stanfield,† and K. Kishi

DEPARTMENT OF ANATOMY AND NEUROBIOLOGY
WASHINGTON UNIVERSITY SCHOOL OF MEDICINE
ST. LOUIS, MISSOURI

I. Introduction 103
II. The Morphology of the Dentate Gyrus in the Rat and Mouse 104
   A. General Form and Cell Numbers............................. 104
   B. Afferent Connections 109
   C. Efferent Connections 114
III. The Development of the Dentate Gyrus 115
   A. The Time and Site of Origin of the Dentate Granule Cells 115
   B. The Migration of the Granule Cells and the Assembly
     of the Stratum Granulosum 121
   C. The Growth and Differentiation of Granule Cell Processes 123
   D. The Development of the Afferent Connections to the
     Dentate Gyrus 130
   E. The Development of Synapses in the Molecular Layer
     of the Dentate Gyrus 139
   F. Some Consequences of the Prolonged Development of the Granule
     Cells for the Distribution of the Commissural and Associational
     Afferents to the Dentate Gyrus 145
IV. Conclusions and Future Perspectives 152
   References 154

I. Introduction

The greater part of the medial edge of the mammalian cerebral hemisphere is formed by a distinctive cortical structure known as the *dentate gyrus* or *fascia dentata*. By any measure, this is the simplest of all cortical areas, and for this, and certain other reasons, one of the most convenient for developmental studies. Whereas most areas of the neocortex consist of up to six superimposed cellular layers each of which may include several different types of neurons, the principal

* This work was supported in part by USPHS grants NS-10943 from the National Institutes of Health, DA-00259 from ADAMAH, and Training Grant EY-00092; K. K. was on leave of absence from Tokyo Medical and Dental University, Bunkyo-Ku, Tokyo, Japan.
† Present address: The Salk Institute for Biological Studies, San Diego, California.

CURRENT TOPICS IN
DEVELOPMENTAL BIOLOGY, Vol. 15

cellular layer of the dentate gyrus, the stratum granulosum, consists of a single class of neuron, and all the cells in this layer are uniformly oriented in such a way that their dendrites arise from the superficial aspect of the cells and ascend into a synaptic, or molecular, layer that extends outward to the pial surface; their axons, on the other hand, arise from the deep or basal aspects of the cells, and extend in the opposite direction into what is termed the hilus of the dentate gyrus. Furthermore, whereas it has been difficult to define the precise site of termination of most afferent inputs to the neocortex, the principal extrinsic afferents to the dentate gyrus all end within the molecular layer, and are arranged in discrete, sharply defined laminae with one class of afferents ending in relation to the distal parts of the granule cell dendrites, while another ends upon more proximal dendritic segments close to their origin from the cell somata. Finally, it is now known in rats and mice (which have been most intensively studied from this point of view) that about 85% of the granule cells are generated postnatally, and it has thus been possible to manipulate certain aspects of the development of the dentate gyrus, without resorting to intrauterine procedures.

Although several details in the development of the dentate gyrus remain to be clarified, as a result of recent studies we can now give a fairly complete account of the major events involved in the assembly of this cortical area, and in the development of its principal afferent connections, both in normal rats and mice, and in the so-called reeler mouse in which the cellular architecture of the dentate gyrus is severely disturbed. In this chapter we shall confine ourselves mainly to what is known about the *development* of the dentate gyrus, and only briefly comment upon those aspects of neuronal plasticity in this system which bear upon its development. In the chapter by Gall and Lynch in this volume, the remarkable capacity of this system to reorganize itself after partial deafferentation is considered at length.

II. The Morphology of the Dentate Gyrus in the Rat and Mouse

A. General Form and Cell Numbers

Before describing the development of the dentate gyrus a brief account should be given of its morphological organization in the rodent brain; this will serve not only to indicate the type of developmental issue to be addressed, but also to define the nomenclature we shall use and the topographic relationships that exist between the dentate gyrus and the other components of the hippocampal formation[1] with which it is so intimately related.

The form of the dentate gyrus is complicated by the fact that the entire hippocampal formation is curved along its longitudinal extent, so that when viewed from the side it has the form of a rather open "C" with the concavity directed rostroventrally. The rostral end of the dentate gyrus reaches almost to the septal region of the brain; for this reason, in what follows, we shall refer to this part of the gyrus as its *septal pole.* The caudal end of the gyrus extends ventrally toward the amygdala in the temporal region of the brain, and is accordingly termed the *temporal pole.* In sections transverse to the longitudinal axis of the dentate gyrus, its appearance is more or less the same at all levels, but in sections cut in either the frontal or horizontal planes its appearance is more complex (see Swanson and Cowan, 1977a).

Figure 1 is a low-power photomicrograph of a frontal section through the septal (or rostral) third of the dentate gyrus and the adjoining hippocampus in an adult rat. In such sections the principal cellular layer of the dentate gyrus is more or less V-shaped and surrounds the medial end of field CA_3 of the hippocampus (Cajal's *regio inferior*). From the relationship of the two blades (or limbs) of the dentate gyrus to the pyramidal cells of the regio inferior they are commonly referred to as the *suprapyramidal* and *infrapyramidal* blades, respectively.[2] A comparable photomicrograph of a horizontal section through the vertically disposed, caudal part of the dentate gyrus is shown in Fig. 2. In such sections the dentate gyrus is more U-shaped, but the two blades bear the same topographic relationship to the regio inferior of the hippocampus. The densely stained cellular layer which contains the closely packed somata of the granule cells is usually called the *stratum granulosum,* while the overlying cell-free zone, in which most of the extrinsic afferents to the dentate gyrus terminate, is known as the *stratum moleculare.* As there is still a good deal of uncertainty about the precise nature of the heterogeneous population of cells located between the two blades (in what is usually called the *hilus* or the *hilar*

---

[1] The term "hippocampal formation" is convenient, if somewhat imprecise. Included in it are: the dentate gyrus, the various fields of Ammon's horn (or hippocampus proper), the subicular complex (subiculum, presubiculum, and parasubiculum), and the medial and lateral parts of the entorhinal cortex (Swanson and Cowan, 1977a).

[2] There is still a good deal of confusion in the literature in the naming of the two blades of the dentate gyrus. What we, and others, refer to as the suprapyramidal blade, is elsewhere termed the dorsal, external, or lateral blade (the terminology usually being determined by the plane of section in which the material is studied), while the infrapyramidal blade is commonly known as the ventral, internal, or medial blade.

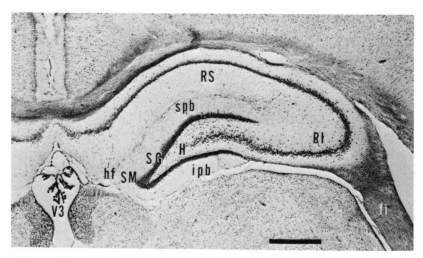

FIG. 1. A low-power photomicrograph of a luxol-fast blue-cresyl violet-stained frontal section through the middle of the septal (or rostral) third of the hippocampal formation. fi, Fimbria; hf, hippocampal fissure; ipb, infrapyramidal blade; spb, suprapyramidal blade; H, hilus of dentate gyrus; RI, regio inferior; RS, regio superior; SG, stratum granulosum; SM, stratum moleculare; V3, third ventricle. Scale: 500 μm. Modified from Swanson and Cowan (1977a) with permission.

region of the dentate gyrus) we shall use the convenient term introduced by Blackstad (1956) for the dentate gyrus and the greater part of the region enclosed within the limits of the supra- and infrapyramidal blades of the dentate gyrus and refer to it as the *area dentata* (see Amaral, 1978, and Fig. 2).

The appearance of individual granule cells is best seen in Golgi stained preparations, which reveal the full, three-dimensional form of the cells, including all their dendrites and, in most cases, the proximal portions of their axons. Figure 3 shows camera lucida drawings of two such cells. In general their form is rather constant. The perikaryon is relatively small (~8–12 μm in diameter) and each cell has several ascending (but no basal) dendrites. Despite their overall similarity there are two significant morphological differences within the population. First, most of the cells that are deeply placed in the stratum granulosum usually have a single primary dendrite which gives rise to secondary branches only as it approaches the molecular layer; the more superficially located cells, on the other hand, generally have two or three dendrites arising from their perikarya. Second, the total dendritic length of the cells varies considerably, over a range of about 700 to 2500 μm, in adult rats (Fricke, 1975). In addition the lateral spread of

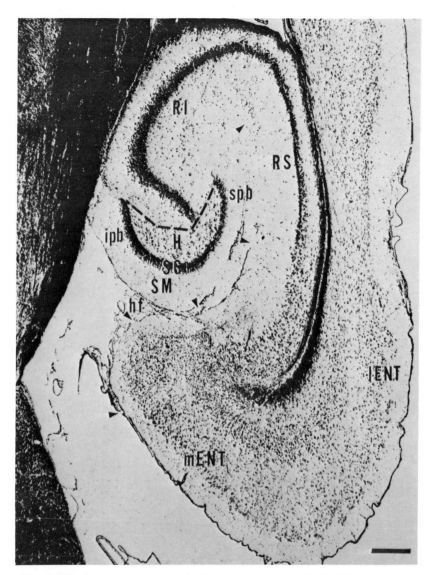

FIG. 2. A horizontal section through the temporal (caudal) third of the rat hippocampal formation. RI, Regio inferior; RS, regio superior; spb, suprapyramidal blade; ipb, infrapyramidal blade; H, hilus of dentate gyrus; SG, stratum granulosum; SM, stratum moleculare; hf, hippocampal fissure; lENT, mENT, lateral and medial entorhinal areas. The arrowheads indicate the borders between the various cytoarchitectonic fields of which only the major ones are labeled; the dashed line indicates the limits of the area dentata. Scale: 250 μm. Modified from Swanson and Cowan (1977a) with permission.

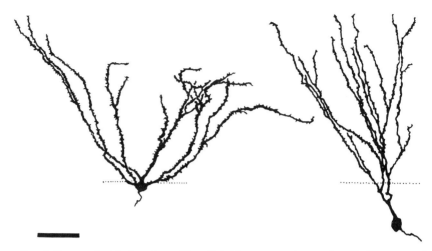

FIG. 3. Camera lucida drawings of two Golgi-impregnated granule cells. The soma of the cell on the left was located immediately deep to the border between the stratum granulosum and the molecular layer (marked by the dotted line), while that on the right was deeply placed within the stratum granulosum and was probably generated at a much later time. Scale: 50 μm.

the dendrites also varies greatly, but three-dimensional reconstructions indicate that most cells tend to be oriented orthogonally to the long axis of the dentate gyrus as a whole (Desmond et al., 1979). In mature animals the secondary and tertiary dendrites are studded with spines. As a rule those on the more proximal dendrites are short and stubby, while those located further out on the secondary and tertiary dendritic branches are both longer (up to 2 μm in length) and more numerous. From electron microscopic studies (Laatsch and Cowan, 1966, 1967; Nafstad, 1967) it is clear that the majority of the afferents to the granule cells terminate upon these dendritic spines, forming asymmetric synapses; from physiological studies these synapses are now known to be excitatory (Anderson et al., 1966; Lømo, 1971, Deadwyler et al., 1975; Steward et al., 1977).

Several estimates have been made of the numbers of granule cells in rats and mice. The relatively small size of their somata and the close packing of the cells make accurate counts rather difficult so that the numbers available in the literature provide only an indication of the order of magnitude involved. In two independent estimates in the rat, the number of granule cells has been found to range from about 600,000 (Schlessinger et al., 1975) to just under 1,000,000 (Gaarskjaer, 1978a). In the mouse, Wimer et al. (1978) have found sizable differences in the numbers of granule cells in different inbred strains, ranging from 270,000 in animals of the C58/J strain to about 450,000 in the

LG/J strain. An independent count in animals of the C57BL strain by Stanfield and Cowan (1979b) gave a figure of 390,000, and in one homozygous reeler animal (of the same genetic background) the number was 260,000. It is of interest that the estimate of the number of granule cells seen in the reeler mouse (which, for technical reasons, is likely to be on the high side) is lower than that recorded in any of the inbred strains studied by Wimer et al. (1978).

B. AFFERENT CONNECTIONS

The extrinsic afferents of the dentate gyrus are derived from several regions; for convenience they may be considered in five groups: (a) entorhinal, (b) hippocampal, (c) hypothalamic, (d) septal, and (e) aminergic. Quantitatively, and possibly functionally, the principal extrinsic input is derived from the medial and lateral parts of the entorhinal cortex (areas 28a and 28b). Recent studies in which the entorhinal afferents have been retrogradely labeled with the enzyme marker horseradish peroxidase (HRP) indicate that the majority of these fibers arise from stellate cells in what is usually designated as layer II of the entorhinal cortex (Steward and Scoville, 1976). They reach the dentate gyrus by passing through the subiculum, from its deep to superficial layers, and for this reason are collectively referred to as the perforant path. The fibers in the perforant path cross the largely obliterated hippocampal fissure to reach the outer two-thirds of the molecular layer of the dentate gyrus. Within this layer the afferents from the two parts of the entorhinal area are spatially segregated: those from the lateral entorhinal area end exclusively within the outer third of the molecular layer while those from the medial entorhinal area terminate in its middle third (Raisman et al., 1965; Hjorth-Simonsen, 1972; Hjorth-Simonsen and Jeune, 1972; Steward, 1976; and see Fig. 4). The distribution of the two groups of afferents is particularly well shown in preparations stained by Timm's sulfide-silver method for heavy metals; although it is not known what intracellular component(s) this method actually stains, empirically the pattern of staining has been found to coincide rather precisely with the sites of termination of certain afferents to the hippocampal formation and other cortical areas (Haug, 1974, 1976). As Fig. 5 shows the zone of termination of the afferents from the lateral entorhinal area is deeply stained while that of the medial entorhinal afferents is very lightly stained.

The hippocampal afferents to the dentate gyrus are derived from a specialized class of fusiform cell in the hilar region of the dentate gyrus of both sides (Zimmer, 1971; Gottlieb and Cowan, 1972a, 1973; Hjorth-Simonsen and Laurberg, 1977; Swanson et al., 1978; West

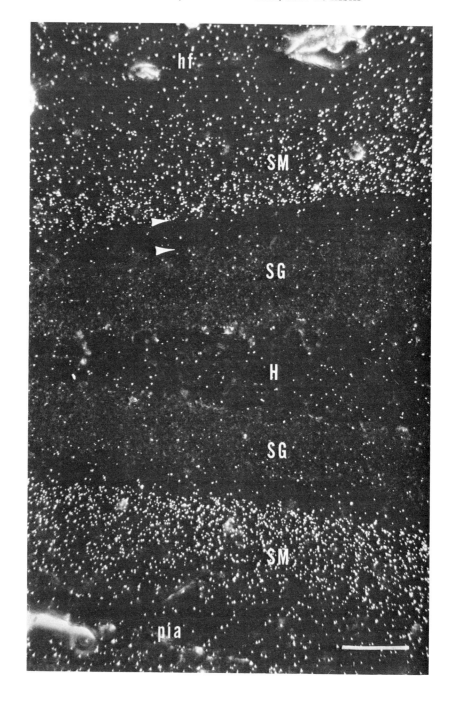

et al., 1979; Laurberg, 1979; Amaral, 1978). These neurons in the *area dentata* are commonly thought to be part of field CA$_4$ as originally defined by Lorente de Nó (1934), but until more is known about the diversity of cell types in this region, final judgment must be suspended on this issue. Whether the inputs from the two sides arise from the same cells, or from different populations of neurons, is also not known. However, it is clear that the axons from both sources terminate within the inner one-fourth to one-third of the molecular layer (Blackstad, 1956; Raisman *et al.*, 1965; Zimmer, 1971; Gottlieb and Cowan, 1972a, 1973). The overlap in the distribution of the ipsilateral (or *associational*) and the crossed (or *commissural*) inputs is essentially complete (Gottlieb and Cowan, 1972a) and there is every reason to believe that the two groups of afferents compete with each other for synaptic sites on the same segments of the granule cell dendrites (see following); both classes of afferents terminate upon the short, sessile spines on the proximal parts of the granule cell dendrites (Laatsch and Cowan, 1967; McWilliam and Lynch, 1978) and are known to be excitatory (Deadwyler *et al.*, 1975; Steward *et al.*, 1977). In Timm's preparations the zone of termination of these efferents is densely stained (Haug, 1974, 1976; and Fig. 5).

The *hypothalamic afferents* have only recently been identified by experiments in which HRP was injected into the hippocampal region; in these a rather diffusely distributed population of retrogradely labeled neurons could be seen extending throughout the lateral preoptic and lateral and posterior hypothalamic areas, but especially in the supramammillary region (Segal and Landis, 1974; Pasquier and Reinoso-Suarez, 1976; Wyss *et al.*, 1979a; Amaral and Cowan, 1980). The complementary type of experiment, in which the afferents were anterogradely labeled by the injection of [^{3}H]amino acids into the supramammillary region, has shown that their site of termination in the dentate gyrus is a narrow band (about 20–30 μm wide in the rat and cat) immediately deep to the zone occupied by the hippocampal afferents (Wyss *et al.*, 1979b). Exactly how they terminate has yet to be determined, but the fact that they are in a zone that extends from the deepest part of the molecular layer into the outermost part of the

FIG. 4. A dark-field photomicrograph of an autoradiograph through the dentate gyrus of a mouse following an injection of [^{3}H]proline into the ipsilateral medial entorhinal area. In such preparations the silver grains—which mark the location of the axonally transported label—appear as bright spots. The two arrowheads indicate the zone occupied by the commissural and associational afferents. hf, Hippocampal fissure; SM, stratum moleculare; SG, stratum granulosum; H, hilus of dentate gyrus; pia, pia mater. Scale: 50 μm.

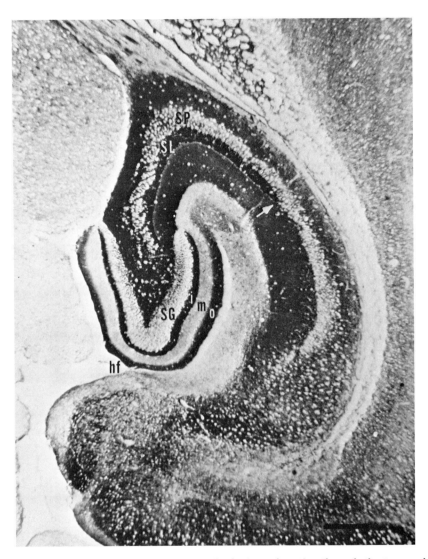

FIG. 5. A Timm-stained preparation of a horizontal section through the temporal portion of the hippocampal formation in an adult mouse. SG, Stratum granulosum; hf, hippocampal fissure; SL, stratum lucidum; SP, stratum pyramidale; i, m, and o, inner, middle, and outer zones of the molecular layer in which afferents from the hippocampus, and the medial and lateral entorhinal areas, respectively, terminate. The arrow marks the end of the mossy fibers close to the boundary between the regio superior and the regio inferior. Scale: 500 μm.

stratum granulosum suggests that they synapse upon the most proximal parts of the granule cell dendrites, and possibly upon some cell somata. Most of the synapses observed at this level in the electron microscope (Laatsch and Cowan, 1966; Gottlieb and Cowan, 1972b) are of the symmetrical variety, with flattened or pleomorphic synaptic vesicles, which elsewhere have often been found to be inhibitory, and there is now physiological evidence to suggest that the hypothalamic afferents may indeed constitute a long-axoned inhibitory pathway (Segal, 1979).

The *septal afferents* to the dentate gyrus are derived from the large-celled medial septal/diagonal band complex (Daitz and Powell, 1954; Raisman, 1966; Swanson and Cowan, 1979). Most of these fibers appear to terminate within the hilar region immediately deep to the stratum granulosum (Raisman *et al.*, 1965; Swanson and Cowan, 1979) but there also appears to be a fairly light, and rather diffuse, distribution of septal afferents to the molecular layer (Mosko *et al.*, 1973; Swanson and Cowan, 1979). The mode of termination of these afferents is not known, but there is some indirect evidence to suggest that they may be cholinergic (Lewis and Shute, 1967). Certainly, the amounts of acetylcholinesterase, and of the enzyme choline acetyltransferase, in the dentate gyrus are significantly reduced after lesions which interrupt the septal afferents (Lewis and Shute, 1967; Mellgren and Srebro, 1973; Cotman *et al.*, 1973a).

The *monoaminergic inputs* to the dentate gyrus are derived from two sources: the noradrenergic afferents arise, bilaterally, within the locus coeruleus (Swanson and Hartman, 1975; Jones and Moore, 1977; Loy *et al.*, 1979), while the serotonergic afferents are derived from the raphe nuclei of the midbrain (Conrad *et al.*, 1974; Moore and Halaris, 1975). Although the evidence on the distribution of these systems within the dentate gyrus is still rather incomplete, it appears that the greater part of both monoaminergic inputs is distributed to the hilar region, but some fibers of both types also ramify diffusely within the molecular layer (Koda and Bloom, 1977; Loy *et al.*, 1979). Their role in the functional activity of the dentate gyrus is obscure, but there is evidence that the noradrenergic input to the adjoining fields of the hippocampus has a long latency, and long-lasting, inhibitory influence on pyramidal cells (Segal and Bloom, 1976).

By comparison to what we know of the extrinsic afferents to the dentate gyrus, our understanding of the connections and functions of the *interneurons* in this region is meager. It is evident from Golgi studies that there are several types of local circuit neuron in the area dentata whose axons do not leave the dentate gyrus. The somata of many of these interneurons are found along the deep aspect of the stratum granulosum and many give rise to axons which ascend into and arborize within the granule cell layer (Cajal, 1893, 1911; Lorente de Nó, 1934; Amaral, 1978). Physiological studies indicate that at least some of these interneurons are involved in the "feed-forward" and "recurrent" forms of inhibition observed when the dentate granule cells are synaptically activated (Anderson et al., 1966; Lømo, 1968; Alvarez-Leefmans, 1976). And more recently it has been shown that they may utilize GABA as their transmitter (Storm-Mathisen, 1976; Nadler et al., 1977). The finding of a differential distribution of GABA receptors within the dentate gyrus is consonant with this view (Chan-Palay, 1978).

C. EFFERENT CONNECTIONS

The efferent connections of the dentate gyrus are formed by the axons of the granule cells which, since the time of Cajal (1893), have been referred to as the mossy fibers. They arise from the basal, or deep, aspects of the cell bodies, are unmyelinated, and of rather fine diameter ($\sim$1–2 μm). Near their origin they generally give off recurrent collateral branches which form a fairly distinct infragranular plexus, that distributes, at least in part, to some of the interneurons within the hilar region. The mossy fibers themselves have large numbers of fusiform swellings along their length, most of which form en passant synaptic connections with the many prominent dendritic spines ("thorns") found on the proximal parts of the apical dendrites of the pyramidal cells in the regio inferior of the hippocampus, and to a lesser extent upon their basal dendrites. Many of the swellings along the lengths of the mossy fibers have small lateral extensions which form additional contacts upon the shafts of the pyramidal cell dendrites (Amaral, 1979, and see below).

The mossy fibers from the suprapyramidal blade of the dentate gyrus form a very prominent bundle immediately above the pyramidal cell bodies in the regio inferior, in the layer known as the stratum lucidum, while those from the infrapyramidal blade form a similar, but less extensive, infrapyramidal bundle that is distributed to the basal dendrites of the pyramidal cells in the deep part of the so-called stratum oriens. Because of their unusually high zinc content the mossy fibers are intensely stained by Timm's method (Timm, 1958; von Euler, 1962; Fig. 5).

The distribution of the mossy fibers tends to be lamellar, in the sense that fibers arising at any one septotemporal level tend to be distributed across the transverse axis of the hippocampus to the pyramidal cells of the regio inferior at more or less the same septotemporal level (Blackstad *et al.,* 1970; Anderson *et al.,* 1971; Rawlins and Green, 1977; Gaarskjaer, 1978b; Swanson *et al.,* 1978). A comparable level-to-level organization is found in the distribution of the entorhinal afferents to the dentate gyrus (Hjorth-Simonsen and Jeune, 1972; Rawlins and Green, 1977), but its hippocampal afferents seem to be organized in a quite different way. The relatively few cells from which the hippocampal afferents arise seem to distribute their axons rather widely. This can be easily demonstrated by small injections of [^{3}H]amino acids into the hilar region of the dentate gyrus at about the middle of its rostro-caudal extent; such injections may label associational and commissural fibers to the greater part of the dentate gyrus of both sides (Gottlieb and Cowan, 1972a; Fricke and Cowan, 1978). The implication of this is that some inputs to the dentate gyrus and its efferent projection are relatively localized, and organized on a level-to-level basis, while others (notably those from the hippocampus, the hypothalamus, and the brainstem) are distributed very widely, to most parts of the dentate gyrus, and often bilaterally.

Some of these anatomical considerations are summarized in Fig. 6A and B. The former schematically illustrates the relative distribution of the various afferents to the granule cells (excluding some of the monoaminergic inputs); the latter is a generalized "flow-diagram" based on what we currently know of the processing of information through the dentate gyrus; although obviously oversimplified this summarizing diagram has the merit of emphasizing the pivotal role that the dentate gyrus plays in the whole hippocampal formation.

III. The Development of the Dentate Gyrus

A. THE TIME AND SITE OF ORIGIN OF THE DENTATE GRANULE CELLS

The precursor population of cells from which the neurons of the dentate gyrus are derived arises from a rather restricted portion of the neuroepithelial lining of the medial wall of the cerebral vesicle between the region which contributes the neurectodermal component of the choroid plexus of the lateral ventricle and the neuroepithelium from which the hippocampus itself arises (Fig. 7). However, whereas the neurons that leave the neuroepithelium to form the hippocampus are postmitotic, having irretrievably lost their capacity for DNA synthesis, the majority, if not all, of the cells which leave the adjoining "dentate zone" are neuroblasts in the strict sense of that word: they continue to divide after reaching the region of the developing dentate gyrus, for periods that may range from a few days to several weeks.

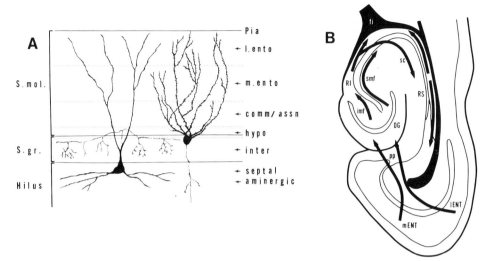

FIG. 6. (A) A schematic representation of a typical dentate granule cell and one variety of interneuron, to show the striking laminar distribution of the different classes of afferents to the dentate gyrus. S. mol., stratum moleculare; S. gr., stratum granulosum; l. ento, m. ento, afferents from the lateral and medial entorhinal areas; comm/assn, commissural and associational afferents; hypo, hypothalamic afferents; inter, interneurons of the "basket cell" type. Based in part on Raisman et al. (1965) and Gottlieb and Cowan (1972b). (B) A schematic "flow-diagram" to illustrate the general sequence of information flow from the entorhinal cortex → the dentate gyrus → regio inferior → regio superior and hence by way of the major outflow tracts to the septal complex and the subiculum. The regio inferior also contributes commissural fibers to the hippocampus of the opposite side; the commissural and associational afferents to the dentate gyrus arise within the hilar region. fi, Fimbria; RI, regio inferior; RS, regio superior; DG, dentate gyrus; lENT, lateral entorhinal area; mENT, medial entorhinal area; SC, Schaffer collaterals; smf, imf, supra- and infrapyramidal mossy fiber bundles; pp, perforant pathway.

After migrating across that part of the marginal zone of the hemisphere that later forms the *fimbria* (which is the major, rostrally directed, efferent pathway of the hippocampal formation) and the region of the future stratum oriens of the regio inferior, the dentate precursor cells establish a second proliferative zone close to the developing hippocampal cortical plate. This proliferative zone persists for about 1 to 2 weeks in most rodents and disappears only as its progeny migrate radially into the developing stratum granulosum. The prolonged period of neuron production, which continues from the latter half of the gestational period, through the first 3 weeks postnatally (Angevine, 1965; Schlessinger et al., 1975; Stanfield and Cowan, 1979c) and, at a much reduced rate, for several more weeks (Kaplan and Hinds, 1977) is most

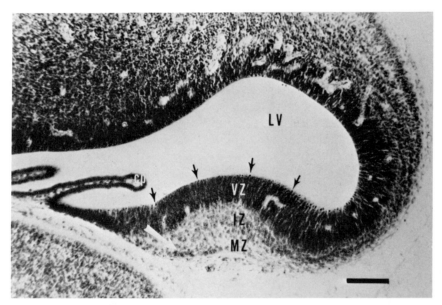

FIG. 7. A low-power photomicrograph of a section through the developing hippocampal region in an ED 14 mouse. The precursor cells of the dentate gyrus arise from the ventricular zone to the left of the series of four arrows which point to mitotic figures in the neuroepithelium. The bold, white arrow indicates the direction taken by migrating neuroblasts from the ventricular zone to the dentate proliferative zone. LV, Lateral ventricle; VZ, ventricular zone; IZ, intermediate zone; MZ, marginal zone; cp, choroid plexus. Scale:100 μm.

unusual. For example, in the same animals hippocampal and most neocortical neurons are generated over a period of only about 4 or 5 days (Schlessinger et al., 1978).

If [³H]thymidine is administered to a series of pregnant animals (to date this has been done in rats, mice, and monkeys) or, during the postnatal period, directly to their offspring, one can map the distribution of granule cells generated at different stages in development by examining autoradiographs of the brain when the dentate gyrus is, to all intents and purposes, fully developed (around the third or fourth postnatal week in rodents). From experiments of this kind several generalizations can now be drawn. First, the granule cells as a whole are generated over a period of some weeks (Angevine, 1965; Schlessinger et al., 1975). Estimates of the numbers of neurons generated on each day (Fig. 8) indicate that in the rat only about 15% of the granule cells are formed prenatally (Bayer and Altman, 1974; Schlessinger et al., 1975), and that the peak period of neurogenesis occurs toward the end of the first postnatal week when cells are being generated at a rate of about

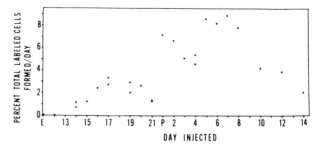

FIG. 8. The numbers of heavily labeled granule cells seen in young rats after the injections of [³H]thymidine at different stages in development between ED 12 and postnatal day 14, expressed as a percentage of the total number of such cells observed in all experiments. It is evident from this that more than 80% of the granule cells are generated postnatally and that during the peak period of granule cell production (toward the end of the first postnatal week) cells are being generated at a rate of about 50,000 per day. From Schlessinger *et al.* (1975) with permission.

50,000 per day in the rat. By the end of the second postnatal week proliferation is at a relatively low level, but some cells continue to divide within the stratum granulosum even as late as the third month postnatally (Kaplan and Hinds, 1977). Whether these very late-formed cells serve to replace other granule cells that die prematurely, or whether the stratum granulosum grows by steady accretion, is not known.

Second, the granule cells are generated along three distinct gradients. The first, and easiest to demonstrate, is that along the transverse axis of the dentate gyrus from the tip of the suprapyramidal blade toward the tip of the infrapyramidal blade. Although at any given time throughout the poliferative period cells destined for both blades are being generated, on the average the majority of the cells in the suprapyramidal blade become postmitotic earlier than those in the infrapyramidal blade. This gradient is clearly reflected in the peak period of proliferation in the two blades and in their subsequent assembly as distinct cytoarchitectonic entities (see the following). The second easily observable gradient is in the radial dimension of the gyrus, perpendicular to the plane of the stratum granulosum. Whereas all other cortical areas show a distinct inside-out gradient[3] in the time of origin of their

[3] The terms "inside-out" and "outside-in," which are commonly used in the literature, are always with reference to the proliferative zone in which the cells are formed. In the case of the dentate gyrus many of the late-formed cells are generated either within the hilar region or even in the stratum granulosum itself. With this caveat in mind, it is reasonable to speak of an "outside-in" gradient, in terms of the final locations of granule cells generated at successively later times.

cells, the cells in the dentate gyrus of normal mice, rats, and monkeys are generated in the reverse sequence: the more superficial cells are formed first and the later-generated neurons are progressively added to their deep aspect (Angevine, 1965; Schlessinger *et al.*, 1975; Nowakowski, 1976; Stanfield and Cowan, 1979c). In a word, they are generated in an "outside-in" sequence. The third gradient is along the septotemporal dimension of the dentate gyrus. Again, although at every stage some cells are being formed at all septotemporal levels, on the average the cells in the more temporal parts of the dentate gyrus are generated earlier than those at more septal levels (Schlessinger *et al.*, 1975; Stanfield and Cowan, 1979c).

Comparable gradients in the time of neuron origin have been found in many parts of the brain, including the rest of the hippocampal formation (Angevine, 1965; Schlessinger *et al.*, 1978). However, probably because the period of neurogenesis in most other regions is relatively compressed, it has often not been possible to recognize the caudal-to-rostral gradient. Some of the implications of this prolonged period of neurogenesis in the dentate gyrus for experimental studies of neural development, and for the patterns of connectivity that are formed are considered in Section III,F.

Third, there appears to be no correlation between the time of origin of the cells in the dentate gyrus and that of the neurons which project to it, or those to which the granule cells themselves project. The evidence for this derives mainly from the rat hippocampal formation which can be briefly summarized as follows. The cells in the entorhinal cortex which give rise to the perforant path are generated between embryonic days (ED) 14 and 18; the cells of origin of the hippocampal afferents are probably formed between ED 13 and ED 18 (Schlessinger *et al.*, 1978); the cells in the medial septal nucleus arise between ED 12 and ED 14 (Swanson and Cowan, 1977b), and the pyramidal cells in the regio inferior upon which the mossy fibers synapse pass through their last round of DNA synthesis between ED 14 and ED 20 (Schlessinger *et al.*, 1978). The simplistic notion that the cells in a group of interconnected regions should be sequentially generated clearly does not hold true in this system, or indeed in any other neuronal system that has been adequately studied from this point of view. One corollary of this fact (which, as we shall see, is especially critical in the dentate gyrus) is that the axons of many of the input cells are unable to establish connections with the granule cells until long after they have reached the dentate gyrus and, conversely some mossy fibers arise only relatively late in postnatal life, when their target neurons are already well-developed.

Fourth, many of the granule cells that are destined for the infrapyramidal blade of the dentate gyrus must remain in a morphologically undifferentiated state for several days, if not some weeks. For example, [³H]thymidine studies indicate that a small proportion of the cells in the infrapyramidal blade of the rat dentate gyrus withdraw from the cell cycle as early as ED 14, yet it is not until toward the end of the first postnatal week that the infrapyramidal blade becomes recognizable as a separate cytoarchitectonic entity, and only some days later does the molecular layer in this region begin to appear. Presumably the early formed granule cells that are destined for the infrapyramidal blade must remain in a state of arrested development, until the infrapyramidal blade begins to be assembled, and only at that time can they begin to form dendrites.

Finally, it is worth mentioning that although in most respects the generation of granule cells in normal mice closely resembles that seen in the rat, in homozygous reeler mice their site of postnatal proliferation is quite different (Stanfield and Cowan, 1979c). As Fig. 9 shows,

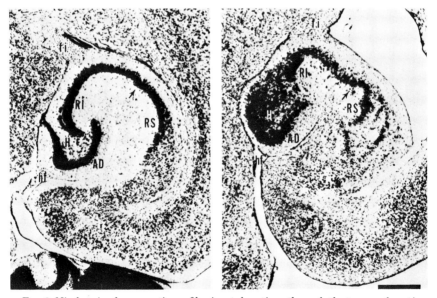

FIG. 9. Nissl-stained preparations of horizontal sections through the temporal portion of the hippocampus and dentate gyrus in a normal (left) and homozygous reeler mouse (right). Note the absence of a distinct stratum granulosum in the reeler dentate gyrus (AD), and that in the mutant granule cells are scattered throughout the hilar region (H). RI, Regio inferior; RS, regio superior; hf, hippocampal fissure. Scale: 500 μm. Modified from Stanfield and Cowan (1979b) with permission.

the major differences in the dentate gyrus of normal and reeler mice are the absence, in the latter, of a distinct stratum granulosum and a more-or-less random distribution of granule cells throughout the hilar zone (Caviness and Sidman, 1973a; Stanfield and Cowan, 1979b). What is of interest in the present context is that in the reeler mouse the period of cell proliferation, the relative rates of granule cell production, and the gradients of neurogenesis in the transverse and longitudinal dimensions of the dentate gyrus are unaffected by the mutation (Stanfield and Cowan, 1979c). However, cellular proliferation across the radial dimension of the area dentata turns out to be reversed. In normal mice, proliferating cells are concentrated during the postnatal period in the depths of the stratum granulosum, but in reeler mice the cells which incorporate DNA are largely confined to the most superficial part of the vaguely defined granule cell zone where it adjoins the stratum moleculare. Thus the sequence of cell proliferation in the reeler is not "outside-in," as in normal animals, but is reversed by the mutation. There is a similar reversal of the reeler hippocampus in the proliferative gradient across the radial dimension (Caviness, 1973; Stanfield and Cowan, 1979c), and to a significant degree this is true also for the neocortex (Caviness and Sidman, 1973b). This suggests that during development the reeler gene expresses itself morphologically in the radial dimension of the cortex rather than across its areal extent or in the arrangement of its various subfields (see Caviness and Rakic, 1978 for review).

B. The Migration of the Granule Cells and the Assembly of the Stratum Granulosum

The granule cells are unusual among neurons in the cerebral cortex in undergoing two distinct migratory phases. Reference has already been made to the early migration of the granule cell precursor population from the neuroepithelium of the lateral ventricle to the secondary proliferative zone close to what will become the hilar region of the dentate gyrus. The route taken by these precursor cells is illustrated in Fig. 10, which is a low-power photomicrograph of the developing hippocampal region in a mouse at ED 16. From the neuroepithelium they sweep caudomedially across that part of the original marginal zone that will (when it is invaded by the axons of the pyramidal cells in the hippocampus and subiculum) later become the fimbria (Altman, 1966). Exactly how many cells migrate in this way, and how long proliferation continues in the relevant zone of the neuroepithelium, are not known. However, the fact that labeled cells are seen along this route in autoradiograms of sections taken 2 hours after the injection of

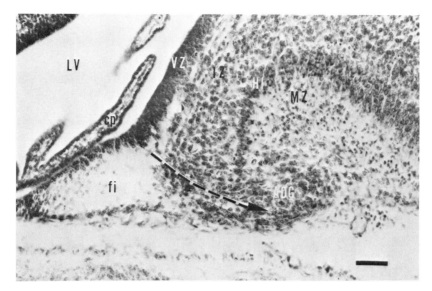

FIG. 10. Photomicrograph showing the migratory route followed by the precursor cells of the dentate gyrus, in an ED 16 mouse. The broken line marks the approximate course taken by the migrating cells from the ventricular zone to the anlage of the dentate gyrus (ADG). LV, Lateral ventricle; VZ, ventricular zone; IZ, intermediate zone; MZ, marginal zone; cp, choroid plexus; fi, fimbria; HI, hippocampal cortical plate. Scale: 50 μm.

[³H]thymidine at the appropriate stage indicates that the cells are apparently capable of DNA synthesis while they are migrating.

The second phase of migration occurs as the cells become postmitotic (or in the case of some of the cells destined for the infrapyramidal blade, some days or weeks later). This migration is essentially directed radially outward from the proliferative zone, so that in normal animals the cells that are formed at progressively later times aggregate along the deep face of the developing stratum granulosum.

In both the rat and mouse, the suprapyramidal blade of the dentate gyrus begins to appear toward the end of gestation, and by the first or second postnatal day is clearly recognizable as a separate cytoarchitectonic entity even though a considerable proportion of its cells are not generated until some days later. The infrapyramidal blade, on the other hand, is not recognizable until near the end of the first postnatal week (even though, as we have seen, a proportion of its cells are generated prenatally). For much of this period spanning the last week of gestation and the first postnatal week, the proliferative zone appears in cross-section as a triangular mass of cells that extends almost to the pial surface, and the infrapyramidal blade can become distinctly recognizable only as the population of precursor cells becomes depleted. Figures 11 and 12 show the gradual emergence of the infrapyramidal blade from what we may refer to as the anlage of the dentate gyrus; it is not until some time later (usually at the end of the first postnatal week) that the molecular layer overlying the granule cells in the infrapyramidal blade makes its appearance.

In keeping with the overall temporal→septal gradient in the time of granule cell proliferation it is evident that at any given stage the temporal region of the dentate gyrus is cytoarchitectonically more advanced than its septal portion. The differences are not dramatic (and certainly not as striking as those seen along the transverse axis from the supra- to the infrapyramidal blade); but until relatively late in development (around the end of the second postnatal week) the septal pole of the dentate gyrus lags behind the temporal pole by the equivalent of about 2 days of development.

C. The Growth and Differentiation of Granule Cell Processes

Our knowledge of the growth of the dendrites and axons of the granule cells is a good deal less complete than about many other aspects of the development of the dentate gyrus, and to a considerable extent it is based on the analysis of Golgi-impregnated and Timm-stained material. Fortunately, because of the wide disparity in the time of generation of the granule cells one can often see in a single Golgi preparation, cells that are at markedly different stages in development and from this it is possible to reconstruct the general pattern of granule cell cytodifferentiation. At the same time these marked temporal differences make it extremely difficult to quantify the development of the cells' processes, and all statements about the appearance or the dimensions of individual granule cells at any one given developmental stage must be qualified by reference to the cell's location (in particular, whether it lies within the septal or the temporal part of the gyrus, and in the supra- or infrapyramidal blades). The most complete analysis of the development of the dendrites of selected granule cells (including three-dimensional computer reconstructions) was carried out by Dr. Russell Fricke while working in our laboratory. His study was based on preparations impregnated by the Golgi method, and the following account is derived largely from his unpublished observations.

In Fricke's (1975) study relatively few granule cells were impregnated in the immediate postnatal period (days 1 and 2); the two cells which he was able to analyze in some detail at this stage were both in the region of the developing infrapyramidal blade. Camera lucida drawings of these cells are labeled a and b in Fig. 13; both cells have

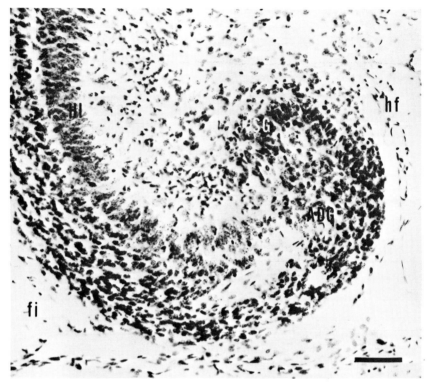

FIG. 11

FIGS. 11 and 12. This group of three photomicrographs taken from Nissl-stained sections of mice at ED 18, and postnatal days 1 and 3, respectively, illustrates: (a) the progressive emergence of first the lateral part of the stratum granulosum (SG) of the suprapyramidal blade from the anlage of the dentate gyrus (ADG, Fig. 11), and later the remainder of the suprapyramidal blade (spb, Fig. 12A), and finally the infrapyramidal blade (ipb, Fig. 12B); and (b) the location of the secondary proliferative zone (pz) in what will later become the hilar region of the dentate gyrus (H). HI, Hippocampal pyramidal cell layer; fi, fimbria; hf, hippocampal fissure. Scales: Fig. 11, 50 μm; Fig. 12A and B, 100 μm.

relatively smooth somata and only rudimentary dendritic branches: the total dendritic length of cell a was 39 μm, that of cell b, 223 μm. Of 15 cells which were reconstructed from a group of 4-day-old animals the total dendritic length was found to range from 89 to 764 μm (mean 370 μm). Two of these cells are also shown in Fig. 13, the cells labeled c and d; as both are taken from the suprapyramidal blade it is perhaps inappropriate to compare them with those from the day 1 animals, but even allowing for this difference it is evident that during this period there is a fairly rapid growth of dendrites, the total dendritic length of

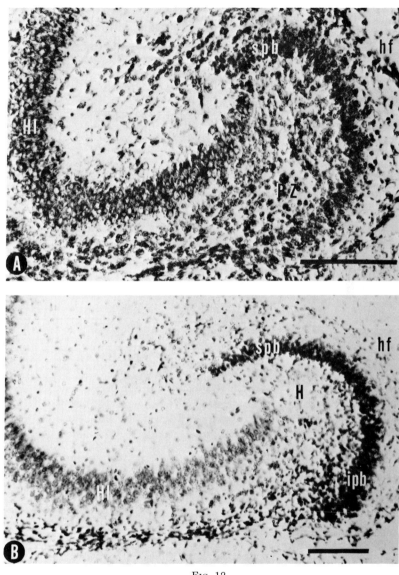

FIG. 12

cell c being 212 μm, and that of cell d, 764 μm. Most of the cells observed at this stage have well-impregnated axons but only one bore spine-like processes on its primary and secondary dendritic trunks.

The cells labeled e and f in Fig. 13 are from a series of 24 examined at day 8; together they indicate something of the range of maturation

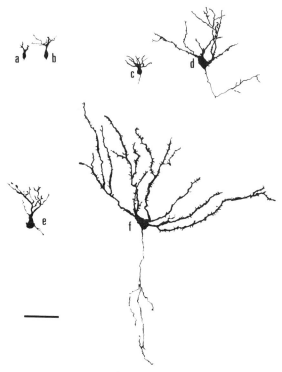

FIG. 13. A group of six camera lucida drawings of Golgi-impregnated granule cells to show the progressive elaboration of their dendrites and the range of variability in granule cell cytodifferentiation at different developmental stages: Postnatal day 1 (cells a and b), day 4 (cells c and d), and day 8 (cells e and f). See text for discussion. Scale: 50 μm. Modified from Fricke (1975) with permission.

seen at this stage, cell e being from the infrapyramidal blade and cell f from the suprapyramidal blade: while cell e is at about the same stage of maturation as cell c at 4 days, cell f is considerably advanced both in terms of the number and lengths of its dendritic branches, and the profusion of spines upon them. Between days 8 and 12 there is a marked increase in the mean dendritic length of the cells examined (to just over 1000 μm). This increase is largely attributable to the disappearance of cells with very small dendritic arbors; this, in turn, reflects the fact that cell proliferation in the dentate gyrus as a whole drops appreciably during the second postnatal week (Schlessinger et al., 1975). Furthermore, by day 12, most of the cells show considerable numbers of dendritic spines, especially upon their secondary and tertiary branches. This pattern continues over the next several days, until by day 20 the cells essentially attain their adult dimensions, the range

in total dendritic length for the six cells that Fricke (1975) has reconstructed at this stage being 1400–2000 μm (Fig. 14).

Given the considerable range of variability in the extent of the
granule cell dendrites at any given stage in development, it is difficult
to generalize from these observations, and rather futile to attempt to
estimate such parameters as the rate of dendritic growth, or to guess at
the factors that may control dendritic branching. Some of these difficulties may be illustrated by a single example. The earliest stage at which
Fricke (1975) has observed a granule cell whose total dendritic length
fell within the range seen in adult animals was day 8. The cell in
question was located rather superficially within the stratum
granulosum of the suprapyramidal blade, within the temporal half of
the dentate gyrus. From what we know of the genesis of granule cells in
this region, this cell probably became postmitotic no later than day 20

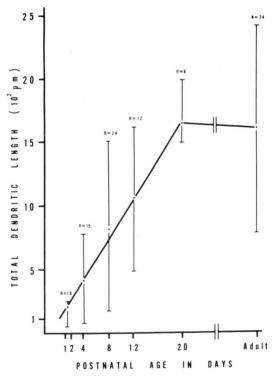

Fig. 14. Graph showing the progressive increase in the average total length of the
dendrites of a series of Golgi-impregnated neurons at various stages in postnatal development; the vertical lines at each stage indicate the overall range of total dendritic
lengths observed at that stage. Redrawn from Fricke (1975) with permission.

of gestation. Assuming that it began to form dendrites almost immediately, one could calculate a rate of growth of individual dendrites of about 22 μm per day (the longest dendrite being approximately 175 μm—measured from the soma to its end). Almost certainly this is a gross underestimate of the rate of dendritic growth because so many relevant factors cannot be taken into account. Among others these include the possibility of a latent period between the cessation of DNA synthesis and the onset of dendritic growth, differential growth rates in different dendrites, the possibility that the longest dendrite might have attained its maximum length some days before the animal was killed, and the possibility that the dendritic tree as a whole may have undergone considerable "remodeling." Our studies of dendritic growth *in vitro* suggest that at least in the case of hippocampal pyramidal cells, remodeling plays a considerable role in determining the final form and the overall size of a cell's dendritic arbor (see Banker and Cowan, 1977, 1979 for discussion), but, as yet comparable studies have not been carried out on dentate granule cells.

The development of the axons of the granule cells has been studied in Golgi preparations by Minkwitz (1976) (and in one special respect by Amaral, 1979), in Timm-stained preparations by Zimmer (1978) and Zimmer and Haug (1978), electron microscopically by Stirling and Bliss (1978), and, to a limited extent, functionally, by Bliss *et al.* (1974) and Stirling and Bliss (1978). In general, the findings in their various studies are consonant, so one can now present a fairly straightforward synoptic view of the process.

Mossy fibers are first seen in Golgi preparations on the day of birth (Minkwitz, 1976); at this stage there is a region of dense Timm staining near the lateral edge of the developing suprapyramidal blade that resembles the characteristic staining of mossy fibers at later stages, and may therefore be regarded as the first indication of the developing suprapyramidal system of fibers; these fibers are probably the axons of the earliest granule cells generated (Zimmer and Haug, 1978). On the day after birth Stirling and Bliss (1978) have observed numerous axons and axonal growth cones around the proximal parts of the dendrites of the pyramidal cells in field CA_{3b}; in addition, there are large, essentially vesicle-free profiles with symmetrical specializations on parts of their surfaces adjoining the pyramidal cell dendrites, and occasional profiles making what appear to be asymmetric synaptic contacts with the dendrites. However, electrical stimulation of the dentate gyrus at this stage did not synaptically activate the pyramids in the regio inferior (Bliss *et al.*, 1974). By day 3, Timm's preparations show distinct staining of what are undoubtedly mossy fiber boutons. By day 5, the infrapyramidal bundles of mossy fibers can be recognized, and the number of vesicle containing profiles with distinct asymmetrical membrane specializations is said to be appreciably greater, while those lacking vesicles are correspondingly less frequent. Stirling and Bliss (1978) have also noted that at this stage many presynaptic profiles of the same type occur in clusters and have suggested that axons from neighboring granule cells (or possibly from cells of the same age) fasciculate together and are distributed in small groups to the regio inferior. At this stage weak synaptic field potentials could be recorded in the regio inferior on stimulating the dentate gyrus, but apparently the cells could not be made to discharge in sufficiently large numbers to produce a population spike (Bliss *et al.*, 1974). By day 7 there are large numbers of fairly characteristic presynaptic profiles, many of which are deeply invaginated by postsynaptic processes bearing distinct asymmetric membrane specializations, and by day 10 many synapses are present that are indistinguishable in appearance from those seen in adults (Fig. 15). Stimulation of the dentate gyrus, at this stage, reliably resulted in depolarization of the regio inferior pyramids, although the cells did not consistently fire in response to each afferent volley.

Toward the end of the second postnatal week, Timm preparations indicate that the mossy fiber system is essentially mature, and, by day 15, Stirling and Bliss (1978) have been able to show that the mossy fiber terminals have attained their mature size and form, and popula-

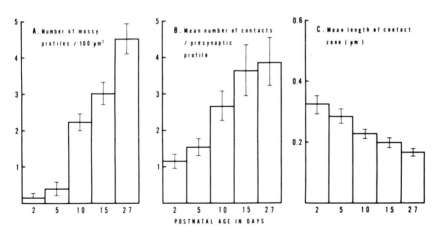

FIG. 15. Three sets of histograms indicating (A) the progressive increase in the density of mossy fiber presynaptic profiles in the regio inferior at five different stages in development; (B) the mean numbers of synaptic contacts made by these profiles; and (C) the mean lengths of the contact zones. Adapted from Stirling and Bliss (1978) with permission.

tion spikes are consistently generated in the regio inferior when the mossy fibers are activated.

From Zimmer and Haug's (1978) study it is clear not only that the supra- to infrapyramidal gradient in granule cell genesis is accurately reflected in the development of the mossy fiber system (the infrapyramidal mossy fibers appearing only some 4 or 5 days after the first indication of the suprapyramidal system), but also that there is also a proximodistal sequence of invasion of the regio inferior (in the direction $CA_{3c} \rightarrow CA_{3b} \rightarrow CA_{3a}$). Moreover, in the case of the suprapyramidal system the earliest formed mossy fibers occupy the deepest part of stratum lucidum while those that arrive later appear to synapse upon progressively more distal parts of the pyramidal cell dendrites.

Amaral (1978) has drawn attention to the existence of small lateral extensions on many of the mossy fiber swellings. In a later, combined Golgi and electron microscopic, study (Amaral, 1979), he has demonstrated that these extensions form synaptic contacts primarily with shafts of regio inferior pyramids. Interestingly, the average combined lengths of these extensions increases to a maximum (of about 226 μm) around day 14, and then declines sharply to about 73 μm by the end of the fourth postnatal week; this reduction is apparently due to a shortening of individual extensions, rather than to a net reduction in their number (the mean number observed at days 14 and 28 being 7.3 and 6.0, respectively). At present this is the only firm evidence for a secondary reorganization of maturing connections in the dentate gyrus, unless the apparent early overlap of entorhinal and hippocampal afferents is to be regarded as an indication of some degree of competitive process elimination comparable to that seen in other systems (see Redfern, 1970; Crepel et al., 1976; Lichtmann, 1977).

D. The Development of the Afferent Connections to the Dentate Gyrus

The introduction of the autoradiographic method for tracing neuronal connections in 1972 has provided a widely applicable, reliable, and sensitive technique for sequentially following the development of relatively long neural pathways (Cowan et al., 1972; Cowan and Cuénod, 1975). In the case of the dentate gyrus it has been possible, using this method, to determine the time of arrival of certain of the extrinsic afferent pathways by making small injections of labeled amino acids into the appropriate regions in young rats at each of several stages in postnatal development, and subsequently mapping autoradiographically the distribution of the resulting axonally transported label in the molecular layer of the dentate gyrus, after postinjection periods of 4–24 hours (Fricke and Cowan, 1977; Loy et al., 1977). In most experiments of this kind the background levels of radioactivity are relatively high (partly because of the systemic uptake of label, and partly because of the proximity of the injection site to the dentate gyrus), but despite this it is usually possible to obtain a reasonable estimate of when the first afferents of a particular class reach the dentate gyrus, and to follow the sequential elaboration of the major afferent fiber systems. At the light microscope level, at which this approach has been used, one cannot, of course, establish when the first synapses are formed or follow the progress of synaptogenesis; for this electron microscopic autoradiography would be necessary, but this has not yet been applied to the developing dentate gyrus.

Two alternative approaches have also been used to follow the development of connections in the dentate gyrus. The first of these is the use of one or another variant of the Nauta method for staining degenerating axons and axon terminals (Singh, 1977; Loy et al., 1977). In general this has proved less satisfactory for studies of developing fiber systems than for the analysis of mature pathways, partly because the various staining methods appear to be somewhat insensitive, and partly because in very young animals the products of degeneration are very rapidly removed (cf. Leonard, 1974). The second approach involves the appearance of certain histochemical or histophysical patterns which seem to be characteristic of some of the afferent fiber systems. Timm's sulfide-silver method is particularly useful in this regard, because, as we have pointed out, although the physicochemical basis for the staining of tissue components with this method remains obscure, it is known empirically to stain selectively the zones of termination of specific classes of afferents to the dentate gyrus. Zimmer and Haug (1978) have used this method very effectively to follow the appearance of the characteristic laminar staining patterns seen in the molecular layer.

1. The Commissural Afferents

In the rat the commissural afferents appear to reach the dentate gyrus shortly after birth. Injections of [³H]proline into the regio inferior and the hilar region on the day after birth (i.e., day 2—if the day of birth is regarded as day 1) result in substantial labeling of the commissural afferents to the hippocampus proper, and there is some indication of labeling in the lateral part of the molecular layer of the suprapyramidal blade of the contralateral dentate gyrus at septal levels (Stanfield et al., 1980) (Fig. 16). In animals injected on the third day after birth the labeling over the inner part of the molecular layer is

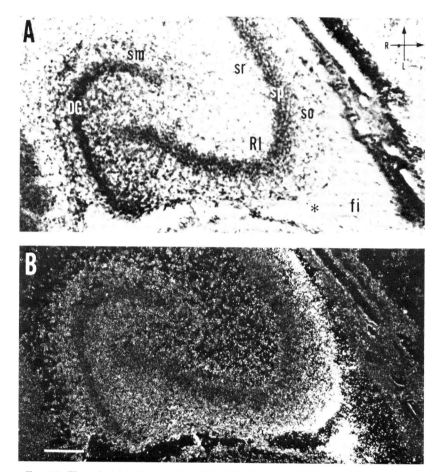

Fig. 16. These bright (A) and dark-field (B) photomicrographs are from autoradiographs through the temporal portion of a 1-day-old rat in which [³H]proline had been injected into the contralateral hippocampus and hilar region 6 hours before death. At this stage the commissural afferents to the hippocampus are quite clearly seen, especially in the fimbria (fi) deep to the stratum pyramidale (sp) in the stratum oriens (so), and to a lesser extent in the stratum radiatum (si), of the regio inferior (RI) but few, if any, appear to have reached this part of the dentate gyrus (DG). At more rostral levels, however, comparable autoradiographs reveal a small number of commissural fibers in the developing molecular layer (sm) over the lateral tip of the suprapyramidal blade. The arrows are for orientation purposes (R, rostral; L, lateral) and the asterisk marks the location of a blood vessel crossing the base of the fimbria. Scale: 100 μm.

quite unequivocal and, on the fifth day after birth, comparable labeling is seen over much of the septotemporal extent of the dentate gyrus. This does not mean that *all* the commissural fibers have reached the contralateral dentate gyrus at this stage, only that by this stage the distribution of the commissural fibers resembles that seen in mature animals. It is probable that additional commissural fibers continue to be added for some time, but the currently available methods do not readily permit this type of quantitative assessment.

The sequence we have described here for the development of the commissural afferents is slightly in advance of that reported by Fricke and Cowan (1977). In the material available to them, there was little or no indication of a commissural projection to the dentate gyrus on the third postnatal day, which was the earliest stage examined. However, in the same brains, there was evidence that the ipsilateral associational fibers were labeled, as were the commissural fibers to the hippocampus itself. Injection of [³H]proline on the sixth postnatal day (the next stage examined in that study) resulted in clear labeling of the commissural fibers in the inner part of the molecular layer of the contralateral dentate gyrus at all septotemporal levels. However, as might be expected, the projection was substantially heavier over the suprapyramidal than over the infrapyramidal blade and, interestingly, grain density estimates over the two blades revealed a pattern that is quite different from that seen in adult animals. After an injection near the middle of the septotemporal extent of the hippocampus (case HN45, Fricke and Cowan, 1977) the number of grains over the suprapyramidal blade of the contralateral dentate gyrus was about three times that over the infrapyramidal blade, whereas in mature animals with injections at comparable levels, the ratio of the number of grains over the two blades is essentially the reverse of this (Gottlieb and Cowan, 1972a; Fricke and Cowan, 1978). Presumably this reflects the fact that even at day 6, most of the commissural fibers to the infrapyramidal blade have not yet invaded it; again, this is hardly surprising considering that a substantial proportion of the granule cells destined for the infrapyramidal blade have yet to be generated.

These findings on the development of the commissural afferents are in essential agreement with those of Loy *et al.* (1977) who have examined their distribution both autoradiographically and using a variant of the Fink–Heimer method following extensive lesions of the contralateral hippocampus. After [³H]proline injections into the hippocampus on the fourth postnatal day they found a distinct band of silver grains in the inner 30 μm of the molecular layer over the suprapyramidal blade of the contralateral dentate gyrus, and over the inner 40 μm after injections on day 10. Loy *et al.* (1977) have pointed out that whereas the width of the molecular layer over the suprapyramidal blade of the dentate gyrus increases markedly during the first 4 weeks of postnatal life (from about 80 to about 170 μm between the fourth and twenty-sixth days, the increase in the thickness of the zone of termination of the commissural fibers does not keep pace with this expansion; thus the commissural zone was found to occupy about 37% of the width of the molecular layer at 4 days, and only about 28% at 26 days. Although Fricke and Cowan (1977) did not specifically address this point, their observations are also compatible with the view that there is either substantially less expansion of the "commissural zone" than the zone occupied by the entorhinal afferents during the second postnatal week, or there must be a significant degree of overlap in the terminal fields of these two classes of afferents at early stages (see the following).

Following lesions of the contralateral hippocampus, Loy *et al.* (1977) could see no evidence of terminal degeneration, stainable by the Fink–Heimer method, in the contralateral dentate gyrus at 4, 6, or 8 days. However, by the tenth postnatal day degenerating terminals were seen in the suprapyramidal blade, in a band about 40 μm wide in the inner part of the molecular layer. Although the width of the zone in which degeneration was seen matches the width of the commissural zone seen in the autoradiographic experiments, and while the time of appearance of terminal degeneration corresponds reasonably well with the period of rapid synaptogenesis in the inner part of the molecular layer, the absence of degeneration before day 10 (when a considerable proportion of the commissural fibers are present) suggests that degeneration methods are not particularly well suited for studying the early development of central neural pathways. And this is even more strikingly borne out by Singh's (1977) study in which the first indication of degeneration in the dentate gyrus, after lesions of the contralateral hippocampus, was seen on the thirteenth postnatal day.

A complementary approach to these studies has been Zimmer and Haugh's (1978) analysis of the appearance of the commissural zone of the dentate gyrus in Timm's sulfide-silver preparations. The characteristic, moderately dense-staining pattern seen in this zone is evident as early as the first postnatal day, and becomes progresively more sharply defined, first over the suprapyramidal blade (by day 3) and later over the infrapyramidal blade (between days 5 and 7). The zone increases only slightly in width during the first postnatal week, and by day 9 is almost as sharply delimited as in the adult animal. Since it is impossible to observe the appearance of the commissural afferents in the absence of the ipsilateral associational system, these observations pertain only to the zone of termination of both the commissural and associational afferents, as a whole. In so far as they go, they are in agreement with the findings in the more analytic studies but, in addition, they have shown even more strikingly the progressive delineation of the zone of termination of the hippocampal afferents that parallels the temporal-to-septal and suprapyramidal-to-infrapyramidal gradients in granule cell proliferation.

2. The Associational Afferents

The very high levels of background labeling seen on the side of an intrahippocampal injection of a labeled amino acid have made it difficult to establish when the ipsilateral associational afferents first reach the molecular layer of the dentate gyrus and to analyze their topographic distribution in relation to that of the commissural and entorhinal afferents. However, from Fricke and Cowan's (1977) study, and our own more recent observations (Stanfield et al., 1980), two general conclusions seem justified. The first is that the associational afferents are present in the molecular layer before the arrival of the first commissural fibers; this is an important finding, and, as we shall see, critical for the "temporal hypothesis" discussed in Section III,F. The second generalization is that although from the earliest stage examined the associational afferents are confined to the inner part of the molecular layer, like the commissural afferents they appear to occupy a relatively greater proportion of the molecular layer than they do in adult animals; again we shall defer discussion of this point until we have considered the development of the entorhinal afferents.

3. The Entorhinal Afferents

The development of the entorhinal afferents has been studied autoradiographically by Fricke and Cowan (1977) and Loy et al. (1977), in Fink–Heimer preparations by the latter authors and by Singh (1977), and in Timm's sulfide-silver preparations by Zimmer and Haug (1978).

It is clear from the two autoradiographic studies that the entorhinal afferents invade the molecular layer of the suprapyramidal blade before the arrival of the commissural afferents (but not necessarily before the ingrowth of the ipsilateral associational fibers). Fricke and Cowan (1977) have described two cases in which [^{3}H]proline injections were made into the entorhinal cortex on the third postnatal day. In one of these the cells in the medial entorhinal area seem to have been most heavily labeled, and this injection resulted in a fairly high grain density at about the middle of the cross-sectional width of the molecular layer of the dentate gyrus. In the second case the injection was more laterally placed and involved principally the lateral entorhinal cortex. Grain density traverses across the stratum granulosum and the molecular layer in this brain showed a high level of radioactivity in the outer third of the molecular layer that fell to near the background level in the inner half of the layer. While there is clearly a considerable degree of overlap in the distribution of the labeled fibers in these two cases, this may simply reflect the fact that neither injection was confined to the relevant field of the entorhinal cortex. However, although there are difficulties in comparing autoradiographs of different brains, prepared at different times and showing different background levels of radioactivity, it seems likely, from a comparison of these cases and those described, that the projections from the entorhinal cortex as a whole overlap that of the associational system at day 3. This is probably true also at day 6 when an injection of [^{3}H]proline into the medial entorhinal area resulted in a rather broad band of labeling occupying much of the middle three-fifths of the molecular layer.

From the sixth day onward the entorhinal projections become progressively more localized and by day 12 their distribution is essentially comparable to that seen in mature animals, being confined to the outer two-thirds of the molecular layer.

4. The Development of Other Afferents to the Dentate Gyrus

At present little is known about the development of the aminergic, septal, or hypothalamic afferents to the dentate gyrus. There are a number of technical problems in the analysis of the development of some of these inputs, but it should be relatively straightforward to follow the appearance of the aminergic inputs using either a variant of the Falck–Hillarp method, or one of the more recently introduced immunohistochemical methods; as far as we are aware this has not yet been done.

The development of the cholinergic afferents to the hippocampus (which are thought to arise within the septum) and dentate gyrus has been studied histochemically by following the increase in acetylcholinesterase (AChE) staining (Mellgren, 1973; Matthews *et al.*, 1974; Vijayan, 1979) and activity (Nadler *et al.*, 1974) and by monitoring the levels of choline acetyltransferase activity (Nadler *et al.*, 1974) and the development of high-affinity choline uptake in the dentate gyrus (Shelton *et al.*, 1979). In general, the results of these various studies are consistent in indicating that cholinergic fibers are present in the lateral part of the hilar region of the dentate gyrus as early as the second postnatal day, and that at this stage small amounts of AChE are present throughout the inner two-thirds of the developing molecular layer over the suprapyramidal blade (Mellgren, 1973). Over the course of the next week activity is seen over the medial part of the hilar region and over the inner part of the infrapyramidal blade. By day 15 the characteristic intense AChE staining seen in adult animals, in the zone immediately above the granule cells, appears. At this stage there is also evidence of activity in the stratum granulosum (between the granule cells) and the staining in the outer part of the molecular layer has a trilaminar arrangement.

Choline acetyltransferase (CAT) levels are very low at 11 days of age, but over the next 2 weeks increase sharply (especially early in the third week) so that the absolute activity of the enzyme increases about 15-fold and its specific activity by a factor of 3–4. In contrast to this the specific activity of AChE in the molecular layer increased only slightly during the second and third postnatal weeks, but effectively doubled between 4 and 7 days (Nadler et al., 1974). As we shall see, the biochemically measured changes in CAT correlate fairly well with the period of rapid synaptogenesis in the molecular layer, but at present there is no satisfactory explanation for the apparent time lag in the capacity of the system to metabolize acetylcholine.

More recently Shelton et al. (1979) have found that high-affinity choline uptake increases 3-fold between the sixth postnatal day and maturity, with most of the increase again occurring around 16–17 days. And interestingly, at 30 days, the rate of choline uptake is considerably above the adult value, and the coupling of choline uptake and acetylcholine synthesis becomes apparent only near the end of the second week. Hunt and Schmidt (1979) have approached this issue in a somewhat different manner, by examining the distribution of α-bungarotoxin receptors in the hippocampus and dentate gyrus. They have found evidence for acetylcholine receptors in the hilus of the dentate gyrus at birth and that their number appears to increase progressively over the next 3 weeks. This increase seems to be wholly independent of the septal afferents since it occurs, apparently at the normal rate, after early postnatal lesions of the septum.

In view of their distinctive pattern of termination, it would be particularly interesting to determine the time of arrival of the hypothalamic afferents. Do they enter the molecular layer before or after the associational and commissural fibers and do they initially extend into the zone of termination of these afferents, or are they strictly segregated from the beginning? These problems are just now

being addressed (Stanfield *et al.*, 1980) since the mode of termination of
the hypothalamic afferents has only recently been determined (Segal,
1979; Wyss *et al.*, 1979).

5. Some Conclusions about the Development of the Afferents to the Dentate Gyrus

Although our knowledge of the development of the afferents to the
dentate gyrus is still far from complete, a few general conclusions
about their development can now be drawn. (*a*) It is clear that each
class of afferents can be recognized in the suprapyramidal blade (at all
septotemporal levels) earlier than in the infrapyramidal blade, and
that in a general sense the development of the afferents that terminate
in the molecular layer parallels the morphogenetic gradients of
granule cell production in both the transverse and longitudinal dimensions. (*b*) The afferents reach the molecular layer when the granule
cells are still very immature, and the formation of definitive synaptic
connections can occur only several days after the afferents arrive. It is
not evident, at present, what happens to the afferent fibers during this
interval, but it is worth pointing out that the situation is similar, in
some respects, to that found in the neocortex where the thalamocortical
and callosal afferents reach the region just beneath the cortical plate at
a relatively early stage, and appear to delay their entry into the cortex,
for several days (Rakic, 1976, 1977; Lund and Mustari, 1976; Wise and
Jones, 1976, 1978; Wise *et al.*, 1977). (*c*) From the earliest stage at
which they can be identified the afferents to the molecular layer are
arranged in a laminar fashion, and although there may be some overlap between the afferents in adjoining laminae, there does not seem to
be a period when one class of afferent occupies the entire thickness of
the molecular layer, although final judgment on this point will have to
wait until we have evidence about the prenatal organization of the
entorhinal and associational afferents. Evidence from the distribution
of the various classes of afferents in the reeler mouse suggests that this
laminar arrangement is determined by some feature *intrinsic* to the
ingrowing afferents themselves rather than to the orderly arrangement
of the granule cells; whether this is due to some form of selective fas-
ciculation of the fibers or to some other (as yet unrecognized factor) can
only be speculated upon (Stanfield *et al.*, 1979). (*d*) It seems unlikely
that the lamination within the molecular layer can be explained solely
on the basis of the *time of arrival* of the various afferents since if this
were the case, we should expect that the late-arriving commissural
afferents would occupy a separate zone within the molecular layer,
either deep or superficial to that occupied by the associational fibers.

The fact that these two classes of afferents share the same region within the dendritic field of the granule cells would seem to argue that they share a common cytochemical specificity and that this, rather than their time of arrival, determines their ultimate distribution. And, if this is so, it would not be unreasonable to assume that the organization of the other afferents is determined on a similar basis. Of course, this notion does not, in any way, contradict or call in question the now substantial body of evidence that under certain circumstances afferents may extend beyond their normal laminar zones, into an adjoining deafferented zone (see Gall and Lynch, in this volume, for discussion). Specificity and plasticity are formally distinct phenomena, and the existence of one does not preclude the occurrence of the other.

E. The Development of Synapses in the Molecular Layer of the Dentate Gyrus

Crain et al. (1973) have given a brief account of the time course of appearance of synapses in the rat dentate gyrus in animals fixed on the fourth, eleventh, and twenty-fifth days postnatally, and in fully mature adults. Essentially what they have found is that there are very few synapses in the molecular layer of the dentate gyrus at the fourth postnatal day (about $0.25/100$ μm^2 in the infrapyramidal and about $2/100$ μm^2 in the suprapyramidal blade). The density of synapses increases relatively little in the suprapyramidal blade over the next week (from ~2 to 9 synapses/100 μm^2) but increases by a factor of almost 25 in the infrapyramidal blade. Between the eleventh and twenty-fifth days synaptic density increases about 3- or 4-fold from about $6-9/100$ μm^2 (in the infra- and suprapyramidal blades, respectively) to about $27/100$ μm^2. While there is no appreciable change in synaptic density after the twenty-fifth day, the proportion of asymmetrical to symmetrical synapses increases markedly (from about $3:1$ to almost $9:1$), continuing a trend that appears to extend throughout the developmental period (as many as two-thirds of the synapses being of the symmetrical variety in their 4-day-old animals). There is, however, no apparent difference in the rate of accumulation of synapses in the inner, middle, or outer thirds of the molecular layer, which suggests that synaptogenesis proceeds more or less uniformly along the length of the dendrites of the granule cells. Since the total volume of the molecular layer also increases considerably during the first 3 or 4 postnatal weeks (Crain et al. estimate that it may increase by a factor of 25 between 4 days and adulthood), the total number of synapses must rise sharply during this period—between 1000 and 2000 times in the infrapyramidal blade. This implies that during the period of most rapid increase, the number of synapses in the infrapyramidal blade more or less doubles every day between 4 and 11 days, which is considerably faster than the rate of increase in the numbers of granule cells (Crain *et al.*, 1973).

Kishi and Cowan (1980) have recently completed a morphometric analysis of the developing molecular layer in rats at 1, 5, 10, 21, and 41 days of age. In general their observations are in agreement with those of Crain *et al.* (1973) and Cotman *et al.* (1973b), but by examining sections taken at each of three septotemporal levels (corresponding approximately to the middle of the septal, middle, and temporal thirds of the dentate gyrus) they have been able to significantly extend this earlier work. Tables I and II, and Figs. 17 and 18, which are taken from their study, make it clear that there are, indeed, very few synapses in the molecular layer on the first postnatal day; only nine were seen in three traverses 14 μm wide across the width of the molecular layer over the suprapyramidal blade, and all but three of these were on dendritic shafts. By day 5 there are appreciably more synapses in this region of the dentate gyrus, and there is a clear gradient along the septotemporal extent of the gyrus in terms of the relative proportions of shaft and spine synapses (see Table II). As might be expected the number of synapses in the molecular layer over the infrapyramidal blade is appreciably smaller than that over the suprapyramidal blade, but the relative proportions of shaft and spine synapses follow the same general pattern.

TABLE I

SYNAPTIC DENSITY (NUMBERS OF SYNAPSES PER 100 μm^2) IN THE MOLECULAR LAYER OVER THE SUPRAPYRAMIDAL (SPB) AND INFRAPYRAMIDAL (PB) BLADES OF THE RAT DENTATE GYRUS AT EACH OF FIVE DIFFERENT DEVELOPMENTAL STAGES[a,b]

Days		Rostral	Middle	Caudal	Total
1	SPB	0.27	0	1.0	0.4
5	SPB	3.2	4.1	2.5	3.2
	IPB	0.82	0.88	0.6	0.8
10	SPB	12.2	8.8	12.1	11.0
	IPB	5.4	8.0	5.0	6.1
21	SPB	32.5	37.7	36.6	35.6
	IPB	36.4	28.4	36.9	33.9
41	SPB	36.6	35.6	38.2	36.8
	IPB	37.0	32.6	39.3	36.3

[a] From Kishi and Cowan (1980).
[b] The figures given for the totals represent the average for the rostral, middle, and caudal thirds of the dentate gyrus.

TABLE II

PERCENTAGE OF SHAFT (sh) AND SPINE (sp) SYNAPSES IN THE MOLECULAR LAYER OF THE RAT DENTATE GYRUS AT DIFFERENT STAGES IN DEVELOPMENT[a]

Age in days			Rostral	Middle	Caudal	Means
1	SPB	sh	100.00	0	50.0	
		sp	0.00	0	16.7	
5	SPB	sh	29.2	46.7	74.1	50.0
		sp	41.7	46.7	22.2	36.9
	IPB	sh	62.5	76.9	71.4	70.3
		sp	12.5	15.4	0.00	9.3
10	SPB	sh	31.6	42.9	47.9	40.8
		sp	56.8	36.0	48.5	47.1
	IPB	sh	49.9	56.5	45.5	50.6
		sp	39.3	37.3	47.5	41.4
21	SPB	sh	17.5	12.1	10.7	13.4
		sp	80.0	86.3	86.7	84.3
	IPB	sh	10.4	16.5	9.9	12.3
		sp	88.3	81.8	88.3	86.1
41	SPB	sh	8.4	10.5	11.8	10.2
		sp	89.7	88.8	86.8	88.4
	IPB	sh	14.2	7.7	9.2	10.4
		sp	84.7	89.6	88.0	87.4

[a] From Kishi and Cowan (1980).

There is a roughly 4-fold increase in the density of spine synapses (i.e., synapses/100 μm^2) in the molecular layer between 5 and 10 days, but since, during this period, the volume of the molecular layer as a whole also increases by about a factor of four (from 0.246 to 1.053 mm^3) there is something like a 16-fold increase in the total number of synapses in the molecular layer between the fifth and tenth days.

Over the course of the next 11 days the density of synapses in the molecular layer of the suprapyramidal blade again increases 3- or 4-fold (from an average of 11 to ~36 synapses/100 μm^2), but over the infrapyramidal blade the increase in density is more than 5-fold (from about 6 to 34 synapses/100 μm^2). Most of this increase is due to the appearance of large numbers of spine synapses, the proportion of shaft-to-spine synapses falling from about 0.9:1 to 0.16:1 in the suprapyramidal, and from 1.2:1 to 0.14:1 in the infrapyramidal blade, respectively. During this period the volume of the molecular layer as a whole expands by a factor of 1.8 (from 1.053 to 1.875 mm^3) so that the total number of synapses must increase 8-fold between 10 and 21 days. By day 21 synaptic density in the infrapyramidal blade closely approximates that in the suprapyramidal blade so that the rate of synap-

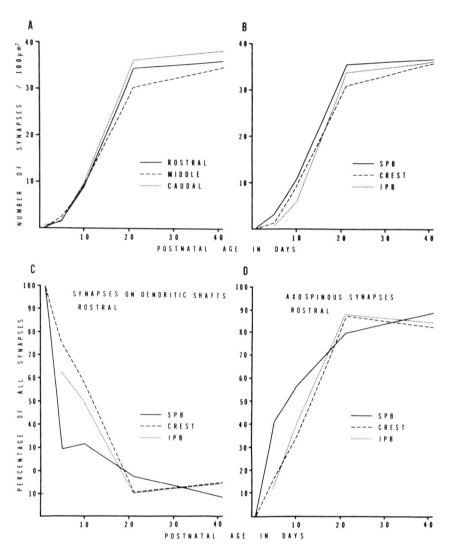

FIG. 17. Four graphs showing the progressive change in synaptic density in the molecular layer of the dentate gyrus at rostral (septal), middle, and caudal (temporal) levels (A), and over the suprapyramidal blade (SPB), the crest of the stratum granulosum and the infrapyramidal blade (IPB, B), and the relative percentages of synapses upon dendritic shafts and dendritic spines in the rostral third of the stratum moleculare (C and D). From Kishi and Cowan (1980).

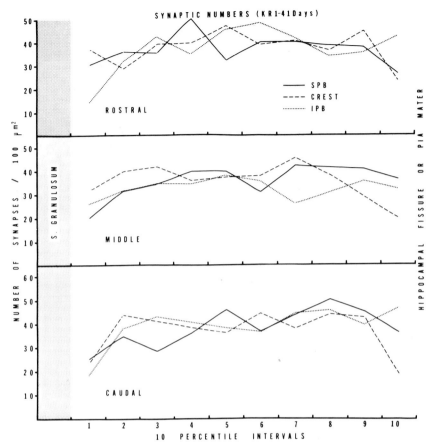

FIG. 18. The distribution of synapses (per 100 μm^2) across the thickness of the molecular layer of the dentate gyrus in a mature rat (41 days of age). For the sake of comparison the data have been plotted as a function of each 10% of the width of the molecular layer. SPB, suprapyramidal blade; IPB, infrapyramidal blade. From Kishi and Cowan (1980).

togenesis in the infrapyramidal blade must be even more accelerated during this period.

There is little change in either synaptic density or the proportions of spine-to-shaft synapses in the molecular layer between 21 and 41 days (the latest stage studied). However, as the volume of the molecular layer is further increased (from 1.875 to 2.671 mm^3 in a 35-day-old animal) the total number of synapses must increase during this 2-week period by a factor of about 1.4.

At most stages there are significantly fewer synapses in the region immediately superficial to the stratum granulosum and less in the zone

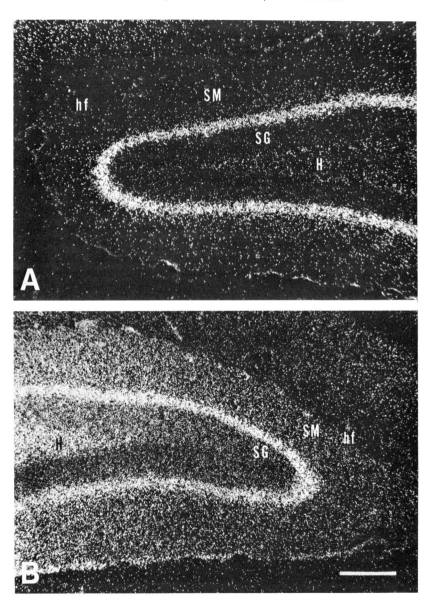

FIG. 19. Two dark-field photomicrographs taken from near the middle of the septal third of the dentate gyrus of a young adult mouse showing the distribution of axonally transported proteins in the commissural (A) and associational afferents (B) following an injection of [³H]proline into the hilar region at a more temporal level. Note that apart from the higher background level of radioactivity on the side of the injection (B) the

immediately deep to the pial surface. This is illustrated for a mature rat (at 41 days of age) in Fig. 18, in which the density of synapses has been plotted as a function of distance across the width of the molecular layer. Apart from this, the only appreciable difference in synapse distribution is that there tend to be more shaft synapses in the deeper part of the molecular layer than elsewhere at different stages. Figure 17 shows the rather sharp decline in the proportion of shaft synapses (expressed as a percentage of all synapses observed in the rostral part of the dentate gyrus) that occurs between days 5 and 20, and the concurrent rise in the relative numbers of axospinous synapses.

F. SOME CONSEQUENCES OF THE PROLONGED DEVELOPMENT OF THE
    GRANULE CELLS FOR THE DISTRIBUTION OF THE COMMISSURAL AND
    ASSOCIATIONAL AFFERENTS TO THE DENTATE GYRUS

An important insight into the possible significance of the prolonged development of the granule cells emerged during an autoradiographic study of the associational and commissural connections (Gottlieb and Cowan, 1972a). This can best be illustrated by reference to a typical experiment. If an injection of a [³H]amino acid is made into the hilar region of the dentate gyrus of a rat or mouse, at about the middle of its septotemporal extent, the commissural and associational afferents to the inner part of the molecular layer of the dentate gyrus are clearly labeled at more rostral levels (Fig. 19). Although, superficially, the labeling of the two pathways appears to be rather similar, counts of the numbers of silver grains found in traverses across the labeled regions at different points along the transverse axis of the dentate gyrus make it clear that there are systematic differences in the distribution of the two classes of afferents. This is illustrated in the series of graphs shown in Fig. 20. Near the tips of the suprapyramidal blades of the dentate gyrus the number of grains (above the background level) that are seen on the side of the injection (due to the labeling of the associational afferents) is roughly 2.6 times that seen at the corresponding point on the contralateral side (due to labeling of the commissural afferents). Near the crest of the dentate gyrus (at points C and D in Fig. 20) the corresponding ratio for the numbers of grains on the two sides is close to 2 : 1, but over the infrapyramidal blade (at points A and B it is close to 1.2 : 1). It seems unlikely that this type of systematic difference (which is consistent from experiment to experiment) can be attributed

distribution of the labeled fibers within the inner one-fourth of the molecular layer (SM) is identical on the two sides. hf, Hippocampal fissure; H, hilus; SG, stratum granulosum. Scale: 100 μm.

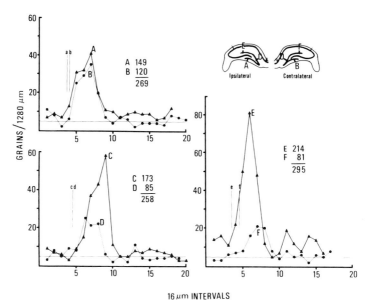

16 μm INTERVALS

Fig. 20. Three series of grain density traverses illustrating the consistent pattern of labeling seen over the molecular layer of the dentate gyrus of the two sides (at the level indicated in the inset drawing) after injections of [³H]amino acids into the hilar region of adult rats at a more caudal level. Near the tips of the suprapyramidal blade (points E and F) the ratio of the numbers of grains (above background) on the side ipsilateral to the injection (due to the labeling of the associational afferents) to that on the contralateral side (due to the commissural fibers) is approximately 2.6 : 1 (as indicated by the numbers to the right of the graphs labeled E and F). Near the crest of the dentate gyrus the corresponding ratio is close to 2 : 1 (graphs C and D), but over the infrapyramidal blade (graphs A and B) it is closer to 1.2 : 1. The consistency of this pattern has led to the formulation of the temporal hypothesis discussed in the text. The horizontal lines indicate the background levels of labeling and the vertical lines marked by the letters a–f, the outer margins of the stratum granulosum. From Gottlieb and Cowan (1972a) with permission.

to differences in the selective transport of different amounts of label in the two groups of fibers because it has been found to be independent both of the amount of isotope administered and the postinjection survival period (within the range of a few hours to a few days). The most reasonable alternative explanation for these grain density profiles is that they provide a fairly accurate measure of the relative numbers of commissural and associational afferents to the different regions of the dentate gyrus, and that the associational afferents dominate the suprapyramidal blade while the synaptic sites available within the infrapyramidal blade are more or less evenly distributed between the two groups of afferents.

Taken together with the evidence for a fairly steep gradient in cell proliferation along the transverse axis of the dentate gyrus, these findings suggest a plausible, and experimentally testable, hypothesis to account for the distribution of the two classes of afferents. The hypothesis requires only three assumptions. First, that the commissural and associational afferents share the same cytochemical specificity; at present the only evidence for this is that they terminate upon the same segments of the dendrites of their target cells, and that they arise from a similar, if not identical, population of neurons in the hilar region. Second, that the two classes of afferents reach the molecular layer of the dentate gyrus at different times in development; as we have seen, there is now good evidence for this: the commissural afferents have to grow across the hippocampal commissure from the opposite side of the brain and arrive some days later than the associational afferents which have to grow only for the relatively short distance from the hilar region to the molecular layer. And third, that the two classes of afferents compete with each other for the available synaptic sites on the proximal parts of the granule cells dendrites, in such a way that the first axons to arrive in the target region have a competitive advantage over those which arrive later.[4]

The associational afferents are presumably in the vicinity of the suprapyramidal blade when the first-formed granule cells are in a position to make synapses and hence monopolize the majority of the synapses in this region. Conversely, by the time the infrapyramidal blade is assembled and ready to form synapses both the commissural and the associational afferents are present in the molecular layer and they can presumably compete on an equal footing for synaptic sites, as they become available. If this is the case, one might expect that the commissural afferents would synapse principally with the later-formed granule cells in the suprapyramidal blade, but with both the early- and late-generated cells in the infrapyramidal blade.

This temporal hypothesis readily accounts for the consistent grain density patterns seen in the supra- and infrapyramidal blades after [³H]amino acid injections near the middle of the septotemporal extent

---

[4] Strictly this "temporal hypothesis" relates, not so much to the time at which the fibers reach the molecular layer, but rather the time at which they can form synapses of the appropriate kind. As we have pointed out, in the case of the entorhinal afferents to the dentate gyrus (and this is likely to be true also of the associational and commissural afferents) the fibers may be in, or close to, the target region for some time before synaptogenesis can occur.

of the dentate gyrus.[5] But if it is of general significance we should expect that there would be comparable systematic variations in grain density distribution after injections at different septotemporal levels, because of the observed temporal-to-septal gradient in the time of granule cell origin. Although this gradient is not nearly as steep as that across the transverse axis of the dentate gyrus, and although the situation appears somewhat complicated for the commissural connections to the caudal pole of the gyrus, Fricke and Cowan (1978) have been able to adduce evidence consonant with the temporal hypothesis.

The first line of evidence is that injections of labeled amino acids into the mid-portion of the hippocampus invariably result in the labeling of associational and commissural afferents over a much greater distance in the septal than in the temporal direction, and in every case the caudal extent of the labeling due to the associational fibers exceeds that due to the commissural afferents. This is exactly what one might predict on the basis of the temporal-to-septal gradient in granule cell neurogenesis, since in the septal direction the growing afferents will encounter increasing numbers of late-generated granule cells, whereas in the reverse (temporal) direction the cells are, on average, more mature, and hence more likely to have already formed synapses with afferents arising from more temporal levels. The second line of evidence derives from estimates of the relative numbers of silver grains seen over the molecular layer at different septotemporal levels following injections of [3H]proline at any one level. For example, after an injection near the middle of the rostrocaudal extent of the hippocampus, the associational and commissural fibers are labeled throughout the septal half of the dentate gyrus. At about the middle of the septal third of the dentate gyrus the pattern of grain density distribution over the molecular layer of the two sides is essentially the same as that reported by Gottlieb and Cowan (1972a) and described above. But at more temporal levels the above-background grain densities due to the labeling of the associational fibers are appreciably greater at all points around the transverse axis of the dentate gyrus (Fricke and Cowan, 1978).

---

[5] As the hypothesis has mistakenly been taken to imply that the entire pattern of distribution of the various intrinsic and extrinsic afferents to the dentate gyrus can be explained on the basis of their time of arrival, it is worth reiterating that it is intended to account only for the *relative* distribution of two classes of afferents that end on the *same segments* of the same population of target neurons (and presumably have the same cytochemical specificity). There is, at present, no compelling evidence to suggest that different classes of afferents that normally synapse on *different parts* of their target neurons compete with each other on the same basis.

The simplest explanation of these findings, and of those in experiments with more rostrally placed injections, is that the associational fibers not only have to compete with the commissural fibers for synaptic sites in the inner part of the molecular layer, but also with other associational afferents arising at more rostral and caudal levels. And the fact that they usually have a much greater rostral distribution is entirely consistent with a temporal-to-septal gradient in the availability of synaptic sites. However, it is also evident from experiments with injections into the temporal region of the hippocampus that the entire pattern of associational and commissural afferents cannot be accounted for solely on temporal factors of this kind. Since in these cases labeling on the contralateral side is usually confined to the temporal third of the dentate gyrus, it seems as though there must also be some degree of topographic (i.e., region-to-region) specificity within the commissural projection. Whether this is true only for the temporal region, or whether it applies, to a greater or lesser extent, at all levels, is difficult to determine, but it is clear that whereas we can account reasonably well for the distribution of the commissural projection from middle and septal levels on the basis of the time of arrival of the fibers, it is impossible to account for the selective distribution of the fibers to the temporal pole, on any other basis than that they can form synapses only in the temporal region.

A more direct test of the temporal hypothesis derives from the observation that after an injection of [^{3}H]amino acid into the mid-portion of the hippocampus, the density of silver grains (due to the labeling of the associational afferents) over the suprapyramidal blade of the dentate gyrus is approximately twice that over the infrapyramidal blade. This is illustrated for normal brains, with appropriately placed injections, in Figs. 21 and 22, taken from the study of O'Leary et al. (1979). Again, the simplest explanation for this pattern (which is strikingly consistent despite very wide variations in the absolute grain densities in different experiments) is that the suprapyramidal blade is dominated by the associational afferents because there is comparatively little competition for synaptic sites in this region from the commissural fibers; conversely, the numbers of synapses available to the associational afferents are smaller in the infrapyramidal blade because here the competition is greatest. If this is indeed the explanation, we might expect to see a significant change in the relative numbers of grains in the two blades after labeling the associational afferents, if all competition from the commissural fibers were to be eliminated. Since, as we have pointed out, in the rat the commissural fibers reach the dentate gyrus only sometime after birth, it is relatively easy to eliminate them

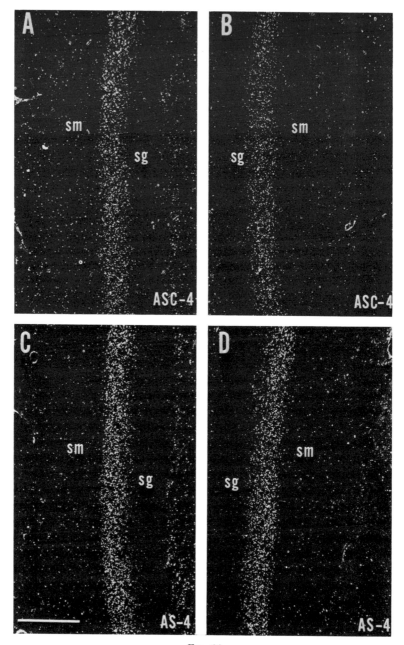

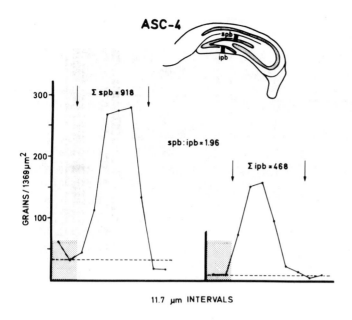

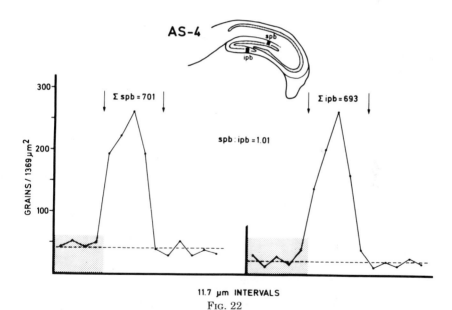

FIG. 22

FIGS. 21 and 22. The upper two dark-field photomicrographs (A, B) in Fig. 21 illustrate the normal grain densities seen over the molecular layer (sm) of the suprapyramidal (ASC-4, left) and infrapyramidal blades (ASC-4, right) after autoradiographic experiments in which the associational afferents are labeled by an injection of [³H]proline into the hilar region of the dentate gyrus at a more caudal level. The density of grains over the suprapyramidal blade (spb) is roughly twice that over the infrapyramidal blade (ipb) as shown in the two upper graphs in Fig. 22. When the hippocampus on one side is destroyed

by ablating the hippocampus on one side within a day or two of birth. When this is done, and injections of [³H]amino acid made into the hilar region several weeks later, there is indeed a change in the ratio of labeling over the supra- and infrapyramidal blades, from a mean of 1.88 : 1 to 1.05 : 1 (O'Leary et al., 1979). Although it is difficult to rule out the possibility that under these circumstances, the removal of the commissural afferents has resulted in some (at this time, inexplicable) change in axonal transport in the associational fibers to the two blades, on the whole this seems unlikely. The most probable interpretation of the change in grain density is that in the absence of the commissural afferents the associational afferents are able to occupy all the available synaptic sites on the relevant parts of the granule cell dendrites. Whether this is brought about simply by a redistribution of the associational fibers, or by an actual increase in the number of associational fiber terminals in the infrapyramidal blade, remains to be determined.

IV. Conclusions and Future Perspectives

That the dentate gyrus is, indeed, a useful model system for the analysis of cortical development has been amply borne out by the various studies carried out during the past 10–15 years. We now know a great deal about the time-course and patterning of cell proliferation both in the dentate gyrus itself and in the adjoining regions in rodents and primates, and about the early and later migration of the granule cells and their precursors, and the sequential assembly of its different parts in normal rats and mice and in one neurological mutant—the reeler mouse. Although we know virtually nothing about the molecular mechanisms that regulate and direct the processes of proliferation, migration, and cell aggregation, at least at the descriptive level their analysis is fairly complete. Perhaps the only major remaining issues in this context concern the numbers of granule cells generated and the factors responsible for the very striking gradients in granule cell production that have been observed.

---

on the day after birth, and the associational fibers labeled by similar injections some weeks later, the grain densities over the two blades appear to be essentially the same as seen in the lower two photomicrographs (C, D) in Fig. 21 (AS-4 left shows the suprapyramidal blade; AS-4 right the infrapyramidal blade). That this is so is borne out by the grain density traverses plotted in the lower part of Fig. 22. Experiments of this kind suggest that normally the commissural and associational afferents compete for synaptic sites in the inner part of the molecular layer, especially in the infrapyramidal blade, and that when this competition is eliminated (by ablating the contralateral hippocampus) the distribution of the associational afferents becomes uniform around the entire transverse extent of the dentate gyrus. sg, Stratum granulosum. Figures 21 and 22 from O'Leary et al. (1979) with permission.

In most neural systems for which quantitative data are available considerably more neurons are formed than finally survive, the definitive numbers of cells being determined by a phase of naturally occurring cell death at a later stage in development (see Cowan, 1978 for review). So far it has been difficult to establish whether or not a similar phase of cell death occurs during the development of the dentate gyrus. Schlessinger et al. (1975) have adduced evidence that is consonant with the view that as many as 30% of the granule cells may not survive to maturity; but, since this was based on estimates of the relative numbers of labeled cells after [^{3}H]thymidine injections, rather than on direct counts of granule cells, it cannot be regarded as definitive. It would be of interest to establish this point in view of the current notions about the etiology of naturally occurring cell death, and to establish whether or not cell death occurs in neural systems in which the connectivity seems to be specified mainly in terms of the segments of the target neurons to be contacted rather than on precise topographic or numerical grounds. As techniques for rapidly counting large populations of neurons become available, this question should be relatively easy to answer.

The elucidation of the factors responsible for the temporal → septal, supra- → infrapyramidal, and outside-in gradients in granule cell production is likely to be extremely difficult. It seems improbable that the types of experimental analysis that have been applied to this type of problem in invertebrates, and in some neural centers in lower vertebrates (Cowan, 1978), can be applied to the mammalian brain and, as yet, the genetic variants have thrown little light on this issue. Again, considering that gradients of this type are such a characteristic feature of the development of virtually all neural systems in the mammalian brain, an imaginative assault on this problem could well yield a rich dividend.

The considerable variability in the form, and in the numbers and lengths of the dendrites of the granule cells, has made the analysis of this aspect of their cytodifferentiation unexpectedly difficult. We may anticipate, however, that as intracellular labeling techniques are applied to this system, it should be possible to generate more reliable quantitative data, and to obtain more statistically significant data, for cells in different regions and at each of several different stages in development. Such material, if examined electron microscopically, should also resolve a number of remaining issues concerning the fine structure and connectivity of the dentate gyrus. But what is perhaps most sorely needed is an approach to the cytochemical differentiation of the granule cells (and, with it, to the differentiation of the various classes of cells with which they are connected). We still do not know the nature of the transmitter used by the granule cells, and have only indirect evidence for the transmitters used by their various intrinsic and extrinsic afferent inputs. Nor do we have any information about such critical physiological parameters as the nature of the principal ion(s) used in the generation of action potentials by the granule cells, and whether or not the cells are electrically coupled at any stage during their development. To our knowledge, no serious study of the physiological properties of the developing granule cells has been undertaken (in part, no doubt because of their relatively small size); again we may anticipate that this will soon be remedied.

The published studies on the time of arrival of the major extrinsic afferents to the dentate gyrus, and on the appearance of synapses of different classes in the molecular layer, have laid an adequate foundation for the next phase in this work. This should see an extension of these studies to the electron microscopic level, and, hopefully, the emergence of cytochemically specific labeling methods for following the development of each of the major afferent pathways. Together these approaches should establish with certainty when specific classes of synapses are formed and whether or not there is a significant degree of overlap between the afferents to different laminar zones, at the time the fibers first enter the molecular layer. If there is such an overlap, the elucidation of the factors that lead to the elimination of some fibers (and synapses) and the persistence of others might well go a long way toward clarifying the nature of the distinctive specificity that exists in this system, and at the same time its unusual capacity for morphological plasticity.

ACKNOWLEDGMENTS

We should like to thank Ms. Ruth Weber for secretarial help and for her careful typing of the manuscript, Ms. Sara Wykes for help with the illustrations, and our colleagues Drs. David Amaral, Russell Fricke, Michael Wyss, and Dennis O'Leary for permitting us to reproduce figures from their published work and/or to cite their unpublished observations.

REFERENCES

Altman, J. (1966). *J. Comp. Neurol.* **128**, 431–474.
Alvarez-Leefmans, F. J. (1976). *Exp. Brain Res. Suppl.* **1**, 229–234.
Amaral, D. G. (1978), *J. Comp. Neurol.* **182**, 851–914.
Amaral, D. G. (1979). *Anat. Embryol.* **155**, 241–251.
Amaral, D. G., and Cowan, W. M. (1980). *J. Comp. Neurol.* (in press).
Andersen, P., Holmqvist, B., and Voorhoeve, P. E. (1966). *Acta Physiol. Scand.* **66**, 448–460.

Andersen, P., Bliss, T. V. P., and Skrede, K. K. (1971). *Exp. Brain Res.* **13**, 222–238.
Angevine, J. B., Jr. (1965). *Exp. Neurol.* **13**, Suppl. 2, 1–70.
Banker, G. A., and Cowan, W. M. (1977). *Brain Res.* **126**, 397–425.
Banker, G., and Cowan, W. M. (1979). *J. Comp. Neurol.* **187**, 469–494.
Bayer, S. A., and Altman, J. (1974). *J. Comp. Neurol.* **158**, 55–80.
Blackstad, T. W. (1956). *J. Comp. Neurol.* **105**, 417–538.
Blackstad, T. W., Brink, K., Hem, J., and Jeune, B. (1970). *J. Comp. Neurol.* **138**, 433–450.
Bliss, T. V. P., Chung, S.-H., and Stirling, R. V. (1974). *J. Physiol. (London)* **239**, 92–94P.
Cajal, S. Ramón y (1893). *Anal. Soc. Esp. Histol. Nat. Madrid* **22**, 53–114.
Cajal, S. Ramón y (1911). "Histologie du système nerveux de l'homme et des vertébrés," Vol. 2. Maloine, Paris.
Caviness, V. S., Jr. (1973). *J. Comp. Neurol.* **151**, 113–120.
Caviness, V. S., Jr., and Rakic, P. (1978). *Annu. Rev. Neurosci.* **1**, 297–326.
Caviness, V. S., Jr., and Sidman, R. L. (1973a). *J. Comp. Neurol.* **147**, 235–254.
Caviness, V. S., Jr., and Sidman, R. L. (1973b). *J. Comp. Neurol.* **148**, 141–152.
Chan-Palay, V. (1978). *Proc. Natl. Acad. Sci. U.S.A.* **75**, 2516–2520.
Conrad, L. C. A., Leonard, C. M., and Pfaff, D. W. (1974). *J. Comp. Neurol.* **156**, 179–206.
Cotman, C. W., Matthews, D. A., Taylor, D., and Lynch, G. (1973a). *Proc. Natl. Acad. Sci. U.S.A.* **70**, 3473–3477.
Cotman, C., Taylor, D., and Lynch, G. (1973b). *Brain Res.* **63**, 205–213.
Cowan, W. M. (1978). *In* "International Review of Physiology" (R. Porter, ed.), Vol. 17, pp. 149–191. Univ. Park Press, Baltimore, Maryland.
Cowan, W. M., and Cuénod, M. (1975). *In* "The Use of Axonal Transport for Studies of Neuronal Connectivity" (M. Cuénod and W. M. Cowan, eds.), pp. 1–24. Elsevier, Amsterdam.
Cowan, W. M., Gottlieb, D. I., Hendrickson, A. E., Price, J. L., and Woolsey, T. A. (1972). *Brain Res.* **31**, 21–52.
Crain, B., Cotman, C., Taylor, D., and Lynch, G. (1973). *Brain Res.* **63**, 195–204.
Crepel, F., Mariani, J., and Delhaye-Bouchaud, N. (1976). *J. Neurobiol.* **7**, 567–578.
Daitz, H. M., and Powell, T. P. S. (1954). *J. Neurol. Neurosurg. Psychiat.* **17**, 75–82.
Deadwyler, S., West, J. R., Cotman, C. W., and Lynch, G. S. (1975). *J. Neurophysiol.* **38**, 167–184.
Desmond, N. L., Levy, W. B., and Hall, D. M. (1979). *Anat. Rec.* **193**, 521.
Euler, C., von (1962). *In* "Physiologie de l'hippocampe" (P. Passouant, ed.), pp. 135–145. Centre National de la Recherche Scientifique, Paris.
Fricke, R. A. (1975). Ph.D. Thesis, Washington University, St. Louis.
Fricke, R., and Cowan, W. M. (1977). *J. Comp. Neurol.* **173**, 231–250.
Fricke, R., and Cowan, W. M. (1978). *J. Comp. Neurol.* **181**, 253–270.
Gaarskjaer, F. B. (1978a). *J. Comp. Neurol.* **178**, 49–72.
Gaarskjaer, F. B. (1978b). *J. Comp. Neurol.* **178**, 73–88.
Gottlieb, D. I., and Cowan, W. M. (1972a). *Brain Res.* **41**, 452–456.
Gottlieb, D. I., and Cowan, W. M. (1972b). *Z. Zellforsch.* **129**, 413–429.
Gottlieb, D. I., and Cowan, W. M. (1973). *J. Comp. Neurol.* **149**, 393–422.
Haug, F.-M. Š. (1974). *Z. Anat. Entwicklungsg.* **145**, 1–27.
Haug, F.-M. Š. (1976). *Exp. Brain Res. Suppl.* **1**, 177–178.
Hjorth-Simonsen, A. (1972). *J. Comp. Neurol.* **146**, 219–232.
Hjorth-Simonsen, A., and Jeune, B. (1972). *J. Comp. Neurol.* **144**, 215–232.
Hjorth-Simonsen, A., and Laurberg, S. (1977). *J. Comp. Neurol.* **174**, 591–606.
Hunt, S., and Schmidt, J. (1979). *Neuroscience* **4**, 585–592.

Jones, B. E., and Moore, R. Y. (1977). *Brain Res.* **127**, 25–53.
Kaplan, M. S., and Hinds, J. W. (1977). *Science* **197**, 1092–1094.
Kishi, K., and Cowan, W. M. (1980). In preparation.
Koda, L. Y., and Bloom, F. E. (1977). *Brain Res.* **120**, 327–350.
Laatsch, R. H., and Cowan, W. M. (1966). *J. Comp. Neurol.* **128**, 359–396.
Laatsch, R. H., and Cowan, W. M. (1967). *J. Comp. Neurol.* **130**, 241–262.
Laurberg, S. (1979). *J. Comp. Neurol.* **184**, 685–708.
Leonard, C. M. (1974). *J. Comp. Neurol.* **156**, 435–458.
Lewis, P. R., and Shute, C. C. D. (1967). *Brain* **90**, 521–540.
Lichtman, J. W.(1977). *J. Physiol. (London)* **273**, 155–177.
Lømo, T. (1968). *Acta Physiol. Scand.* **74**, 8–9A.
Lømo, T. (1971). *Exp. Brain Res.* **12**, 18–45.
Lorente de Nó, R. (1934). *J. Psychol. Neurol.* **46**, 113–177.
Loy, R., Lynch, G., and Cotman, C. W. (1977). *Brain Res.* **121**, 229–243.
Loy, R., Koziell, D. A., Lindsey, J. D., and Moore, R. Y. (1979). *J. Comp. Neurol.* (in press).
Lund, R. D., and Mustari, M. J. (1976). *J. Comp. Neurol.* **173**, 289–305.
McWilliams, R., and Lynch, G. (1978). *J. Comp. Neurol.* **180**, 581–616.
Matthews, D. A., Nadler, J. V., Lynch, G. S., and Cotman, C. W. (1974). *Dev. Biol.* **36**, 130–141.
Mellgren, S. I. (1973). *Z. Zellforsch.* **141**, 375–400.
Mellgren, S. I., and Srebro, B. (1973). *Brain Res.* **52**, 19–36.
Minkwitz, H. G. (1976). *J. Hirnforsch.* **17**, 213–231.
Moore, R. Y., and Halaris, A. E. (1975). *J. Comp. Neurol.* **164**, 171–184.
Mosko, S., Lynch, G., and Cotman, C. W. (1973). *J. Comp. Neurol.* **153**, 161–174.
Nadler, J. V., Matthews, D. A., Cotman, C. W., and Lynch, G. S. (1974). *Dev. Biol.* **36**, 142–154.
Nadler, J. R., White, W. F., Vaca, K. W., Redburn, D. A., and Cotman, C. W. (1977). *J. Neurochem.* **29**, 279–290.
Nafstad, P. H. J. (1967). *Z. Zellforsch.* **76**, 532–542.
Nowakowski, R. S. (1976). Ph.D. Thesis, Harvard Medical School.
O'Leary, D. D. M., Fricke, R. A., Stanfield, B. B., and Cowan, W. M. (1979). *Anat. Embryol.* **156**, 283–299.
Pasquier, D. A., and Reinoso-Suarez, F. (1976). *Brain Res.* **108**, 165–169.
Raisman, G. (1966). *Brain* **89**, 317–348.
Raisman, G., Cowan, W. M., and Powell, T. P. S. (1965). *Brain* **88**, 963–996.
Rakic, P. (1976). *Nature (London)* **261**, 467–471.
Rakic, P. (1977). *Phil. Trans. R. Soc. London B* **278**, 245–260.
Rawlins, J. N. P., and Green, K. F. (1977). *Exp. Brain Res.* **28**, 335–344.
Redfern, P. A. (1970). *J. Physiol. (London)* **209**, 701–709.
Schlessinger, A. R., Cowan, W. M., and Gottlieb, D. I. (1975). *J. Comp. Neurol.* **159**, 149–176.
Schlessinger, A. R., Cowan, W. M., and Swanson, L. W. (1978). *Anat. Embryol.* **154**, 153–173.
Segal, M. (1979). *Brain Res.* **162**, 137–141.
Segal, M. E., and Bloom, F. E. (1976). *Brain Res.* **107**, 513–525.
Segal, M., and Landis, S. (1974). *Brain Res.* **78**, 1–15.
Shelton, D. L., Nadler, J. V., and Cotman, C. W. (1979). *Brain Res.* **163**, 263–275.
Singh, S. C. (1977). *Anat. Embryol.* **151**, 183–199.
Stanfield, B., and Cowan, W. M. (1979a). *Anat. Embryol.* **156**, 37–52.

Stanfield, B. B., and Cowan, W. M. (1979b). *J. Comp. Neurol.* **185**, 393–422.
Stanfield, B. B., and Cowan, W. M. (1979c). *J. Comp. Neurol.* **185**, 423–460.
Stanfield, B., Amaral, D. G., and Cowan, W. M. (1980). In preparation.
Stanfield, B. B., Caviness, V. S., Jr., and Cowan, W. M. (1979). *J. Comp. Neurol.* **185**, 461–484.
Steward, O. (1976). *J. Comp. Neurol.* **167**, 285–314.
Steward, O., and Scoville, S. A. (1976). *J. Comp. Neurol.* **169**, 357–370.
Steward, O., White, W. F., and Cotman, C. W. (1977). *Brain Res.* **134**, 551–560.
Stirling, R., and Bliss, T. V. P. (1978). *Prog. Brain Res.* **48**, 191–198.
Storm-Mathisen, J. (1976). *In* "GABA in Nervous System Function" (E. Roberts, T. N. Chase and D. B. Tower, eds.), pp. 149–168. Raven, New York.
Swanson, L. W., and Cowan, W. M. (1977a). *J. Comp. Neurol.* **172**, 49–84.
Swanson, L. W., and Cowan, W. M. (1977b). *In* "The Septal Nuclei" (J. F. DeFrance, ed.), pp. 37–64. Plenum, New York.
Swanson, L. W., and Cowan, W. M. (1979). *J. Comp. Neurol.* **186**, 621–655.
Swanson, L. W., and Hartman, B. K. (1975). *J. Comp. Neurol.* **163**, 467–506.
Swanson, L. W., Wyss, J. M., and Cowan, W. M. (1978). *J. Comp. Neurol.* **181**, 681–715.
Timm, F. (1958). *Z. Zellforsch.* **48**, 548–555.
Vijayan, V. K. (1979). *Neuroscience* **4**, 121–137.
West, J. R., Nornes, H. O., Barnes, C. L., and Bronfenbrenner, M. (1979). *Brain Res.* **160**, 203–216.
Wimer, R. E., Wimer, C. C., Vaughn, J. E., Barber, R. P., Balvanz, B. A., and Chernow, C. R. (1978). *Brain Res.* **157**, 105–122.
Wise, S. P., and Jones, E. G. (1976). *J. Comp. Neurol.* **163**, 313–343.
Wise, S. P., and Jones, E. G. (1978). *J. Comp. Neurol.* **178**, 187–208.
Wise, S. P., Hendry, S. H. C., and Jones, E. G. (1977). *Brain Res.* **138**, 538–544.
Wyss, J. M., Swanson, L. W., and Cowan, W. M. (1979a). *Neuroscience* **4**, 463–476.
Wyss, J. M., Swanson, L. W., and Cowan, W. M. (1979b). *Anat. Embryol.* **156**, 165–176.
Zimmer, J. (1971). *J. Comp. Neurol.* **142**, 393–416.
Zimmer, J. (1978). *Prog. Brain Res.* **48**, 171–189.
Zimmer, J., and Haug, F.-M. Š. (1978). *J. Comp. Neurol.* **179**, 581–618.

CHAPTER 6

THE REGULATION OF FIBER GROWTH AND SYNAPTOGENESIS IN THE DEVELOPING HIPPOCAMPUS

Christine Gall* and Gary Lynch

DEPARTMENT OF PSYCHOBIOLOGY
UNIVERSITY OF CALIFORNIA
IRVINE, CALIFORNIA

I. Introduction 159
II. Regulation of the Size of a Developing Afferent Field 160
    A. Afferent Distribution within the Dentate Gyrus of the
       Adult Rat 160
    B. The Competition Hypothesis: Redistribution of Dentate
       Gyrus Afferents after Selective Removal of Input 161
    C. Selective Retention and Loss of Early Axonal Branches 163
    D. Limits on the Capacity for Growth 163
    E. The Role of Relative "Preferences" in Governing the
       Distribution of Dentate Gyrus Afferents 164
    F. Summary, Conclusions, and Some Possible Cellular Mechanisms 167
III. Regulation of Synaptogenesis within the Target Region 169
IV. The Later Stages of Development 171
    A. "Equilibrium" between Afferent Populations 171
    B. Tonic Inhibition versus Qualitative Changes in the Neurons ... 173
    C. Limits of Growth Imposed by Capacity or Self-Recognition
       Processes 175
    D. Time-Dependent "Stop" Signals 177
    E. Residual Growth Capacity in the Adult 177
    References 179

I. Introduction

The process by which the neurons of the brain connect together surely represents one of the basic problem areas of neurobiology—it is, after all, through this step in development that the operating characteristics of the central nervous system become defined. In this chapter we will attempt to elucidate certain mechanisms by which the precise organization of fiber and synaptic systems is achieved. Specifically,

* Present address: Department of Neurology, School of Medicine, State University of New York at Stony Brook, Long Island, New York.

CURRENT TOPICS IN
DEVELOPMENTAL BIOLOGY, Vol. 15

three questions concerning sequential though overlapping events in development will be discussed:

1. What regulates the size of the dendritic field which is captured by an ingrowing afferent?
2. What factors determine the speed with which an input innervates its targets?
3. Why does the growth process ultimately stop?

In order to approach these questions we will follow the story of a group of fibers after they enter one brain structure under normal circumstances as well as under conditions in which neighboring inputs or particular cellular targets have been removed. Our discussion then will be restricted to a small part of the brain of one species as well as to a limited portion of its ontogenetic history. While these constraints preclude a general review of the literature of axon–target tissue interactions, they allow us to go into the detail needed to evaluate several of the more recent theories of how brain circuits are formed

II. Regulation of the Size of a Developing Afferent Field

A. AFFERENT DISTRIBUTION WITHIN THE DENTATE GYRUS OF THE ADULT RAT

In two respects the dentate gyrus of the rat hippocampal formation has proved extremely useful in studies of developing fiber systems: (a) it is an unusually simple structure consisting of a single row of granule cell bodies whose radiating dendrites generate a homogeneous and largely cell-free molecular layer, and (b) the afferents to this layer are rigidly laminated (Fig. 1). Because of these features it is possible, using several anatomical techniques, to describe in precise quantitative terms the distribution of the afferents, the development of that distribution, and finally any changes in growth produced by experimental manipulations.

Within the dentate gyrus molecular layer of the adult rat two distinct innervation fields are defined by the segregated termination of the principal afferent systems. The proximal 27% of the dendritic field receives input from the hippocampal commissural and associational systems (which arise from the regio inferior pyramidal cells of the contralateral and ipsilateral hippocampal formations, respectively) while the outer 73% of the same dendritic field receives almost all of its input from the ipsilateral entorhinal cortex (see Lynch and Cotman, 1975 for a review of the extensive literature relating to these points).

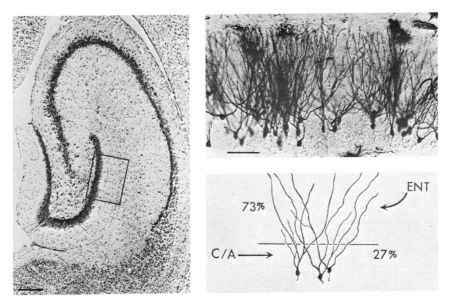

FIG. 1. This figure illustrates the basic features of dentate gyrus anatomy discussed in the text. Within the horizontal Nissl-stained section of the hippocampal formation seen on the left, the dentate appears as a compact curve of granule cells. The micrograph on the upper right is taken from a length of the granule cell and molecular layers comparable to the boxed-in portion of the Nissl section, impregnated by the Golgi technique. Both micrographs illustrate the strict definition of the cellular and dendritic lamina as well as the homogeneous saturation of the dentate's molecular layer by granule cell dendrites. The accompanying drawing indicates the position and relative proportion of the primary afferent lamina defined by the terminal fields of the entorhinal (ENT) and commissural/ associational (C/A) afferent systems. Calibration bar on left micrograph indicates 300 μm; bar on upper right, 100 μm.

The commissural, associational, and entorhinal axons arrive in the dentate gyrus during the first week of life and quickly become restricted to the appropriate portions of the granule cell dendrites and remain in these positions for the life of the animal (Loy et al., 1977; Fricke and Cowan, 1977). The question that faces us now is what dictates this organization, or why do these fibers fail to invade and occupy neighboring regions of the developing dendritic field.

B. THE COMPETITION HYPOTHESIS: REDISTRIBUTION OF DENTATE GYRUS AFFERENTS AFTER SELECTIVE REMOVAL OF INPUT

The exquisitely precise distribution of the afferents to the dentate gyrus suggests that these fibers and synapses may in some way be

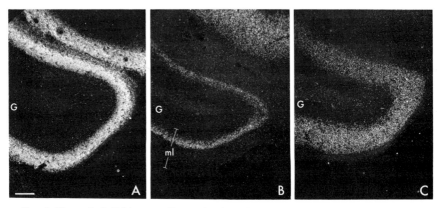

FIG. 2. These dark field autoradiographs show the expansion of the dentate's commissural afferent field following neonatal removal of input from the ipsilateral entorhinal cortex. Each micrograph includes the tip of the sharply curving layer of granule cells (G) and the surrounding molecular field (ml). In (A) and (B) the normal entorhinal (A) and commissural (B) terminal fields, labeled by [^{3}H]leucine transport, can be seen to occupy adjacent and strictly exclusive lamina. However, following neonatal removal of the ipsilateral entorhinal cortex before 2 weeks of age, the commissural terminal field expands distally to occupy the deafferented field (C). Calibration bar in (A) indicates 200 μm tissue distance for all three micrographs.

rigidly programmed to terminate within discrete and defined dendritic zones. However, there is evidence that this may not be the case. In the experiment illustrated in Fig. 2, the mature distribution of the dentate's commissural input was analyzed in rats in which the ipsilateral entorhinal cortex had been removed at 14 days of age. This manipulation, which removes the major afferent to the outer molecular layer, results in the distal expansion of the commissural terminal field. Therefore, following the removal of an adjacent afferent system, the commissural axons, normally restricted to the proximal dendritic lamina, grow to occupy the full depth of the molecular layer (Lynch *et al.*, 1973; Zimmer, 1973a; Gall and Lynch, 1978). The associational fibers show similar expansion (Zimmer, 1973a).

Such sprouting effects involving afferent field expansion (or, in other systems, intensification) following neonatal removal of a potentially competitive afferent system have been demonstrated throughout the neuroaxis. For example, retinal ganglion cells which project predominantly to the contralateral superior colliculus intensify their ipsilateral projection following unilateral enucleation (Lund and Lund, 1973, 1976). The visual cortex normally projects to the superior colliculus only on the ipsilateral side but develops an abnormal crossed projection when the contralateral colliculus is deprived of its normal visiocortical input at birth (Mustari and Lund, 1976). Similarly, following unilateral neonatal lesions of the motor cortex the contralateral cortex develops an enlarged projection to lower motor centers on the ipsilateral side (Hicks and D'Amato, 1970; Leong and Lund, 1973).

These sprouting experiments suggest a series of important hypotheses about the factors which regulate the distribution of the commissural/associational projections to the dentate gyrus. First, these fibers are not rigidly "specified" to terminate within a given dendritic zone; instead it appears that they are excluded from the distal dendritic region by the presence of the entorhinal input. Second, the axons are capable of much more growth than they ever express during normal development (see Section II,D for further discussion of this point). However, other interpretations of these sprouting experiments are possible and we shall now consider several of these; this will also provide the opportunity to consider hypotheses other than the "competition" idea just discussed.

C. SELECTIVE RETENTION AND LOSS OF EARLY AXONAL BRANCHES

An increasing body of evidence suggests that developing axons will generate a certain number of connections which become lost or resorbed during development. (cf. Rakic, 1976). It is not at all clear how common this effect is, but its existence suggests an alternate explanation for the aforementioned experiments; namely, that the commissural axons in the middle and outer molecular layer found after lesions of the entorhinal cortex represent the retention of contacts formed in those dendritic zones during early development but which are normally lost.

However, light and electron microscopic studies have shown that at the time of the lesion used in the above study, 14 days postnatal, both commissural and entorhinal afferent systems are present and innervate adjacent, nonoverlapping lamina as seen in the adult (Fricke and Cowan, 1977; Loy et al., 1977; Gall and Lynch, 1978). In fact, no period of mixed areal occupancy has been demonstrated at any point in the development of this system. Therefore, although this criticism *may* apply to the interpretation of other "sprouting" studies, the commissural projection is not in this case retaining an earlier more diffuse terminal pattern; instead the expansion of these afferents must be viewed as an invasion of dendritic space normally held by another input.

D. LIMITS ON THE CAPACITY FOR GROWTH

It has been suggested that one of the major factors which dictates the extent of an afferent's projection is a genetic limit on the amount of arborization a given axon can achieve. This idea receives support from experiments showing that sprouting of an afferent into one area will often reduce the size of the terminal field generated by that system within its normal target region (Devor and Schneider, 1975; Devor, 1976). It can be appreciated that the sprouting study described does not accord well with this hypothesis; instead, the results of that experiment suggest that the afferents of the dentate gyrus possess the capacity for growth far in excess of that which they express under normal circumstances. After all, the commissural terminal field in rats subjected to neonatal removal of the entorhinal cortex more than doubles the dendritic space it occupies in the normal animal.

Nevertheless, there is a real possibility that this sprouting represents not a hypertrophy of the commissural innervation of the dentate gyrus but, instead, a redistribution of the normal number of fibers and terminals across a wider than normal dendritic space. This explanation would be consistent with both the field expansion observations and the growth limitation hypothesis. If the redistribution idea is correct, one would expect that the commissural projection would generate fewer synapses within its normal, proximal, terminal lamina as the commissural axons spread across a larger dendritic field. However, this is not the case. Ultrastructural degeneration studies analyzing the distribution and density of commissural synapses within the inner (normal-commissural) and outer (neonatally deafferented) molecular layers demonstrate that the commissural afferent innervates both regions with the same density observed within the proximal field of the normal rat (Fig. 3; Gall et al., 1979a). It must be concluded then that the commissural projection has grown into the deafferented territory without expense to its normal terminal field; sprouting in this case represents a genuine axonal hypertrophy.

E. The Role of Relative "Preferences" in Governing the Distribution of Dentate Gyrus Afferents

The sprouting experiments suggest that the commissural projections are not excluded from the middle and outer molecular layers by any type of rigid specification. However, it remains possible that milder forms of matching or specification might still be responsible for the development of the laminated afferent distribution. That is, the two major subzones of the granule cell dendrites may possess relative preferences for certain inputs (presumably expressed through biochemical matching of the pre- and postsynaptic elements): Such preferences could play a major role in segregating the ingrowing afferent systems. Sprouting then would represent a case in which a dendritic target was

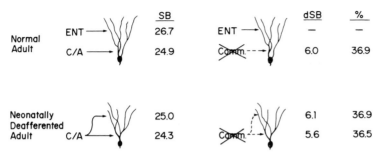

FIG. 3. Summary of data obtained in the ultrastructural analysis of commissural sprouting induced by removal of the entorhinal cortex in the 14-day-old rat. The average synaptic bouton (SB) density (per 100 μm^2) within the inner and outer molecular layers of the normal and neonatally deafferented adult rat is presented on the left. It can be seen that, despite the removal of the input from the entorhinal cortex (ENT) in the neonate, the experimental outer molecular layer eventually recovers its "normal" innervation density. Results from commissural degeneration studies are presented on the right where the density of degenerating synaptic boutons (dSB) per 100 μm^2 and the percentage synaptic bouton loss (%) produced by contralateral hippocampal aspiration are tabulated for each subject group. From these data it is clear that the commissural afferent assumes a large proportion (36.9%) of the innervation of the neonatally deafferented outer molecular layer without reducing the density of its inner molecular layer innervation.

denied its primary choice of input and consequently accepted a less preferred afferent. Alternatively, denervation might cause the loss of normally present specification mechanisms and thereby create a situation in which any input could invade and successfully innervate the deafferented territory. However, another experimental paradigm, one in which each developing input remains intact, has been used to substantiate the notion that competition between afferents for terminal space is, indeed, a strong influence in organizing afferent topographies.

The majority of the dentate gyrus granule cells arise postnatally and, therefore, are selectively vulnerable to X-irradiation during the first 2 postnatal weeks. This treatment can effectively reduce the granule cell population to 15% of the normal value (Bayer and Altman, 1975; Gerbrandt et al., 1978). As mentioned previously, the commissural afferents of the dentate gyrus are restricted to the proximal 27% of the dendritic field while the entorhinal afferents occupy the more distal 73% (supplying about 90% of the innervation of this zone; Lee et al., 1977). In the pyramidal cell fields of the hippocampus proper a similar laminar arrangement is observed, but with the relative balance of input reversed. The more proximal 79% of the dendritic field receives commissural innervation while the distal 21% contains moderate input from the entorhinal cortex. Thus, while destruction of the granule cells

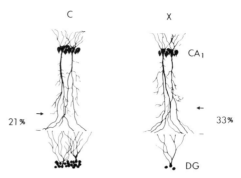

Fig. 4. Drawing illustrating the influence of removing the majority of the dentate gyrus granule cells upon the distribution of the entorhinal projections to the hippocampal pyramidal cells. In the normal hippocampal formation (C) the distal-apical edge of the dentate gyrus (DG) molecular layer abuts that of the pyramidal cell field (CA₁). Afferent fibers from the entorhinal cortex occupy the more distal region of each dendritic field with the outer molecular layer of the dentate gyrus representing their primary synaptic target. X-Irradiation applied during the first 2 postnatal weeks can be used to reduce the granule cell population of the dentate gyrus to 15% of the normal level (X), thereby depriving the entorhinal fibers of their major dendritic target. Following such treatment the entorhinal cortical input is found to increase its pyramidal field occupancy such that in field CA₁ this afferent increases its dominion from 21% of the apical dendritic field in the normal animal to 33% in the X-irradiated rat.

with X-irradiation removes only a small fraction of the normal inner-vation field of the commissural fibers this treatment effectively elim-inates the major target of the entorhinal fibers.

As illustrated in Fig. 4, the X-ray-produced reduction of the granule cell population significantly disrupts the normal balance of afferent termination in regions of the hippocampus not directly affected by the treatment. The entorhinal axons deprived of their normal target in the dentate gyrus terminate more heavily and extensively in the pyrami-dal cell molecular layer and, most interestingly, this shift displaces the commissural afferent from some of its normal innervation field (Ger-brandt *et al.*, 1978). Therefore, in this case the loss of the normal target region for one afferent system appears to have changed the competitive balance between the commissural and entorhinal axons within another terminal field; the enlarged entorhinal termination in the second area apparently excludes a normal, intact, afferent to that zone.

Similar target removal effects have been observed in other systems. Schneider first demonstrated that removal of the superior colliculus in the newborn hamster causes the normal retinal afferents to the ablated region to form aberrant synapses in the remaining superior colliculus as well as to intensify their projection to other normal terminal fields

(Schneider, 1973; Devor and Schneider, 1975). Similar observations have also been made in the rat (Miller and Lund, 1975). In each case, the growth of the target-deprived axons into the remaining superior colliculus acted to exclude the normal contralateral retinal afferents from this region, thereby revealing what appears to be a competitive interaction between the two axonal populations.

These experiments demonstrate that axonal systems can penetrate target zones which they normally would not occupy even if: (a) the dendritic regions in question have not been deafferented and (b) the normal afferents to the zone are present. This provides further reason to reject the idea that dendrites and their inputs are rigidly matched and supports the "simple" competition explanation for the above described sprouting results. Beyond this, target removal studies suggest some clues about the factors which dictate the outcome of competitive interactions between developing fiber systems. That is, it appears that the success the entorhinal projections experience in invading the more proximal dendritic zones of regio superior (thereby displacing the normal afferent to that region) is somewhat dependent upon the extent to which this system is forming or has formed synapses in the dentate gyrus. At first glance this may seem at odds with the conclusion made earlier that axonal systems have large reservoirs of unused growth potential. By way of integrating the two sets of observations we would advance the following hypotheses: Growth slows as contacts are formed but stops well before the capacity of the neurons is reached. Growth rate might well influence the outcome of competitive interactions but further study on the basic idea is needed.

F. SUMMARY, CONCLUSIONS, AND SOME POSSIBLE CELLULAR MECHANISMS

To summarize, it does not appear that the precise lamination of the commissural and associational afferents to the dentate gyrus can be explained by a selective loss of more extensive contacts or by an exhaustion of growth capacity. Furthermore, the expansion of these projections into distal dendritic territories indicates that they are not *rigidly* coded to terminate only within the proximal dendritic zone. Instead the hypertrophic development of the commissural/associational projections seen after removal of the entorhinal axons suggests that the growth of the former is suppressed by the later, in a word, that a form of competitive exclusion appears to exist between the various inputs to the dentate gyrus. From this perspective one might consider an afferent's dominance of its normal terminal field as representing that afferent's successful competition for the space. A relative preference by the target neuron for a particular input system may still exist, but, if the competitive balance is shifted away from the norm, as in the target-removal experiments discussed above, the effect of this preference can be overcome. We would emphasize that there is nothing in the data so far discussed which requires such a preference device.

The mechanisms by which this competitive interaction between growing afferents is realized are a matter of speculation. It has been suggested that the proportion of the innervation of the dentate gyrus inner molecular layer held by its commissural and associational afferents merely reflects the temporal sequence of afferent arrival with the earlier arriving afferent gaining more synaptic space than the later (Gottlieb and Cowan, 1972; Fricke and Cowan, 1978). Such an explanation works fairly well in this case of overlapping projection fields but it is far from satisfactory when considering the apparent exclusive nature of the competition that can exist between adjacent terminal fields. To find analogs for the mutual inhibitory influence observed between these afferents we must look to very different systems.

In the case of peripheral cutaneous innervation of the salamander it has been demonstrated that colchicine treatment of one sensory nerve, and thereby the blockage of axoplasmic transport, results in the extension of the sensory fields of adjacent nerves into the affected area—a consequence similar to that expected had the original (blocked) nerve been cut (Aguilar et al., 1973). The simplest, and least assuming, interpretation of these results would be that the colchicine treatment impaired the treated nerve's ability to exclude the collaterals of adjacent sensory fibers from invading its normal cutaneous field. In this case it was suggested that the treated nerve normally excluded adjacent fibers from its peripheral domain by the release of trophic substances (supplied via fast axoplasmic transport) that prohibit this incursion. An alternate interpretation might be that the affected cutaneous zone was no longer sufficiently served by the colchicine-treated fibers and, as a result, the cutaneous tissue in some way induced the ingrowth of the intact sensory fibers from nearby fields [this would be consonant with the hypothesis sometimes offered to explain the development of aberrant innervation into the muscle targets of anesthetized nerves (Jansen et al., 1978)].

A similar mutually repellant effect between nerve fibers has been demonstrated in tissue culture although in this case neurite outgrowth was repelled only when the processes came into contact (Dunn, 1971). Interestingly, this repellant interaction was expressed only under certain culture-substrate conditions such that growing neurites would predictably fasiculate or repel upon contact when grown in either semifluid or more solid plasma clots. Thus, changes in the local growth environment could elicit seemingly opposite interaxonal influences on growth. Nevertheless, both the tissue culture and cutaneous sprouting data indicate that particular axonal populations have the ability to "protect" their "space" by the expression of some characteristic that actively excludes the growth of neighboring fiber systems.

III. Regulation of Synaptogenesis within the Target Region

Once the fiber has arrived in its target region the formation of synaptic connections begins. What determines the rate at which this proceeds? It seems reasonable to assume that it is set by some property of either the pre- or postsynaptic cell that limits the capacity to generate the components of the synapse. Recent experiments, however, suggest that to a large extent synaptogensis is regulated by local interactions rather than general properties of pre- and postsynaptic neurons.

The experiment illustrated in Fig. 5 takes advantage of the sprouting effect described earlier. It will be recalled that removal of the entorhinal cortex in 14-day-old rats eliminates the great majority of

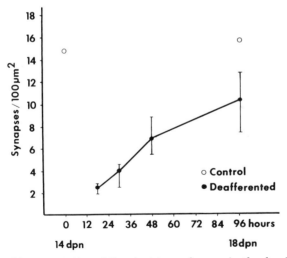

FIG. 5. Graphic presentation of the short-term changes in the density of synaptic boutons within the outer molecular layer of the rat dentate gyrus deafferented at 14 days postnatal (dpn). The normal density in this region at 14 and 18 days of age is indicated by open circles. Within 18 hours of ipsilateral entorhinal ablation this index has fallen to less than 20% of the normal value. Approximately 60% of this loss is recovered in the next 78 hours. The rate of synaptogenesis during this period is clearly much more rapid than that accomplished during this same age interval in the normal rat.

synapses in the outer molecular layer; it also involves a concomitant loss of the spines and postsynaptic densities from that area. If the rate of synaptogenesis is determined by a general property of the neuron (either pre- or postsynaptic) then we would expect that the commissural/associational axons which sprout into the denervated territory would generate new contacts at about the same rate as their parent fibers in the inner molecular layer. However, this is clearly not the case. Synaptogenesis in the denervated territory progresses at a rate greatly in excess of that seen during normal development— quantitative electron microscopic studies have shown that over half the normal density of synapses in the middle molecular layer is recovered by 96 hours postlesion (Gall et al., 1980b).

The early onset in the return of intact synapses is not surprising in light of the recent autoradiographic data demonstrating that the growth of the commissural afferent fibers into the deafferented zone is well under way by 24 hours postlesion (Gall and Lynch, 1978). The rate of reinnervation, however, is surprisingly high as compared to the normal rate of synaptogenesis in this region during the period of the study. As can be seen in Fig. 5, the normal increase in the density of synaptic boutons within the outer molecular layer between 15 and 18 days of age is quite modest (from approximately 15 to 16 synapses per $100 \mu m^2$); a similarly slight increase (14 to 15 synapses per $100 \mu m^2$) is observed within the more proximal, normal-commissural, dendritic zone (Gall et al., 1980b). The actual accumulation of new synapses would be somewhat greater than these values indicate because the dendritic zone is also enlarging during this period. Nevertheless, the rate of synaptogenesis during the period of outer molecular layer reinnervation is clearly much more rapid than that observed in the normal innervation of this, or the more proximal, zone.

Despite the intense synaptogenesis in the deafferented zone, the innervation of the inner molecular layer seems to proceed at the normal pace. Therefore not only do these results demonstrate that the commissural/associational systems are capable of forming connections much more rapidly than is expressed during normal development, they also indicate that single afferent systems (and probably collaterals of the same fiber) can form connections at different rates within two target regions on the same dendrites. (Note that this argument holds as well for the dendrites of the granule cells since they are clearly forming spines and appropriate postsynaptic sites much more quickly in their denervated outer segments than is the case in their innervated inner regions.) Taken together, and expressed in more general terms, these results strongly suggest that "local conditions" rather than some limitation on or program for growth of the pre- or postsynaptic element dictates how quickly synapses are formed.

IV. The Later Stages of Development

In previous sections we have considered some of the possible regulatory processes which restrict fibers to defined subzones of the dendritic field and determine the rate at which they form synapses; we come then to the last stages of development, that period when afferent fields cease to expand and the density of synaptic contacts no longer increases. The question we should now like to consider is why this occurs.

A. "Equilibrium" between Afferent Populations

As discussed previously, it appears that growing afferents restrict one another's expansion and, within a field, there is reason to believe that increasing densities of contacts slow the process of synaptogenesis. It is conceivable then that a point is reached in development at which the number of afferent axons and the density of the synaptic population are great enough to prevent further fiber expansion or the addition of new contacts; in essence, a point at which inhibitory influences balance the tendency toward growth and a kind of anatomical "homeostasis" is achieved. To test this idea we repeated the sprouting study described above using rats of different postnatal ages (Gall et al., 1979b).

As shown in Fig. 6 sprouting by the commissural projections at 14 dpn results in an expanded terminal field which covers nearly all of the granule cell dendrite; however, if this experiment is carried out in the adult only about 50 μm of the denervated zone is successfully invaded (Lynch et al., 1973). Furthermore, the onset of the sprouting is considerably delayed in the adult compared to the immature rat (Gall and Lynch, 1978; Lynch et al., 1977).

Originally we interpreted these findings as indicating that a single sprouting process became restricted in both scope and time over the course of development but recent work examining the neonatal sprouting effect with a light microscopic neurofibrillary technique has led to a very different explanation. Surprisingly, the expansion of the commissural/associational plexus revealed by this method is about the same in the 14 dpn rat as it is in the adult—yet the autoradiographic and electron microscopic experiments show that the terminal field generated by the commissural fibers extends much farther after entorhinal lesions in the neonate than it does after comparable damage in the mature animal. Careful examination of the fiber-stained material after deafferentation of the 14 dpn dentate gyrus indicates that long collat-

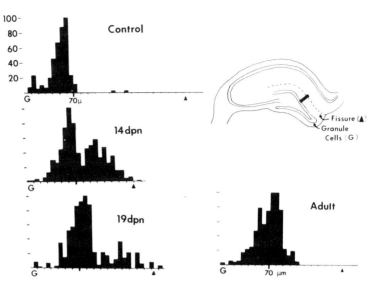

FIG. 6. The distribution of the commissural projections in the dentate gyrus of mature rats which had received unilateral lesions of the entorhinal cortex at 14 or 19 days postnatal (14 dpn, 19 dpn) or as adults ("Adult"). Radiolabeled amino acid was injected into the regio inferior contralateral to the lesion (the origin of the dentate gyrus commissural afferents) 2 days before sacrifice and the relative density of autoradiographic grains was measured at various depths in the molecular layer of the dentate gyrus ipsilateral to the lesion; the site of grain counting is shown in the schematic in the upper right-hand side of the figure. The bar graphs illustrate the results with the abscissa expressing the distance from the layer of granule cell bodies (G) to the hippocampal fissure (indicated by filled arrowhead; see schematic). Note that in the control rat (no lesion) the projection is restricted to a zone with a distal boundary 70 μm above the granule cell bodies. Following removal of the entorhinal cortex in the adult the terminal field expands outward by some 35–50 μm; in rats so lesioned at 14 dpn the degree of distal enlargement of the field is considerably greater. The effects of lesion placement at 19 dpn are intermediate—the terminal field extends throughout the dendritic field but it is somewhat less dense in the outer zones than was seen after entorhinal ablation in the younger rats.

eral branches emerge from the commissural and associational plexus and travel for considerable distances in the denervated dendritic zones—apparently it is these fibers which are responsible for the rapid proliferation of terminals in those regions.

This suggests that two forms of sprouting are present in the neonate: (a) a modest outward enlargement of the commissural/associational plexus which is readily detected by fiber stains, and (b) an uneven generation of long collateral branches which quickly reinnervate the more distal dendritic territories. Furthermore, and most important, the second form of growth (which for convenience we will refer to with the older term "collateral sprouting") appears to drop out with development leaving only the local expansion of commissural/associational fibers to be seen in the adult (G. Lynch and C. Gall, unpublished). Work still in progress suggests that the robust collateral type of sprouting disappears gradually between 14 and 21 dpn. From these studies we conclude that a change transpires in the hippocampal formation during the second week of life such that the regio inferior pyramidal cell (commissural) axon can no longer generate long collateral sprouts or alternatively that such collaterals begin to encounter barriers to growth.

Studies of the developmental diminution of the sprouting response have also been conducted in other brain areas and a selection of these results are presented in Table I. Both the similarities and differences between these effects and those obtained in hippocampus are of interest—note in particular that collateral sprouting appears to cease much earlier in some areas than others. We will return to this point shortly.

We can conclude then that something happens in the hippocampal formation (and many other sites in brain) probably starting before the third week of life such that collaterization is progressively repressed. The nature of this "something" is, to say the least, obscure and in the following sections we can do little more than touch upon the broader possibilities and issues.

B. TONIC INHIBITION VERSUS QUALITATIVE CHANGES IN THE NEURONS

Conceivably the cessation of growth might represent the addition of some continuously acting inhibitory factor rather than a loss of capacity by the neurons themselves. The time period during which the collateral sprouting response becomes retarded and ultimately disappears is one in which numerous extraneuronal events are occurring in the hippocampus. During this period the astrocytes begin process extension (Gall et al., 1980a) and rapid vascularization occurs—slightly later oligodendroglia and microglial cells begin to appear in large numbers. These changes could result in the appearance of inhibitory factors which serve to prevent the extension of collaterals from parent axons.

There are two lines of admittedly inconclusive evidence which mitigate against such an explanation. First, the argument would not predict that two afferents terminating in the same target region would show a loss of sprouting at different times—yet this appears to be the case for the retinal and cortical inputs to the tectum (Lund and Miller, 1975; So and Schneider, 1976; Mustari and Lund, 1976; Lund, 1978; see Table I). Second, there is the fact that axons and neurons undergo

TABLE I

SUMMARY OF STUDIES DEMONSTRATING DEVELOPMENTAL DIFFERENCES IN THE CAPACITY FOR MORPHOLOGICAL PLASTICITY IN THE MAMMALIAN CENTRAL NERVOUS SYSTEM[a]

Projection system	Morphological plasticity			References
	Maximal	Decremental	Mature	
Olfactory bulb → olfactory cortex	P1	P3–P17		Devor (1976)
Retina → tectum	E16-(approx.)P3	–P10	P12	Lund and Miller (1975)
Retina → tectum	Up to P6	P10, P12	P14	So and Schneider (1976)[b]
Visual cortex → tectum	Up to P10	P15, P20	Post-P20	Mustari and Lund (1976)
Motor cortex → lower motor centers (pons, spinal cord, etc.)	Up to P3	P3–P20[c]	Prior to P20 in most areas	Leong (1976) (also Leong and Lund, 1973; Hicks and D'Amato, 1971)
Intrinsic hippocampal circuits (commissural/associational)	Up to P14	P15–P21	Post-P21	Lynch et al. (1973); Zimmer (1973a,b); Gall and Lynch (1978), Gall et al. (1979b)

[a] A summary of data from a variety of systems in which developmental differences in the magnitude of lesion-induced anatomical plasticity has been reported. Three developmental phases are generally described. During the earliest phase, "maximal" growth of remaining axonal systems into aberrant target regions is observed. This is followed by a "decremental" period in which there is a progressive reduction in the magnitude of the experimentally induced growth with lesion placement at progressively later ages. Finally, the "mature" lesion responsiveness is attained. The last pattern is generally assumed well before the system being analyzed can be considered to have received its mature complement of innervation. P, Postnatal age; E, embryonic age such that P10 represents postnatal day 10.

[b] Study conducted on the Syrian hamster; in all other cases the rat was used.

[c] Lesion induced plastic changes "faded out" sooner in some areas than others.

marked qualitative changes over the course of development. This is apparent through ultrastructural analyses of normal development and can be seen perhaps even more clearly in the response of neurons to damage. Axons and terminals separated from their parent cell are very quickly removed from the immature brain (Gall *et al.,* 1980b; Schoenfeld *et al.,* 1979). However, in the adult a significant proportion of the degenerating elements enter a period in which they are "electron dense"; in this form they will often persist for several days or, in the case of axons, even weeks. Light microscopic studies fully confirm the extreme persistance of degenerating axons in the adult as compared to the neonatal brain (cf. Lynch *et al.,* 1973; Leonard, 1974). Thus it appears that axons undergo some type of qualitative change over the course of development. It hardly need be emphasized that the changes seen in the ultrastructure of axons or in their degenerative process may not be related to the loss of collateral sprouting; yet the simple fact that mature and immature fibers *are* different encourages the belief that the decreased "plasticity" of the former reflects a basic change in their character. The case for the "tonic inhibition" hypothesis is certainly not closed but from the few data that are pertinent a qualitative, maturational change in the neurons appears to be a more likely explanation for the loss of collateral sprouting.

C. Limits of Growth Imposed by Capacity or Self-Recognition Processes

The final size and shape of the neuron's processes might reflect some type of genetic code which tells its dendritic tree, for example, to assume a granule or pyramidal form—this idea would require that the cell also have a "self-recognition" mechanism such that once its desired geometry and size were achieved growth would cease. Tissue culture experiments have provided some reason to believe that neurons are to a degree specified to develop toward some idealized form (Privat, 1975; Banker and Cowan, 1977), but from the evidence reviewed it is unlikely that the dimensions of an axonal projection or its synaptic domain is genetically determined. The evident hypertrophy of the commissural afferents indicates that these axons will grow well beyond normal limits if the appropriate space is made available; hence it seems unlikely that they stop growing under normal circumstances because of an internal signal generated when a certain level of arborization is reached. It remains possible though that the end of axonal growth is secondary to the target dendrites responding to their own, intrinsically programmed "off" signal. However, there is evidence which suggests that again, given the right conditions, postsynaptic targets will hyperdevelop.

It has been shown that removal of the bulk of the dentate's granule cell population by neonatal X-irradiation results in the hyperinnervation of the somata of the remaining granule cell bodies (Lee, 1978). Thus it appears that the number of postsynaptic sites generated per unit membrane by the target cell is not set by some rigid internal code but instead can be significantly modified by altering the neuron's microenvironment. Golgi analyses of these X-irradiated brains have also revealed the presence of neurons with extremely long dendritic processes (Laurberg and Hjorth-Simonsen, 1977; Fig. 7). While more detailed analyses are clearly needed these data suggest that removal of one segment of a homogeneous pool of neurons results in the hyperdevelopment of the remaining members of that pool. This observation, combined with axonal hypertrophy in the presence of partial deafferentation, argues that the neuron has no clear "program" which dictates

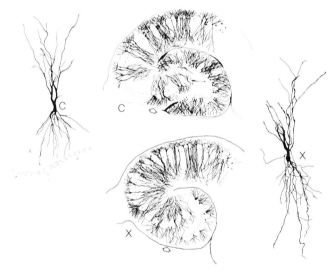

FIG. 7. Camera lucida drawings illustrating the influence of the X-irradiation elimination of the majority of dentate gyrus granule cells upon the dendritic arborization of hippocampal CA3c and CA4 neurons. In the low-magnification drawing of the normal adult rat hippocampal formation (C) the external blade of the granule cells seems to set a limiting boundary on the length of the basal dendrites of CA3c/CA4 hippocampal pyramidal neurons (in the region of the arrow). In animals subjected to neonatal X-irradiation (X) this boundary (in the form of granule cells) is missing and the pyramidal basal dendrites extend to the external surface of the hippocampal formation achieving dendritic lengths much greater than ever seen in the untreated rat. Higher power drawings of individual CA3c neurons from these same control (C) and X-irradiated (X) tissue sections further illustrate this effect. The basal dendritic arborization, extending down, is clearly much longer in the X-irradiated case.

the size of either its axonal or dendritic ramifications and thus the ultimate form assumed by these processes must be due to some other factors.

D. TIME-DEPENDENT "STOP" SIGNALS

In Sections IV, B and C we have discussed evidence that the reduction in the capacity for collateral growth (at least as manifested in the sprouting response) cannot be explained by the appearance of a tonically active inhibitory influence or by the achievement of genetic limits or "goals." A third possibility is that at a certain stage in development the neuron is qualitatively altered by some type of signal, altered so that collateralization no longer occurs. There are two variants of this hypothesis that we might consider:

1. The neuron could have an internal, presumably genetic, "clock" which at some point after the birth of the cell begins to emit "stop" signals.
2. Extrinsic events might change the cell such that growth is blocked (note that this can be distinguished from the "tonic" extrinsic influence hypothesis—in the present case the signal alters the quality of the cell after which it, the signal, might well disappear).

At this time there are few data which bear directly on either of these ideas, at least as they apply to the development of the dentate gyrus. It is clear that local interactions play a major role in molding the ultimate shape of a cell (ample evidence for this has been cited throughout this article), but this cannot be taken as strong evidence against the idea that internal signals appearing at a fixed time after the birth of the cell limit the phase of free growth. Extrinsic events which shift the neuron (or its processes) toward the mature state could be derived from the environment of the neuropil (hormones, glia, vascular elements) or could simply be the accumulated effect of extensive process extension and synapse formation. Unfortunately these are questions which do not readily lend themselves to experimentation.

E. RESIDUAL GROWTH CAPACITY IN THE ADULT

In the above sections we have stressed the finding that robust collateral sprouting disappears over the third postnatal week of life. However, we should not overlook the second form of sprouting by the commissural/associational fibers that is present in the young animal as well as in the adult and to about the same degree. Light (Parnavalas *et al.*, 1974) and electron microscopic (Matthews *et al.*, 1976a,b) experiments have provided substantial evidence that the postsynaptic components of the synaptic complex disappear after their preterminal elements are removed and reappear as the local sprouting response begins. Thus it seems that neurons retain the capacity to form paraterminal fiber branches, terminals, and spines well into adulthood. These effects are not unique to the hippocampus; synaptogenesis by intact afferents following partial denervation has been found in several areas of the adult mammalian brain. One must ask then if this capacity for growth plays some function in the normal operation of the mature brain and if so what controls it.

Sotelo and Palay (1971) have made the interesting suggestion that degeneration and sprouting-like phenomena are part of the day-to-day life of the brain. In electron microscopic studies of the vestibular nuclei of the brain stem they found occasional degenerating terminal profiles and structures which appeared to be growth processes. This leads to the idea that synaptic connections may slowly turn over in the central nervous system (CNS) and that residual growth capacity is needed to replace those that are lost. Structural growth in the brain may be required for other purposes as well. A number of experiments have suggested that environmental experiences over a period of weeks results in growth of both dendritic branches and postsynaptic spines (see Greenough, 1976, for a review). This certainly invites the speculation that synaptic growth can be triggered by behavioral events or the hormonal effects attendent to them. More surprising still, recent electron microscopic experiments have provided evidence which indicates that repetitive stimulation of synapses in the hippocampus results in the formation of new synaptic connections and that this is accomplished in a matter of minutes (Lee *et al.*, 1979). If so, this provides yet another possible function for residual growth capacity.

The capacity of fiber systems in the adult to form new contacts raises some intriguing questions regarding the development and maturation of the brain. Specifically should such abilities be viewed as a stable property of the mature nervous system, much as synaptic transmission is, or are they lingering characteristics of immaturity. Put another way, is it possible that some developmental phenomena decline so slowly that they persist (albeit to ever reduced degrees) throughout much of the animal's life? Perhaps maturation, in terms of the growth of fiber systems of the brain, is never truly reached but, instead, should be described as a series of developmental events which take varying times to reach conclusion.

REFERENCES

Aguilar, C. E., Bisby, M. A., Cooper, E., and Diamond, J. (1973). *J. Physiol. (London)* **234**, 449–464.

Banker, G., and Cowan, W. M. (1977). *Brain Res.* **126**, 397–425.

Bayer, S., and Altman, J. (1975). *J. Comp. Neurol.* **163**, 1–20.

Devor, M. (1976). *J. Comp. Neurol.* **166**, 49–72.

Devor, M., and Schneider, G. (1975). *In* "Aspects of Neural Plasticity/Plasticite Nerveus" (F. Vital-Durand and M. Jeannerod, eds.), Vol 43, pp. 191–200. INSERM

Dunn, G. (1971). *J. Comp. Neurol.* **143**, 491–508.

Fricke, R., and Cowan, W. (1977). *J. Comp. Neurol.* **174**, 231–250.

Fricke, R., and Cowan, W. (1978). *J. Comp. Neurol.* **181**, 253–270.

Gall, C., and Lynch, G. (1978). *Brain Res.* **153**, 357–362.

Gall, C., McWilliams, R., and Lynch, G. (1979a). *Brain Res.* **175**, 37–47.

Gall, C., McWilliams, R., and Lynch, G. (1979b) *Anat. Rec.* **193**, 554.

Gall, C., Ishibashi, P., and Lynch, G. (1980a). In preparation.

Gall, C., McWilliams, R., and Lynch, G. (1980b). *J. Comp. Neurol.* (in press).

Gerbrandt, L., Rose, G., Wheeler, R., and Lynch, G. (1978). *Exp. Neurol.* **62**, 122–132.

Gottlieb, D. I., and Cowan, W. M. (1972). *Brain Res.* **41**, 452–456.

Greenough, W. (1976). *In* "Neural Mechanisms of Learning and Memory" (M. Rosenzweig and E. Bennett, eds.), pp. 255–278. MIT Press, Cambridge, Massachusetts.

Hicks, S., and D'Amato, C. (1970). *Exp. Neurol.* **29**, 416–438.

Jansen, J. K. S., Thompson, W., and Kuffler, D. (1978). *In* "Maturation of the Nervous System, Progress in Brain Research" (M. Corner, ed.), Vol. 48, pp. 3–18. Elsevier, Amsterdam.

Laurberg, S., and Hjorth-Simonsen, A. (1977). *Nature (London)* **269**, 158–160.

Lee, K. (1978). *Anat. Rec.* **190**, 457–458.

Lee, K., Stanford, E., Cotman, C., and Lynch, G. (1977). *Exp. Brain Res.* **29**, 475–485.

Lee, K., Oliver, M., Schottler, F., Creager, R., and Lynch, G. (1979). *Exp. Neurol.* **65**, 478–480.

Leonard, C. M. (1974). *J. Comp. Neurol.* **156**, 435–458.

Leong, S. K. (1976). *Exp. Brain Res.* **26**, 235–247.

Leong, S., and Lund, R. (1973). *Brain Res.* **62**, 218–221.

Loy, R., Lynch, G., and Cotman, C. (1977). *Brain Res.* **121**, 229–243.

Lund, R. (1978). "Development and Plasticity of the Brain." Oxford Univ. Press, London and New York.

Lund, R., and Lund, J. (1973). *Exp. Neurol.* **40**, 377–390.

Lund, R., and Lund, J. (1976) *J. Comp. Neurol.* **169**, 133–154.

Lund, R., and Miller, B. (1975). *Brain Res.* **92**, 279–289.

Lund, R., Cunningham, T., and Lund, J. (1973). *Brain Behav. Evol.* **8**, 51–72.

Lynch, G., and Cotman, C. (1975). *In* "The Hippocampus" (R. Issacson and K. Pribram, eds.), pp. 123–155. Plenum, New York.

Lynch, G., Stanfield, B., and Cotman, C. W. (1973). *Brain Res.* **59**, 155–168.

Lynch, G., Gall, C., and Cotman, C. (1977). *Exp. Neurol.* **54**, 179–183.

Matthews, D. A., Cotman, C., and Lynch, G. (1976a). *Brain Res.* **115**, 1–21.

Matthews, D. A., Cotman, C., and Lynch, G. (1976b). *Brain Res,* **115**, 23–41.

Miller, B., and Lund, R. (1975). *Brain Res.* **91**, 119–125.

Mustari, M., and Lund, R. (1976). *Brain Res.* **112**, 37–44.

Parnavalas, J., Lynch, G., Brecha, U., Cotman, C. W., and Globus, A. (1974). *Nature (London)* **248**, 71–73.

Privat, A. (1975). In "Advances in Neurology, Physiology and Pathology of Dendrites" (G. Kreutzberg, ed.), Vol. 12, pp. 201–216. Raven, New York.
Rakic, P. (1976). Nature (London) 261, 467–471.
Schneider, G. E. (1973). Brain Behav. Evol. 8, 73–109.
Schoenfeld, T., Street, C. and Leonard, C. M. (1979). Neuroscience 5, 177 (Abstr.).
So, K.-F., and Schneider, G. E. (1976). Anat. Rec. 184, 535–536.
Sotelo, C., and Palay, S. (1971). Lab. Invest. 25, 653–672.
Zimmer, J. (1973a). Brain Res. 64, 293–311.
Zimmer, J. (1973b). Brain Res. 64, 313–326.

CHAPTER 7

MOTONEURON HISTOGENESIS AND THE DEVELOPMENT OF LIMB INNERVATION

Margaret Hollyday

DEPARTMENT OF PHARMACOLOGICAL AND PHYSIOLOGICAL SCIENCES
THE UNIVERSITY OF CHICAGO
CHICAGO, ILLINOIS

I. Introduction 181
II. Spinal Motoneurons and the Muscles of the Limbs 182
   A. Anatomical Organization of the Motor Pools of the Lateral
      Motor Column 182
   B. Muscle Precursor Position Represented in the Adult
      Motor Pool Map 184
   C. Functional Organization of the Motor Pools of the Lateral
      Motor Columns 188
III. Development of the Lateral Motor Column 189
   A. Regional Differentiation of Spinal Segments 189
   B. Motoneuron Production and the Control of Cell Numbers 190
   C. Cell Death and the Control of Neuron Numbers 192
IV. Development of Limb Innervation 194
   A. Motor Axons Grow into Undifferentiated Limb Buds 195
   B. Specificity of Initial Innervation in Normal Embryos 197
V. Experimental Manipulations of Developing Limb Innervation 200
   A. Rotations of Limb Axes 201
   B. Manipulations of Motor Pool or Target Size.................. 203
VI. Developmental Mechanisms to Account for
   Experimental Observations 209
   References 212

I. Introduction

Since the pioneering studies of Sherrington (1892) it has been known that each muscle of the limb receives innervation from specific segments of the spinal cord. The developmental mechanisms responsible for the establishment of specific patterns of connections between nerves and muscles have remained elusive although this problem has received considerable experimental attention since the early 1900s. In many systems there is evidence suggesting that outgrowing axons can recognize their appropriate targets (Harrison, 1935; Sperry, 1951, 1965; Sperry and Arora, 1965). However, experimental manipulations of the source of limb muscle innervation have failed to show strict

CURRENT TOPICS IN
DEVELOPMENTAL BIOLOGY, Vol. 15

selectivity (Sperry, 1945 review; Bernstein and Guth, 1961; Mark, 1969 review; Grimm, 1971).

Does the inability to demonstrate an exclusive recognition of motoneurons for target muscles mean that nonselective developmental mechanisms such as timed outgrowth, mechanical guidance, and the exclusion of late-arriving fibers are sufficient to account for the normal stereotyped pattern of limb innervation? The thesis of this article is that the answer is "no." Recent experiments have shown that certain motoneurons *do* selectively innervate particular groups of limb muscles after the normal relationships between nerves and muscles have been perturbed in the embryo. And, as I will argue, the rules describing the resulting patterns of connections cannot be fully explained without attributing to the motor axons, at the minimum, an ability to discriminate between dorsal and ventral embryonic muscle mass tissue in the limb bud.

In Section II of this chapter I will describe the anatomical organization of the motor pools supplying limb muscles and show how this organization can be viewed as a continuous representation of the position of the muscle precursors within the developing limb bud. I will then discuss the development of limb innervation at two levels of precision. The first will treat the entire lateral motor column as a unit considering the control of cell numbers by proliferation and cell death, and also the parallel early development of the lateral motor column and the limb bud. Then I will consider the problem of how specific patterns of connections are formed between the clusters of motoneurons that make up the lateral motor columns and the limb muscles. This will include consideration of both normal development and experimental perturbations of the normal relationships between motor pools and muscle. A major issue is the possible relationship between pattern formation and cell death. Finally, I will attempt to synthesize our current knowledge about the development of limb innervation and propose a theory to account for the experimental observations. I will deal with the development of limb innervation in several species, but will concentrate on the chick embryo because more detailed information is currently available about the chick than about other species.

II. Spinal Motoneurons and the Muscles of the Limbs

A. ANATOMICAL ORGANIZATION OF THE MOTOR POOLS OF THE LATERAL MOTOR COLUMN

All of the motoneurons which innervate the limb muscles are located within the lateral motor columns (l.m.c.) in the spinal cord. The population of motoneurons innervating a given muscle comprises the motor pool for that muscle. A description of the normal relationships between motor pool position and the position of the muscles of the limbs is a necessary introduction to the analysis of the ways in which the normal pattern of connections becomes established during embryogenesis.

The relatively recent introduction of horseradish peroxidase (HRP) as a neuronal tracer has made possible a more detailed analysis of patterns of connections between motoneurons and muscles than tracing techniques based on retrograde neuronal degeneration had previously allowed. When HRP is injected into a muscle, the enzyme can be picked up by the axons and transported retrogradely to the motoneuron soma in the spinal cord where it can be made visible following an appropriate histochemical reaction (Kristenssen, 1975). A careful application of HRP tracing methods can be used to map the position and extent of the motor pool for individual muscles.

In species where motor pool maps have been obtained using both anatomical tracing and electrophysiological methods, the data are in essential agreement. These include the frog, *Rana catesbiana* (Cruce, 1974), chick (Landmesser and Morris, 1975; Landmesser, 1978a; Hollyday, 1980a), and cat (Romanes, 1951; Swett *et al.*, 1970; Burke *et al.*, 1977). Motor pool maps for *Ambystoma* (Székely and Czéh, 1967), *Xenopus laevis* (Lamb, 1976), and human (Sharrard, 1955) based on a single method have also been reported. In all animals, a majority of motoneurons belonging to a given motor pool tend to be situated close to one another, although in amphibians neurons belonging to different motor pools tend to be more intermingled than in birds and mammals.

In birds and mammals, the l.m.c.s are composed of histologically distinct groups or clusters of motoneurons (Huber, 1936; Sprague, 1948; Romanes, 1942, 1951, 1964; Sharrard, 1955; Hollyday, 1980a). The number of clusters identifiable in a transverse section through the l.m.c. varies depending on the species and on the spinal cord segment, but typically ranges from 3 to 10 clusters per section. Serial reconstruction of the clusters along the entire length of the l.m.c. reveals that these groups of cells are longitudinally oriented columns of motoneurons of various lengths, shapes, and relative positions to neighboring columns (Romanes, 1951; Sharrard, 1955). The topographical relationships of the motoneuron clusters to each other at the various rostrocaudal and mediolateral positions within the l.m.c. are quite constant between different animals of the same species. Experimental determination of the positions of various motor pools indicates that a muscle's motor pool is always found in the same neuron cluster within the l.m.c. Thus, the position of a motoneuron cluster can be used to identify and name particular motor pools. This clearly holds for birds and mammals; however, it should be noted that in amphibians, motor pool identification based on motoneuron position criteria alone is probably not reliable except perhaps for the rostral, caudal, medial, and lateral extremes of the l.m.c. There is significant segmental overlap of the motor pools and there are no intrinsic cell groupings within the l.m.c. in these species.

The significance of the cytoarchitectural differentiation of the l.m.c. into neuron clusters is not entirely clear. The motoneurons comprising a given motor pool are all located within one motoneuron cluster, but a given cluster can be made up of the motor pools for several (closely related) muscles (Romanes, 1964; Burke *et al.*, 1977; Hollyday, 1980a). Certain clusters appear to be more tightly organized and separated from their neighbor clusters than others. These well-circumscribed clusters tend to supply one muscle exclusively. Other more loosely organized clusters tend to comprise the somewhat intermingled motor pools for several muscles. In the cat and chick, all of the motoneurons of a single cluster tend to have their major dendritic branches oriented similarly (Sprague and Ha, 1964; Hollyday, unpublished), while dendrites of motoneurons in other clusters are oriented in different directions. Motoneuron clusters in different segments of the l.m.c. but in similar mediolateral/dorsoventral positions tend to have similarly oriented dendrites in the transverse phase.

B. MUSCLE PRECURSOR POSITION REPRESENTED IN THE ADULT MOTOR POOL MAP

Investigators have long sought an explanation for the arrangement of the motor pools within the lateral motor columns. Unlike the mammalian motor cortex and many of the primary sensory systems, there have been no descriptions of a somatotopic representation of the limb muscles within the motor pools of the l.m.c. A few generalizations which relate certain features of the motor pool map to either the position or the function of the muscle in the adult limb have been described (Romanes, 1964 review), however no unifying scheme to explain the overall anatomical organization of the motor pools has previously been suggested. This inability to see somatotopic representation of the limb muscles in the l.m.c. stemmed in part from the unavailability of detailed motor pool maps and from the focus on the arrangement of the adult limb muscles. A somatotopic representation of the limb muscles can be detected if the analysis is based on the position of the embryonic precursors of the muscles within the dorsal and ventral premuscle masses.

All vertebrate limbs develop from limb buds which are initially composed of a morphologically homogeneous mass of mesenchyme. The initial stages of limb differentiation involve the condensation of a central precartilagenous mass flanked on either side by a dorsal and a ventral premuscle mass. The central precartilage forms the skeletal elements while the dorsal and ventral premuscle masses subsequently subdivide and separate into individual limb muscles (Romer, 1927, 1964; Wortham, 1948; Sullivan, 1962; Shellswell and Wolpert, 1977). The most detailed descriptions of limb muscle morphogenesis have been made in the chick embryo; however, the studies of Romer have shown this general pattern in other vertebrate embryos.

One recently proposed simplifying principle to explain the position of a given motor pool in the l.m.c. relates the mediolateral position of a motor pool in the l.m.c. to the embryonic origin of the muscle (Cruce, 1974; Landmesser, 1978a; Hollyday, 1978). Limb muscles derived from the embryonic ventral mass are innervated by medially located motor pools; muscles derived from embryonic dorsal muscle mass are innervated by motor pools in more lateral positions. This simplifying principle can be successfully applied to the limb motor pool maps for a number of vertebrate species (see Fig. 1).

In addition, our recent analysis of the map of the motor pools sup-

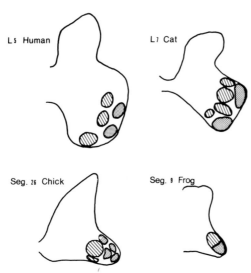

FIG. 1. Outlines of spinal cord gray matter in four species showing the relationship of motoneuron pool position to the embryonic origin of the limb muscles. Medially positioned motor pools supply muscles derived from the ventral muscle mass. Laterally positioned motor pools supply muscles derived from the dorsal muscle mass.

Human motor pool data taken from Sharrard (1955). Cat motor pool data from Romanes (1951). Chick motor pool data from Hollyday (1980a). Frog data from Cruce (1974) and Lamb (1976).

plying chick leg muscles suggests a second general principle of motor pool organization: muscles derived from neighboring positions within each of the two separate sheets of primary embryonic muscle mass are innervated by adjacent motor pools. For any given muscle, the position of its motor pool is best explained by the position of its embryonic precursor and not its position within the adult limb. Although most muscles maintain the same relative positions with their neighbors as their precursors, a few muscles undergo translocations during limb muscle morphogenesis. The motor pools supplying muscles which acquire new neighbor relations are adjacent to motor pools supplying their original neighbors and not neighboring muscles in the adult limb. This conclusion is based on a comparison of Romer's (1927) description of chick leg morphogenesis with a detailed map of motor pool position for muscles in the hatched chick (Hollyday, 1980a).

The generalization that adjacent motor pools innervate muscles derived from adjacent precursors holds only for pairs of muscles sharing a common origin from either dorsal or ventral muscle mass. This is because the motor pool representation of the proximodistal axes of each muscle mass sheet has been somewhat distorted by folding and stretching, and the motor pool representation of each muscle mass is not perfectly aligned with the other. This second type of motor pool discontinuity is fundamentally different from discontinuities produced by translocations of originally adjacent muscle mass tissue and has important implications for the developmental mechanisms of limb innervation.

In order to test the general applicability of these two general principles of motor pool organization, it will be necessary to obtain more detailed motor pool maps and descriptions of limb muscle morphogenesis in other species. However, we know already that the relationship between motor pool position and the origin of the muscle from either of the two embryonic muscle masses is the same for all species of higher vertebrates studied so far. Only the motor pool map for the limb muscles of *Ambystoma* based on electrophysiological stimulation experiments (Székely and Czéh, 1967) seems to be an exception to the general rule which relates motor pool position to the embryonic origin of the muscles. It would be interesting if the organization of the motor pools in urodele amphibians differed from anurans and the higher vertebrate classes. Alternatively, a reinvestigation of the motor pools in *Ambystoma* using an anatomical tracing technique might reveal the same pattern of organization as described for other vertebrate species.

It also seems most likely that the chick is not a unique example of the second principle. Future studies of motor pool organization in other

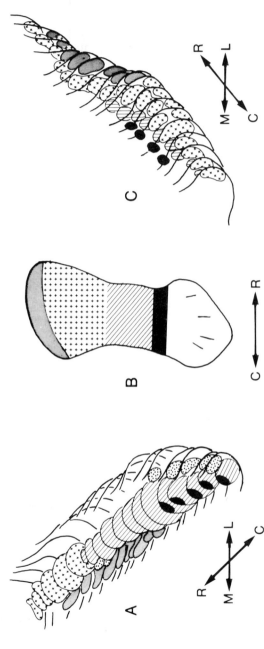

FIG. 2. The relationship of adult motor pool position to embryonic muscle precursor position. (A and C) Reconstructions of a right l.m.c. showing motor pools supplying leg muscles derived from the ventral (A) and dorsal (C) sheets of embryonic muscle mass, respectively. Part (A) is drawn as viewed from the medial aspect; (C) is drawn as viewed from the lateral aspect; (B) shows an outline of a stage-28 chick leg bud. The various presumptive regions for hip (stippling), thigh (crosses), calf (diagonal lines), and intrinsic foot muscles (black) are indicated. The corresponding motor pools supplying muscles derived from each of these four limb regions are shown in (A) and (C). The adult motor pool map can be viewed as being composed of two maps, each of which is a continuous, though distorted, representation of muscle precursor position on one sheet of embryonic muscle mass. It should be noted that the effect of these distortions is to produce several places where motor pools for neighboring muscles in the limb bud are discontinuous. These discontinuities occur at boundaries between dorsal and ventral mass motor pools and rule out the possibility that the motor pool map is a continuous representation of the entire limb bud. R, Rostral; C, caudal; M, medial; L, lateral. From Hollyday (1980a).

species may demonstrate that muscles derived from neighboring positions within the embryonic dorsal and ventral muscle mass receive innervation from adjacent motor pools.

C. FUNCTIONAL ORGANIZATION OF THE MOTOR POOLS OF THE LATERAL MOTOR COLUMNS

Some previous investigators have suggested that certain aspects of the anatomical organization of the motor pools can be best explained by functional relationships rather than by spatial relationships to the limb muscles (Romanes, 1964; Székely and Czéh, 1967). Other investigators have pointed out the general inability of functional considerations to describe the anatomical organization of the motor pools (Cruce, 1974; Landmesser, 1978a). Our own electromicrographic studies of walking in the hatched chick suggest that there is a longitudinal functional organization of the motor pools as defined by activity recorded during three distinct behavioral phases of the step cycle: swing-flexion, swing-extension, and stance. The perikarya of cells which innervate stance muscles lie in two major regions: a large medial cluster and a smaller dorsolateral cluster. The perikarya of cells innervating swing muscles are in motor nuclei which lie between the two stance clusters. In addition, every segment of the lumbosacral cord has motor pools innervating stance muscles and motor pools innervating swing muscles. Thus, muscles that are coactive during the step cycle have motor pools in similar topologic positions along the rostrocaudal extent of the l.m.c. (R. Jacobson, 1979). A similar analysis of the available data for the cat using Romanes' (1951) motor pool map and the muscle activity data from Engberg and Lundberg (1969) and Rasmussen *et al.* (1978) suggests that this is also true for the cat.

As pointed out previously, motoneurons within a single cluster tend to have similarly oriented dendrites, whose orientation differs from neighboring clusters (Sprague and Ha, 1964). In addition, motoneuron clusters in different segments of the l.m.c. but in similar mediolateral/ dorsoventral positions tend to have similarly oriented dendrites. Some regions of dendritic overlap between adjacent motor nuclei are also present but other dendrites are in unique positions. Longitudinally oriented motoneuron dendrites and dendrite bundles have also been described (Sterling and Knypers, 1967; Scheibel and Scheibel, 1970). In this way, different motor pools composed of neurons whose dendrites are in homologous positions within the l.m.c. might be expected to receive common presynaptic inputs. The functional organization of the motor pools might depend more on the morphology of the dendritic arborizations of the various motoneuron clusters than on motoneuron position within the l.m.c. per se.

One of the challenges for future investigations is to understand how a motor pool map which seems most easily explained in terms of muscle primordia position within the limb bud is also organized to produce a behaviorally meaningful motor output.

III. Development of the Lateral Motor Column

A. REGIONAL DIFFERENTIATION OF SPINAL SEGMENTS

Different spinal cord segments normally innervate different sets of muscles. Only certain spinal segments have motoneurons grouped together to form the lateral motor columns which supply the limbs. A pair of l.m.c.s is present in each limb-supplying spinal segment, one for each limb. The axial body musculature is supplied by a ventral, more medial column of neurons, the median motor column (m.m.c.) found primarily in thoracic and cervical spinal segments.

Whether or not a l.m.c. is formed in a given segment of the spinal cord seems to depend on developmental events occurring during gastrulation. In both birds and amphibians, determination of the anterior–posterior neural axis and the regionalization of the spinal cord segments takes place between primary neural induction which accompanies gastrulation and the closure of the neural folds (Spemann, 1938; Spratt, 1952), before any motoneurons complete their terminal DNA synthesis and leave the mitotic cycle. Technical difficulties in performing experimental manipulations of the neural plate have limited the ability to determine more precisely the time course of regional determination.

Wenger (1951) has shown that at the time of neural tube closure, the ability of the various spinal segments to form either medial or lateral motor columns has been determined. In addition, the limb-moving capabilities of the presumptive limb segments have also been determined (Straznicky, 1963; Narayanan and Hamburger, 1971). This has been demonstrated by transplantation of neural tube from various presumptive spinal cord regions into other presumptive regions of the spinal cord. In the chick, lateral motor columns are formed only in segments taken from presumptive limb regions; they are formed even when grafted into presumptive thoracic or cervical regions (Wenger, 1951). Likewise, only medial motor columns are formed in segments taken from presumptive thoracic or cervical regions when they are grafted into limb (brachial) regions. Limbs receiving innervation from

spinal segments with only a medial motor column fail to develop normal movements and the limb musculature gradually atrophies
(Székely and Szentágothai, 1962; Straznicky, 1967; Hollyday and
Mendell, 1975; Morris, 1978). Limbs receiving innervation from segments with a lateral motor column develop movements; the nature of
these movements is determined by the spinal segments supplying the
limbs. If brachial (wing) segments are grafted so that they innervate
the legs, the legs move synchronously as in wing-flapping (Narayanan
and Hamburger, 1971). Wings supplied by lumbar spinal segments
move in alternation as in stepping (Straznicky, 1963).

   These observations and experimental results suggest that certain
regions of the ventricular epithelium produce a unique population of
motor cells destined to innervate muscles of the limbs and form the
lateral motor columns. The production of the spinal interneurons capable of generating patterns of limb movements may also be restricted to
certain spinal segments.

B. MOTONEURON PRODUCTION AND THE CONTROL OF CELL NUMBERS

   Motoneurons are among the first neurons formed in the spinal cord.
This has been known since the first descriptions of spinal cord development by Cajal (1890, 1929) and Tello (1922). More recent studies of
regional mitotic indices (Hamburger, 1948; Corliss and Robertson,
1963) and [³H]thymidine antoradiography (Fujita, 1964; Langman and
Haden, 1970; Prestige, 1973; Nornes and Das, 1974; Hollyday and
Hamburger, 1977; Nornes and Carry, 1978) give the same picture.
Motoneurons are derived from cells of the ventral ventricular
epithelium. After leaving the mitotic cycle they migrate laterally to
settle in the ventral mantle layer. There are differences in the birthdates or time of origin of different motoneurons within the spinal cord.
A rostral-to-caudal sequence of motoneuron birthdates has been described for *Xenopus* (Prestige, 1973), the rat (Nornes and Das, 1974),
and the chick (Hollyday and Hamburger, 1977). Some motoneurons in
cervical and brachial spinal segments are born before any in thoracic
and lumbar segments have left the mitotic cycle although there is
substantial overlap of the periods of motoneuron proliferation between
the various regions of the spinal cord.

   After motoneurons leave the mitotic cycle, they migrate away from
the ventricular epithelium to settle in a ventrolateral position in the
intermediate zone. In the chick, a continuous morphologically homogeneous primary motor column is formed throughout the entire length of
the spinal cord (Levi-Montalcini, 1950). The migration and peripheral

settling pattern of motoneurons of the lateral motor columns follows an inside-out or medial-to-lateral assembly order (Prestige, 1973; Nornes and Das, 1974; Hollyday and Hamburger, 1977). It is not known whether the entire embryonic motor column is formed in a medial-to-lateral sequence, or whether this assembly pattern is specific for the lateral motor columns.

The number of motoneurons generated for the l.m.c.s is relatively fixed among individuals of a given species and is not affected by either limb bud addition or removal (Prestige, 1970; Hamburger, 1975; Hollyday and Hamburger, 1976; Oppenheim and Willard-Majors, 1978). The factors that control the numbers of neurons produced for the l.m.c. are not known but one might speculate that the ventricular epithelium is a mosaic of cells whose progeny are already determined to form a limited number of cell types. Some of the germinal cells may be committed to producing only neurons for the l.m.c. This population might first increase its own cell number with replicating mitoses and then produce l.m.c. neuroblasts. The timing of the terminal mitoses must also be carefully programmed because we know that not only is the total number of neurons produced quite constant, but the stage when particular populations of neurons within the l.m.c. leave the cell cycle is also fixed (Hollyday and Hamburger, 1977).

Following the assembly of the primary embryonic motor columns, further shaping of the motor columns in the limb and nonlimb innervating segments takes place through secondary neuron migration and selective cell death. These events have been described in most detail for the chick (Levi-Montalcini, 1950). In the cervical (neck) segments, the loss of a substantial proportion of the original population via cell death produces a small median motor column. In the thoracic segments, the primary column is also reduced in cell number, but, in these segments, neurons undergo a secondary migration to form the visceral preganglionic column of Terni. As in the cervical segments, the number of neurons generated for the l.m.c.s of the brachial and lumbar segments is greater than the number of motoneurons which innervate the limbs in the adult. The number of neurons which die in the cervical spinal segments has not been quantified, but the impression one gathers from Levi-Montalcini's descriptions is that this loss is greater than that occurring among neurons of the l.m.c. In the chick, the naturally occurring cell death of cervical motoneurons seems to have a clear morphogenetic explanation—the amount of cervical axial musculature to be innervated is relatively small. A similar explanation for the normal cell loss of l.m.c. neurons is not intuitively obvious.

C. CELL DEATH AND THE CONTROL OF NEURON NUMBERS

We now know that there is an overproduction of neurons in the motor columns of the spinal cord (Hughes, 1968; Hamburger, 1975), in the spinal ganglia (Hamburger and Levi-Montalcini, 1949; Prestige, 1967, 1970), and in most other neuronal populations whose development has been carefully studied (see Cowan, 1973). The amount of cell death among motoneurons has been estimated to range from 40 to 75% during normal development.

Motoneuron death in response to peripheral injury or limb amputation was known long before it was generally recognized that cell death is common among embryonic neuronal populations (Glucksmann, 1951). Amputation of a limb bud in the embryo produces extensive degeneration of the l.m.c. neurons (Shorey, 1909; Hamburger, 1934, 1958). It is now known that injury-induced motoneuron loss occurs at approximately the time as the normal cell death (Prestige, 1967; Hughes, 1968; Fortune and Blackler, 1976; Oppenheim et al., 1978). As mentioned previously, the initial formation of a numerically complete l.m.c. does not depend on the presence of a limb bud. Motoneuron differentiation including the initiation of axon outgrowth, development of dendritic processes which form morphologically recognizable synapses, and synthesis of certain enzymes involved in acetylcholine metabolism can also be accomplished in the absence of their normal synaptic targets, the limb muscles. Motoneuron survival past a certain critical stage in the embryo does depend however on the presence of a limb.

One of the general principles of neuronal development is that the size of a neuronal center depends on the size of its peripheral innervation field (Twitty, 1932; Detwiler, 1936 review; Hamburger and Levi-Montalcini, 1949; Hamburger, 1958; Cowan and Wenger, 1967; Hughes, 1968 review; Prestige, 1970). This generalization is easily demonstrated for the case of limb innervation; total limb bud amputation results in the death of all neurons in the l.m.c. whereas partial removal results in neuron loss proportional to the amount of limb tissue removed (Hamburger, 1958; Prestige, 1967). Enlargement of the peripheral innervation field by the surgical addition of a supernumerary limb reduces the number of neurons lost at the time of normal cell death, although it does not eliminate it entirely (Hollyday and Hamburger, 1976).

It is interesting to note that a typical l.m.c. is formed in the embryo of *Anguis fragilis*, a limbless lizard (Raynaud et al., 1977). These motoneurons subsequently degenerate and disappear entirely, presumably because no limbs are ever formed for them to contact. In this species then, the ventricular epithelium has not lost its ability to produce a l.m.c.; the presumptive limb motoneurons simply degenerate during later development. Perhaps evolutionary selective pressure on the control of cell production is less than on the final match between neuron number and target size. However, the ability to generate a l.m.c. has not been conserved by all vertebrate classes; the true snakes (e.g., *Python* and *Tropidonotus*) never produce a l.m.c. in the region of their rudimentary limb girdles.

These observations are consistent with the idea that in normal development, cell death may be involved in matching the size of the innervating population to the size of the limb muscles, whatever the mechanism for cell death per se. We have seen that the number of l.m.c. neurons initially generated is fixed and is unaffected by peripheral manipulations. The later sensitivity of the motoneurons to the presence or absence of peripheral tissue suggests that there may also be a two-step process for matching the size of the motor pool to the size of the muscle. If cell death is the second step of a two-step process for assuring an exact match between neuron number and target size, then one might expect to find greater or lesser numbers of degenerating neurons in different motor pools related to the ultimate size of the adult muscle or to the size of the motor units within a muscle. Hamburger (1975) reported that greater numbers of neurons degenerated at both the rostral and caudal ends of the l.m.c., but did not otherwise notice any selective distribution of dying cells in other regions of the l.m.c. Now that information is available concerning the location of motor pools for individual muscles, a reexamination of the distribution of cell deaths might reveal consistent differences between motor pools. Such differences could possibly suggest why certain neurons survive and why others die. It should be noted, however, that if neuron survival depended *entirely* on the amount of muscle tissue available, then one might expect more than the observed 10 to 25% increased cell survival when the peripheral innervation field was enlarged by grafting a supernumerary limb (Hollyday and Hamburger, 1976). This limited increased survival suggests that factors in addition to size matching play a role in the control of cell death.

A second suggested role for cell death was that it might account for the elimination of polyneuronal innervation of embryonic muscle fibers (Bennett and Pettigrew, 1974). However, we now know that the time course of motoneuron degeneration and the withdrawal of axons from multiply innervated muscle fibers does not overlap (Hamburger, 1975; Harris-Flannagan, 1969; Brown *et al.*, 1976; Oppenheim and Majors-Willard, 1978). The major period of motoneuron death accompanies the original formation of synaptic connections and is essentially completed at the time when multiple innervation is lost. A third possible role for cell death is that it participates in forming the final pattern between motoneurons and muscles by eliminating projection errors. This possibility will be considered in Section IV.

The relationship between the size of the periphery and the number of neurons which innervate it has suggested to many investigators that some aspect of the peripheral tissue regulates cell death (Hughes, 1968; Prestige, 1970, 1978; Cowan, 1973; Landmesser and Pilar, 1974, 1976; Hamburger, 1975). Whether this involves competition among motor axons for a limited number of synaptic sites (Guillery, 1972; Cowan, 1973; Hamburger, 1975) or for a maintenance factor (Prestige, 1967, 1970), and the degeneration of neurons which either fail to make or receive the appropriate synaptic connections (Cowan, 1973; Clarke and Cowan, 1976; Lamb, 1976, 1977) is unclear. Except for our desire for simplicity, there is no reason to require that all naturally occurring neuron deaths be attributable to the same cause.

Recent experiments (Pittman and Oppenheim, 1978; Laing and Prestige, 1978; Olek and Edwards, 1978) demonstrating the prevention of *all* cell death when the embryo is treated with a variety of neuromuscular blocking agents suggest that functional synapses are required for the expression of cell death. Contrary to expectation (cf. Changeaux and Danchin, 1976), preventing activity at the neuromuscular junction with both presynaptic and postsynaptic blocking agents did not cause all of the neurons to die as did limb removal, rather none of the cells died. The role of synaptic activity or transmitter release for the expression of cell death is not yet understood, but should stimulate further investigations into the role of activity in the formation and maintenance of neuronal connections.

IV. Development of Limb Innervation

One of the basic questions about the development of limb innervation is whether the initial projection patterns of motoneurons to the limb bud is highly specific and adult-like, or whether it is initially unordered and requires extensive modification. The latter might be accomplished by the natural cell death known to occur during synaptogenesis. As will become clear in the discussion that follows, the limb bud is relatively undifferentiated when motor axons first grow into it. Only the dorsal and ventral premuscle masses have formed, separated by the central condensation of precartilage. It is therefore inappropriate to ask whether axons grow specifically to a particular target muscle. One can only ask whether axons grow to specific regions of the muscle masses which are known to separate later into particular adult muscles.

A. MOTOR AXONS GROW INTO UNDIFFERENTIATED LIMB BUDS

Motor axons leave the neural tube and grow toward the limb bud at very early stages, probably shortly after the neuron has completed its terminal mitosis. The relationship of axon outgrowth to neuronal migration is not entirely clear. Most neurons with an axon in the ventral root are located peripherally in the marginal zone. However, a few neurons have been observed in the intermediate zone having a central process extending to the ventricular epithelium and having an axon which could be traced into the ventral root (Cajal, 1929; Barron, 1943). These neurons are presumed to be in the process of migrating. While this does not seem to be the typical pattern, these observations have been confirmed in our laboratory for rat thoracic motoneurons (Grobstein, 1979) and chick lumbar motoneurons (M. Hollyday, unpublished). Heaton et al. (1978) have reported a similar finding for trigeminal motoneuroblasts indicating that migrating motoneurons can have an axon in peripheral tissue.

The possibility that neuron migration and axon outgrowth are not necessarily independent developmental events suggests that the initial formation of the l.m.c. following peripheral manipulations should be reinvestigated using autoradiographic techniques. It has always been assumed that because the number of neurons produced was not affected by limb bud addition or removal, the l.m.c.s are normal in every respect. In light of our current assertion that motoneuron position within the l.m.c. can be used to name motoneuron pools, the possibility that the patterns of neuronal migration are altered by peripheral manipulations should be carefully reinvestigated. If it is found that peripheral manipulations do perturb the normal patterns of neuronal migration, then many of our later conclusions regarding developmental mechanisms will have to be revised.

Motor axons leave the spinal cord via the ventral roots and grow ventrally, medial to the myotomes, to enter the limb adjacent to their segment of origin. Motor axons first enter the limb when the first condensations of the mesenchyme, the dorsal, and ventral premuscle masses on either side of the central core of precartilage are beginning. The exact sequence of events relating the time and order of axon arrival to the separation of the muscles from the embryonic muscle masses has not yet been described in detail, but the differentiation of the limb takes place after some, if not all, of the motor axons have entered the limb (Harrison, 1907; Romer, 1927; Taylor, 1943; Wortham, 1948; Lamb, 1974; Sullivan, 1962; Roncali, 1970; Fouvet, 1973; Hamburger, 1975; Oppenheim and Chu-Wang, 1977; Lance Jones and Landmesser, 1979; Pettigrew *et al.*, 1979). The obvious possibility that normal limb morphogenesis with respect to muscle separation and skeleton formation depends on innervation has been disproved (Harrison, 1904; Hunt, 1932; Hamburger and Waugh, 1940; Eastlick, 1943; Shellswell, 1977), although it is necessary for maintaining the muscle and promoting its subsequent differentiation (Eastlick and Wortham, 1947; Zelená, 1962).

The growth of the motor axons into the limb bud is neither diffuse nor random. Bundles of axons are found in specific positions, especially along the borders of the central precartilage condensation and the premuscle masses (Harrison, 1907; Hamburger, 1975). The axons subsequently distribute themselves within the muscle masses in patterns which are recognizable as the peripheral nerves of the adult limb (Taylor, 1943; Roncali, 1970; Fouvet, 1973; Lance Jones and Landmesser, 1979). Although the major peripheral limb nerves can be recognized at the time the axons initially grow into the limb bud, their final distribution pattern is formed as the premuscle masses in the limb bud condense and separate to form the muscles of the adult limb. Experiments involving manipulating the source of limb innervation by limb bud transplantation have shown that the peripheral branching pattern and gross distribution of the nerves is determined by the limb itself and not by the segmental source of innervation (Harrison, 1907; Detwiler, 1936; Piatt, 1942). These observations indicate that certain aspects of initial limb innervation are accomplished by relatively nonspecific processes. Nerves adjacent to a limb bud grow into it and are distributed within the premuscle masses in specific patterns. The factors which influence the growth trajectories and the final distribution pattern of the motor axons within the limb bud are unknown although the experiments discussed in the following section suggest that under normal conditions, the majority of the axons grow specifically to particular regions of the premuscle masses.

Examination of the chick embryonic l.m.c. during the time of axon outgrowth but before neuron death reveals that groups of neurons in particular positions already have their major dendritic branches oriented in the same way (Hollyday, unpublished; but see also Cajal, 1929; Barron, 1943; Hamburger, 1958). The adult pattern of motoneuron clusters emerges during the period of natural cell death and appears to be derived from the initial groups of motoneurons within the l.m.c. having similarly oriented dendrites. These observations suggest but in no way prove that there are intrinsic differences between populations of motoneurons at the time of axon outgrowth. The extent to which the differentiation of motoneuron clusters within the l.m.c.s of birds and mammals is dependent on interactions with the muscles or on the formation of central interneuronal or reflex connections remains to be determined.

B. SPECIFICITY OF INITIAL INNERVATION IN NORMAL EMBRYOS

Only a few studies have examined the development of specific innervation of the limb using techniques capable of addressing questions of target and pathway selectivity of subpopulations of motoneurons. Some of the first studies of the period of initial innervation have been done by Lamb (1974, 1976, 1977) who has studied the projection patterns of motoneurons to the developing leg in *Xenopus* using localized limb bud injections of HRP at various development stages (staging according to Nieuwkoop and Faber, 1956). He has mapped the projections of motoneurons into four limb regions beginning at stage 50 (spherical limb bud) and continuing through metamorphosis when the limbs assume their adult structure. At the earliest stages of limb innervation, he found that some motoneurons located in incorrect positions within the l.m.c. projected to the two presumptive thigh regions of the limb bud which he tested. After the period of cell death, HRP injections into each thigh region labeled neurons in the appropriate adult motor pool position exclusively. In contrast, the two foot regions studied showed initial specific projections from the earliest stages when motoneurons could first be labeled with distal injections of HRP (stage 52).

In order to demonstrate the removal of early projection "errors" to the presumptive thigh region by cell death, Lamb injected stage 51 tadpoles and sacrificed them at various subsequent stages. According to the birthdate data for the *Xenopus* l.m.c. (Prestige, 1973), only the medially positioned motoneurons which normally project to the flexor muscle (derived from ventral muscle mass) are born at stage 51. The motoneurons which supply the extensor muscle (derived from the dorsal mass) in the adult are born at stage 52. Injections of the presumptive extensor muscle mesenchyme at stage 51 labeled motoneurons in the l.m.c. of tadpoles at stages 51 through 53. Labeled degenerating cells were found in stage 53 and 54 tadpoles. No labeled cells at all were found in most tadpoles at stages 54 and 55. That the loss of HRP-labeled neurons in older tadpoles was not simply due to degradation of the enzyme in living cells was shown by injections of the posterior and medial thigh region at stage 51; labeled motoneurons were found in the appropriate medial position within the lateral motor column from stages 51 through 55. These data suggest that initially inappropriate motoneuron projections are eliminated by cell death. Although Lamb's evidence supports the idea that projection errors are removed by cell death, the number of motoneurons which die (estimated to be at least 75% in *Xenopus*) during the period of naturally occurring cell death far exceeds the number of misdirected motor axons (see the following).

The available data on the development of motor innervation to the chick limb suggest that some projection errors may also occur during the initial stages of axon outgrowth and be eliminated during cell death. However, as in the frog, the majority of motor axons project to the appropriate region of the specific muscle mass (Landmesser, 1978b; Pettigrew *et al.*, 1979) before the period of natural cell death. As studied with silver stains, motor axons reach the base of the limb bud at stages 23 to 24 (staging according to Hamburger and Hamilton, 1951), reach the level of future knee or elbow by stage 25, and attain a recognizable adult innervation pattern by stage 28 to 29 (Roncali, 1970; Fouvet, 1973; Hamburger, 1975). Roncali (1979) also observed an early (stages 22–24) abnormal contribution to the wing plexus by segments 12 and 17. In the adult, the wing is innervated by segments 13 through 16. By stage 26, these abnormal projections were no longer observed.

A recent study by Pettigrew *et al.* (1979) has used both electrophysiological and HRP tracing methods to study the development of segmental projections to the proximal ventral muscle mass of the chick wing. Of particular interest are their findings concerning the biceps muscle. At all stages studied, the greatest density of HRP reaction product was found in segments 14 and 15. These are the segments which normally innervate the biceps in the adult. However, prior to stages 29–30, the stage when the presumptive biceps separates from the other ventrally derived proximal limb muscles (Sullivan, 1962), these investigators report segmental projection errors. At stage 26, cells in segments 12–17 were labeled following injection of HRP into the presumptive biceps area. At stage 28, labeled cells were found in segments 13–17, and at stage 29 the labeled cells were located in segments 14–16. From stage 31 onward, only motoneurons in segments 14 and 15 were labeled. These investigators also recorded extracellular compound action potentials from what they assumed were motor axons following stimulation of the various segmental nerves. At stage 29, they recorded potentials in the presumptive biceps muscle when nerves 14, 15, and 16 were stimulated. After muscle separation, only nerves 14 and 15 produced contractions of biceps. The reported time course of the progressive reduction in the segmental projection to the biceps corresponds to the period of naturally occurring cell death among brachial motoneurons (Oppenheim and Majors-Willard, 1978). However, this is also the period of biceps muscle separation from the original sheet of muscle mass tissue (Sullivan, 1962). Undetected HRP leakage and widespread electrical coupling between cells within the undivided muscle mass sheets could also account for their findings of transient projection errors. Different experimental techniques will be required to address these possible technical difficulties.

The pattern of segmental projections to the leg muscles of the chick has been studied from stage 28 onward (Landmesser and Morris, 1975; Landmesser, 1978b) when the ingrowth of motor axons to the limb is thought to be completed and when the dorsal and ventral muscle masses of the limb have just begun to subdivide into groups of limb muscle precursors using both electrophysiological and HRP tracing methods. In contrast to the data of Pettigrew *et al.* (1979), Landmesser's data suggest that motoneurons project specifically to particular regions within the embryonic muscle masses by stage 28, which is before the onset of the major period of cell death, during which at least 40% of the motoneurons die (Hamburger, 1975). As in the wing, some small portion of the earliest arriving population may project initially to an incorrect target in the leg bud and be lost before stage 28 thereby remaining undetected in these studies. A few degenerating motoneurons have been reported in lumbar segments as early as stage 26 (Oppenheim and Chu-Wang, 1977) which would be consistent with this possibility. However, no major changes in either the segmental contribution or in the relative position of the motoneurons within the lateral motor column have been observed during the period of maximal cell death, using either anatomical or electrophysiological techniques.

Bekoff's (1976) electromyographic study of leg muscle activity during periods of spontaneous embryonic motility has shown that by stage 31 (7 days) the adult alternating pattern of EMG activity could be recorded from two antagonist calf muscles. These results suggest that the initial pattern of functional *connections,* as well as initial *projections,* to limb muscles is also correct from the beginning.

Although the issue is not entirely resolved, the existing evidence suggests that in normal development the *majority* of motor axons grow initially to the appropriate dorsal or ventral muscle mass of the differentiating limb bud as defined by the position of the motoneuron within the l.m.c. Furthermore, most axons seem to grow to a specific region or subdivision of the muscle masses. If it were possible to define the presumptive target of a motor axon more precisely than a specific region of an embryonic muscle mass, then perhaps one could conclude that cell death served to remove small projection errors and thus be important for fine tuning the specific pattern of limb innervation. However, the current evidence says that most of the cells that die have not made gross projection errors.

One possible explanation for the occurrence of transient projections or "errors" is that they are not errors at all but rather these axons play a necessary role in establishing the final projection pattern. No estimates of the numbers of neurons involved in the transient projections have been published, but inspection of the data indicates that the percentages are small in comparison to the total number of motoneurons which die during normal cell death. It is also not known whether the transient projections are formed exclusively by the earliest arriving fibers although for *Xenopus* this would seem to be the case. These axons might provide pathway guides for later arriving fibers, or they might provide some information or trophic stimulus to the premuscle mass to initiate further muscle development. While Lamb's data from *Xenopus* suggest that the transient projections may be removed by neuron death as opposed to a rearrangement of the peripheral terminals of these axons, there is no evidence in either frog or chick that extensive modification of the projection pattern takes place during the period of cell death.

V. Experimental Manipulations of Developing Limb Innervation

We have seen that in the adult there is an ordered and stereotyped pattern of connections established between clusters of motoneurons and the limb muscles. Furthermore, this pattern can be viewed as a continuous, although distorted, representation of the positions of muscle primordia within each sheet of embryonic muscle mass. However, while descriptions of the normal organization and developmental sequence of neuromuscular connections are important, they cannot demonstrate the developmental mechanisms responsible for establishing those normal patterns. Perturbations of the normal relationships between innervation source and limb muscles are useful for analyzing the involvement of particular developmental mechanisms in the normal innervation process.

Numerous developmental mechanisms have been suggested to account for certain aspects of limb innervation or the formation of specific connections in other developing neuronal systems including mechanical guidance, timed outgrowth, chemoaffinity, and chemotropism. Rather than focusing on mechanisms and selecting data which tend to support or refute particular possibilities, I will review the data we have about the development of limb innervation in embryos whose motor pools or limb muscles or both have been experimentally manipulated in specific ways. In each situation we want to describe the patterns of connections which are formed between motor pools and limb muscles. It may then be possible to generate rules which encompass several sets of experimental results. Descriptive rules about the order and peripheral distribution patterns of identified outgrowing motor axons and the sequence of limb muscle development in experimentally altered situations, as well as the final distribution pattern between motor pools and muscles, should suggest or on the other hand eliminate certain developmental mechanisms.

In the long run, the evidence may indicate that several different or redundant developmental mechanisms are capable of generating the normal pattern of connections between motor pools and muscles, and that certain processes may be detected only under particular circumstances. Although as yet we can only speculate about the existence or relative importance of particular mechanisms, any developmental model of limb innervation should follow the rules which describe the behavior of the developing system under both normal and experimental circumstances.

A. ROTATIONS OF LIMB AXES

One way to examine the relationships between motoneurons and limb muscles is to rotate the limb experimentally about either the anterior–posterior (A-P) or dorsoventral (D-V) axis. Proximodistal inversions, while theoretically interesting, have not been used because such grafts generally do not "take." If the formation of connections between motoneurons and muscles were related to the position of muscles in real space, as opposed to the position of muscles with respect to the intrinsic limb axes, then rotations of the limb about either the anterior–posterior or dorsoventral axes would be expected to reverse the pattern of projections from the motor pools to the limb muscles. If motoneurons form connections with muscles based on some other criteria, then rotations about the limb axes would not be expected to produce rotated maps.

Limb rotations about the dorsoventral axis have been performed by replacing a right limb bud with a left limb bud, keeping the A-P axis fixed (Ferguson, 1978) at stages before motor axons had reached the periphery. Motor pools supplying three calf muscles have been mapped and in each case, the normal motor pool supplied its muscle in the D-V reversed leg. Although muscles derived from the dorsal mass were oriented ventral with respect to the spinal cord and the ventral mass was dorsal in the experimental animals, motoneurons found their normal appropriate target muscle. This is an important result in that it suggests whatever characteristics define dorsal and ventral muscle mass, they are intrinsic properties of the limb and are not defined by the orientation of the limb in real space. Further, it suggests that motoneurons are capable of recognizing these properties.

Is there any evidence to suggest that the anterior–posterior axis of the limb is likewise detected by the outgrowing axons in order to maintain the normal relationships between motor pools and limb muscles? Simple A-P rotations have not yet been reported. However, wing bud rotations of 180° reversing both A-P and D-V axes have been recently performed by Stirling and Summerbell (1979). Unfortunately, these investigators did not examine the innervation of the wing muscles by motor pools. These investigators have made electrophysiological recordings of activity in each of the wing segmental nerves in response to tactile stimulation of the skin. They have also used cobalt chloride to trace the peripheral contributions of each of the segmental nerves forming the brachial plexus of the chick in both normal and wing-rotated embryos. In all cases, they found that the axons from each of the segmental nerves tended to maintain their relative anterior or posterior position in the limb plexus and in their subsequent branchings to form the various peripheral nerves. Although these studies dealt with mixed peripheral nerves, the results are consistent with studies of motor innervation of supernumerary limbs discussed below. Of particular interest is their finding that reversing the anterior–posterior wing axes before axon outgrowth did not result in a compensatory crossing of the axons as they entered the reversed limb. Rostral (anterior) spinal segments entered the originally posterior portion of the rotated wing bud and formed the appropriate posterior portion of the peripheral innervation pattern. Thus, unlike the results obtained from rotations of the limb about its D-V axis, at least certain characteristics of the A-P distribution pattern of the peripheral nerves seem to be determined by the orientation of the limb on the body.

As noted, inversions of entire proximodistal (P-D) axis are not generally experimentally possible; however, other surgical manipulations can test the ability of motor axons to establish patterns of connections in the face of P-D axis perturbations. Duplications or deletions of particular limb segments, the foot, calf, or thigh or the homologous segments of the wing, alter the P-D axis of the limb. Although wings with specific duplications or deletions have been produced experimentally to study pattern formation in the chick (Saunders et al., 1957; Summerbell et al., 1973; Tickle et al., 1975) and the formation of the peripheral nerves (Stirling and Summerbell, 1977), these studies have not yet dealt with the motor innervation of such manipulated limbs.

B. MANIPULATIONS OF MOTOR POOL OR TARGET SIZE

A second general way to test the fixity of the normal pattern of connections between motoneurons and muscles or the ways in which they can be altered is to expand the possible innervation territory of spinal nerves. This can be accomplished in two ways: by grafting an additional limb so that the spinal nerves are divided between two limbs (Hollyday et al., 1977; Morris, 1978; Hollyday, 1978, 1980b) or by removing some of the spinal cord segments and testing the ability of the remaining segments to expand into the territory normally occupied by the deleted motor pools (Lance-Jones and Landmesser, 1978; Lamb, 1979). In each type of experiment, a reduced number of spinal segments is given the opportunity to establish a complete map. If complete and normally ordered maps are formed in each situation, then one could conclude that interactions among the outgrowing axons alone could account for their distribution patterns within the limb. If instead, the maps are incomplete or are rearranged in some consistent way, then one could conclude that interactions between motor axons and limb bud tissue influence the match between motor pools and target muscle. And further, the details of the abnormal maps might indicate something about the nature of the inferred axon–tissue interactions. Different patterns of connections between motor pools and limb muscles have been obtained from these two kinds of experiments. Possible explanations for the differences will be discussed.

1. Supernumerary Limbs

Since the experimenter can control to a large degree the segmental innervation of grafted limbs by placing the limb bud in specific positions on the flank of the embryo, we can compare the normal relationships between muscles and motor pools with those obtained when foreign nerves supply the limb or when a limb receives only a portion of its normal segmental supply. (The reader is reminded that the chick leg is normally supplied by seven or eight spinal segments and that the motor pools for individual muscles rarely extend through as many as four segments.) In the chick, histological reconstruction of the innervation patterns and electrical stimulation of the segmental nerves both show that when a supernumerary limb is grafted close to the limb of a host, the nerves of the limb plexus are divided between them (Hollyday and Hamburger, 1976; Morris, 1978). This experimental situation provides an opportunity to examine the target specificity of motor pools for their particular muscles. One possible outcome is that the neurons of a given motor pool always manage to innervate their own muscles, perhaps because each limb muscle precursor secretes a specific neurotropic agent or a specific motoneuron nerve growth factor. The same muscles in each of the two legs would then be supplied by neurons from the same motoneuron cluster. Individual motoneurons might supply only one of the two target muscles, or they might supply both via axon branching. Another possible result is that the two adjacent limbs are each supplied by separate and complete somatotopically organized groups of motoneuron clusters, with each group of motor pools a reduced duplication of the normal motor map. The data indicate that neither possibility completely describes the relationships between motor clusters and limb muscles in the case of supernumerary limbs. In the initial set of experiments, simultaneous HRP injections of the lateral gastrocnemius muscle in the host and supernumerary leg yielded labeled motoneurons in two places in the lateral motor column, separated by several segments of completely unlabeled neurons (Hollyday *et al.*, 1977). Only one of the two motor pools was in the normal segmental position; the muscle of the supernumerary leg was innervated by foreign motoneurons. Furthermore, in all six cases studied, the foreign motoneurons were consistently located in a particular cluster of neurons within the l.m.c. and not randomly scattered throughout the l.m.c.

Subsequent experiments have mapped the motor pools supplying five different leg muscles in more than 30 embryos with supernumerary legs (Hollyday, 1978, 1980b). The muscles tested include lateral gastrocnemius and flexor hallicus brevis, both derived from the embryonic ventral muscle mass, and femorotibialis, posterior iliotibialis, and peroneus, all derived from dorsal mass. Consistent with the results from earlier studies on manipulated limb innervation, all of the neurons supplying the grafted limb are located in the spinal segments whose ventral roots form the limb's plexus. Of the five individual muscles that were tested, they each received innervations from their normal motor pool if the spinal segments containing that pool gained access to the leg. In most cases, a normal pattern of peripheral nerve distribution to the various limb muscles was formed by the reduced number of innervating segments. However, in some embryos, motor axons even traversed abnormal pathways in the leg to innervate their normal targets. This observation suggests that while motor axons may be capable of recognizing particular pathways within the limb bud, target recognition takes precedence. In addition, for muscles deprived of their normal segmental innervation, *selective mismatching* between motoneurons and muscles was found. In these cases, the muscles were always innervated by neurons whose normal target was derived from the same embryonic muscle mass as the experimental muscle.

Our interpretation of the results is that motoneurons exhibit target selectivity. Their first "choice" is their normal muscle. Motoneurons will express alternative or second choice innervation preferences for muscles if those muscles are deprived of innervation by their normal motor pool. Motoneurons will innervate foreign muscles if those muscles are derived from the same embryonic muscle mass as their normal target muscle.

We had previously suggested that the selective mismatch between motoneurons and one foreign target muscle could be interpreted as an expression of a "hierarchy of chemoaffinities" (Hollyday et al., 1977). The preceding experiments suggest that this hierarchy might be based on a selectivity for either dorsal or ventral muscle mass. The data also indicate that the selectivity of motoneurons for foreign target muscles apparently extends beyond the simple distinction between dorsal and ventral muscle masses. Only certain motor pools of all the possible motor pools which normally supply dorsal mass muscles will innervate a given foreign muscle derived from the dorsal mass. The same has been found for motor pools for ventral mass muscles. An analysis of the rules of this additional selectivity shows that motor pools selectively innervate muscles derived from the same first subdivision of the muscle masses (e.g., superficial vs deep) as the muscles they normally innervate.

If the distribution patterns between motoneurons and muscles were determined exclusively by motoneuron birthdate or the order of axon outgrowth and not by recognition of dorsal or ventral mass tissue, then one should be able to predict the pattern of the mismatching by determining the relative birthdate order of the various motor pools. As described previously, the l.m.c. is formed in an overall medial-to-lateral sequence. However, an analysis of the motor pool birthdates in normal embryos shows that there are some motoneurons born at every stage which supply both dorsal and ventral mass muscles (Hollyday, 1980a). One of the five muscles tested in the supernumerary legs (flexor hallicus brevis) received innervation from a late-born motor pool, one that normally supplies hip retractor muscles derived from the ventral muscle mass. Neurons belonging to a second motor pool, which normally supplies hip protractor muscles (derived from the dorsal muscle mass), undergo their terminal DNA synthesis at the same time as hip retractor motoneurons. Thus, assuming that motoneuron birthdates and

l.m.c. assembly patterns are unchanged by the addition of a supernumerary limb, it is not possible to explain the selective mismatch
between the hip retractor motor pool and flexor hallicus brevis by
motor pool birthdate alone. It seems necessary to attribute to the outgrowing motor axons the ability to discriminate between tissue derived
from either dorsal or ventral muscle mass. The possibility that certain
other features of the mismatch among groups of muscles all derived
from a common embryonic muscle mass could possibly be explained by
a developmental mechanism based on timed axon outgrowth as opposed to a more refined selectivity capability requires further study.

Supernumerary wings have also been grafted next to the leg so that
they receive innervation from lumbar segments. A similar pattern of
mismatching between motoneurons and muscles has been found: wing
muscles derived from the ventral muscle mass receive innervation from
leg motor pools whose normal targets are muscles derived from the
ventral muscle mass; wing muscles derived from the dorsal mass are
innervated from dorsal mass motor pools (Hollyday, 1978, 1980b). To
date, no exceptions in either the leg or wing have been found to the
"rule" that if motoneurons innervate a foreign muscle, that muscle is
derived from the same type of embryonic muscle mass as its normal
target.

The experiments discussed previously deal with the evidence that
suggests motoneurons have the ability to recognize either dorsal or
ventral muscle mass tissue. Certain features of the limb innervation
pattern may be determined by nontarget selective developmental
mechanisms such as timed axon outgrowth or the position of the growing axons as they approach the base of the limb bud. The results obtained from A-P wing rotations (Stirling and Summerbell, 1979), described previously, suggest that the gross distribution pattern of a
segmental nerve is determined by the position of that nerve as it enters
the limb bud. Studies on the motor innvervation of A-P reversed supernumerary limbs have shown that the most rostral lumbar nerve (or
even thoracic nerves) can enter a A-P reversed limb and make functional connections with muscles normally supplied by the most caudal
lumbar segments (Morris, 1978; Hollyday, 1979b). There is no evidence
at present from either simple limb rotations (Ferguson, 1978) or from
rotated additional limbs that motor axons respond to the A-P axis of
the limb and shift their peripheral pathways appropriately to find their
normal target, although in both situations, motoneurons continue to
exhibit a selectivity for either dorsal or ventral muscle mass.

The relative order of the segmental contribution to the limbs' innervation pattern tends to be preserved irrespective of the segments

involved or the orientation of the limb (Morris, 1978; Stirling and Summerbell, 1979). If the segments innervating a supernumerary leg are varied by grafting the leg at different positions on the flank, the branching patterns of the peripheral nerves remain essentially unchanged despite a progressive systematic shift in the segmental innervation to a given muscle (Hollyday, 1980b). This experimentally forced variation of segmental innervation is mirrored by shifts in the location of motoneurons whose axons supply the muscles while preserving the target selectivity for dorsal or ventral muscle mass. These observations suggest that populations of motor axons maintain neighbor relationships with each other during axon outgrowth and that the limb itself is largely responsible for the gross distribution patterns of those axons within the limb.

2. Deletion of a Few Spinal Cord Segments

Surgical removal of a few rostral lumbar spinal cord segments in the young embryo produces an experimental situation theoretically similar to the supernumerary limb experiment: a reduced number of spinal segments is challenged to provide innervation for an entire limb. Early experiments by Castro (1963) involving the removal of a portion of the spinal cord segments normally supplying the chick wing produced specific deletions of the wing nerves normally formed by the extirpated segments. Experiments by Lance Jones and Landmesser (1978) in the chick and by Lamb (1979) in *Xenopus* have shown that muscles normally innervated from the extirpated spinal segments fail to receive innervation from the remaining intact segments. There is no expansion into foreign muscle territories by the nerves which enter the limb and which innervate only their normal target muscles. These observations have been confirmed in our laboratory for the chick (Hollyday, unpublished).

An explanation for the different patterns of connections between motor pools and limb muscles which are found when a reduced number of spinal segments enters a limb in a limb-grafting experiment as opposed to a spinal cord segment deletion experiment might possibly be found in a consideration of the local environmental conditions found in the limb bud by the outgrowing axons. As we have seen, there is no evidence to suggest that motor axons travel any significant distance within the spinal cord before exiting the ventral roots to reach a distant target. Motor axons grow out from the ventral roots and enter the limb tissue closest to it. In the case of the spinal cord segment deletions, one presumes that a portion of the limb bud was not invaded by outgrowing fibers, whereas in the supernumerary grafts, the entire limb

bud was penetrated by outgrowing axons. (The grafted limb is positioned so that it overlaps with the host's limb bud.) These data and the
progressive shifts in motor pool position observed in A-P reversed
supernumerary limbs described previously suggest that nerve fibers
interact with each other and with the tissues they enter in a local and
not in a global way. Once motor axons grow into the limb bud their
growth trajectories and possible target sites become somewhat restricted.

3. Reduction of Innervation Territory

Partial limb bud removal at stages before axon outgrowth to the
limb provides an experimental situation where certain aspects of competition and the role of order of axon outgrowth could potentially be
investigated. Preliminary results have been obtained from experiments on chick embryos whose legs were amputated at the knee (Hollyday, unpublished). This distal deletion was produced by removing the
tip of the limb bud including the apical ectodermal ridge in a stage 20
or 21 embryo (before the entrance of nerve axons into the limb bud). At
12 days (stage 38), individual muscles of the thigh were injected with
HRP. The location of the thigh motor pools was normal in every respect;
they did not extend beyond their usual segmental or mediolateral
boundaries. The motor pools for calf and foot muscles were absent,
presumably lost by cell death. These results suggest that motoneurons
whose normal target is removed do not find an alternative target if the
motoneurons which normally supply the available target are present.
The target-deprived motoneurons die. This might be restated in the
following way: motoneurons can successfully compete with foreign
motoneurons and can exclude them even if the foreign neurons are
target-deprived.

One would like to know if analogous results are obtained if a thigh
deletion experiment is performed where a calf and foot are attached to
the body at the knee. The results from such experiments might indicate
whether target selectivity can be influenced by pathways or by the
order in which axons grow into the limb. As discussed previously, the
order of axon outgrowth is insufficient to account for the observed selectivity of mismatched motoneurons for either dorsal or ventral muscle
mass in all cases. However, since we know that there is a slight gradient
in the rostrocaudal order of birthdates of the motoneurons, it should be
possible to test the hypothesis that the later born motoneurons innervate calf muscle derived from a particular muscle mass instead of the
thigh because certain thigh pathways or terminal sites are occupied by

earlier arriving thigh motoneurons. If thigh motor pools were found to innervate calf and foot muscles when the thigh was deleted, one could conclude that the order of fiber arrival could help establish the normal pattern of connections. If only the normal calf and foot motor pools supplied the limb, then one would conclude that motoneuron-target affinity was a stronger developmental mechanism than another mechanism dependent on sequential fiber outgrowth in the temporal or spatial domain.

VI. Developmental Mechanisms to Account for Experimental Observations

It should be clear to the reader by now that no single developmental mechanism that has been previously proposed appears adequate to explain the complexities of pattern formation involved in limb innervation. Yet sufficient evidence has accumulated to allow one to speculate that certain mechanisms are more prominently involved in establishing the final pattern of connections between motoneurons and limb muscles. The realization that the relationship between motor pools and limb muscles is a continuous map when analyzed at the stage when limb innervation is initially formed, and not an adult map, simplifies our search for developmental mechanisms considerably, since it indicates that within certain limits neighboring motoneurons establish connections with neighboring muscles.

The consistent observation that, irrespective of limb orientation, target size or neuron density motoneurons selectively establish connection with target muscles derived from only one of the two embryonic muscle masses, strongly implies the existence of a developmental mechanism which endows growing axon tips with the capacity to discriminate dorsal and ventral mass tissue. This conclusion depends critically on our ability to recognize and name motor pools in the l.m.c. by their segmental position and spatial relationships to other motoneuron clusters. In experimental situations where this is not possible (for example, when the limb muscles have been perturbed in a way that produces extensive degeneration in the l.m.c.), some other criteria such as [³H]thymidine labeling of birthdates would be necessary to provide an independent identification of the motor pool. Although the pattern of connections formed between motor pools and limb muscles after certain experimental perturbations could possibly be explained by a nonselective ordered outgrowth of axons arriving at sequentially differentiating muscle masses (cf., Horder, 1978), there are also clear examples of a selective mismatching of motor pools and muscles of a supernumerary limb which are inconsistent with a timed outgrowth/contact guidance hypothesis. This conclusion depends, at present, on the assumption that birthdate order accurately reflects the sequence of axon outgrowth.

One developmental mechanism which could possibly explain the selectivity of motoneurons for either dorsal or ventral muscle mass is a specific affinity between certain classes of axon growth cones and the differentiating limb tissues into which they grow and distribute themselves. Sperry (1963) originally suggested that the specific affinity between optic nerve fibers and their target cells in the optic tectum might be based on the presence of specific chemical labels on both cells which could be responsible for the matching between pre- and postsynaptic neurons. If a similar chemoaffinity model can explain limb innervation, the data suggest several points about the nature of the "chemoaffinity labels" on the motoneurons and on the muscles or on their embryonic precursors. First, a single unique label for each muscle and members of its motor pool is not required. Rather, a unique lineage-dependent label could be derived from sets of several "specifiers," perhaps specific membrane proteins, some of which might be shared in common with other muscles derived from the same embryonic muscle mass. One specifier might demarcate dorsal muscle mass, another might indicate ventral muscle mass. A second set of specifiers could be added to delineate the various subdivisions of the muscle masses as they separate to form the various muscles of the adult limb. A label would comprise a unique set of specifiers which ensure the proper match between motoneurons and muscles.

One might imagine that the labels are initially present on the dorsal and ventral premuscle mass tissues at the time the axons enter the limb and that axons would grow selectively into either dorsal or ventral mass tissue. A differential distribution of the specifiers for the various subdivisions of the muscle masses could already be present within the muscle masses which could account for the formation of a recognizable adult innervation pattern before the muscle masses have separated completely into the adult muscles.

The results obtained from limb rotation experiments and partial spinal cord removals indicate that ingrowing axons interact with the labels in their immediate environment and do not sense their A-P position within the limb as a whole although they discriminate dorsal and ventral muscle mass tissue. The axons enter whatever limb tissue is in their path and then perhaps make a series of choices based on the best available match between axon and tissue specifiers. This aspect of a model for limb innervation could account for the results obtained from A-P limb rotations which indicate that axons tend to maintain neighbor relationships and distribute themselves within the limb according to their position when they enter the base of the limb. It could also explain the normal variability found in the limb plexuses of some animals. A slight variability of the position of the limb bud with respect to the limb innervating segments of the spinal cord could be compensated for while preserving the central organization of the motor pools necessary for proper motor function.

A selective developmental mechanism involving a scheme of lineage-dependent labels could also provide the basis for the selective mismatching observed in supernumerary wings and muscles when muscles are deprived of innervation from their normal motor pool. Only particular motoneurons would selectively innervate a foreign muscle because more of their specifiers were similar to those of the target muscle than were the specifiers on other motor axons also growing into the limb bud. A scheme of multiple specifiers constituting a label is also consistent with a model of competition between motor axons and muscles both in normal and manipulated development. In the cases where axons from the normal motor pool grew into the limb bud, they would be able to compete successfully for synaptic sites on their target muscle because their specifier labels were exactly matched with those of the muscle. When axons from the normal motor pool did not enter the limb, then those axons with the best matched set of specifiers would successfully compete for synaptic sites on target muscles.

This aspect of the model is consistent with a mechanistic explanation for the naturally occurring cell death among motoneurons that involves competition among neurons for a limited number of possible synaptic sites that could be based on the degree of matching between pre- and postsynaptic specifier labels. Competition for synaptic sites and the displacement of inappropriate motor axons have been demonstrated in the absence of cell death (Yip and Dennis, 1976; Bennett and Raftos, 1977), but a similar mechanism might also account for some of the fine-tuning of the projection pattern between motoneuron and target muscle at the time of muscle separation and peak cell death.

The teleological explanation for the substantial overproduction of motoneurons and their subsequent loss is not readily apparent since we have evidence that several types of developmental mechanisms may each be capable of establishing a moderately specific pattern of limb innervation. Katz and Lasek (1978) have suggested that this overproduction of neurons could allow for normal evolutionary changes in the size of the target muscle. Another possible evolutionary explanation for excess neuron production and the sensitivity of developing motoneurons to the presence of muscle tissue is that these processes have allowed evolutionary changes in the limb structure to take place more easily.

Perhaps the information encoded in an individual's genome is for a set of developmental mechanisms which can provide for the normal innervation of any limb, and not detailed instructions about the organization of its motor pool map in the adult. Another set of genetic developmental instructions would control the pattern of limb muscle morphogenesis and be responsible for the differentiation of a forelimb or a hindlimb, or a wing and a leg. A read-out of the same developmental program would form different limb-specific motor pool maps within either the brachial or lumbar l.m.c. Changes in limb structure could be accommodated without requiring a corresponding change in the genetic instructions for the motor pool map because the developmental mechanisms would have sufficient flexibility to establish a map that reflected changes in the peripheral structures.

ACKNOWLEDGMENTS

This work was supported by PHS grant #NS-14066 and The Spencer Foundation. I would like to thank Dr. Paul Grobstein, Carolyn Smith Grobstein, Sally Hoskins, and Richard Jacobson for valuable discussions and their critical reading of earlier versions of this manuscript.

REFERENCES

Barron, D. H. (1943). *J. Comp. Neurol.* **78**, 1.
Bekoff, A. (1976). *Brain Res.* **106**, 271.
Bennett, M. R., and Pettigrew, A. G. (1974). *J. Physiol.* **241**, 515.
Bennett, M. R., and Raftos, J. (1977). *J. Physiol.* **265**, 261.
Bernstein, J. J., and Guth, L. (1961). *Exp. Neurol.* **4**, 262.
Brown, M. C., Jansen, J. K. S., and VanEssen, D. (1976). *J. Physiol.* **261**, 387.
Burke, R. E., Strick, P. L., Kanda, K., Kim, C. C., and Walmsley, B. (1977). *J. Neurophysiol.* **40**, 667.
Cajál, S. R. y. (1890). *Anat. Anz.* **5**, 111, 609, 631.
Cajál, S. R. y. (1929). "Études sur la Neurogenèse de quelques Vertébrés." Madrid. (L. Guth, trans.). (1960). "Studies on Vertebrate Neurogenesis." Thomas, Springfield, Illinois.
Castro, G. d. O. (1963). *J. Exp. Zool.* **152**, 279.
Changeaux, J. P., and Danchin, A. (1976). *Nature (London)* **264**, 705.
Clarke, P., and Cowan, W. M. (1976). *J. Comp. Neurol.* **167**, 143.
Corliss, C. E., and Robertson, G. C. (1963). *J. Exp. Zool.* **153**, 125.
Cowan, W. M. (1973). *In* "Development and Aging in the Nervous System" (M. Rockstein, ed.), p. 19. Academic Press, New York.
Cowan, W. M., and Wenger, E. (1967). *J. Exp. Zool.* **164**, 267.
Cruce, W. L. R. (1974). *J. Comp. Neurol.* **153**, 59.
Detwiler, S. R. (1936). "Neuroembryology. An Experimental Study." Macmillan, New York.
Eastlick, H. L. (1943). *J. Exp. Zool.* **93**, 27.
Eastlick, H. L., and Wortham, R. A. (1947). *J. Morphol.* **80**, 369.

Ebbesson, S. O. E. (1976). *In* "Frog Neurobiology" (R. Llinás, ed.), p. 679. Springer-Verlag, Berlin and New York.
Engberg, I., and Lundberg, A. (1969). *Acta Physiol. Scand.* **75,** 614.
Ferguson, B. (1978). *Soc. Neurosci. Abstr.* **4,** 111.
Fortune, J. E., and Blackler, A. W. (1976). *J. Embryol. Exp. Morphol.* **36,** 453.
Fouvet, B. (1973). *Arch. Anat. Microsc. Exp.* **62,** 269.
Fujita, A. (1964). *J. Comp. Neurol.* **122,** 311.
Glücksmann, A. (1951). *Biol. Rev.* **26,** 59.
Grimm, L. M. (1971). *J. Exp. Zool.* **178,** 479.
Grobstein, C. S. (1979). *Soc. Neurosci. Abstr.* **5,** 161.
Guillery, R. W. (1972). *J. Comp. Neurol.* **144,** 117.
Hamburger, V. (1934). *J. Exp. Zool.* **68,** 449.
Hamburger, V. (1939). *J. Exp. Zool.* **80,** 347.
Hamburger, V. (1948). *J. Comp. Neurol.* **88,** 221.
Hamburger, V. (1958). *Am. J. Anat.* **102,** 365.
Hamburger, V. (1975). *J. Comp. Neurol.* **160,** 535.
Hamburger, V., and Hamilton, H. (1951). *J. Morphol.* **88,** 49.
Hamburger, V., and Levi-Montalcini, R. (1949). *J. Exp. Zool.* **111,** 457.
Hamburger, V., and Waugh, M. (1940). *Physiol. Zool.* **13,** 367.
Harris Flanagan, A. E. (1969). *J. Morphol.* **129,** 281.
Harrison, R. G. (1904). *Am. J. Anat.* **5,** 121.
Harrison, R. G. (1907). *J. Exp. Zool.* **4,** 239.
Harrison, R. G. (1935). *Proc. R. Soc. London B* **118,** 155.
Heaton, M. B., Moody, S. A., and Kosier, M. E. (1978). *Neurosci. Lett.* **10,** 55.
Hollyday, M. (1978). *Neurosci. Abstr.* **4,** 115.
Hollyday, M. (1980a). *J. Comp. Neurol.* In Press.
Hollyday, M. (1980b). Submitted.
Hollyday, M., and Hamburger, V. (1976). *J. Comp. Neurol.* **170,** 311.
Hollyday, M., and Hamburger, V. (1977). *Brain Res.* **132,** 197.
Hollyday, M., and Mendell, L. (1975). *J. Comp. Neurol.* **162,** 205.
Hollyday, M., Hamburger, V., and Farris, J. M. G. (1977). *Proc. Natl. Acad. Sci. U.S.A.* **74,** 3582.
Horder, T. J. (1978). *Zoon* **6,** 181.
Huber, J. F. (1936). *J. Comp. Neurol.* **65,** 43.
Hughes, A. F. W. (1968). "Aspects of Neural Ontogeny." Logos, London.
Hunt, E. A. (1932). *J. Exp. Zool.* **62,** 57.
Jacobson, R. D. (1979). *Soc. Neurosci. Abstr.* **5,** 374.
Katz, M. J., and Lasek, R. (1978). *Proc. Natl. Acad. Sci. U.S.A.* **75,** 1349.
Kristensson, K. (1975). *In* "The Use of Axonal Transport for Studies of Neuronal Connectivity" (W. M. Cowan and M. Cuénod, eds.), p. 69. Elsevier, Amsterdam.
Laing, N. G., and Prestige, M. C. (1978). *J. Physiol.* **282,** 33.
Lamb, A. H. (1974). *Brain Res.* **67,** 527.
Lamb, A. H. (1976). *Dev. Biol.* **54,** 82.
Lamb, A. H. (1977). *Brain Res.* **134,** 145.
Lamb, A. H. (1979). *Dev. Biol.* **71,** 8.
Lance Jones, C., and Landmesser, L. (1978). *Soc. Neurosci. Abstr.* **4,** 118.
Lance Jones, C., and Landmesser, L. (1979). *Soc. Neurosci. Abstr.* **5,** 166.
Landmesser, L. (1978a). *J. Physiol.* **284,** 371.
Landmesser, L. (1978b). *J. Physiol.* **284,** 391.
Landmesser, L., and Morris, D. (1975). *J. Physiol.* (*London*) **249,** 301.

Landmesser, L., and Pilar, G. (1974). *J. Physiol. (London)* **241**, 715.
Landmesser, L., and Pilar, G. (1976). *J. Cell Biol.* **68**, 357.
Langman, J., and Haden, C. C. (1970). *J. Comp. Neurol.* **138**, 419.
Levi-Montalcini, R. (1950). *J. Morphol.* **86**, 253.
Mark, R. F. (1969). *Brain Res.* **14**, 245.
Morris, D. G. (1978). *J. Neurophysiol.* **41**, 1450.
Narayanan, C. H., and Hamburger, V. (1971). *J. Exp. Zool.* **178**, 415.
Nieuwkoop, P. D., and Faber, J. (eds.) (1956). "Normal table of *Xenopus laevis* (Daudin): A systematical and chronological survey of the development from the fertilized egg till the end of metamorphosis." North-Holland Publ. Amsterdam.
Nornes, H. O., and Carry, M. (1978). *Brain Res.* **159**, 1.
Nornes, H. O., and Das, G. D. (1974). *Brain Res.* **73**, 121.
Olek, A. J., and Edwards, C. (1978). *Soc. Neurosci. Abstr.* **4**, 122.
Oppenheim, R. W., and Chu-Wang, I.-W. (1977). *Brain Res.* **125**, 154.
Oppenheim, R., and Majors-Willard, C. (1978). *Brain Res.* **154**, 148.
Oppenheim, R., Chu-Wang, I.-W., and Maderdrut, J. (1978). *J. Comp. Neurol.* **177**, 82.
Pettigrew, A., Lindeman, R., and Bennett, M. R. (1979). *J. Embryol. Exp. Morphol.* **49**, 115.
Piatt, J. (1942). *J. Exp. Zool.* **91**, 79.
Pittman, R. H., and Oppenheim, R. W. (1978). *Nature (London)* **271**, 364.
Prestige, M. C. (1967). *J. Embryol. Exp. Morphol.* **18**, 359.
Prestige, M. C. (1970). *In* "The Neurosciences Second Study Program" (F. O. Schmitt, ed.), p. 73. Rockefeller Univ. Press, New York.
Prestige, M. C. (1973). *Brain Res.* **59**, 400.
Rasmussen, S., Chan, A. K., and Goslow, G. E. (1978). *J. Morphol.* **155**, 253.
Raynaud, A., Clairambault, P., Renous, S., and Gasc. J.-P. (1977). *C. R. Acad. Sci. Paris* D **285**, 1507.
Romanes, G. J. (1942). *J. Anat. London* **76**, 112.
Romanes, G. J. (1951). *J. Comp. Neurol.* **94**, 313.
Romanes, G. J. (1964). *Prog. Brain Res.* **11**, 93.
Romer, A. S. (1927). *J. Morphol. Physiol.* **43**, 347.
Romer, A. S. (1964). "The Vertebrate Body." Saunders, Philadelphia, Pennsylvania.
Roncali, L. (1970). *Monit. Zool. Ital. N. S.* **4**, 81.
Saunders, J. W., Cairns, J. M., and Gaseling, M. T. (1957). *J. Morphol.* **101**, 57.
Scheibel, M. E., and Scheibel, A. B. (1972). *Exp. Neurol.* **28**, 106.
Sharrard, W. J. W. (1955). *J. Bone Joint. Surg.* **37B**, 540.
Shellswell, G. B. (1977). *J. Embryol. Exp. Morphol.* **41**, 269.
Shellswell, G. B., and Wolpert, L. (1977). *In* "Proc. Symp. Vertebrate Limb and Somite Morphogenesis" (D. A. Ede, M. Balls and J. Hinchcliffe, eds.), p. 71. Brit. Soc. Dev. Biol., Cambridge Univ. Press, London and New York.
Sherrington, C. S. (1892). *J. Physiol. (London)* **13**, 621.
Shorey, M. L. (1909). *J. Exp. Zool.* **7**, 25.
Spemann, H. (1938). "Embryonic Development and Induction." Yale Univ. Press, New Haven, Connecticut.
Sperry, R. W. (1945). *Rev. Biol.* **20**, 311.
Sperry, R. W. (1951). *In* "Handbook of Experimental Psychology" (S. S. Stevens, ed.), p. 236. Wiley, New York.
Sperry, R. W. (1963). *Proc. Natl. Acad. Sci. U.S.A.* **50**, 703.
Sperry, R. W. (1965). *In* "Organogenesis" (R. L. Dehaan and H. Ursprung, eds.), p. 161. Holt, New York.

Sperry, R. W., and Arora, H. L. (1965). *J. Embryol. Exp. Morphol.* **14**, 307.

Sprague, J. M. (1948). *Am. J. Anat.* **82**, 1.

Sprague, J. M., and Ha, H. (1964). *Prog. Brain Res.* **11**, 120.

Spratt, N. T. (1952). *J. Exp. Zool.* **120**, 109.

Stirling, R. V., and Summerbell, D. (1977). *J. Embryol. Exp. Morphol.* **41**, 189.

Stirling, R. V., and Summerbell, D. (1979). *Nature, (London)* **278**, 640.

Straznicky, K. (1963). *Acta Biol. Acad. Sci. Hung.* **14**, 145.

Straznicky, K. (1967). *Acta Biol. Acad. Sci. Hung.* **18**, 437.

Sullivan, G. E. (1962). *Aust. J. Zool.* **10**, 458.

Summerbell, D., Lewis, J. H., and Wolpert, L. (1973). *Nature (London)* **244**, 492.

Swett, J., Eldred, E., and Buchwald, J. S. (1970). *Am. J. Physiol.* **219**, 762.

Székely, G., and Czéh, G. (1967). *Acta Physiol. Acad. Sci. Hung.* **32**, 3.

Székely, G., and Szentágothai, J. (1962). *J. Embryol. Exp. Morphol.* **10**, 140.

Taylor, A. C. (1943). *Anat. Rec.* **98**, 379.

Tello, F. (1922). *Z. Anat. Entwicklungsgesch.* **64**, 348.

Tickle, C., Summerbell, D., and Wolpert, L. (1975). *Nature (London)* **254**, 199.

Twitty, V. C. (1932). *J. Exp. Zool.* **61**, 333.

Wenger, B. S. (1951). *J. Exp. Zool.* **116**, 123.

Wortham, R. A. (1948). *J. Morphol.* **83**, 105.

Yip, J. W., and Dennis, M. J. (1976). *Nature (London)* **260**, 350.

Zelená, J. (1962). *In* "The Denervated Muscle" (E. Gutmann, ed.), p. 103. Publ. House of the Czechoslovak Academy of Sciences, Prague.

CHAPTER 8

POLYCLONES AND PATTERNS IN GROWING
Xenopus EYE

Kevin Conway, Katharine Feiock, and R. Kevin Hunt

THOMAS C. JENKINS DEPARTMENT OF BIOPHYSICS
THE JOHNS HOPKINS UNIVERSITY
BALTIMORE, MARYLAND

I. Introduction 217
    A. Clonal Analysis and Cell Lineage 220
    B. Tracking Cells in Clones and Lineages 223
    C. Cell Marking in *Xenopus* Visual System 229
    D. The Developing Eye and Visual System in *Xenopus* 239
II. Polyclone Patterns in Pigment Retinal Epithelium 245
    A. Polyclones and Their Boundaries in Half-Eye Mosaics 246
    B. Pole-Grafts: Size and Metamorphic Variations 251
    C. Local Irregularities in Polyclone Boundaries 259
    D. PRE as a Model for Clonal Organization 262
III. Iris, Choroid, and Neural Retina 264
IV. Retinotectal Patterns 273
    A. Retinotectal Patterning in the Embryo 278
    B. Polyclones and Retinotectal Patterns 285
    C. Retinotectal Patterns following Pole-Grafts 291
V. Some Unanticipated Results 300
    Supernumerary Eye Tissue 302
VI. Conclusion 307
    References 313

I. Introduction

An old anecdote tells of the man crawling about under the porch light of his home. When asked, "What are you looking for?" he replied, "My keys." His wife, with patient wisdom, questioned him further. "Where did you lose them?" He admitted, "Out in the garden." Calmly, she pursued. "Why are you looking for them here on the porch?" "Because," he concluded, "the light is better here."

Scientific investigation is often beset by such limitations. The development of an embryo, for example, is a mysterious and wonderful process, whose most intriguing features seem to be sequestered in its most inaccessible nooks and poorly illuminated crannies. One feature of consuming interest (and maddening inaccessibility) is the way embryonic cells, each containing the same quota of genetic information,

217

develop specific and reliable differences of form and function. Another is the way the *right* differences arise at the right times and places in the embryo. If it is remarkable that a single zygote cell can produce the exquisitely specific entities we call a retinal ganglion cell and a pigment epithelial cell, it is equally remarkable that these cells are produced *only* in the eye, *only* in their correct retinal layers, and *only* in accordance with a strict developmental timetable.

The entire repertoire of cellular behavior can be forced into a simple-minded set of categories. For example:

1. Cell division (birth) and death
2. Propagation of cell properties through division
3. Cell differentiation
4. Cell migration and displacement
5. Establishment of cell–cell contacts, associations, and alignments
6. Determination of cell or tissue type by induction and other cell–cell interactions
7. Specification of individual cell properties or fates by positional information.

These are arranged roughly in order of our decreasing understanding (and, for these authors, increasing interest); yet the same sequence reflects a more subtle parallel order. That is, the extent to which they are a property of one cell or of the whole embryonic system. Positional information and pattern formation are clearly "systems" constructs, understood only in terms of the whole organism or at least some rather large subdivision of the whole. Cell division, by contrast, can be largely a property of the individual cell, and many aspects of cell division can be studied without reference to the rest of the animal. For the many cellular behaviors in between, assignment is more difficult, and the inability to make the assignment (or at least break down a complex behavior into its "individual cell" and "systems" components) has been a major block to understanding complex systems like embryos and their organ buds. In addition, embryos present a special difficulty. As they change and become more complex with time, individual cell properties may give way to a transient "systems" property that orchestrates, and decays back to, a new set of individual properties. A pattern that appears in the 3-day embryo, for example, may be constructed from the individual properties of 2-day cells, specified by a prepattern in the 1-day embryo. Thus, understanding a developing system depends not only upon identifying the properties of its individual components and the global properties of the system as a whole, but also upon recognizing the relationships between the two.

This statement may appear obvious, even pedantic, but the history of embryology has not been especially distinguished for appreciating the interdependence of (individual) cell properties and (multicellular) systems properties. Early in this century, an arbitrary dividing line was drawn, bisecting the continuum of processes described above, and lumping the two subsets under the umbrellas of "differentiation" and "morphogenesis." The former went on to benefit greatly from advances in cell physiology which identified many of the proteins and other speciality products that distinguish the various terminal cell types in adult organisms. These specialty products were then used as markers, whose *appearance* in development could be studied as model steps in cell diversification and maturation (Whittaker, 1968; Holtzer, 1970; Kafatos, 1972; Cohen, 1972; McDevitt and Brahma, 1973). Likewise, the province of "differentiation" benefited from advances in genetics, extending studies from the specialty products themselves to the genes coding for them and to the control mechanisms attending the expression of these genes. Finally, in rare multicellular moments, differentiation annexed a few two-cell systems, in which the expression of some cell-specific property was induced by an adjacent cell type (Holtzer, 1968) or triggered by a hormone produced by an endocrine cell some distance away (Hamilton, 1968; Schimke *et al.*, 1975). Arguments can, of course, be made for simplifying complex problems, and it is true that what we *do* know about cell specialization probably derived, in part, from such a simplification. Yet it is also the case that particular diversification steps occur *only* at particular places (and times) in the embryo, and one cannot help wondering whether investigations of *why it happens there* might not have broadened our understanding of how it happens.

In any case, fate was far less kind to the leftovers, grouped under the umbrella of "morphogenesis." Bequeathed in the early 1900s to a small group of imaginative but isolated investigators, problems of organogenesis, assembly of tissue patterns, and spatial control of differentiation gradually become lost in a dark underworld of phenomenology and private language, of gradients and fields, of organizers and axes (Runnstrom, 1928; Spemann, 1938; Harrison, 1945). Many of these observations and concepts were elegant, and they remain useful today. But the more elaborate they became, the more private they became, and the more they appeared utterly immiscible with the ordinary chemistry and biology of differentiating cells.

Beginning with a few voices in the wilderness—Holtfreter (1939), Sperry (1950), Stern (1968), and Sturtevant (1932) come to mind—a new view of "multicellular embryology" has slowly begun to emerge. Catalyzed by Wolpert (1969, 1971), it is a view in which the assembly of tissue patterns reflects the newly differentiated traits of the participating cells—properties of cell alignment and migration, adhesion, and recognition—whose emergence in development and molecular basis are no more mysterious than the onset of globin synthesis in an erythroblast. It is a view in which questions about growth and sculpting of organ rudiments are first directed to the histogenetic properties of their cells—their mitotic rates and alignment, the tendency of progeny to disperse or stay together, the survival of some cells and planned death of others. It is a view in which the place-specific behavior of cells, the appearance of particular differentiated states at particular positions in the embryo, is examined from many different angles: Is it a simple expression of information the cells had already acquired earlier? Does it reflect input cues of a more global nature, informing the cell of its context or position? And if so, to what extent does the response depend upon the cells' interpretive machinery, itself a differentiated state evolved from their clonal ancestry? In short, what used to be considered *pattern formation* in development is, in part, simply an aggregate phenomenon driven by the individual properties and ordinary differentiated traits of the cells involved. The other part—the "systems" components of patterning processes—is simply what is left over after summing the individual cellular properties and behavior, and subtracting that sum from the total repertoire of the system.

This then is the basis for the special relationship between clonal analysis and the study of pattern formation. Without a knowledge of cell birthdates and movements, of cell lineage and sibship relations, it is impossible to relate emerging patterns and spatial constraints in development to a set of ordered but ordinary molecular events in the participating cells.

A. CLONAL ANALYSIS AND CELL LINEAGE

The histories of cell divisions and cell movements in an embryo are related. The concept of a clone includes both processes. A clone references some antecedent single cell and is defined as all of that cell's mitotic progeny. The concept of a clone is independent of the final whereabouts of individual progeny and of the final set of cell types produced. However, in many cases properties of the initial cell are heritable, so that the cells of a clone share many traits. A second and related concept is that of cell lineage. The lineage concept also references a single cell but looks backward in developmental time toward a definition of its cellular *family tree*. That is, a lineage defines a cell's birthdate, identifies its mitotic ancestors, and characterizes the sibship relations of the cell and other cells derived from those same ancestors.

Lineage is also independent of cell position and fate in the sense that cells are placed in a lineage solely on the basis of ancestral or sibling relationships to the reference cell and not on the basis of common position or common specializations.

Both concepts depend for their power upon a judicious selection of reference cells. Asking, "What is the lineage of a two-cell blastomere?" is an unfocused inquiry, merely reformulating the entirety of development. When reference cells are judiciously selected, the concepts of lineage and clone are useful even if the analysis is open-ended or incomplete. Thus, a cell's clone may be tracked through development only to the point where two interesting subpopulations emerge among its progeny. For example, a limb bud cell is an important reference cell; showing that its progeny includes both myoblasts and fibroblasts (Deinstman and Holtzer, 1975) is significant, even though the clone is incompletely defined in the sense that the fibroblasts are still dividing. Similarly, the lineage of a judiciously selected cell can be highly informative, even if it is traced back only a few generations. It is important to know that erythroid cells and leukocytes have a common grandmother, even though the ancestors of the grandmother have not been completely identified (for review, see Stohlman, 1970).

Lineage is important because it directs attention to the time and places in the embryo at which cells may have diversified primarily as a function of having divided. Holtzer (1970) and others have proposed that the molecular steps involved in turning on a battery of genes is linked to the chemistry of DNA replication and cell division. Indeed, a delay of DNA synthesis or mitosis is sufficient to prevent some cell types from differentiating (for review, see Weintraub, 1975; Dientsman and Holtzer, 1975; Holtzer *et al.*, 1975; Hunt, 1975b). In addition, both clone and lineage data may help to point out the diversification steps which preordain the emergence of particular cell types and which control and specify future multicellular patterns. Three examples may be illustrative.

A sensory neuron, bristle, and two associated base cells form a functional quartet in the insect cuticle. It is now known that the four cell types are produced by a terminal set of two cell divisions: one precursor cell divides and its two daughters divide again and yield one of each of the four types (Lawrence, 1966, 1975). To ask, in this case, "What global positional signal managed to produce a bristle, a sensory neuron, and two support cells at the same location?" becomes a less than burning question when the clonal relations are known. Moreover, to ask how a neurogenic cell population mixed and associated with a cuticular cell population is now meaningless. The lineage information permits an altogether different investigation based on yet another formulation of the questions: How did one parent generate this 4-fold diversity in the space of two cell divisions? And how did the parent cell decide to generate a "bristle" quartet, as opposed to "hair"?

By contrast, a trio of melanin-producing cell types arise at the dorsal periphery of the metamorphosing frog eye: the pigment retinal epithelial cell (PRE), the choroidal melanocyte, and the iris cell all arise at the same time and place. One could easily devise many reasonable experiments based on how a melanogenic precursor cell, not unlike the cuticular grandmother cell in the insect, could diversify, in two divisions, to produce these three cell types. In fact, analysis of cell clones from reference cells in the *early larval* eye shows that the three cell types have separable cell lines dating back to the first 2 days of embryonic life (Feiock *et al.*, 1980). Obviously, a search for diversification steps in the precursor cell present at metamorphosis would be misdirected.

Finally, a more complicated case is provided by the retinal ganglion cells of the frog eye. These cells undergo refined specializations related to their individual addresses within the retina, and use their place-specific properties to make selective axonal connections in the midbrain visual center (review Sperry, 1950, 1965; Gaze, 1970, 1978; Hunt and Jacobson, 1974a; Meryer and Sperry, 1975). This pattern of connections, the so-called *retinotectal map,* recreates across the midbrain tectum a "map" of the respective ganglion cell positions in the retina. Early speculation considered how positional signals along the embryo's body might inform each cell of its two-dimensional address in body space. Indeed, very early in development, interactions between the eye cup and extraocular tissues can modify the future connection patterns between eye and brain (Stone, 1944; Szekely, 1954; Jacobson, 1968a; Jacobson and Hunt, 1973; Hunt, 1975a, 1976a; Hunt and Piatt, 1978; Cooke, 1977). Yet, even at these stages a sufficient *plan for patterning* already exists within the eye (Hunt and Jacobson, 1973). By 2 days of development (embryonic Stage 31), the plan for ganglion cell patterning is completely insensitive to external cues (Jacobson, 1968a; Hunt and Jacobson, 1972), and the 99% of the ganglion cells which *do not yet exist* must reference their "address" to landmarks within the eye. Can we ask then if global signals *across the retina* convey positional information to new ganglion cells added to the growing retina? Clonal studies indicate that this too is unlikely. When a small group of cells is moved from one place in the 2 day eye-bud to another, the resulting "polyclone" can lay down orderly address information independent of the new position and thus independent of global context (Hunt and Ide,

1977; Ide and Hunt, 1978). In short, a detailed appreciation of clonal patterns shows that (a) global interaction can *change the plan* in rather abrupt ways early in development; but (b) the address information conveyed to individual ganglion cells—the *execution* of the plan at the single cell level—involves more local interactions within growing clones.

This last case is indeed complicated, but it represents the focal interest of investigations in our laboratory and an exemplary case of the power of clonal analysis to address not only diversification problems, but their spatial control and patterning as well. We will return in some depth to this system later.

B. TRACKING CELLS IN CLONES AND LINEAGES

Tracing cell clones and cell lineages depends upon some method of identification. That is, one must be able to recognize a cell's ancestors or progeny. In one spectacular system, the nematode worm, the embryos have large transparent cells that have been followed individually under Nomarski optics. Simple inspection of neural lineages in the ventral nerve cord revealed a standard lineage, common to all segments. Then cell types not needed in a particular segment were eliminated (Sulston and Horvitz, 1977). In the harder to visualize world of small-celled animals, however, cell marking techniques are needed. These fall into the general categories of vital dyes, [³H]thymidine labeling, genetically induced mosaicism, and surgical chimerae.

Vital dyes mark the surface of a cell or small group of cells. The mark is easily visualized, is passed on to daughter cells following mitotic division, and its introduction requires no surgical perturbation. However, the mark rarely lasts more than a week, is diluted by growth and mitosis, and may be transferred from one cell to another by simple contact. Moreover, most vital dyes are oxidizing or reducing agents that may alter, in some way, the surface of the marked cell. Cautiously used, however, this marking method can provide a rapid, preliminary survey of cell clones, and cell migration. Early in this century, the lineages of many cells in marine invertebrate embryos were detailed by this method (for review, see Whittaker, 1973). More recently, dye-marking has been used to provide a basic plan of regional determination in the vertebrate neural plate (Jacobson, 1959, 1964) and to sort out the geometrical scheme of cell movements during gastrulation (Keller, 1975) and neurulation (Burnside and Jacobson, 1968).

A particularly promising variant of dye-marking has recently been developed by Stent and his colleagues. The histochemical marker, horseradish peroxidase, was microinjected into embryonic cells in the leech nervous system (Weisblat et al., 1978). Although this marker eventually disappears and microinjection is somewhat intrusive, the marker can be reliably introduced into single cells, and exchange between cells is rare or nonexistent. Thus, Weisblat et al. (1978) were able to show that the leech CNS is formed from a very few founder cells and that individual identified cells arise from highly invariant lineages in this invertebrate. Recently, Jacobson and Hirose (1978; Hirose and Jacobson, 1980) applied this method to blastula cells of Xenopus frogs. Their very first experiments produced some startling observations. The frog CNS is formed from eight founder clones. These clones are organized into long "barrels" running from head to tail. Each eye derives from three founder clones, one of which began on the other side of the embryo (Fig. 1a). The general strategy of tracking cell clones by intracellular microinjection may have even broader applicability, as larger and more inert tracers, as well as low-molecular-weight dyes which pass between cells in association with gap junctions, are deployed together with the peroxidase tracer. Goodman and Spitzer (1978), in particular, have demonstrated the extraordinary promise of Lucifer yellow for studies of intercellular communication *within* an evolving neural cell lineage.

Radiolabeling with [³H]thymidine provides an alternative method for cell marking. It is generally believed that any dividing cell will incorporate tritiated nucleosides and that, if a labeled cell dies, surrounding cells will not reincorporate isotope in sufficient concentration to appear labeled (Trinkaus, 1969; Weston, 1963, 1970). Although microinjection per se is rather unobtrusive, many experiments require selective marking of reference cells. Thus, the whole embryo is often labeled, and select cells from that embryo are transferred into an unlabeled host embryo (Fig. 1b).

A most intriguing feature of [³H]thymidine marking is mitotic dilution. Consider a labeled cell which continues to divide after [³H]thymidine is no longer present. This cell has a fixed number of radioactive chromatids and parcels them out through its clone. After two to four divisions, single progeny cells now may not have a sufficient number of hot chromatids to expose an autoradiographic emulsion. Both the power and the limitations of thymidine marking derive from this dilution effect. Studies on neuron birthdates have cleverly exploited the dilution effects. An embryo is pulsed with isotope at some time in development. Many precursor cells incorporate label, but those destined to divide many more times dilute their label. At the time of sacrifice at young adult stages, the only labeled neurons are those which become postmitotic immediately following the pulse. In species

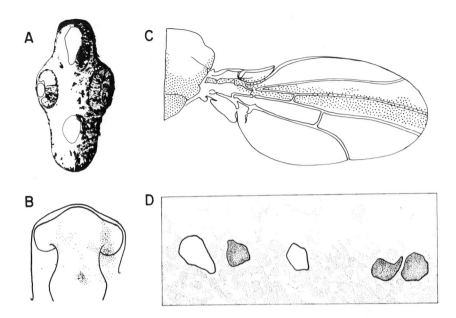

FIG. 1. Four of the many methods that have been used to mark cell clones and lineages in developing embryos. (a) An intracellular tracer, horseradish peroxidase, was microinjected into a single blastula cell in *Xenopus*. Histochemical staining of tissue sections, cut many hours later in the 3-day embryo, revealed a cell clone which was largely confined to one side of the body. A small region of the eye-bud behaved differently and stained on the *opposite* side of the body. The tracer method was developed by Weisblat *et al.* (1978) and applied to the frog by Jacobson and Hirose. Redrawn from Jacobson and Hirose (1978). (b) [³H]Thymidine labeling has been used to trace neural crest cells in the chick embryo. The dots show the distribution of label, 13 hours after an early orthotopic graft of cephalic neural crest. Redrawn from Noden (1975). (c) *Drosophila* imaginal discs show *compartments* during development. A recessive cell marker was genetically coupled to the developmental *minute* gene which causes disc cells to divide very slowly. In an embryo which is heterozygous for both mutations, a somatic recombination event produced a single wing disc cell that was double-recessive for the marker and wild-type at the *minute* locus. Despite the fact that descendants of this cell can now divide much faster than the other (M/+) cells of the wing disc, the clone (shown by stippling) confined itself to the anterior half of the wing. All clones initiated after a certain stage of development respect the imaginary line (a so-called compartment boundary) which divided the wing into anterior and posterior. Redrawn from Garcia-Bellido (1976). (d) An enzyme histochemical marker has been used to study clonal relationships in the mouse cerebellum. Tetraparental mice were created, in which one pair of parents was positive for the marker. The dark silhouettes show the outlines of cerebellar Purkinje cells, and the results showed a random intermixing of Purkinje cells from different clones. Redrawn from Mullen (1977).

such as frog and chick, where [³H]thymidine is not cleared from the embryo, a "negative labeling" method has been devised in which isotope is presented continuously from some timepoint in development until the time of sacrifice. Here the *unlabeled* neurons are judged to be those which had become postmitotic before the isotope was first intro-duced. These paradigms have been used to chart the inside-out assem-bly of mammalian cortex (Angevine and Sidman, 1962; Rakic, 1977), for example, and to show that ganglion cells are the first neurons to be born in the retina of frog, chick, and mammal (Sidman, 1961; Jacobson, 1968b; Kahn, 1974).

On rare occasions, birth date information can provide insights into lineage. Cerebellar Purkinje cells, for example, are born on prenatal days 11–14 of mouse development; granule, basket, and stellate cells, by contrast, are formed weeks later in a secondary germinal zone. Hence, the "common grandmother" hypothesis is eliminated. In other fortuitous circumstances, dilution itself can be used to construct lineage information. In a classic series of experiments on the grasshop-per optic lobe, Nordlander and Edwards (1969) used thymidine dilution to show that a primary "neuroblast" divides asymmetrically: one daughter, a ganglion mother cell, divides again to make neurons; the other daughter, retaining the "neuroblast" character, proceeds into a second asymmetric division. Finally, a few investigators have been able to follow a radiolabeled population that was both dividing and migrat-ing. Weston (1963), for example, characterized the major migratory pathways of neural crest cells and identified many of the cell types that differentiate among crest progeny. Weston's (1963) experiments, re-markable for their time, provide a poignant example of both the strengths and limitations of this method. He identified many new cell types which had been missed in dye-marking studies of crest deriva-tives. Yet the radiolabel, in turn, failed to report some progeny cell types which proliferate extensively before differentiating. Identifica-tion of these cell types awaited the introduction of chimeric methods.

Genetically induced mosaicism has been used to mark cells in *Drosophila*. *Gynandromorphs* are flies in which some of the cells are male (XO) and the rest are female (XX). Genetically female embryos are produced in which one of the sex chromosomes is an unstable *ring-X* chromosome. This kind of X chromosome has a chance of being lost during one of the early nuclear divisions in the zygote. The clone of such a nucleus, following cellularization of the blastoderm and subse-quent development, is comprised of XO cells, which are recognizable if the surviving X chromosome contains a recessive allele for some marker gene. Somatic recombination makes use of X-rays to induce a crossing-over event in mitotic cells. Using a recessive marker such as *yellow*, heterozygous embryos (*Yy*) are irradiated at designated cells will experience a recombination event involving the chromosome region carrying the *Yy* genes. One daughter (Y/Y) is indistinguishable from the heterozygous background, but the other (y/y) yields a clone that can express the *yellow* phenotype.

Both methods suffer from an inability to predict *which cell* will undergo the genetic event that leads to marking. The clones of gynandromorphs are large by definition, and the gene must be X-linked. In addition, most of the available markers involve genes that are normally expressed only by adult cuticular cells. Multiple wing hair provides a convenient, if somewhat exaggerated, example. Brain cells do not make wing hairs, single or multiple; and hence, recessive clones cannot be tracked into brain. Likewise, wing cells make hairs only when they fully differentiate, so clones cannot be followed in the developing wing. Instead, one must view the clone in the *adult* wing and make retrospective inferences about the course of its development. Nevertheless, the availability of other mutants and genetic manipulations in *Drosophila* have made both methods exceedingly powerful. Using an X-linked marker for eye color, Ready *et al.* (1976) constructed gynandromorphs and showed that the boundaries between XO and XX populations often cut through single ommatidia. This observation proves that the receptor cells comprising a single ommatidium are not the clone of a single preommatidial cell. Somatic recombination clones in *Drosophila* wing show startling geometries and, when induced sufficiently late in development, are never observed to cross certain territorial lines on the wing (Garcia-Bellido, 1975). By using recombination methods together with mutants affecting the rates of wing growth, Garcia-Bellido and his co-workers showed that clones which overgrow dramatically will only fill up their territorial *compartment* (Fig. 1c). Recently, geometrical analysis of clones has been extended to the eye of *Drosophila* (Campos-Ortega, this volume) and the detailed lineage of *Drosophila* photoreceptors has been characterized (Lawrence and Green, 1979). The discovery of new histochemical markers that are expressed in embryonic and internal cell types (Kankel and Hall, 1976; White and Kankel, 1978; Hall *et al.*, 1980) further enhance the promise of these methods for clonal analysis of nervous system development.

Finally, *surgical chimerae* are produced by physically combining cells from genotypically different embryos into one mosaic embryo. In mice, this is accomplished by joining embryonic blastula cells from one mouse embryo with those of another, and reimplanting the composite in a foster mother. The mouse methods depend upon the serendipity of integration of the two cell groups (a variable fraction of one or both may divert to form placental structures) and have been limited by a lack of cell markers in the mouse. Recently, however, Mullen (1977) has applied a new enzymatic marker to cerebellum mosaics with the exciting result that Purkinje cell "clones" mix and intermingle extensively during the migration to cerebellar cortex (Fig. 1d). Classic experiments by Mintz and her associates have used isozyme markers to show that muscle cells form by cell fusion *in vivo* and that normal brain cells can be produced from teratoma-derived clones (Mintz and Ilmensee, 1975; Ilmensee and Mintz, 1976).

In birds and amphibia, surgical chimerae can be constructed by classical embryonic grafting. A designated bit of embryonic tissue is excised and replaced by a tissue graft whose cells carry some mark, in much the same strategy as that used for implanting [³H]thymidine-labeled cells. Here, however, the marker is genetic or cytogenetic, and a variety of marker sources have been used. As in the case of [³H]thymidine-labeled grafts, this method is limited on two general counts. The surgery is intrusive, and many controls must be done to confirm the normality of the specimen; and grafts contain *groups of cells*, not a single cell, and give rise to *polyclones* rather than true clones descended from a single cell. The chief advantage lies in the investigator's ability to choose in which cells, and at what stage of development, to introduce the marker. A variety of special limitations attend individual marking schemes, based on the properties of the marker and the degree to which donor and host embryos develop in true parallel with one another.

In birds, for example, bits of chick embryo tissue can be replaced by bits of analogous tissue from a quail embryo (LeDouarin, 1973). This marking scheme is limited in that only some embryonic cell groups and tissues develop with a sufficiently parallel schedule in the two birds to treat the chimera as something like a normal composite system. Certain kinds of limb-bud grafts, for example, produce very different results in quail-into-chick versus chick-into-quail reciprocals (Keiny, 1977). The marker itself, however, is nearly ubiquitous, in that the nuclei of the two species stain differently in virtually all embryonic and adult cell types. The method is thus ideal for systems like neural crest, in which chimerae are viable and achieve reasonably normal structure and in which a large variety of cell types are eventually produced from the polyclone (LeDouarin, 1973, 1979). Very recently, Bronner and Cohen (1979) have succeeded in microinjecting a *clone* of neural crest cells, raised *in vitro* from a single cell plated from quail neural crest, back into a chick embryo host. Their demonstration that a homogeneous clone can give rise to both melanocytes and adrenergic neurons is particularly powerful (Bronner-Fraser and Cohen, this volume). In particular, the microinjection method may have provided a way around the two general limitations to the grafting strategy: microinjection is much less intrusive, and by injecting a clone one can extend the analytical resolution to that of true clonal analysis.

A variety of marking schemes have been applied to amphibian development. All have had great success on a very few questions but suffer from severely limited applicability. *Interspecies* chimerae have established the migratory pathway and placodal origin of lateral line cells (Harrison, 1945); *ploidy* chimerae have been used to show that many of the new muscle cells in a regenerated limb derive from the old muscle of the blastema (Steen, 1970); and *light and dark strains* of embryos have been used to follow a variety of tissue grafts in the axolotl (Van Deusen, 1973; Dellaney, 1978; Ide, 1978). A few of these marking schemes suffer from limited resolution. Most suffer from perturbation artifacts. Amphibian species rarely show parallel developmental schedules; indeed, most interspecies chimerae have been created to exploit developmental differences. In a typical experiment, Harrison (1939) showed that *A. tigrinum* eyes develop at their own (rapid) growth rate in a (slow-growing) *A. maculatum* host. The point of the whole experiment—whether eye growth is intrinsically or extrinsically controlled—turned on the fact that the two eye systems do *not* develop in parallel. Ploidy markers may also introduce a serious perturbation, as the number of cells is inversely related to their ploidy and size. A more detailed critique of amphibian cell marking has recently been published by Harris (1980).

The power of grafting methods, as noted above, lies in the ability of the investigator to choose the cells he wishes to mark. As such, the methods can be combined with experimental designs, so that marked cells can be followed under conditions in which their developmental contexts have been changed (Harrison, 1945). Yoking markers with the classic paradigms of experimental embryology, one can examine the effects, on the resultant polyclone, of moving the graft to a different place in the embryo, or to a different stage in development.

C. CELL MARKING IN *Xenopus* VISUAL SYSTEM

Our own research and the remainder of this chapter are focused upon the development of the eye and its visual connections with the brain, in the African clawed frog, *Xenopus laevis*. We use microsurgical methods to replace a bit of tissue in an embryonic eye-bud with another bit of tissue carrying a genetic marker. The chimeric eye is then allowed to mature and grow, and a variety of analyses are performed to determine the patterns of genetic mosaicism in various layers and cell types of the eye, and to relate these histogenetic patterns to the patterns of connections which the eye has developed with the midbrain.

Our current strategy is built around the use of two marker mutant strains. One is *periodic albinism* (alb^p). Homozygotes for this mutation have greatly reduced levels of pigmentation, both in the retinal pigment epithelium and in melanocytes derived from neural crest. The other strain is the *Oxford nucleolar marker*. Heterozygotes for this mutation have only one nucleolus per cell.

Periodic albinism, characterized by Tompkins (1977), is inherited as a simple Mendelian recessive. Homozygotes (alb^p/alb^p) are pure white at fertilization and remain so until early larval stages (Fig. 2a). Beginning at about 3 days after fertilization, tissues which normally synthesize melanin begin to show limited levels of melanin accumulation, acquiring a gray appearance in the dissecting microscope (Fig. 2c) and in histologic section. Toward the end of the larval period, however, these tissues have again become amelanotic and the adults are white once again (Tompkins, 1977) (Fig. 2b). By exchanging tissues between wild-type and (alb^p/alb^p) embryos, Thompkins showed that the mutation is largely cell autonomous. During the larval phase of transient pigmentation, the albino melanocytes accumulate slightly more melanin and assume more normal morphology if they have been grafted into a wild-type host. However, the transiently pigmented cells were sufficiently abnormal to remain distinguishable from the normal (host) melanocytes in the larva. Moreover, the white phenotype of embryonic albino cells, the timecourse of transient melanin accumulation, and the return to a white phenotype in the late larva and adult were unchanged by the wild-type host environment.

The Oxford nucleolar marker, discovered by Elsdale *et al.* (1958), has been characterized by Wallace (1960) and by Brown and Gurdon (1964). It is a deletion mutation for ribosomal DNA. The genes for heavy ribosomal RNAs are contained in the nucleolus, and wild-type cells have two nucleoli per nucleus, one from each parental chromosome set (Fig. 2d). At least one set of ribosomal genes is required for development after the maternal stocks of ribosomes become inadequate. For this reason, a full dose of the Oxford mutation, the so-called *0-nu* condition, is lethal at about 3 days. Heterozygotes for the mutation, however, contain one set of ribosomal genes (and hence one nucleolus per cell) and are termed *1-nu*. They are sufficiently normal in their development to be indistinguishable from *2-nu* siblings upon external examination (Wallace, 1960). Matings of a *1-nu* parent with a

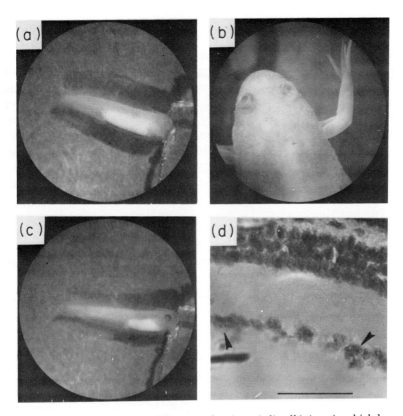

FIG. 2. The marker mutants of *Xenopus*. One is *periodic albinism*, in which homozygous recessive individuals are white at (a) embryonic stages (×10) and (b) adult stages (×2.3), but show transient and limited accumulation of melanin at (c) tadpole stages (×8). (d) The other marker is the Oxford nucleolar marker, in which individual cells contain only one nucleolus. The high-power photomicrograph shows *1-nu* cells (left) and *2-nu* cells (right) in a chimeric neural retina (bar equals 20 μm).

wild-type parent produce equal numbers of *1-nu* and *2-nu* offspring, while crosses of two heterozygotes yield a Mendelian mix of *0-nu* lethals, *1-nu* marker embryos, and *2-nu* embryos. The *0-nu* homozygotes have a special utility, because their cells die on schedule even after transplantation into a normal host embryo. That is, the homozygotes behave as a cell-autonomous cell lethal. We have used them in occasional control experiments because they simulate the surgical perturbation of a marked graft without actually contributing a clone to retina. However, most of our experiments using the Oxford strain have been based on the marker properties of the *1-nu* heterozygotes.

Each marker has characteristic limitations and strengths. The *1-nu* marker has the potential resolution of one cell. In practice, this cannot be achieved because it is not possible to score every last cell with certainty. Sectioning through a *2-nu* cell can yield what appear to be two *1-nu* cells lying in adjacent sections. Overlap of two nucleoli within one nucleus can make a *2-nu* cell appear to be *1-nu,* while overlap of two *cells* can create the appearance of multiple nucleoli within a single nucleus. Some nuclei contain other particles which could be confused with a true nucleolus. In the main, these ambiguities can be resolved by high-power examination, adjustment of focus and comparison of nuclear profiles in adjacent sections. Yet there remain occasional cells for which no definitive assignment of nucleolar number can be made. A second advantage is that nucleoli are not a special property of one or a few differentiated cell types; the marker should be expressed independently of how a marked cell finally differentiates, and should be visible even in the morphologically "undifferentiated" tissues of the tadpole. In practice, the possibility of nucleolar fusion or fragmentation and/or naturally occurring polyploidy makes it necessary to validate the assumption of ubiquity in control experiments. Fortunately, most cell types of the frog retina reliably exhibit their nucleolar genotype at late larval and early juvenile stages. The major disadvantage of the *1-nu* marker in our experience is our inability to see it in the living animal. Reconstruction of mosaic patterns in the eye can be achieved only from histologic material, and this eliminates the chance of studying the same specimen over time. Selection of *1-nu* embryos for grafting is severely limited, since *1-nu* and *2-nu* siblings can be distinguished only by elaborate tail-squash procedures. Finally, because a small percentage of grafts either fall out or fail to heal into place, it is impossible to determine whether a successful mosaic was created until the animal has matured and its tissues have been processed for the final histologic analysis. In summary, then, the *1-nu* marker is laborious; but it is a definitive cell marker where it can be observed, and it can be observed in the great majority of the eye's cells if not in every last individual cell.

Pigment markers also have single cell resolution and have strengths and limitations that, in many respects, complement those of cytogenetic markers such as *1-nu.* At the cellular level, the albino phenotype is simply an unpigmented cell. This phenotype is meaningful only in tissues whose normal repertoire of specializations includes the production and accumulation of melanin, and only at stages of development when pigmentation is normally present. In some respects, melanogenic cells are less than ideal subjects for clonal analysis. While it is easy to resolve a black spot the size of one cell, heavy pigmentation also obscures intracellular detail within the spot. Thus, it is hard to determine whether a black spot in a white surround really represents only one cell, and impossible to assign nucleolar number to such a cell. Most melanocytes derive from the neural crest, an extremely versatile and notoriously migratory embryonic cell line. Some melanocytes can be stimulated to reenter the mitotic cycle, and even to dedifferentiate (Whittaker, 1968). In short, the mere absence of pigment (in a place where pigment is expected) may be a meaningless correlate of having introduced albino cells. Finally, pigment cells are a prime candidate for departures from strict cell autonomy. In addition to the general worry (attending all specialty product mutations) that a missing gene product may be supplied to mutant cells by neighboring wild-type cells, frank phagocytosis of pigment is known to occur following the death of melanocytes. In one major respect, however, pigment cells are *the* ideal subject for clonal analysis in surgical chimerae, especially in a species like *Xenopus* where the embryos are translucent and the larvae transparent. Pigment cells can be observed directly on external inspection of the living chimera.

Fortunately, the eye of *Xenopus* contains two full cell layers that produce and accumulate melanin. The *choroid* contains a number of interspersed cell types, including melanocytes derived from the neural crest. The pigment retinal epithelium (PRE) is made up exclusively of melanotic cells and may be the only true melanocyte in the body that is not derived from the neural crest. It forms from the back wall of the eye-bud and thus is a true neural plate derivative. In addition to these two layers, the *iris* of the frog eye appears to produce and accumulate large amounts of melanin.

The pigmented layers of the eye are visible on external view of the animal, and the timetable of pigmentation in the normal embryo is perfect for external observations of chimeric eyes prepared from 1- to 3-day eye-buds. In wild-type embryos, visible levels of egg pigment mark the cells until about 3 days of development; and by 2.5 days of development, the choroid and PRE have begun to synthesize and store their own melanin. A number of other concerns have been allayed by the special properties of PRE cells and by some fortuitous aspects of the clonal data obtained on it. The PRE cells assume an orderly monolayer, become mitotically quiescent under normal developmental conditions, and seem to be relatively resistant to the migratory impulse. In a very small fraction of cases, a PRE clone evokes a graft-rejection response. These cases, although annoying in some respects, have allowed us to assess directly the appearance of non-PRE cells which have phagocytosed PRE pigment. Such cells are easily distinguished from true PRE cells: their morphology is different, they are not part of the true PRE monolayer.They also provide a model cell for comparing the levels and intracellular distribution of pigment in a cell which has phagocytosed melanin to those in a cell which makes and accumulates its own melanin. Again the phagocytic cell is clearly different: its pigmentation is spotty and much reduced from that of the PRE cell storing its own melanin. PRE cells with reduced levels of melanin (comparable to our model phagocyte) are not observed in PRE mosaics. Moreover, the assumption that the alb^P gene shows cell-autonomous expression within a mosaic PRE receives additional support from two observations that will be discussed in more detail later: mosaics show strict black/white boundaries ("gray" cells are not seen); and occasionally boundaries show finger-like projections which attenuate to a point at which a single unpigmented cell is virtually surrounded by pigmented cells. Definitive confirmation of this assumption should be obtainable by photographing the exact pigment pattern in a 1-nu/albino mosaic, bleaching out the PRE pigment during histologic preparation (Beach, 1977), and then reconstructing the photographic pattern by 1-nu reconstruction of the PRE.

Our methods also reflect the general strengths and limitations of the surgical chimerae discussed earlier. Only grafts introduced early in development (here by stage 40 or roughly day 4) escape immune rejection. The surgery is intrusive, requiring a wealth of sham-graft and 0-nu controls to show that a phenomenon correlated with a particular clonal pattern was not really caused by the carving up of the host eye-bud.We can introduce small groups of marked cells but not one solitary marked cell. This limits the data in two ways. First, the patterning behavior of true clones is not observed directly, but must be inferred from the collective behavior and boundary configurations of *polyclones*. Second, a polyclone made up of several cell types does not distinguish between pluripotential founder cells and a *diversified set* of founder cells, each specific for a particular cell type. Thus, if a pair of final cell types really does derive from a single, pluripotential precursor cell, we could never prove it. Only the *other* answer is obtainable with our methods, and even this depends on some measure of luck. *If* precursor cells are specific for particular cell types, and *if* our individual grafts contain a varying mix of such precursors, we will obtain a few clones which lack a particular cell type or which contain this cell type but not others. Last, all marking methods are limited to the extent that the marker genotype—either the mutation itself or the inbred strain in which it has been maintained (Sotello and Changeux, 1974)—may be abnormal, that idiosyncracies of mosaicism are more a function of aberrations in the mutant stock than of the normal proper-

ties of growing clones. In the case of the albino mutant, and its application to eye development and retinotectal patterns, such worries are not
unfounded. In every mammalian species studied, albino mutants show
paradoxical abnormalities in the pattern of central connections from
the retina to the brain (Guillery *et al.*, 1974). One cardinal
abnormality—that too many optic fibers cross at the midline and innervate the visual centers on the opposite side of the brain—may be
irrelevant to our studies, since the retinotectal patterns we study are
nearly entirely contralateral in the wild-type frog (Scalia, 1977). Moreover, we have taken great pains to determine that the physiology of
optic fibers in the normal albino frog is at least grossly normal. However, the abnormal fiber-crossing in mammalian albinos may well reflect more basic abnormalities in positional information and patterning
in the retina itself, and the latter could introduce significant perturbation artifacts in our studies of retinal patterning in frogs.

To a large extent, our experimental strategy has been shaped in
ways that circumvent or minimize these limitations, and that exploit
both the special strengths of each marker and the general strengths of
the surgical method: the ability of the investigator to choose precisely
which cells are to be marked; and the ability to yoke the marking
methods with the many transplantation maneuvers of experimental
embryology. Many features of our strategy are evident in Fig. 3, which
shows the life cycle and analytical history of one illustrative chimera.
The chimera is constructed by surgically transplanting a bit of eye-bud
tissue from a pigmented *1-nu* embryo into the eye-bud of a host embryo
which is albino (*alb^P/alb^P*) and which contains the wild-type complement of two nucleoli per cell (Fig. 3a). Here the surgery was performed
upon 2-day embryos (stage 32), and we have excised a bit of tissue at
the *posterior* rim of the host eye-bud and replaced it with a bit of tissue
from the *anterior* rim of the donor eye-bud, thus changing both
genotype and position. The putative chimera is photographed postoperatively (Fig. 3b), and the presence of a small black wedge in the
composite eye confirms that a successful chimera has been created and
marks the initial size and angular position of the marked cell group.
The chimeric eye may be photographed again, at tadpole stages of
particular interest, as the chimera is being reared through metamorphosis. In the young juvenile frog, the chimeric eye is photographed a
final time (Fig. 3c), and the animal is prepared for electrophysiologic
analysis of the visual projection from the chimeric eye and its midbrain
visual center, the contralateral optic tectum (Fig. 3d). The frog is then
sacrificed, and its eye cut into tissue sections at 7 or 10 μm. Individual
sections are traced through a drawing tube, noting the positions of
pigment boundaries and of *1-nu* and *2-nu* cells, and, in some cases,

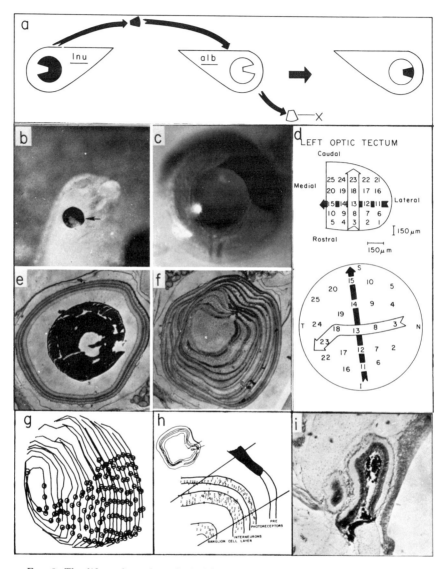

FIG. 3. The life cycle and analytical history of one chimera. (a) As shown in the schematic diagram, the chimera is prepared by exchanging a bit of eye-bud tissue between a pigmented *1-nu* donor embryo and a 2-day *albino (2-nu)* host embryo. The genotypes at embryonic stage 32 (according to the normal table of Nieuwkoop and Faber, 1956) are given on the silhouettes of the embryos; eye-bud tissue which is genotypically destined to become pigmented (i.e., wild-type and *1-nu*) is black. (These conventions are maintained in the operative schemata that appear in subsequent figures.) (b) Postoperative photography through the dissecting microscope confirms the success of the operation; a small bit of pigmented tissue is healing into the host eye (×7.5). (c) The eye is photographed for the last time in the juvenile frog, prior to electrophysiological analysis (×17). (d) Electrophysiological assay, of the visual field projection from the experimental

photographed through the microscope (Fig. 3e). Serial sections, aligned by best fit superposition of ocular and extraocular landmarks, are processed for three-dimensional reconstruction. In some instances, micrographs of serial sections are assembled into photographic montages (Fig. 3f) to display the fine detail of polyclone boundaries. More routinely the contours of every fifth section are entered into a DEC-10 computer, and displayed in three-dimensional Cal-Comp plots (Fig. 3g), using computer programs which rotate the position of the observer and which subtract contours and parts of contours which are hidden by the solid geometry of the eye. Finally, a variety of overlay maneuvers are performed to examine how marked cells in one retinal tissue or layer overlay with those in another tissue or layer (Fig. 3h).[1]

[1] In addition to the analytical steps illustrated, which followed directly from our overall rationale, other analyses were engendered by entirely unexpected findings. This chimera, for example, developed a discrete, small supernumerary eye in addition to the main chimeric eye (Fig. 3i). The incidence of supernumerary eyes and some aspects of their structure are considered, together with several other unexpected findings, later.

---

eye to the midbrain visual center on the opposite side of the animal (the contralateral optic tectum), reveals the pattern of the retinotectal map assembled by the chimeric eye. Analysis of visual projections is explained in more detail in Fig. 5. A photomicrograph of an individual section, showing the boundary of polyclones in the various eye layers, is shown in (e). This tissue was fixed in Bouin's fixative, imbedded in paraffin, sectioned at 10 μm, and stained with a composite stain of hematoxylin and Picro Panceau. The plane of section in this and all other chimerae (although the *exact* plane varies somewhat from case to case) was roughly perpendicular to the optic axis: that is, tangential to the cornea and parallel to the plane of the ciliary margin. Magnification is given by the bar (500 μm). (f) Montages, assembled from photomicrographs of serial sections, trimmed on the contours of PRE, display the detailed boundaries of the polyclone in the PRE. (g) By inputting traced contours of every fifth section through the eye, we can obtain computer-generated Cal-Comp plots of the three-dimensional structure of the eye and the positions, in three dimensions, of the polyclone boundaries. The boundaries and representative points of the polyclone are displayed as open circles. By means of a hidden line program, developed in this laboratory by Dr. Gregory Stock, the computer subtracts contours and parts of contours that are hidden by the solid structure of the eye. By repositioning the observer relative to the data points, it is possible to view the eye and its polyclone from any angle. (h) The polyclone in the PRE is overlaid with that in the neural retina, to show the correspondence of position of marked cells in different tissue types. Similar maneuvers, here applied over a more limited range of sections, allow comparison of clonal boundaries within neural retina and between PRE and iris. (i) Photomicrograph of a supernumerary eye which formed outside the main eye (500 μm). This phenomenon is treated in more detail in Fig. 21. This chimeric individual and all others described in this paper were prepared from embryos obtained by gonadotrophin-induced amplexus, dejellied mechanically, anesthetized for surgery in Tricaine methane sulfonate, operated, and reared at 22°C in 20% saline (5% Steinberg's and 15% Holtfreter's), raised to metamorphosis in plastic trays containing nettle powder and frog brittle in the above saline, and maintained after metamorphosis on Tubefex worms and chopped liver.

In the particular case shown, the anterior pole cells of the donor eye-bud grew out a contiguous polyclone that occupied a "sector" of the final chimeric eye. This sector occupied an anterior position, and extended radially outward from the optic nerve head at the back of the eye, to the margin of the pupil in the front of the eye. Although the polyclones include many layers and cell types in the eye, marked cells in different layers did not line up exactly. Last, though both the method and the result will be described in more detail later, the visual projection in Fig. 3e indicates that the graft sustained its "anterior character" after it was transplanted from a *left* eye-bud, but failed to "remember" the inversed handedness appropriate to left eye tissue. As the polyclone grew, the ganglion cells were assigned "anterior" address information and mapped into the brain's visual center in a manner appropriate to anterior retinal cells in a *right* eye.

The latter result illustrates the enhanced power of clonal methods when they are used together with the transplantation methods of experimental embryology (here a graft from left eye-bud to right). That the pigment marker is visible in the living animal allows postoperative confirmation that a bona fide chimera has been created and also allows kinetic analysis of the polyclone over time. In addition, external photography provides a straightforward and reliable image of the pigment pattern in a chimeric eye. We know of no better way to validate our methods for tracing and alignment of tissue sections and for computer display of three-dimensional reconstructions than to produce a computer image that matches what a camera sees. The histologic methods are essential, however, not only for *1-nu* reconstruction of the nonpigmented of the layers of the retina, but to confirm *which* pigmented tissue is contributing to the externally visible pigment. Assembling the composite pigment image from the interlocking "pieces" in the PRE, choroid, and iris provides a useful model for developing *overlay* procedures to compare neural layers with one another and neural retina with pigment retina. Because the *1-nu* patterns in the neural retina are laborious to reconstruct, it has proved useful to use the PRE as the model retinal layer on which to apply the theory and from which to derive an overview of results on polyclone patterns. By transplanting grafts from offspring of *1-nu* matings into albino host embryos, even those donors which prove to be *2-nu* offspring generate chimerae that provide pigment data and important internal controls. The pigment data also provide a backdrop, against which the (harder to obtain) *1-nu* data can be counterpointed, especially in experiments like the stage 32 pole-graft shown in Fig. 3, where neural retinal (*1-nu*) patterns and PRE (*pigment*) patterns are in good general agreement. Yet this agreement must be established empirically for each category of experiment, and each category permuted over a variety of genotypic combinations, including reciprocals for each pair of genotypes, and including *1-nu* with wild-type as well as various pairings of pigmented with albino phenotypes. Only then can one be certain that the experiment in question, and its results, are reporting on the normal process of clonal growth rather than on defects in an abnormal mutant stock.

D. THE DEVELOPING EYE AND VISUAL SYSTEM IN *Xenopus*

Juvenile *Xenopus laevis* are smooth-skinned aquatic frogs, about 5 gm in weight and 2 to 5 cm in length. Their eyes are rather small, perhaps 2 mm across, nearly immobile, and positioned to look upward and forward. The structural integrity of the eye is maintained by two supporting structures that will not concern us further: a tough, transparent outer capsule and a pressure-generating internal "fluid," the gelatinous vitreous. The outermost layer of interest for our analysis is the *choroid,* a vascularized layer which forms a pigmented "skin" of the eyeball and encapsulates the retina. A second layer of melanin-containing cells, the pigment retinal epithelium (PRE), lies between the choroid and the neural retina. The neural retina displays the laminated organization of vertebrates in general, with no histologically identifiable fovea: proceeding toward the vitreal fluid from the PRE, one encounters a layer of photoreceptors (rods and cones), a layer of neuropil, a layer of interneurons (horizontal, bipolar, and amacrine cells), a second layer of neuropil, a layer of ganglion cells, and a fiber layer which contains the axons of the ganglion cells as they course to the optic disc and on to the brain. The eye, to this point then, can be viewed as a truncated sphere made up of many layers: six layers of neural tissue, one inside the other, all surrounded by a PRE shell which is, in turn, encapsulated in the choroidal shell (Fig. 4). The adult eye contains some 30,000–70,000 ganglion cells, several hundred thousand interneurons and photoreceptors, and unknown numbers of PRE and choroidal cells.

The eye "sphere" is truncated in front, with the many layers converging in a histologically undifferentiated *ciliary margin*. One can think of the ciliary margin as framing the porthole of the pupil (Fig. 4). Suspended around the fringe of this porthole is the *iris,* a pigmented structure, which forms the immediate perimeter of the pupil and which is attached to the lens internally. Light enters the eye through the pupil, passes through the lens and through the neural retina, and is transduced into an electrochemical signal by the photoreceptors. The signal is passed on to the ganglion cells, via the interneurons, and then

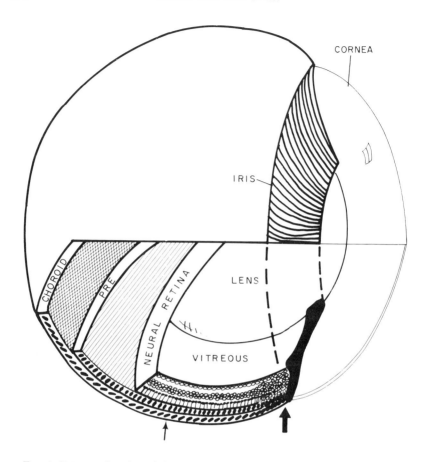

FIG. 4. Cutaway drawing of the eye showing the anatomical relationships of tissues relevant to chimera analysis in the authors' laboratory. The choroid is a pigmented layer, derived from neural crest, which encapsulates the PRE, which in turn encapsulates the neural retina. In all regions of the eye, except one, the neural retina is a layered structure (light arrow), made up of alternating layers of cell bodies and neuropil. The one exception is the ciliary margin (heavy arrow), which contains undifferentiated germinal cells. The germinal cells form a bilayer which is pigmented in the outermost layer, and describe a ring between the iris and the rest of the eye. The internal space of the eyeball is filled with a gelatinous fluid, the vitreous.

conveyed to the brain, in the form of action potentials, along the ganglion cell axons.

The ganglion cell axons form the fibers of the optic nerve. The nerve extends centrally from the eye to the optic chiasm where its fibers meet those from the other eye, and form two optic tracts which continue on to the brain's visual centers. The primary and best-studied visual center in *Xenopus* is the midbrain optic tectum. The two tecta form prominent lobes, and each lobe is innervated exclusively, or nearly so (Scalia, 1977), by optic fibers from the opposite eye. That is, the left tectum entertains only *crossing* optic fibers from the right eye. The optic fibers connect in the contralateral tectum with precise topographic order, such that the pattern of connections forms a kind of map of the corresponding cell positions in the retina. Thus, proceeding from the side edge of the tectum to the midline, one finds connections from ganglion cells ever more ventral in their retinal position; proceeding backward from the front edge of the tectum, one encounters connections from successively more anterior retina. The visual world forms an inverted image on the retina, and the topographic pattern of retinotectal connections allows that image to be relayed intact to the brain. Presentation of small stimuli in the visual field, while probing various tectal positions with a microelectrode, provides a simple electrophysiologic assay for the pattern of connections between eye and brain (Fig. 5).

The eye originates in the neural ectoderm of the gastrula. Its progenitor cells lie far anterior, very close to the neural ridge in the neurula. As the neural tube closes, the eye outpockets toward the ectoderm. There it induces overlying ectodermal cells to form a lens, and pinches down to form a two-cell layered cup attached to the neural tube by the optic stalk ventrally, and surrounded by mesoderm. During early tailbud stages, the layer closest to the ectoderm produces the neural retina cell types, the ganglion cell, bipolars, and amacrines and horizontal cells, and photoreceptors. The second layer produces the PRE. The surrounding mesoderm forms the choroid, sclera, and ocular muscles. Neural crest pigment invades these layers at 1.5 to 3 days. By 2.5 days, an optic nerve can be observed growing out of the ventral fissure; by 3 days of age, the nerve has reached the chiasm, the eye is a functional tiny organ of several hundred cells, the heart and other organs are functioning, and the tadpole is feeding.

Between 1 and 2 days of embryonic life, the eye grows by cell division throughout the bud (Jacobson, 1968b; Straznicky and Gaze, 1971; Bergey *et al.*, 1973), and gap junction-like structures are evident (Dixon and Cronly-Dillon, 1974). After embryonic stage 30, mitosis is primarily limited to a ring of germinal cells at the ciliary margin (Fig. 6a), and junctions are likewise confined to the region of mitotic activity. The germinal ring is in fact bilayered. The inner layer, made up of unpigmented pseudostratified epithelial cells, is continuous with the neural retina and is the source of new neurons that are added to the neural retina during growth. The outer layer is pigmented and continuous with the PRE and the iris. Throughout development, mitosis is

MULTIUNIT VISUAL PROJECTION   OPTIC FIBER SINGLE UNITS

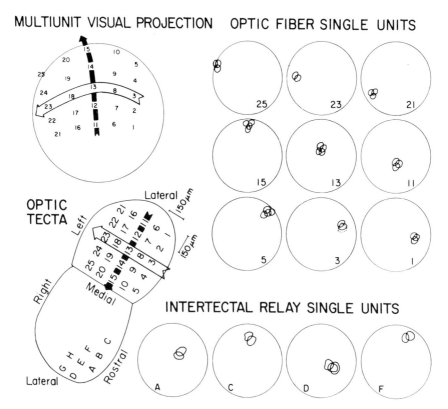

FIG. 5. The visual field projection from right eye to left optic tectum in a normal juvenile *Xenopus*. The large circle at the upper left represents 200° of the right eye's visual field. The numbers represent the center of an area in the right eye's visual field at which a spot of light evoked neural activity at the correspondingly numbered positions on the outline of the left optic tectum (lower left). A platinum–iridium microelectrode is used to penetrate the tectum at each numbered position, and the neural activity it detects consists mainly of action potentials from terminal arborizations of optic fibers. The analysis can be carried further by isolating the electrical activity of a single optic-fiber unit in the tectum, and determining the receptive field area within the visual field from which the light spot can excite the unit. *Optic fiber single units* are displayed as closed, irregularly shaped contours, within the nine numbered visual field circles at the upper right. All representations of the right eye's visual field are similarly oriented (*nasal* right, *superior* up). Note that the receptive fields for several different single units, detected at or beneath a single numbered position on the tectum, overlap and are confined to a small patch in the eye's visual field. For example, the three distinct optic fiber single units recorded at position *25* are clumped in temperosuperior visual field. These results show that optic fibers form point-to-point, topographically ordered patterns of innervation in the tectum. *Intertectal relay single units* (bottom right) also have receptive fields within the right eye's visual field and can be detected by recording from the *ipsilateral* (right) optic tectum. At lettered positions (A,C,D,F) on the right optic tectum,

confined to a germinal ring at the ciliary margin. Thus, embryos, tad-poles, and frogs all show a ring of label at the ciliary margin, when fixed immediately after a pulse of [³H]thymidine (Fig. 6b). The germi-nal cells are believed to add new differentiated cells to the retinal periphery, in the main by asymmetric division. That is, a round of division in the germinal ring produces an annulus of new neurons and pigment cells, on the "rim" of our truncated sphere, and a new genera-tion of germinal cells which are now displaced "one annulus further away" from the back of the eye. At any stage of development, then, autoradiographs prepared a week after a thymidine pulse show a labeled annulus of cells some few cell diameters back from the ciliary margin; additional annuli of more lightly labeled cells and finally un-labeled cells are interposed between the two, having been added to the retina (diluting their label with each round of division) in the week following the pulse. Not surprisingly, a series of pulses at 10-day inter-vals throughout development (Jacobson, 1976) produce a series of labeled annuli, rather like the growth rings of a tree, when autoradio-graphs are prepared from the adult eyeball (Fig. 6c). Annuli abutting the optic nerve at the back of the eye were added at the earliest stages of development; annuli located farther and farther from the optic nerve (and thus ever closer to the ciliary margin of the adult eye) were formed at successively later stages of development. It follows that the plane of section used to display our chimeric eyes (Fig. 3e) yields a set of tissue sections whose serial order roughly mimics the temporal order by which the cells were produced (Fig. 6d).

Although the geometry of cell accretion is invariant throughout development, the absolute rate of cell accretion (e.g., numbers of annuli added per week) may vary over development; and during certain phases of development, different relative rates may exist at different an-gular positions around the eye periphery. Grant and Rubin (1980) feel that for the first week or two of larval life, growth is greater in the dorsal retina. This is consistent with the appearance of the eye at these stages, and with the fact that the optic nerve head lies ventrally during this time. Jacobson (1976) and Beach (1977) have studied cell division during the later part of larval life in some detail. They report that mid-larval tadpoles have approximately the same growth dorsally and ventrally. Concurrent with the development of hindlimb buds, how-

the four samplings of intertectal units (shown in the lettered visual field circles at bottom right) were recorded. Since nearly all retinotectal fibers from the right eye cross to the contralateral (left) tectum, these ipsilateral units represent an indirect, polysynaptic projection relayed through the left tectum.

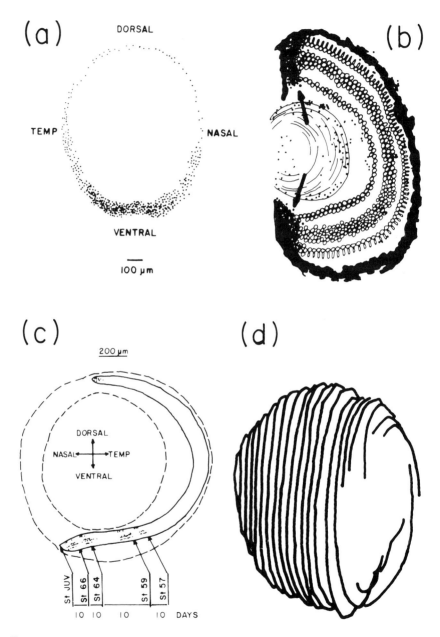

FIG. 6. Annular growth of *Xenopus* eye. (a) A ring of germinal cells resides at the ciliary margin. Dots show the positions of all mitotic figures in the eye of a stage 63 tadpole, 1 day after injection of colcemid. Redrawn from Beach (1977). (b) A camera

ever, there is a large increase in the number of ventral cells synthesizing DNA. There is no decrease in the cell cycle (20 hours). Thus the number of dividing cells must have increased. This increase in stem cells ventrally can be induced precociously in one eye by intraocular thyroxin implants. Beach and Jacobson (1979a,b) also report that the growth of the eye remains symmetric with respect to the nasotemporal axis through mid- to late larval life. The dorsoventral asymmetry peaks during metamorphic climax, but some measure of asymmetry remains throughout juvenile life. After metamorphosis, the absolute rate of cell accretion drops greatly and remains low. Over many many months, however, this low rate of cell accretion enables the eye to increase about 3-fold in cell number. The ganglion cell population grows from 10,000–20,000 cells in a new froglet to 70,000 cells in an old (2 kg) adult.

II. Polyclone Patterns in Pigment Retinal Epithelium

In this system, then, something is already known about the pattern of cell division during growth. It can be likened to a "moving" boundary which leaves a trail or *stream* of cells in its wake. What then are the clonal relationships among the cells of the retina? Do the germinal cells at 12 o'clock on the early larval eye lay down a clonal stream of their own that remains contiguous and constant at its 12 o'clock position throughout all subsequent growth? Are the germinal cells which occupy the 12 o'clock position in the metamorphosing eye descended from germinal cells which had occupied the 12 o'clock position in the early eye-bud? Will a population of marked germinal cells, introduced at the 12 o'clock position in the embryonic eye-bud, lay down perfectly

---

lucida drawing, from a coronal section through the eye, shows the confinement of [³H]thimidine label (arrows) to the ciliary margin in stage 45 animals fixed 2 hours after injection of isotope. Redrawn from Straznicky and Gaze (1971). (c) Following many such thymidine injections, administered at 10-day intervals throughout larval development, autoradiographs of coronal sections show a banding pattern (dots and arrows), here rendered in camera lucida. Redrawn from Jacobson (1976). (d) Computer-generated three-dimensional image of a *Xenopus* eye recapitulates the time course of development. The eye has been sectioned in a plane roughly perpendicular to the optic axis, such that the first sections pass through the cornea, then through the front of the eye including the iris, then through the fattest part of the eye, then the back, and finally through the optic nerve. The series of contours generated from such a set of sections represents, to a first approximation, a "time series" of cell birth dates in development: thus all the cells in one section were born at or near the same developmental stage. The back sections (to the left) contain cells that were formed earliest in development, while cells nearest the front of the eye (to the right) contain cells formed late in development, very near in time to the day of sacrifice.

overlapping streams in all layers of the eye? Do streams dissipate, indicating that cells move and mix among one another after they have been added to the differentiated retina? Does one contiguous stream split into two over its outward course, indicating, for example, that a group of germinal cells, originally residing at 12 o'clock, split during development into two smaller groups at 1 o'clock and 11 o'clock? Do streams widen or narrow over their outward course, reflecting local *temporal* fluctuations in cell accretion rate? Do streams laid down at the dorsal (12 o'clock) position differ from those laid down at the anterior or ventral pole, reflecting *spatial* differences in histogenesis at different angular growth points around the eye?

In the discussion to follow, we reserve the term *boundary* to describe points and lines between the polyclone (derived from a marked graft) and the adjacent host cells. However, the notion of the ciliary margin as a slowly moving boundary, depositing a stream of cells in its wake is a helpful construct in relating the geometries of polyclones to the histogenetic processes that gave rise to them. In fact, most grafts do lay down a coherent stream of cells in the PRE; and the variations on this theme, seen in certain types of grafts or in other eye tissues, provide an affirmative answer to virtually all of the questions posed.

A. POLYCLONES AND THEIR BOUNDARIES IN HALF-EYE MOSAICS

Consider, for example, a simple *half-eye* graft in which half of the eye-bud is excised from a 2-day albino host embryo (embryonic stage 32) and replaced by the corresponding half of a donor eye-bud from a 2-day pigmented embryo (of the same stage). Figure 7a–f shows a typical anterior/posterior mosaic, in which the posterior half of the albino bud was replaced by the posterior half of a wild-type bud (Fig. 7a). Viewed in the postmetamorphic frog (Fig. 7b), a large, contiguous patch of pigmentation is seen encompassing the posterior "half" of the eyeball. In this case, the external photograph also shows strict black–white boundaries, running radially outward from the back of the eye to the rim of the pupil (Fig. 7c–f). Three-dimensional reconstruction confirms that roughly the posterior half of the PRE is clonally descended from the graft, and that pigmented and albino cells are cleanly segregated on opposite sides of a strict radial boundary. An analogous pattern of black and white sectors is seen in dorsal/ventral mosaics prepared by replacing the dorsal half or the ventral half of the 2-day eye-bud.

The "half-eye" mosaics illustrated in Fig. 7 are typical in that the PRE is not partitioned into precisely equal "halves." The exact fraction of the PRE derived from the graft is rarely 50%, and varies from case to

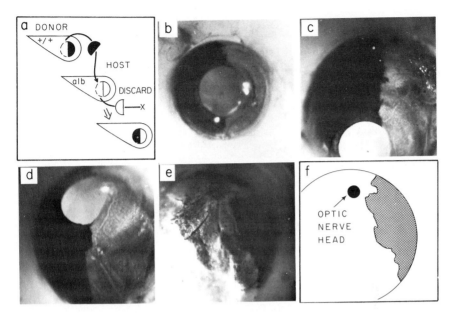

FIG. 7. Polyclone boundaries, in pigmentation mosaics, prepared by half-eye replacement in stage-32 embryos. (a) Operative schemata of the surgery used to prepare an anterior/posterior half-eye mosaic. (b–e) External photomicrographs and tracings showing detailed boundary relations of the pigmentation polyclone in the juvenile frog. (b) Front view of the eyeball at low power (×14). (c) Higher power view of dorsofrontal boundary (×21). (d) Similar ventrofrontal view (×21). (e,f) Boundary of the polyclone at the back of the eye (here viewed after the eye has been dissected free from the frog and aided by the accompanying schematic) showing irregularities and departures from strict radial lines (×21).

case in individual half-eye mosaics. The animal illustrated in Fig. 7 is also typical in that, however the angular extent is divided up between graft and host cells, the fractions remain fairly constant, and the boundary resides at a roughly constant angular position—over most of the eye's *radial extent* from the optic nerve in back to the ciliary margin in front. Thus, one anterior/posterior mosaic may show boundaries at 11 o'clock and 6 o'clock on the back of the eye (with the graft occupying 40–45% of the eye's angular extent), but the boundaries are likely to remain at or near 11 o'clock and 6 o'clock over most of the eye surface. Another anterior/posterior mosaic may show boundaries at 12 and 5 o'clock, but these are similarly consistent over most of the eye surface.

To be sure, polyclone boundaries do not follow a perfect *radial line* running at precisely the same angular position from the optic nerve to the ciliary margin. There are exceptions at the extreme back of the juvenile eye (where boundaries are irregular) and at the extreme front of the eye (where different types of graft show characteristic "metamorphic variations") and occasionally even a local irregularity in the boundary regions in between. Some of these are evident in Fig. 7, and all will be treated later. Yet the fact remains that all PRE polyclones are grossly bounded by radial lines, and many boundaries follow *strict* radial lines over much of their course. The concept of a radial line boundary and the notion of *consistency* in the size and position of a polyclone over its outward course are central. Following a radial line outward on a juvenile eye (from the optic nerve in back to the ciliary margin in front) recapitulates the sequence of "cell accretion annuli" added to the retina during its growth. If the polyclone really does occupy exactly 150° of arc around the eye over much of its radial extent, it is likely that: (*a*) descendants of the graft occupied 150° of arc on the germinal ring at some early stage of tadpole development; (*b*) later generations of marked germinal cells *continued* to occupy 150° of arc on the germinal ring for a long time thereafter; and (*c*) mature regions of the PRE (away from the germinal zone) must *maintain* the boundary indefinitely. If the 150° of arc lie at the exact same angular location over this radial course (such that a boundary follows a radial line at, say, 11 o'clock) it implies that descendants of the graft maintained a *constant position* on (as well as a constant fraction of) the germinal ring over much of development, and that pigmented PRE cells likewise remain within a constant angular domain within the mature PRE cell sheet. In simple terms, the "stream" is laid down from a constant angular position and, once formed, does not move or mix with adjacent streams.

The legitimacy of this interpretation—indeed of the "stream" analogy itself, and the whole notion of relating where a boundary is on the juvenile eye to where a boundary *may have* existed in the germinal ring when that part of the eye was formed—depends upon the natural history of boundary regions in the PRE. For boundaries could in principle, be maintained (or even created) by active sorting (Steinberg, 1970; Garber and Moscona, 1972) rather than by the absence of cell mixing. We have used external photography at several stages of development, to follow a few special boundary configurations which we will describe later: boundaries are equally sharp in the tadpole, metamorphosing froglet, and juvenile frog. Corroborative information can be obtained within one juvenile eye by simply comparing an "old" PRE boundary some distance away from the ciliary margin with a "young" PRE boundary near the ciliary margin, and comparing the latter with the boundary within the germinal ring itself. In fact, the boundary is equally sharp in all three regions.

At an old boundary, some rate constant (k_{mix}) exists for a *mixing* event, in which a black cell jumps across the boundary and joins the group of albino cells; and another rate constant (k_{sort}) exists for the sorting event in which such a cell either jumps back or is eliminated by cell death.[2] The fact that the old boundary is just as sharp as the young boundary (and the polyclone is contiguous on one side of it) indicates the boundary is being maintained over time and that k_{sort} is much greater than k_{mix}. A complete absence of cell mixing is but a special case of this; if cells which make the jump return quickly and actively to their side of the boundary (or simply are killed), we would also observe a very sharp boundary as a steady state configuration. The key observation, however, is that the boundary is equally sharp within the growth zone. The pigmented germinal cells, contiguous with the PRE, are themselves contiguous and bounded from albino germinal cells within the ciliary margin. Thus, new annuli possess a boundary even as they are added to the retina. This rules out the alternative that PRE cells are generated from the germinal ring in a salt-and-pepper configuration and then (because $k_{sort} >> k_{mix}$) *construct* a boundary from scratch by active sorting. Our stream analogy is justified, in the sense that a bounded stream is laid down (from the growth zone) and maintained thereafter (in mature regions of the PRE). The maintenance of boundary configurations, both within the germinal zone itself and in mature regions of the PRE, may reflect an absence of cell mixing or a rapid, compensatory cell sorting. Shortly, we will consider a few special boundary configurations that suggest that both mixing and sorting may be rare, and that (at least within the germinal ring) the rare mixing events which do occur engender not a sorting response but a compensatory change in the rate of cell accretion. Perhaps more important than the specific conclusions are the analytical keys by which the interpretation was reached. Tracing a polyclone over its outward radial course (following and comparing boundaries in old and young regions of mature PRE as well as in the growth zone itself) samples a succes-

---

[2] We consider only a formal transition between two states: S, in which our test cell is on its correct side of the boundary; and M, in which our test cell is translocated to the wrong side of the boundary and is surrounded by clonally unrelated cells. Thus the rate constants simply reflect the average probabilities of state transitions:

$$M \underset{k_{mix}}{\overset{k_{sort}}{\rightleftharpoons}} S$$

and we make no assumptions about whether the probabilities are affected by distance from the boundary, whether more than one cell move together, etc.

sion of growth annuli in roughly the same order as they were added to the retina. Such a sampling, when radial contiguity exists and boundaries are smooth and continuous into the germinal ring itself, provides a tachistoscopic view of the succession of configurations through which the germinal zone evolved during development. The second key involves external photography applied to the same eye at several stages of development. Photography provides corroborative evidence that stability or fluctuations in a polyclonal stream really do reflect stability or fluctuations in the germinal ring over time, in the way it adds cells to the retina.

The extreme back of the eye provides our first exception to the general rule of radial straight-line boundaries—there boundaries are sharp but irregular—and may provide clues to the nonequivalence of pigmented and nonpigmented "halves." At day 2 or 3 of development, when the surgery is performed, the eye-bud already contains a few hundred nongerminal cells. In the 2 or 3 days between the time a graft is introduced and the time graft and host tissues have healed to form a single coherent eye, many more postmitotic cells would normally be added to the retina. This central and pericentral population is destined to reside at the extreme back of the eye, immediately encircling the optic nerve. When a half-eye replacement is performed, the eye-bud fragments undergo an elastic deformation. Over the healing period, each half-bud begins to round-up and the recombinant assumes a "dumbbell" configuration. Only after 2 or 3 days does the "dumbbell" smooth into a rounded, spherical shape. Occasionally, the two fragments show different degrees of initial deformation or subsequent rounding, so that, as the dumbbell forms, it is somewhat asymmetric. As its shape becomes more spherical, the recombinant retains a configuration in which slightly more or less than half of the pupil margin is ringed with pigmented cells. Moreover, further back on this small sphere, the boundaries between black and white cells, although still sharp, often follow highly irregular contours.

It is likely that the nonequivalence of "halves" in half-eye mosaics can be traced to subtle asymmetries in the initial construction of the chimeric eye. One source of this asymmetry is the healing process itself. As they fuse to form a single eye, the two fragments may experience different amounts of deformation, and one or both fragments may show altered rates of cell accretion in response to the healing conditions (Horder and Spitzer, 1973; French *et al.,* 1976) as we shall see later. A second source of asymmetry is the graft itself. Attempts to make a "half" eye-bud cannot be sufficiently controlled to produce a fragment that contains precisely 50% of the bud's cells. In fact, when "half" eye-buds were prepared on wild-type embryos using procedures very similar to those used in our mosaic eyes, Berman and Hunt (1975) found that the "half" buds were rather variable in size upon reconstruction. Some bud fragments contained as few as 40% of the cell numbers in the unoperated eye-bud on the opposite side, others as many as 60%.

In summary, then, the extreme back of the eye in a juvenile half-eye mosaic may show some "wobble" in the black/white boundary, but rather strict radial boundaries emerge a short distance out from the optic nerve. Both the initial irregularities, and the positioning of the radial boundaries that are eventually established (and hence the size or nonequivalence of pigmented and albino territories), are likely the result of subtle variations among half eye-buds and in the dynamics of the healing process. That the boundaries *continue* to follow the same radial lines over the remainder of their course to the ciliary margin indicates that an *initial mosaic configuration,* established in the germinal ring of the healed recombinant, *was perpetuated* in the germinal ring over most of subsequent development. Finally, we can use a hypothetical case to take the analysis one step further. Any polyclone which has established strict radial boundaries on the back of the eye and which shows a local or systematic *deflection* in the front of the eye (such that the boundary no longer follows the radial line) must have (a) established an initial mosaic configuration in the germinal ring of the healed recombinant, (b) perpetuated it for days or weeks as many annuli of cells were added to the tadpole retina, and then (c) *changed the mosaic configuration* abruptly at some late stage of development. In fact, subtle variations on the radial theme do exist in the boundaries of half-eye mosaics as they curve round the front of the eye (Fig. 7d–f). Such variations are richly informative, but we shall consider them, in the main, in connection with pole-graft mosaics, to which we now return.

B. POLE-GRAFTS: SIZE AND METAMORPHIC VARIATIONS

Pole-grafts, an example of which was shown in Fig. 3, involve transplantation of a small bit of eye-bud tissue, smaller than a quadrant, and, in the smallest cases, no more than a few dozen cells. A full-thickness wedge of tissue (a "pie-slice" extending inward from the rim of the bud into the lens rudiment) is excised from a designated angular position on the host eye-bud. As with the simple half-eye replacements, so-called *orthotopic* pole-grafts attempt to replace the excised bit of host tissue with a donor wedge that is precisely matched in size and bud position. For example, we might excise a 30–45° sector at the dorsal pole and replace it with a similar sized wedge from the dorsal pole of the donor eye-bud. By contrast, *heterotopic* grafts purposefully *mismatch* the positions of graft origin and graft implantation to examine how the behavior of anterior pole cells, for example, may change if they are made to grow out from a posterior position on the eye. Finally, as with the half-eye grafts, our experiments span a number of genotypic combinations. Unless otherwise stated, however, observations on PRE polyclones will emphasize chimerae in which a pigmented (wild-type or *1-nu*) graft was introduced into an albino (*2-nu*) host.

Pole-grafts grow out polyclones in the PRE which adhere to the general principles derived from half-eye mosaics: The "stream" is sharply bounded over its entire course and in the germinal zone itself. Neither gray cells nor salt-and-pepper intermingling of black and white cells is seen. The exact contour of the boundary is irregular at the very back of the eye; but radial-line boundaries are established a short distance from the optic nerve, and they continue over most of the eye surface. Not surprisingly, pole-grafts lay down a much narrower "stream" than half-eye grafts. Thus, the boundaries may be only 30–75% apart, with the pigmented cells occupying a *sector* that radiates outward from the nerve to the ciliary margin in the juvenile eye (Fig. 3c and e–g; Fig. 8).

In practice, any set of orthotopic grafts, involving (what we intend to be) the same transplantation maneuver, yields polyclones which differ slightly from one another in size and position. As we argued in treating variation among half-eye mosaics, it is likely that these differences reflect our inability to control the precise size and position of both hole and graft, as well as individual variation in the way grafts heal into place. Thus, a bit of individuality is built into the *initial* mosaic configuration on the germinal ring of each healed recombinant, and is simply perpetuated on future germinal rings during growth. In fact, observations on healing pole-grafts lend further credence to this explanation. Individual pole-grafts establish a variable "arc" around the rim of the pupil in the healed recombinant. Those in which the arc is noted as small in the postoperative individual nearly always produce a polyclone of narrow angular representation on the adult PRE. Moreover, in a few cases, pigmented cells never abut the rim of the pupil in the healed recombinant. That is, they fail to establish any "arc"-territory on the pupillary rim and, by inference, fail to populate the germinal ring at all. These cases fail to grow out a polyclone and, when reared to juvenile stages, show only a tiny patch of pigmented cells, abutting the optic nerve at the extreme back of the eye.

Pole-grafts provide insights, perhaps more direct than those from half-eye grafts, into the local properties of cells at different angular positions around the eye. For this reason, we have focused our attention upon the pole-graft mosaics in examining the way clone size varies with graft position and in treating two phenomena alluded to in the discussion of half-eye mosaics: deflection of a polyclone boundary from an established radial line, and local mismatch between the real boundary and the idealized line over a short stretch of boundary region. Programs developed in this laboratory will eventually allow the computer to (a) correct for the case-to-case variation in the exact plane of section, (b) reassign the reconstruction data to a coordinate system that *exactly* matches the spatiotemporal sequence of cell birthdate in the eye, and (c) calculate the relative size of individual polyclones, at various radial distances between the optic nerve head and the ciliary margin (Conway *et al.*, 1980). This will allow more quantitative treatment of the relative growth dynamics at different angular positions around the eye, at various stages of development. For the moment, we confine our discussion to the more marked quantitative variations between clones and to the qualitative variations in their geometry.

Despite the presence of individual variation within each group, polyclones derived from different grafted poles show conspicuous differences in their overall size, Ventral pole-grafts lay down a wide "stream," and it remains wide from the point where strict radial boundaries are established on the back of the eye around the front of the eye to the ciliary margin. Dorsal pole-grafts, on the other hand, lay down extremely narrow streams, much narrower even than the streams laid down by anterior and posterior grafts. These differences can be seen in Fig. 8. Since the position of radial-line boundaries and thus the width of the polyclone are presumed to reflect the *construction* of the initial mosaic configuration, it appears that local regions of the eye-bud possess marked differences in the 2-day embryo. Whether these position-dependent properties affect cell survival, deformation, or mitosis during healing cannot yet be determined; and the final result may well reflect a composite of several parameters.

What we can determine, from the behavior of these same types of poles when implanted as *heterotopic* grafts, is whether these properties can be expressed by the graft itself, independent of the healing site. The results offer clear evidence that the grafts themselves possess intrinsic differences. Many dorsal pole-grafts, transplanted to an anterior or posterior hole, grow out the narrow polyclone that is the hallmark of orthotopic dorsal pole-grafts. Most ventral pole-grafts likewise produce an unusually wide polyclone at these same positions. This is not to say

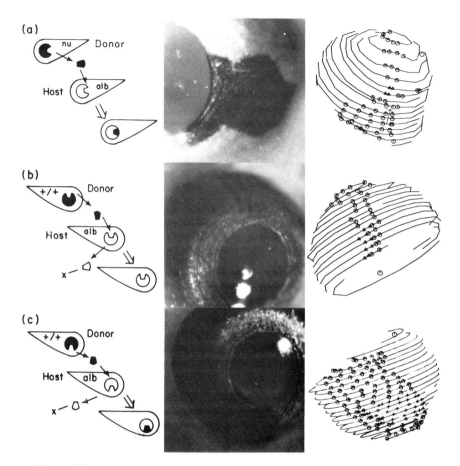

FIG. 8. PRE polyclones from three types of pole-grafts. For each graft, a schematic diagram of the pole-graft surgery is provided on the left, a photomicrograph of the eye (taken through the dissecting microscope immediately before histological material was prepared) is shown in the center, and rotated images displaying the PRE polyclone reconstructed from tissue sections are shown at the right. (a) A posterior pole-graft and polyclone (×25). (b) A dorsal pole-graft and polyclone (×20). (c) A ventral pole-graft and polyclone (×20). In the three eyes displayed, serial reconstruction revealed noncontinuous patches of pigment in the PRE. In (b), this discontinuity is also evident in the external appearance of the animals. Different symbols (+, △) were used to differentiate these areas.

that the implantation site is devoid of local properties which affect polyclone size: ventral pole-grafts, for example, may grow out slightly *wider* polyclones from an anterior hole than from a ventral one. Nevertheless, the maintenance of local properties in some heterotopic pole-grafts provides compelling evidence that local cell groups around the eye have already been programmed with distinct differentiated traits, as early as 2 days of age.

An even more intriguing set of phenomena, supporting the same conclusion, is observed on the front of the juvenile eye (Hunt and Ide, 1977). Having established a "stream" on the back of the eye that roughly follows radial-line boundaries, the polyclones derived from different grafted poles weave characteristic variations on the radial theme as they course around the front of the eye to the ciliary margin. Viewed in the juvenile frog, this part of the PRE is made up of annuli added to the retina during and after metamorphic climax. Remarkably, at least some heterotopic pole-grafts show the specific metamorphic variation appropriate to the *original position* of the graft in the donor eye-bud.

Dorsal polyclones, narrow in their angular representation throughout their course, often become narrower still on the front of the eye. They appear to show a steady *decline* in their angular representation as they approach the ciliary margin. Thus a polyclone appears to shrink over the final stretch of its course. In addition, many dorsal polyclones which began as typical single streams on the back of the eye, split into two streams as they approach the ciliary margin (Fig. 8b). When both *declining angular representation* and *splitting* occur in the same dorsal polyclone, the pattern of pigmentation presents a dramatic image. One black stripe, curving around the eye, gives way smoothly to two stripes, each of which taper down to a "point" at or just before the ciliary margin. Pole-grafts at other eye-bud positions give rise to polyclones with their own metamorphic variations. Ventral polyclones, wide throughout their course, appear to become ever wider as they approach the ciliary margin (Fig. 8c), although (as will be described later) the iris greatly exaggerates this pattern in external views of the eye. Anterior and posterior polyclones, especially those which grow out at a slightly dorsal position (e.g., "2 o'clock"), tend to veer toward an ever more dorsal position near the ciliary margin (Figs. 3a and 8a).

Applying the same analytical keys used in treating radial-line boundaries, we believe that these metamorphic variations reflect changes in the way the polyclonal "stream" is laid down (that is, changes in the germinal zone itself) rather than alterations in the morphology of the stream over time *after* it has been laid down. One key lies in the geometry of the polyclones themselves. Even as they split, narrow, widen, or veer off, they remain as a radially contiguous "stream" with smooth and continuous boundaries. Moreover, if these variations can be viewed as an orderly *aberration* from a strict radial plan, each aberration is continuously graded in extent with the "most aberrant" cells in the ciliary margin itself. For example, we do not observe a dorsal shift in *already-formed* regions of an anterior poly-clone, while the pigmented cells on the germinal ring retain their an-terior position. To the contrary, the most dorsal cells in an anterior polyclone are those at the ciliary margin. External photography exploits the external visibility of the pigment marker and provides a second line of evidence. It is possible to judiciously select individuals in which the external pattern of pigmentation clearly displays the poly-clone in the PRE (and confirm this later, in each case, by histologic reconstruction). Such individuals, examined at tadpole and juvenile stages, provide a direct confirmation that the *mosaic configuration* at the ciliary margin is changing over time.

The final key is provided by the autoradiographic data and mitotic counts of Beach and Jacobson (1979a,b; Jacobson, 1976; Beach, 1977). They observed graded differences in the rate of cell accretion, from a minimum at the dorsal pole to a maximum at the ventral pole, around the eye of the metamorphosing tadpole and juvenile frog. They also reported that the germinal ring became correspondingly "cell poor" at the dorsal pole and "cell rich" at the ventral pole. Our results comple-ment their findings. Dorsal polyclones, whose representatives on the germinal ring must decline in numbers at late larval stages, appear to constrict their angular territory as well. In some cases, adjacent albino cells on the germinal ring simply encroach on this territory; in other cases, they may become interposed between two waning groups of dor-sal germinal cells. Polyclones more ventrally disposed on the eye must build up increasing numbers of representatives of the germinal ring over successive cell generations at metamorphic climax, and may gradually grab up an increasing angular territory on the ring. The veering of anterior and posteriod polyclones may reflect the push and pull, on their intermediate number of precursors, of declining numbers on their dorsal flank and a population explosion on their ventral flank.

Heterotopic pole-grafts provide spectacular, if somewhat inconsis-tent, evidence that these metamorphic variations reflect position-dependent properties already specified in the 2-day eye-bud. Many ven-tral polyclones, though not all, show characteristic widening near the ciliary margin of the juvenile eye, even when made to grow out from an anterior or posterior implantation site. Some, but not all, dorsal poly-clones similarly show the characteristic narrowing during metamor-phosis in the same ectopic positions. The fact that some heterotopic pole-grafts fail to retain their characteristic metamorphic variation is annoying, but it does not compromise the basic conclusion. The paradigm of heterotopic grafting is considerably more complex than it seems. If the eye-bud contains regional properties that might be retained in a pole-graft, it is axiomatic that implantation sites would also show similar regional differences. One component of the regional uniqueness of implantation sites concerns simply the milieu in which the polyclone grows. Thus if a ventral polyclone is preordained to increase its precursor numbers at metamorphosis, the extent to which it increases its angular representation may be limited by the degree to which neighboring cells are destined to increase or decrease their precursor numbers. An example is provided by the behavior of anterior and posterior polyclones in heterotopic grafts. Anterior polyclones, growing out from a posterior implantation site, show characteristic veering as they approach the ciliary margin. They still veer toward a more dorsal position, however, rather than toward ventral. Thus the *occurrence* of veering is likely to represent properties within the polyclone (relating to modulation of precursor numbers during metamorphosis), but the *direction* of veering is governed by the local environment of overgrowing and undergrowing neighbors. A second prospect of regional differences in implantation sites is even more dramatic: as is known in many embryonic systems, regional properties in the implantation site may simply overrun the programmed properties in the graft. Thus, from a few hours after implantation, the polyclone may be reprogrammed with the local properties appropriate to its new region. These concerns will be treated in detail when we consider modes of "embryonic regulation" in Section IV. For the moment, it is sufficient to point out that some ventral polyclones retain their uniquely "ventral" metamorphic variation even when growing out from a heterotopic site, and some drosal polyclones retain their uniquely "dorsal" metamorphic variations under similar conditions. This can be explained only by the presence of programmed differences at different angular positions around the 2-day eye-bud. Unlike the case of the general width variations described previously (ventrals lay down wide streams, dorsals lay down narrow streams), the metamorphic variations cannot reflect trivial differences in the early eye-bud. Simple differential survival of cells in the graft, or differences in packing density or healing vigor, cannot account for changes which commence weeks or months after the graft was performed. Rather, these regional differences specify a unique response, which much later generations of polyclone-derived germinal cells will show, many weeks later, in response to the changing environment at metamorphosis.

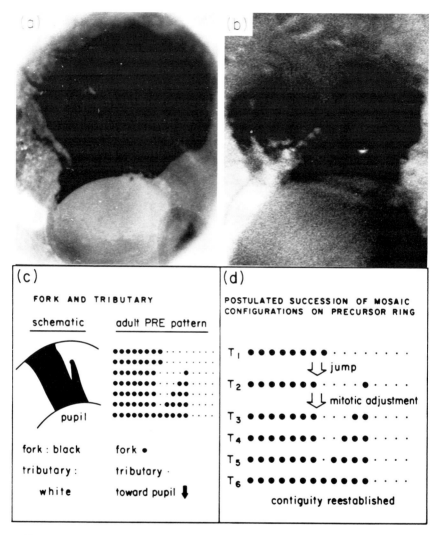

FIG. 9. External photographs of two chimeric eyes showing interlocking *fork* and *tributary* configurations at a polyclone boundary. (a) External photograph of a juvenile chimeric eye prepared at stage 32 by transplanting a pigmented posterior pole-graft into the posterior position on the rim of an albino host eye-bud. A schematic for orthotopic posterior pole-grafts is shown in Fig. 8a. The present eye is viewed from a posterior and frontal position such that posterior is up and dorsal is to the left (×35). At the dorsal edge of the polyclone, a *black* tributary has formed, in which a new secondary stream starts at some angular distance from the main polyclone boundary, widens toward the front of the eye, and eventually rejoins the main stream of the polyclone. A very small subpopulation (perhaps as small as one germinal cell) may have become separated from the main group and, by gradually *increasing* its contribution to cell accretion over time, reestablishes continuity with the main polyclone. The interlocking configuration of fork is formed by the intervening albino cells: a part of the "stream" appears to have veered off from the main part, and attentuates to a point at some further distance from the back of the eye. A subpopulation of

C. Local Irregularities in Polyclone Boundaries

Over the vast stretch of the eye surface where their boundaries generally follow a strict radial line, individual polyclones (from many different types of pole-grafts) may show a *local* irregularity over a short stretch of boundary region. These irregularities, in which the boundary makes a local departure from its established radial line, occur in three rather stereotyped forms. In keeping with our stream analogy, we have called them delta, fork, and tributary. In *deltas,* a side trail diverges smoothly from the main trail at some radial distance from the optic nerve head and then rejoins the main trail after some further radial distance between the divergence point and the ciliary margin. *Forks* (Fig. 9a and c) also begin as a substantial side trail but then narrow to a point and vanish. *Tributaries* begin as a point some distance from the polyclone boundary, and their trail widens (especially in the direction toward the main boundary) and rejoins the main body of the polyclone (Fig. 9a and c). Forks and tributaries, once formed, persist at considerable distances from the growth zone. Both irregularities involve a triangular configuration that intersects the main boundary of the clone at a point; and the two irregularities are reciprocally coincident, in the sense that a fork in the polyclone is necessarily accompanied by a tributary in the adjacent host tissue and vice versa (Fig. 9a and c).

The spatial configuration of these "side streams" in the radial direction provides clues to the *temporal* sequence of events by which they were laid down. All three irregularities are radially contiguous, and the boundary (even as it departs from the radial line) remains sharp and smooth. This suggests that the precursor cells which deposit the trail, rather than the trail itself, underwent the translocation leading to the laying down of two trails. Indeed, when such a precursor translocation occurs very early, during or just after healing of the recombinant eye-bud, a boundary irregularity may be propagated for weeks of subsequent growth, and may remain evident on the front face of the juvenile eye (Fig. 9b). When these local configurations are confined to a rather modest radial distance over the eye surface, we infer that (*a*) two separate trails were being laid down for only a brief period during

marked germinal cells may become separated from the main group at some stage of development and thereafter gradually ceases to contribute new cells to the eye. (b) External photograph of another juvenile chimeric eye (×50). At the left edge of the polyclone the black cells form a fork configuration at the rim of the pupil and a tributary configuration further back along the polyclone boundary. This tributary itself represents rejoining of an early fork that formed far back on the eye (not illustrated). This case illustrates that complex boundary configurations can arise which are not permanently resolved into two completely contiguous polyclones.

development and that (*b*) the translocated precursor cell(s) *rectified the translocation,* actively and rather promptly, in the days immediately following the day on which the translocation occurred. Exactly how this rectification occurs is unclear, but we have yet to observe "tributaries" that start from a point and course over a long (radial) distance while maintaining a constant "trail width" or failing to rejoin the main body of the polyclone. Similarly, forks may resolve them-selves over a short distance. The splitting of dorsal poles—the metamorphic variation described previously—involves the mainte-nance of two streams, with only a very gradual attentuation of stream width, over a long period from metamorphic climax into juvenile life. Local forks, by contrast, involve a rapid attenuation in which the rec-tification is completed within a few days or weeks. Although we have just begun to apply external photography at a succession of develop-mental stages, to watch the detailed evolution of these local configura-tions, preliminary evidence supports the view that they arise and are resolved by a shifting configuration in the germinal ring.

The reciprocal configurations of fork and tributary may begin by a rather long *jump* translocation, spanning several cell diameters on the growth ring. This translocation, which may involve only one or a very few cells undergoing a mixing event, is inferred from the configuration seen on the juvenile eye in the "annulus" closest to the optic nerve head in which the local irregularity appears. In contrast to the normal boundary (wwwwwwwwwwww*BBBBBBBBBB*), a "mixed" configuration appears (wwwww*B*wwww*BBBBBBBBBB*), as shown in Fig. 9d. The tributary established by the translocated (*B*) cell is a trail which *widens* over its course, indicating that the cell(s) which established the trail either divided more rapidly or underwent "symmetric" divisions to produce more precursor cells of the same kind. The fork, established by the isolated island of (w) cells, is a trail which attenuates over its course, indicating that the cells which established it either gradually died off or divided more slowly or underwent "symmetric" divisions to produce two *non*germinal cells, and eventually lost their territory on the growth ring altogether. That the tributary widens smoothly (with the greatest angular representation nearest the ciliary margin), and the fork narrows smoothly in the same direction provides a parallel to the widening and narrowing of ventral and dorsal polyclones during metamorphosis. We favor the view that the formation of fork and tributary involves modulations in the number of precursor cells (over successive generations on the germinal ring) derived from the translo-cated individuals. In any case, it appears that a low level of cell mixing can occur on the germinal ring itself, although such events may be rare. Rather than compensatory sorting, however, such mixing events appear to be resolved by dynamic fluctuations in growth that reestablish, only gradually, angular contiguity within the polyclone.[3]

In addition to insights into growth-zone dynamics, forks and tributaries provide definitive comment on the mechanism by which a boundary is maintained by PRE cells which have *left* the growth zone. At the point of union between the triangle and the main boundary of the polyclone, only a minimal sorting translocation is needed to bring cells into complete contiguity with clonally related cells. If sorting by fully differentiated PRE cells were possible, forks and tributaries should eventually be self-eliminating. That they persist, even maintaining the sharp junction point, is strong evidence that fully differentiated PRE cells, spatially removed from the growth zone, do not actively establish contiguity by sorting. Thus, unless these configurations reflect some major aberration of mechanism, it is likely that the absence of mixing, rather than mixing with *rapid complementary sorting,* is the prime mechanism for maintaining clonal contiguity in the PRE.

Finally, forks and tributaries offer comment on two other questions. The apex of each of the "interlocking" pair of triangles features a single cell or a few cells that is surrounded on all but one side by clonally unrelated cells. The persistence of such a point, and the fact that it is as sharp a black/white boundary as any in the PRE, indicates that mixing in the radial direction is also unlikely. This confirms the finding from [³H]thymidine autoradiography, that labeled "annuli" do not disperse or intermingle with unlabeled annuli over time (Jacobson, 1976). The configuration also provides strong evidence that the expression of the alb^P/alb^P genotype is cell autonomous in mosaic PREs. If any cell were a candidate for passive acquisition of wild-type gene product from its neighbors, an albino cell at the apex of a boundary triangle is such a cell. Apparently, the wild-type cell remains black even when largely surrounded by albino cells; the albino cell remains white even when largely surrounded by black cells. It would appear from the hypothe-

---

[3] It remains, of course, for mitotic counts and autoradiographic studies to confirm that isolated germinal cells reestablish contiguity on the precursor ring by adjusting growth rates, and to define the adjustments involved. Yet other questions remain. How do isolated cells sense their separation from the main group of graft-derived germinal cells? Why do isolated cells not increase their angular representation in the direction *away* from the clone? The latter question is even more compelling in the case of *heterotopic* grafts, where the polyclone shows fork or tributary configurations, and where the direction away from the clone is the direction toward the cell's correct angular position in the eye.

sized origin of the tributary (from a single translocated germinal cell) that germinal cells can maintain this autonomy of phenotype as well.

Deltas reflect a different resolution of what may be a similar jump translocation. Here the translocated cells appear to respond as if initiating the interlocking configuration of fork and tributary, but then show a reversal of their respective growth dynamics such that the isolated pool begins to decline once more. The result is a delta and its interlocking configuration of an *island*. At present we have not studied deltas extensively, and we have observed configurations in which a "trapped" population of albino cells appears to be perpetuated on the germinal ring for an extensive period of time (Fig. 9d). In fact, forks occasionally persist over a long distance traceable to the very back of the eye. It is possible that deltas are more complicated than we presently appreciate. At least some deltas (and the occasional prolonged fork) may actually reflect an *initial mosaic configuration* in which the pigmented cells were not contiguous on the germinal ring of the healed recombinant. Further details on the etiology of forks and tributaries as well as deltas await more direct scrutiny of the growth zone at stages immediately following their initiation.

D. PRE as a Model for Clonal Organization

In summary then, patterns of mosaicism in the pigment retinal epithelium have served their function as a highly visual model for deriving principles of polyclonal organization in the retina. Viewed in the juvenile frog, polyclones in the PRE extend radially outward as contiguous "sectors" from the optic nerve head to the ciliary margin. Boundaries are everywhere sharp, completely segregating black from white cells, and, over most of their course, the boundaries follow strict radial lines. The size of the polyclone (the number of degrees of angular representation around the eye) is fairly constant throughout and commensurate with the fraction of the eye-bud replaced by the initial graft. Thus, pole-grafts produce narrow polyclones occupying a quadrant or less on the adult PRE; half-eye replacements give rise to wide polyclones occupying roughly half of the angular representation around the juvenile PRE. Within each general category, however, some case-to-case variation exists in the size of the polyclone derived from ostensibly identical grafting procedures. Moreover, pole-grafts at different angular positions on the eye-bud show somewhat different size distributions in the set of polyclones they generate. Finally, the boundaries show slight irregularities at the extreme back of the juvenile eye (the region which contains cells formed around the time of surgery and healing), and they also show spectacular "metamorphic variations" at the front of the juvenuile eye (the regions formed during and immediately after metamorphosis). Dorsal polyclones show a decline in their angular representation and may split from one stream into two; anterior and posterior polyclones often veer toward a more dorsal position; and ventral polyclones may increase their angular representation somewhat as they approach the ciliary margin. Polyclones derived from heterotopic grafts indicate that both the general size of polyclones (derived from different regions of the eye-bud) and the metamorphic variations they show reflect, at least in part, the position-dependent properties already assigned to precursor cells at different angular positions around the 2-day eye-bud.

It would appear, then, that graft and host heal together to establish an initial mosaic configuration. Slight variations in individual surgeries and in the healing response may lead to slight irregularities in the back of the eye, and slight case-to-case variation in the size and position which the "arc" of pigmented cells on the germinal ring of the healed recombinant. Once established, this mosaic configuration is maintained throughout most of development. Annuli are added already containing sharp boundaries between black and white cells. These boundaries are maintained over time, in the mature regions of the PRE, by an absence of cell mixing and perhaps also by a compensatory cell death or sorting event in response to an accidental mixing event. Slight irregularities in the boundary, which we have termed forks and tributaries, suggest that the absence of mixing is the predominant factor by which boundaries are maintained in the mature regions of PRE. These irregularities also show that occasional mixing events can occur at the boundary on the germinal ring, and that they lead to a compensatory response in which the transposed cells adjust their precursor numbers over several generations, allowing one population to overrun the other and to reestablish clonal contiguity. Finally, the presence of metamorphic variations suggests that (at least during metamorphosis and perhaps throughout juvenile life) a dynamic competition exists for maintenance of territory on the germinal ring. At metamorphic climax and thereafter, dorsal cells appear to be the losers in this competition, showing declining angular representation and encroachment into their territory by adjacent anterior and posterior cells. Ventral cells appear to be modest winners in this competitive process, encroaching in toward the anterior or posterior pole and contributing (perhaps as cause or consequence or both) to the dorsal displacement of anterior and posterior cells. Heterotopic grafts show dorsal displacement of anterior and posterior polyclones, indicating that the twist reflects *environmental* competition during metamorphosis rather than an intrinsic bias within the cells to twist in one direction rather than the other. That dorsal pole-grafts and ventral pole-grafts, in some heterotopic transplantations, retain their characteristics toward metamorphic variation provides strong evidence that programmed differences exist around the eye-bud as early as the second day of embryonic life. Precursor cells at different angular positions on the germinal ring already possess a plan for unique responses to the metamorphic environment that will arise many weeks later.

III. Iris, Choroid, and Neural Retina

Because the pigment marker is externally visible, we can compare an external photograph of each eye to the computer-generated image reconstructed from its tissue sections. A successful match of what the camera sees provides a final common validation of the entire methodology for sectioning, tracing, aligning, inputting, storing, and displaying mosaic data from histologic sections (Hunt *et al.*, 1979b; Feiock *et al.*, 1980). Because *several* pigmented tissues exist in the eye, the pigment marker allows us to develop general paradigms for comparing the way polyclones in one eye tissue *overlay* with polyclones in another. In practice, the maneuvers of overlay and of reconstituting an external image are inextricably related. In many chimeric eyes, the eye-bud graft has given rise to pigmented cells in two or more of the eye's melanogenic tissues. It follows that reconstitution of the external image will require not only histologic reconstruction of the polyclones in each pigmented tissue, but also a successful execution of an overlay of these polyclones so as to produce a composite pattern of pigmentation for the eye as a whole. Figure 10 shows a stylized example of the relationships of the eye's pigmented tissues, and of the way, in an extreme case, three very different polyclones in choroid, iris, and PRE could sum together to produce a composite pattern of pigmentation seen on external view.

In many cases, the external image and the polyclone reconstructed from the PRE show a remarkable match over most of the eye surface. As it turns out, these cases also represent instances in which the polyclone contributes few if any cells to the choroid (see Fig. 12a and b). When a few pigmented cells are present in the choroid, they are confined to a small patch in the extreme back of the eye, suggesting that the graft contributed a few choroidal cells to the back of the healed recombinant, but *failed* to populate whatever precursor pool gives rise to most of the choroid later on. In any event, these cases are sufficient to validate our general methodologies for tissue tracing alighment and computer display. Not surprisingly, however, a local disagreement may

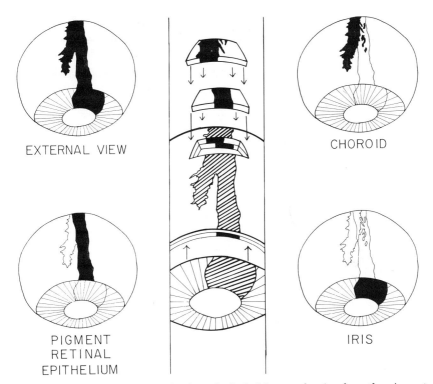

EXTERNAL VIEW

CHOROID

PIGMENT
RETINAL
EPITHELIUM

IRIS

FIG. 10. Schematic diagram of a hypothetical chimera, showing how the pigment pattern seen on external view (top left) can be a composite of polyclone cells in PRE, choroid, and iris. The disassembled eye in the center shows the relationships between the three structures.

exist between external image and PRE polyclone at the extreme front of the eye. The "mismatch" is such that the patch of pigmentation seen on external view is *inclusive* of the PRE polyclone: matching it exactly over most of the eye's surface, yet containing "something extra" in the region near the pupil. This something extra consists of graft-derived cells which have contributed to the iris.

Reconstruction of the iris has been a laborious process. The tissue is very fragile, and it may be even more fragile in some albino individuals. Like the PRE, it is smoothly continuous with the pigmented cells of the ciliary margin (Fig. 11e). Fortunately, some serendipitous cases (Figs. 11 and 13c and d) contained pigmentation in only one or the other of the two tissues and enabled us to determine with some accuracy where the PRE ends and the iris begins. Our analysis has been further complicated by the lack of baseline autoradiographic data on the

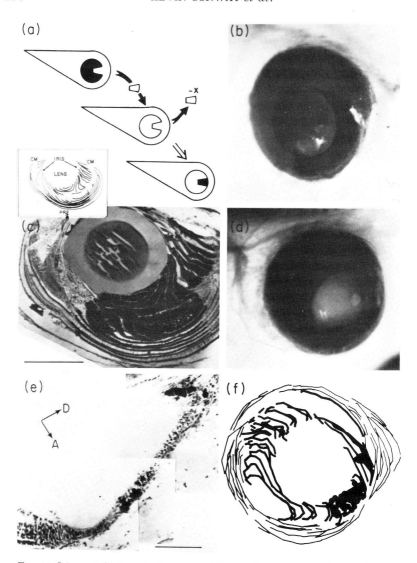

FIG. 11. Iris contributions to the pigmentation pattern seen in external photographs.
(a) A pole-graft of a *ventral* fragment into a nasal hole grows out a polyclone which, in the
juvenile animal (b), appears markedly and abruptly wider at the edge of the pupil than at
any other radial position between the optic nerve and pupil (×15). (c) Montage (500 µm),
prepared from consecutive sections through this eye, reveals that most of the apparent
"overgrowth" is confined to the iris (see insert). That is, the angular representation of the
polyclone in the iris is much greater than that in the PRE. A pole-graft of a *dorsal*
fragment into the same position (d) grows out a polyclone with much less angular representation in the iris (×15). The iris contained two clones; one in apposition to the PRE
and a smaller clone located more dorsally. (e) A montage of one section shows both

way the iris grows. It seems reasonable that the iris forms from the ciliary margin as well, simply adding cells in the opposite direction from the rest of the eye's layers. Until this hypothesis can be confirmed directly, however, we are severely limited in our ability to relate polyclone geometries in the iris to the histogenetic processes by which the iris is formed. What can be said at present is that polyclones in the iris are also contiguous, and thus are likely to derive from a spatially circumscribed subpopulation of precursor cells. They also contain sharp boundaries and thus the principles for interpreting boundaries (mixing is absent or compensatory sorting occurs) are likely to hold for the iris as well. It is also clear that the precise angular representation of a polyclone in the iris may differ somewhat from the angular representation of a polyclone in the PRE of the same (Fig. 11a, b, and c). As in our stylized case in Fig. 10, the polyclone may extend further around the eye in the iris than it has throughout its course in the PRE. This discontinuity between iris and PRE, though poorly understood at present, has enabled us to use the iris in developing overlay maneuvers. By reconstructing the iris and superimposing the reconstructed image on that derived from the PRE (Fig. 11d and f), it is possible to reconstruct this discontinuity in a composite, computer-generated image. It should be noted here that the iris tends to exaggerate the dorsal undergrowth and ventral overgrowth phenomena discussed earlier. For instance, dorsal iris adjacent to a dorsal clone may not be pigmented at all. Interpretation of external photos can be confirmed by subsequent histological analysis.

A substantial minority of black-into-white mosaics do not show a sharply bounded "stream" of pigmentation on external view of the juvenile eye. Instead, they show a more irregular pattern which ranges at one extreme from a rather jagged but spatially circumscribed streak of pigment to a generally mottled appearance at the other extreme (Fig. 12c). An even more peculiar exception was discovered when we attempted to prepare "reciprocal" mosaics, by replacing a bit of pigmented eye-bud tissue with an albino graft. Because albino pole-grafts are very difficult to visualize postoperatively (and thus to exclude the possibility that the graft has failed to heal into place), we emphasized half-eye replacements in these reciprocal experiments. Despite obvious evidence of mosaicism in the healing recombinant, nearly all of the

patches of pigment in the iris as well as the ciliary margin (100 μm). (f) Computer displays, superimposing the reconstructions of the iris (heavy lines) and PRE (light lines), faithfully duplicate the pattern seen in external view.

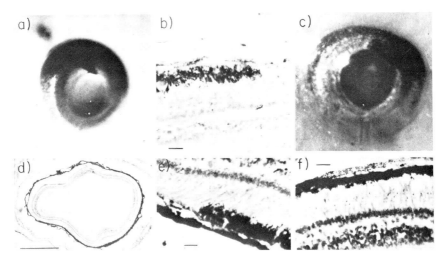

FIG. 12. Clonal analysis of the choroid. (a) Externally, some animals showed very clear clonal boundaries (×12). Subsequent histologic preparations revealed that the choroid in these animals was either very sparsely pigmented, or was amelanotic (b) (20 μm). In other grafts, the external appearance (c) was markedly different (×16): the clone did not contain "clean" boundaries. Sections through a "half" eye mosaic, prepared by implanting a graft from an albino animal into a wild-type host, which were completely black externally (d), showed a heavily pigmented choroid (500 μm) and a sharply bounded *polyclone* of pigment in the PRE (e) (20 μm). In grafts involving a pigmented donor and an albino host, the choroid typically shows varying degrees of pigmentation, often even within the same eye. Transitions from pigmented to nonpigmented choroid were sometimes gradual and made over long angular distances around the eye (f) (20 μm). The choroid clearly represents a very different clonal pattern from that seen in the PRE.

juvenile eyes were completely black on external view. In both instances, the external image reflects the presence of pigmented cells in the choroid. In the latter case, the uniformly black choroid belies the presence of typical sector mosaicism in the underlying PRE of white-into-black mosaics (Fig. 12d and e).

Even when the choroid is extensively pigmented, there may be no clear pattern or boundary. Choroid polyclones are perhaps best described as an amorphous "cloud" of pigmentation. In some regions of a black-into-white mosaic, the pigmentation is highly dense, giving the choroid an appearance of contiguity among pigmented cells in histologic sections. In other regions of the same eye, however, the density of pigmentation simply attentuates in space, producing a "graying-out" of the polyclone in lieu of a sharp black–white boundary (Fig. 12f). In contrast to the PRE, the choroid shows many cells of limited individual pigment density. Both the presence of "gray" cells, and the absence of sharp boundaries and of radial contiguity in many regions of individual chimerae, make it impossible to reconstruct choroidal polyclones by our current methods. Further, it is impossible to rule out (a) extensive cell migration within the choroid, (b) cell division in established regions away from the germinal ring, (c) exchange of pigment between wild-type and albino cells, or even, among the white-into-black mosaics, and (d) a late invasion of the choroid by pigmented cells from extraocular tissues in the host. Nevertheless, the peculiar characteristics of choroidal polyclones are amply demonstrated in histologic sections (Fig. 12), and they indicate a radically different histogenetic process from that seen in the PRE. In fact, the *variability* of mottling in different regions of a single black-into-white mosaic—from discrete patches in one region to a diffuse "gray-out" in others—suggests that choroidal histogenesis may involve both local and invasive processes of cell accretion and perhaps two or more very different varieties of precursor cell. Until autoradiographic studies can be completed on the mosaics, these issues will remain unresolved.

Reconstructions of the neural retina, using the *1-nu* marker, are also in progress at the present time. As noted in our initial critique of this marker, the methodologies are much more laborious; and, for a variety of reasons, an apparent *1-nu* cell is occasionally seen in histologic material from wild-type retina. Thus it has been necessary, in our preliminary reconstructions of neural retina, to use a signal averaging method in which we score a cell as *1-nu* only when it contains at least one neighbor that is also *1-nu*. Despite this limitation and the absence of large numbers of cases, preliminary evidence offers a few clear comments on the histogenesis of the neural retina. Polyclones in the neural retina are similar in their general form to those in the overlying PRE, in chimerae produced by *1-nu* grafts into albino hosts at 2 days of development (embryonic stage 32). That is, the neural retina shows generally contiguous polyclones with gross radial organization extending from the optic nerve radially outward to the ciliary margin. Thus the general principles for establishment and maintenance of a mosaic configuration which we derived for the PRE appear to hold in the main for the neural retina as well. Second, the boundaries within the neural retina are *generally* sharp but they may not be quite as exquisitely sharp as those within the PRE. Some local intermixing of *1-nu* and *2-nu* cells can be seen at the boundary within a neural retinal layer.[4] No conspicuous differences exist in the sharpness of boundaries, when neural retina boundaries at the front of the eye (new boundary) are compared with neural retina boundaries at the back of the same eye (old boundary). This suggests that the intermixing is not a *chronic* process; it may occur during the period when young neurons leave the growth zone and spread out slightly to achieve the lower packing density seen in the mature neural retina. Finally, it is clear that the overlay of polyclones within the same chimeric eye—between neural retina and PRE and between one layer of the neural retina and another—show only *general* agreement. Locally, the boundaries are not always precisely matched. For example, neural retinal polyclones may split in one layer but not another, or may split in a region of the eye in which the overlying PRE polyclone remains a single contiguous arc (Fig. 13a and b). The result is a stretch of retina in which graft-derived PRE is overlain by host-derived neurons, or graft-derived photoreceptors are overlain by host-derived interneurons in the internuclear layer. These and other configurations also suggest that polyclones in the neural retina will offer a rich variety of local forms whose interpretation can be pursued along the lines used for the PRE.

It is clear that a complete treatment of the overlay problem will require many more cases, as well as the application of our quantitative analysis programs, which correct for angle of section, and which measure clone widths and positions as function of true radial position between the optic nerve and the ciliary margin (Conway *et al.,* 1980). We do not yet know whether neural retina will show the range of metamorphic variations seen in PRE. Moreover, our data on the *overlay* of polyclones in neural versus pigmented retina are entirely confined to mosaics prepared at embryonic stage 32, when the 2-day eyebud is a fully formed optic cup (Jacobson, 1968b). Thus, our inference that clonal organization of the growing neural retina is similar (but not identical) to that of the growing PRE pertains *only* to growth between

---

[4] To be sure, the markers used to analyze boundaries in PRE (albino) and neural retina (*1-nu*) are different. We believe, however, that the differences between the generally sharp boundary in the neural retina and the exquisitely sharp boundary in the PRE reflect real biological differences between the two tissues. Most histologic sections through mosaic PRE show absolute segregation of black and white cells; even sections through a fork or tributary often appear as two absolutely segregated "arcs" of pigmentation. Conspicuously rare are boundary configurations in which the pigmented zone(s) gives way to an albino zone through a transition zone in which black spots, the size of one PRE cell, interdigitate with single albino cells BBBBBBBBBBwBwwBwBwwww-wwwwwwww). Such configurations *are* seen in the nucleolar mosaicism of neural retinal boundaries (11111121122211222222222), as seen in Fig. 13a and b).

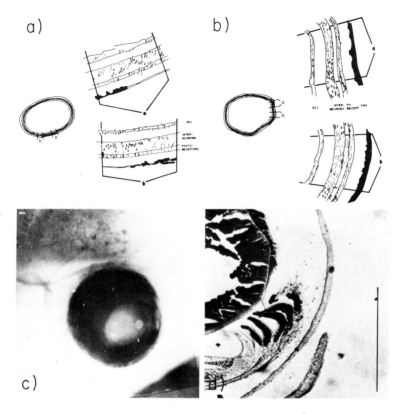

Fig. 13. Reconstruction of neural retinal tissue. Sections are traced through a camera lucida drawing tube at low power (a) for exact orientations of high-power scoring of individual *1-nu* and *2-nu* cells. In most cases, the transition from areas of *2-nu* to *1-nu* cells was relatively sharp, occurring over three or four cell diameters. The boundaries were also near, although not directly aligned with, the boundaries for the PRE. One of the few cases studied with this method, however, showed a definite split in the neural retinal clone (b). This area was adjacent to a cohesive (undivided) clone in the PRE. Both areas of *1-nu* cells can be seen, and the area between the reconstructions was scored as *2-nu*. Occasional cells contained no recognizable nucleoli and are displayed as *0-nu*. These cells probably contained nucleoli but were sectioned in such a way as to leave these markers in adjacent sections.

Resolution of distinct precursor cell types between iris and PRE. One fortuitous chimera showed a cohesive clone, confined to the front face of the eye, on external view (c) ($\times 15$). Histologic examination revealed that pigmentation was confined to the iris and ciliary margin, as shown in the montage (d) (500 μm), and to the PRE in the extreme back of the eye, around the optic nerve head. In this case, the graft appeared to grow out a polyclone in iris while failing to grow out a polyclone in PRE. This result suggests that the eye-bud contains, by as early as day 2, separate precursor cell types for both iris and PRE.

the optic cup stage and the juvenile. The very early eye-bud has a very different geometry, and founder cells for neural and pigmented retina are undergoing complex movements as the bud transforms from optic vesicle to optic cup. Whether the two presumptive tissues show similar clonal organization at these early stages remains to be determined.

Nevertheless, a number of principles have already begun to emerge: the histogenetic processes mediating larval growth of the choroid are clearly different from those underlying larval growth of PRE and neural retina; the mosaic configuration from which the PRE is generated is different from the mosaic configuration which gives rise to the iris; polyclones in various layers of neural retina correspond generally but not always precisely with one another and with those in the PRE, in their growth from embryonic stage 32 through metamorphosis. One particularly important principle, discussed much earlier in this article, concerns the diversity and specificity of precursors from which these different cell types derive. The subtle mismatch between polyclones in iris and PRE provides suggestive evidence that separate precursor cells exist for the two tissue types, but a few serendipitous cases have begun to provide a definitive answer. It is possible to obtain chimeric eyes in which the only pigmented cells are present in the iris (Fig. 13) and no polyclone grew out in the PRE. This indicates that at least some precursor cells for the iris give rise to no other tissue type. That a continuous arc of pigmented iris is present, in the absence of a PRE polyclone, strongly suggests that most or all of the precursor cells for iris are similarly unique. The negative image of the same case, as well as cases in which the PRE is pigmented and the iris is not, confirm the reciprocal inference. That is, at least some of the precursors which give rise to PRE are specific for PRE and do not give rise to iris as well.

Configurations of mismatch between choroid and PRE suggest that the same inference can be made about the uniqueness of precursors for these two layers. Many eyes show a polyclone in PRE with no choroidal pigmentation. A few eyes show patches of pigmentation in choroid at a considerable angular distance from the polyclone in PRE; a few others failed to grow out a polyclone in the PRE, yet show extensive pigmentation in the choroid. White-into-black mosaics show a pigmented choroid throughout while the underlying PRE contains an albino polyclone over half of the angular extent of the eye. This inference is in keeping with the earlier observation that the neural crest contributes melanocytes to the choroid, while PRE melanocytes derive from the back of the optic cup (Coulombre, 1965). Finally, the local mismatch of polyclone boundaries within the retina, between neural layers and PRE and between one neural layer and another, remains to be pursued.

We hope cases in which a polyclone resides in only one neural layer, or in neural retina but not PRE, would provide a definitive answer about the uniqueness of precursor cells for different retinal layers and for the neural retina versus the pigmented retina. The presence of splits in one layer with respect to another, however, provides provocative evidence in support of this hypothesis (Hinds and Hinds, 1974; Hunt, 1975b). Some years ago, in their studies of neuronal birthdates in the neural retina, Sidman (1961) and Jacobson (1968b) proposed that a single precursor cell divides to produce a functional unit of one ganglion cell, several subtending interneurons, and several more subtending photoreceptors, all of which become hooked up into a functional "cartridge" at a particular point in the retinal cell sheet. The present results, if they can be extended to include a definitive demonstration that normal "cartridge-like" connections exist between clonally unrelated cells in these mismatched regions, would strongly suggest that this elegant hypothesis of clonally related "functional cartridges" may not be correct for regions of the retina formed during larval growth.

IV. Retinotectal Patterns

The retinotectal map brings an added dimension to the study of cell patterning in the growing eye. In forming topographically ordered connections with the contralateral optic tectum (Fig. 5), each ganglion cell must send its axon over a long distance to the midbrain and select a connection site that is appropriate for the ganglion cell's position in the retinal cell sheet. Although the formation of connections likely involves group interactions among optic fibers, each axon carries some individual property or properties (termed *locus specificity*) that define its reacting to other fibers and cells in selecting its terminal site. Retinotectal connections, therefore, allow us to consider individual cell properties which reference (and at some earlier stage must have been orchestrated by) a more global parameter of tissue *address,* and to examine how the positional properties of clones are related to the assignment of this address information to individual cells within the clone.

Even as the eye is growing, the tectum is also growing and fibers are continuously striking out from the eye on their journey to the tectum. The tectum arises from a more posterior cell group in the neural plate (Chung and Cooke, 1975). Early morphogenesis of the tectum is not well understood, and later cell accretion has not been as well characterized as that in the growing eye. Nevertheless, preliminary evidence suggests that the tectum grows by adding *bands* or arcs of new cells to its medial and back edges, and completes its histogenesis by the time metamorphosis has ended (Straznicky and Gaze, 1972; Jacobson, 1976). Throughout larval and early juvenile life, the cells of the tectum are maturing in form and function, with the (more recently added) cells at the back lagging behind those in front (Lazar, 1973; Currie and Cowan, 1974; Chung *et al.*, 1975).

Only general agreement exists on the exact stage at which optic fibers first leave the eye, reach the tectum, and establish the first retinotectal synapses. Optic fibers leave the eye around 2.5 days of embryonic life and reach the tectum over the next half day. Retinotectal responses are evident in the tectum by day 4, although at this time there is no topographical order to the visual projection (Gaze *et al.*, 1974). By 1 week postfertilization the visual projection shows a rudimentary topographical order, and retinotectal synapses are evident in laminar field potentials. New optic fibers continue to leave the eye, as new annuli are formed, throughout larval and juvenile life (Jacobson, 1977). Similarly, the visual projection continues to mature and, for most of the larval period, shows nonlinear metrics and some silent zones at the caudomedial back of the tectum (Gaze *et al.*, 1974; Chung *et al.*, 1974, 1975).

Long before its histogenesis was even vaguely understood, the retinotectal system was exploited by Sperry (1945, 1950) in a classic series of behavioral studies on the *regenerating* optic nerve. Sperry showed that optic fibers, from a rotated or transplanted eye, regenerate connections that are behaviorally maladaptive. Months of experience never succeeded in modifying the maladaptive behavior. Against the functionalist view, Sperry proposed his *theory of neuronal specificity,* in which synaptic specificity was but a special case of cytochemical recognition among embryonic cells (Holtfreter, 1939). Individual neurons underwent a refined differentiation, ultimately deploying cytochemical labels which defined their affinity for other neurons. Among several special theories (for the acquisition of labels in different neuronal tissues), Sperry (1950) proposed that the retina and tectum underwent a "polarized," field-like differentiation. Each acquired a graded set of labels. At corresponding positions in the two tissues—points destined to become interconnected in the retinotectal map—retinal labels and tectal labels were proposed to match in some complementary fashion. At corresponding positions in retina and tectum—points destined to become interconnected in the retinotectal map—labels were "complementary" allowing the ingrowing optic fiber to recognize its "matched" target and form a synapse. Later histologic studies showed that a half-retina would indeed pass up "unmatched" regions of an intact tectum and terminate selectively in its appropriate target zone

(Attardi and Sperry, 1963). Attardi and Sperry (1963) also confirmed that fibers are scrambled when the optic nerve is severed and made the observation that fibers attempt to reestablish topographic order (and adjust their path) even before they reach the tectum. Thus, Sperry (1963, 1965) refined his ideas and proposed the so-called chemoaffinity model, in which fibers not only possessed labels complementary to those on specific tectal cells, but also possessed an ability to read the landscape even as they grew and to "home in" on their target from afar.

A variety of experiments have since been carried out on the mechanisms by which the retinotectal map is assembled (Chung, 1974; Cook and Horder, 1977; review Jacobson, 1978; Edds *et al.*, 1979; Fraser and Hunt, 1980; Gaze, 1980; Meyer, 1979a,b; Horder and Martin, 1979). It is clear that optic fibers can exhibit some plasticity in their choice of tectal connections. A half-eye, given enough time, will eventually spread its optic fiber map over the entire tectal surface; a whole retina will eventually compress its retinotectal map onto a tectal fragment (Gaze and Sharma, 1970; Yoon, 1972; Meyer and Sperry, 1975; Scott, 1977; Udin, 1977; review Hunt and Jacobson, 1974a). In at least some of these experiments, the altered mapping does not reflect a simple "rearrangement of the labels" among the surviving cells but appears instead to reflect interactions and competition among the optic fibers themselves. In *Xenopus,* a single patch of retina in the same eye can make a normal map on one tectum, and an expanded map on the other, based on the presence or absence of other "competing" retinal fibers (Fraser and Hunt, 1979a; Fig. 14a). A growth-suppressed larval eye (Hunt, 1977; Fig. 14b and c) often expands its map over the tectum, but late innervation by a normal full-sized eye chases the tiny eye's fibers back to a small shared region of the tectum appropriate to the cells around the optic nerve head. Various kinds of half-eyes in goldfish have been subjected to a similar competitive assay (Sharma and Tung, 1979; Schmidt, 1978; Meyer, 1978, 1979a,b). In fact, the disparate modes of growth in the frog retina and tectum have led some investigators to speculate that *normal development* involves ongoing mismatch and that optic fibers must continuously shift their connections in the tadpole tectum (Gaze *et al.*, 1974).

At the same time, other experiments leave little doubt that optic fibers do possess unique informational properties for map assembly. Small bits of tectum, translocated from one region to another, can entice the appropriate subpopulation of optic fibers to "break ranks" with other fibers and track down their targets in the graft (Fig. 14d; Sharma and Gaze, 1971; Levine and Jacobson, 1974; Jacobson and Levine, 1975a,b; Yoon, 1975; Hunt, 1976a; Hope *et al.*, 1976; Rho, 1978;

LATE LARVAL EYE REMOVAL

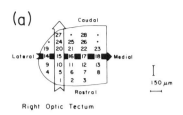

(a)

Right Eye Visual Field

GROWTH-SUPPRESSED (TINY) EYE

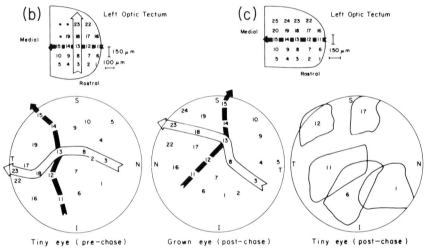

Tiny eye (pre-chase)   Grown eye (post-chase)   Tiny eye (post-chase)

FIG. 14. Projections of *Xenopus*, showing that some plasticity exists in the mapping function between retina and tectum. Here, two different experimental procedures are used to show that a partial retina can assemble an abnormal retinotectal map, in the absence of changes in the map-making processes of the retinal ganglion cells. (a) Following late larval extirpation of the left eye, the right retina innervates both the contralateral tectum and the ipsilateral tectum. The projection to the contralateral tectum is nearly normal (not shown), and the posteroventral region of the retina confines its projection to the rostral and medial edges of the tectum. The same posteroventral region of the retina projects alone to the ipsilateral tectum; and, as shown on the visual field and tectal diagrams, it expands its representation over most of the tectal surface and shows distortions in the topographic ordering of the map. Thus, the presence or absence of (competing) retinal fibers from other regions of the retina can substantially alter the selection of synaptic sites by a subset of retinal ganglion cells. Redrawn from Fraser and Hunt (1979a). Treatment of an early larval eye *in vitro* with fluorodeoxyuridine produces a tiny eye consisting of less than 10% of the normal ganglion cell complement; those ganglion cells are destined to abut the optic nerve head at the back of a normal eye. Alone, the tiny eye spreads its map to cover most of the dorsal tectum (b). This visual field projection, taken at metamorphic climax (stage 57–58), shows the visual field of the

Rho and Hunt, 1980). Similarly, bits of translocated retina can track down their appropriate targets (Hunt and Ide, 1977; Hunt *et al.*, 1980a,b). Optic fibers do reestablish orderly connections and subgroups of fibers will pass up much of the tectal surface (at least in the short run) and confine their projection to the appropriate patch of tectum.

Still other experiments have examined so-called "passive" ordering mechanisms which could make a topographic map in the absence of cytochemical labels (Horder and Martin, 1979). Many of these ordering mechanisms undoubtedly serve a helper role in establishment of the map, but are either unnecessary or insufficient to be the predominant force in map assembly. Cell death occurs (Glucksman, 1940; Hunt, 1976a; Jacobson, 1976) but is insufficient to create a topographic map out of chaos. Retinotopy in the developing frog nerve is imprecise; errors do occur in the selection of synaptic sites, and these errors are systematically eliminated (Longley, 1978). The timing of optic fiber arrivals, while seriously restricting traffic on the tectum in normal development, can be seriously disrupted without perturbing the final map (Feldman *et al.*, 1971; Hunt and Jacobson, 1972; Hunt, 1975a,b). Fibers which take the wrong path can still reach their correct terminal position (Hibbard, 1967; Sharma, 1972; Horder, 1974; Gaze and Grant, 1978; Udin, 1978; Meyer, 1980). Finally, it is in no way established that these processes should be viewed as *passive* at all. Ordering within the optic nerve and tract and the pursuit of ordered pathways might well reflect a different level of expression of the optic fiber specificities (Meyer, 1980; Fraser and Hunt, 1980).

The conclusion now seems inescapable that optic fibers do possess position-dependent qualities, but that the *mapping function* is somewhat more complex than one-to-one complementarity with a specific

---

tiny eye projecting over most of the tectal surface. By contrast, the tiny eye's projection is "chased" back to a small region of the tectum, when a normal "full-sized" eye is allowed to coinnervate the tectum with the tiny eye (c). Here, a second frog has been prepared with one growth-suppressed and one untreated eye grafted into a shared right orbit of a (larval stage 39) host embryo. At metamorphosis, the visual field of the grown eye (left) projects over the whole region, while the visual field of the tiny eye is compressed (with large multiunit response areas) onto a small patch of tectum. This final configuration is obtained, regardless of whether coinnervation proceeds from early larval stages, or whether the tiny eye is first allowed to expand its map before delayed coinnervation by the normal eye. Thus, both expanded and compressed states can be recorded in the same frog (Hunt, 1977), before and after contralateral transplantation of the host's untreated left eye. The shared patch of tectum is appropriate to the region surrounding the optic nerve head. Thus, ganglion cells of the central retina assemble different retinotectal maps, based on the presence or absence of (competing) fibers from peripheral retina. The conventions in this figure and all subsequent visual diagrams are explained in Fig. 5a.

tectal cell. The expression of locus-specificity may occur not only between optic fiber and tectal cell, but between optic fibers themselves
and between growth cone and the landscape between the retina and the
brain. Fraser (1980) has proposed a quantitative model which includes
strong generalized attraction (fiber-tectum) and repulsions (fiber-fiber)
as well as weaker locus-specific interactions both (*a*) among optic fibers
and (*b*) between fibers and cells. The generalized forces are energeti-
cally predominant, forcing less than ideal locus-specific matchings to
achieve maximal retinotectal adhesions (compression of a whole retina
onto a partial tectum) or minimal fiber–fiber repulsion (expansion of a
partial retina over the whole tectum). The key refinement of the model
over previous cell-adhesion models (Barondes, 1970; Marchase *et al.*,
1975) is a class of chemical interactions in which attraction is based on
identity rather than complementarity, thus allowing the fibers to order
among themselves as well as by interaction with tectal cells. Synthetic
models go a long way toward addressing the mixed results of many
plasticity experiments (Fraser and Hunt, 1980) for they predict that
multiple interactions occur and that several stable configurations may
exist in a particular experimental setting. For our present purposes,
however, it is sufficient to point out that general agreement exists for
the presence of individual properties on optic fibers.

A. RETINOTECTAL PATTERNING IN THE EMBRYO

A number of questions immediately come to mind. What is the
molecular basis of optic fiber uniqueness? How do optic fibers learn of
their address in the eye? How is cellular address—so-called "positional
information" (Wolpert, 1969, 1971)—coded in retinal space? Does each
ganglion cell possess one unique address state, or a combination of
several coding states: for example, separate markers for radial distance
and angular position, or separate markers of anteroposterior position
and dorsoventral position? How is the assignment of address information to individual ganglion cells related to their clonal origins? Are
regional differences around the eye-bud, expressed as metamorphic
variations in polyclone growth, accompanied by local differences in
information for assigning cellular address to retinal ganglion cells?
"Positional information" may influence many differential traits of eye
cells, such as attachment points of ocular muscles or layering of neural
retina. Here we would like to continue to concentrate on tectal location
of innervation as an assay for the positional properties of retinal ganglion cells.

As indicated in Section I, something is already known about the early
phenomenology of patterning in the retina. At early optic vesicle stages

in the 1- to 2-day embryo, rotation or transplantation of the eye-bud can induce dramatic modifications in the resulting retinotectal patterns. Although investigators disagree on the mechanisms underlying such pattern regulations, modifications in retinotectal pattern resulting from interactions between an early eye-bud and the surrounding tissue have been documented in many species in many laboratories (Stone, 1944, 1960; Szekely, 1954; Jacobson, 1966, 1968a; Jacobson and Hunt, 1973; Hunt and Piatt, 1980; Cooke, 1977; Crossland *et al.*, 1974; Goldberg, 1976). Moreover, all investigators agree that (a) a full and complete spatial plan sufficient for patterning the entire retinotectal map is present at the earliest optic vesicle stages in *Xenopus* (Jacobson and Hunt, 1973; Gaze, 1980), and that (b) at 2 days (stage 31) of development and thereafter this spatial plan is completely refractory to modifications by interactions with the embryonic surround (Hunt, 1975a; Gaze and Keating, 1972; Gaze, 1980). The later observation is especially dramatic, given that more than 99% of the adult ganglion cell population is not yet present in the 2-day eye-bud. Nevertheless, translocation or rotation of the eye-bud at stage 31 invariably produces a completely rotated retinotectal pattern in conformity with the original spatial plan prior to surgery.

A rich phenomenology of modified patterns, however, has arisen in experiments which ablate or surgically recombine *parts* of 2 day and older eye-buds. In principle, partial ablation of an eye-bud or fusion of two eye-bud fragments can produce two categories of result: one category, *mosaic development,* features a simple expression of what one expects from the participating fragment(s). That is, in their new (surgically modified) context, the bud fragments produce the same subset(s) of address values and pattern parts that they produce in their normal context as regions of an undisturbed bud. For example, a half eye-bud might simply produce half of the adult ganglion cell population, and this half might map as expected to the appropriate half of the tectum. Or two halves fused together might produce two separate independently mapping units which reflect the position-dependent properties expected for these two half eye-buds as they grow within the normal eye. The second category of result is termed *regulative development.* At the simplest level, it involves any process in which the emergent pattern contains parts or address values that are "extra" or different from those expected from the participating fragment(s). Thus a half eye-bud might produce more or different address values from that expected from its normal context or two half eye-buds might produce a composite of address values that differ radically from those expected from their normal origins. Classically, embryologists have distinguished two categories of such regulative development. So-called *epimorphic* regulation (Wolpert, 1971) involves rearrangement of the spatial plan in only a few cells: most cells develop in their normal way, but a few cells undergo a dramatic regeneration response filling in cells and address values corresponding to the missing part of the tissue. So-called *morpholactic* regulation (Wolpert, 1971) involves a more wholesale remodeling of the anlage such that all or most of its cells ultimately adopt address values and show patterning behavior that is different from that expected were their normal context not altered. Typically, epimorphic systems are metrically invariant: whatever pattern parts are produced, they are of normal size. In morpholactic systems, tissue remodeling may produce a "scale model" of the normal pattern, in which the topological organization is normal but the metrics are expanded or compressed.[5]

Analysis of regulative behavior in the eye-bud is somewhat complicated by the finding that *plasticity* can exist in the mapping function itself, as seen in the brain. That is, even in the *absence* of modifications in the spatial plan or the subset of address values in a partial retina, the partial retina may show modified behavior in mapping to the midbrain such that regions of the midbrain not normally innervated by this partial retina now received expanded innervation. Some of these ambiguities can be eliminated by competitive assays (Hunt and Jacobson, 1974a). Because it is known that a half-eye or a growth-suppressed eye will restrict its connections to the appropriate part of the tectum under competition from a normal eye (Hunt, 1977; Sharma and Tung, 1978;

---

[5] These categories of mosaic and regulative development help to systematize a problem alluded to earlier in discussion of polyclone variations in heterotopic pole-grafts. A pole-graft could contain unique regional properties, yet fail to express them in a heterotopic site, because local properties of the implantation site (or more global properties in the eye as a whole) overrun any intrinsic properties and reprogram the graft in accordance with its new (heterotopic) position. Such a process is indeed a form of regulative development.

It should also be pointed out that mosaic and regulative patterns, while alternatives for the individual case, need not be mutually exclusive within a system or even within a single experimental series. Grafts from some regions may possess local properties that are more easily overrun than those in grafts from other regions. Some *implantation sites* may possess more dominant local cues. Indeed, a dynamic tension may exist between local properties of graft and site that is so nearly balanced that some cases will show a mosaic pattern and others a regulated pattern, *within* a single experimental series. Finally, it is very likely that a variety of experimental conditions might well bias a particular type of transplant toward one or the other mode of patterning. In insect imaginal discs, for example, culture conditions (which suppress the regenerative cell division required for epimorphic regulation) can bias disc fragments toward mosaic development.

Meyer, 1978), it is possible to challenge eyes resulting from embryonic eye-bud fragments with such competitions. Thus, for example, half-eye ablation in a 2- to 3-day *Xenopus* embryo (stages 31–38) often produces a normal map that covers the whole tectum, and such normal maps persist even when the rounded-up fragment is forced to innervate the same tectum with a normal eye (Berman and Hunt, 1975; Hunt and Berman, 1975). This suggests that address values which would have arisen in the ablated region of the bud were somehow reconstituted in the rounded-up fragment. In other words, embryonic regulation occurred to produce a whole eye's address values; full coverage of the tectum reflected the full set of address values rather than an expansion of a half-eye into unappropriate tectal areas.

Other categories of regulative mapping, however, show more frank alterations in pattern. A minority of half eye-bud ablations give rise to twinned projections that are characteristic of the fragment left behind (Feldman and Gaze, 1975; Berman and Hunt, 1975). Anterior halves may produce a "double anterior" twinned map (also called "double-nasal," Gaze *et al.*, 1963) in which the posterior half of the adult retina maps as a "mirror image" duplicate of the anterior half, with each tectal locus innervated by ganglion cells from *two* retinal positions, symmetrically disposed about the vertical meridian. Similarly, posterior halves may produce an analogous "double posterior" twin (also called "double-temporal," Gaze *et al.*, 1963) and ventral halves a "double ventral" twin. Slightly smaller anterior, posterior, and ventral fragments almost invariably produce the corresponding, twinned projections; pieces larger than a half bud almost never produce them (McDonald, 1975, 1977; Ide *et al.*, 1979; Ling *et al.*, 1979; Fig. 15a–f).

Clear evidence for some form of regulative interaction has also been obtained from surgically recombinant eyes prepared by fusion of two "half" eye-bud fragments. Recombination of a right anterior and a left posterior (A_R/P_L) fragment gives rise to a "double anterior" twin in which the posterior half of the final retina maps to the brain in a markedly different manner from that expected under mosaic development of a posterior half-bud (Hunt and Frank, 1975). As hinted in Section I, these pattern regulations appear to involve a *rapid* reprogramming of the spatial plan for mapping, rather than persistence of a new global signal for address assignment across the growing recombinant retina. When right anterior and left posterior fragments are combined, the interaction leading to twinned mapping is completed within 30 hours, as shown by fusion and separation of the fragments and the resulting behavior of the posterior (slave) piece (Hunt and Frank, 1975). Similarly, interaction of small anterior and posterior fragments, each of

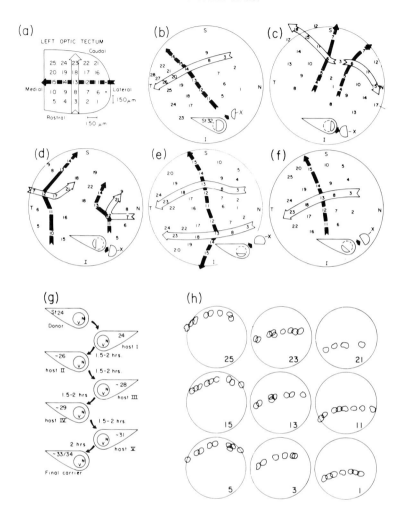

FIG. 15. Visual projections in young adult *Xenopus,* following surgical manipulation of the eye-bud in the embryo. (a) Left optic tectum; a standard series of electrode recording positions was used in all experiments illustrated, and only one tectum is shown. (b–f) Operative schemata (insets) and typical visual projections, illustrating the occurrence of "twinned" retinotectal patterns following partial ablation of the eye-bud at 2 days of development (stage 31/32). As shown in the schema on each map, fragments were prepared by a single straight-line cut through the eye-bud, roughly separating the bud into a larger (2/3) and a smaller (1/3) fragment, and complete excision of one of the two pieces; the remaining fragment was allowed to round-up of its own accord and map to the tectum. (b) Normal visual projection from a large anterior fragment; large posterior fragments and large ventral fragments also give normal visual projections. (c) "Double-nasal" visual projection from a small anterior fragment. (d) "Double-temporal" visual projection from a small posterior fragment. (e) "Double-ventral" visual projection (twinned about the DV axis) from a small ventral fragment. (f) Normal visual projection, which

which would twin if left by itself, can suppress twinning within a similar time course (Ide *et al.*, 1979).

Other studies have investigated the coding properties of address in the eye, exploiting signals between the eye and its surround at early stages, and between fragments of eye-buds at later stages. Hunt (1976b) has analyzed retinotectal maps that are systematically disorganized with respect to retinal space. Totally disorganized maps, nevertheless, assemble orderly lamination in the tectum with "sustained," "event," and "dimming" cells (Chung *et al.*, 1975) segregating their axon terminals to the appropriate tectal layers. More dramatically, some eyes reflect disorganization of address information in only one Cartesian dimension of visual space. Optic fibers can retain the capability for orderly discrimination of their mediolateral levels in the tectum, even when they map at random with respect to rostrocaudal level in the tectum (and concomitantly to anteroposterior position in the eye (Fig. 15g and h). Reciprocally, optic fibers can accurately discriminate rostrocaudal level in the tectum while mappng randomly with respect to mediolateral level.

A second strategy for analysis of coding has been brilliantly exploited by French *et al.* (1976) in various limb systems. They have analyzed the geometrical logic of twinning and nontwinning following partial ablations and fusion of rudiment fragments. Thus, in systems as diverse as *Drosophila* imaginal disc and regenerating newt limb, twinning specifically attends the ablation of more than half of the circumference and is independent of the position of the fragment with respect to major body axes. This logic, or geometrical layout, of the limb rudiment has led these authors to suggest that address in these systems is coded in two polar coordinates, a radius and an angle. In *Xenopus* eye-bud simple radial models have not proved readily appli-

---

typically results from small fragments prepared by diagonal cuts, as in the posteroventral fragment shown. (g,h) Operative schema and resulting single-unit data, from a frog showing a scrambled visual projection. (g) Repeated transplantation of the eye-bud from right orbit to left orbit to right orbit continually changes the anteroposterior orientation of the bud over a 12-hour period, beginning at 1.5 days of development (embryonic stage 24). (h) The circles all depict the visual field of the same frog; all are oriented with nasal to the right and superior right. Each numbered circle shows the location of receptive fields detected beneath a single recording position in the tectum, following the conventions of Fig. 5b. The map is disorganized in the rostrocaudal dimension on the tectum (anteroposterior dimension of the retina), yet the ganglion cells have accurately discriminated their proper mediolateral level on the tectum. Analogous procedures, systematically varying dorsoventral orientation of the eye-bud in the orbit, produce analogous maps that are disorganized in the mediolateral dimension of the tectum but accurate in the rostrocaudal dimension. Redrawn from Hunt (1976a).

cable to coding address information. Small anterior, ventral, or temporal fragments reliably twin, but fragments prepared by diagonal ablations (e.g., a posteroventral small fragment) very rarely twin (Fig. 15f). Moreover, in the few instances in which such twinning is observed, the topography of the twinned pattern does not systematically reflect the radial organization of its position in the eye. Instead only three families of twinned patterns are observed—double-anterior, double-posterior, and double-ventral—and the occasional twinning by diagonal fragments produces simply a rotated version of one of the three archetypes (Tosney *et al.*, 1978; Hoskins *et al.*, 1980). These experiments have led Bodenstein and Hunt (1978, 1980) to propose a hybrid model in which both radial and Cartesian parameters are present and used for specifying address. The model takes into account the radial growth mechanics of the eye, and also the special relationship between eye fragments and the major axes of the eye.

They propose that each ganglion cell ultimately acquires two Cartesian *address values* which reference the cell's anteroposterior and dorsoventral position in the retina. However, the final address values are not conveyed to the ganglion cell directly. Instead, each newborn ganglion cell receives, by clonal inheritance on the precursor ring, two additional parameters called *operators*. One operator marks the cell's anteroposterior (AP) position on the ring, the other its dorsoventral (DV) position; thus, the two operators specify the new cell's *angular position* around the eye circumference. Operators are clonally inherited by successive generations of germinal cells as well, and thus are stable at each angular growth point. The new ganglion cell attempts to "match" directly the (AP and DV) *address values* of the immediately subjacent ganglion cell, born one generation earlier at the same angular position on the eye rim. Each of the operators governs a transduction event by which anteroposterior and dorsoventral address values are modulated, leading to a slight "overshoot" or "undershoot" of AP and DV address values from that of the previous cell generation. The overshoot and undershoot are quantitatively appropriate for elaboration of Cartesian address values at each angular growth point.

The emphasis of the model, unlike many of its most elegant counterparts (French *et al.*, 1976), has not been one of systemizing the regulative behavior of eye-bud fragments based on their size and position in the bud. Moreover, such an effort may be best deferred until more kinds of fragments can be studied and until some of the more paradoxical results of fragment recombination (Ide *et al.*, 1979) are fully analyzed by chimeric methods. Yet, the model can produce exact simulations of all the major categories of experimental map, with simple and rapid regulation events that require no changes in the address values of already differentiated neurons and no appeals to plasticity in the mapping function itself.

B. POLYCLONES AND RETINOTECTAL PATTERNS

An appreciation, however limited, of the early phenomenology of patterning allows us to pose more refined questions for clonal analysis. When an eye fragment rounds up to produce a so-called whole eye, particularly when such a fragment will produce mapping patterns that differ from those expected under mosaic development, is the regulation epimorphic or morpholactic in nature? That is, do only some of the cells dramatically regenerate a large region of the final eye while others retain their original plan specifying cellular address? Or does more large-scale remodeling occur in which nearly all of the cells change both their growth patterns and the resulting assignment for cellular address? Similarly when half eyes fuse, how does a rapid interaction take place to reset the spatial plan in one or both fragments and how is that new spatial plan propagated during clonal growth? Finally, if certain fragments have the capability of reprogramming others by such interactions, can putative "strong fragments" retain local information in tiny pole-grafts grafted to heterotopic locations?

The mechanism for regulation of rounded-up half-eyes has been studied in this laboratory (Conway *et al.*, 1980; Fig. 16). Small pole-grafts marking the dorsal or anterior or posterior pole are introduced early in development at 1.5 days of embryonic life (stages 24–27). Twelve to twenty-four hours later (stages 37–38), after the pole-grafts have healed into place, an ablation is performed, eliminating about half of the eye-bud and leaving either the top edge or some distal position in the surviving fragment marked by a genetic marker. The eye is followed over the next few days (Fig. 17), and the resulting behavior of the marked polyclone is compared to that in a normal eye. Such studies have revealed that both an epimorphic and a morpholactic component exist in the rounding-up of eye fragments. A dorsal marker left at the edge comes to occupy a large adjacent area as the eye fragment rounds up. A dorsal graft in an unablated eye would give rise to a small and narrow stream, but a dorsal graft followed by an anterior ablation may produce an entire anterior-dorso quadrant marked with the pigmented marker. However, even positions at a great distance from the ablation also show some change. Thus, for example, a posterior pole-graft in a thereafter undisturbed eye would produce a posterior polyclone (Fig. 8a). Anterior half-bud ablation, however, produces a slightly larger polyclone in a posterior-dorso position, rather

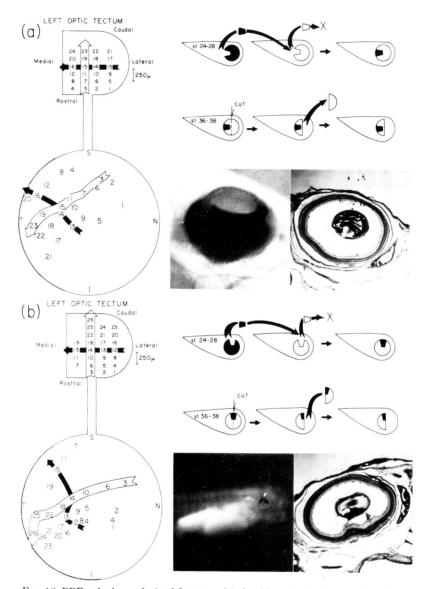

FIG. 16. PRE polyclones derived from two kinds of "marked pole plus delete" experiments. For each case, a schematic diagram of the eye-bud surgery is shown at the upper right. The retinotectal map of the juvenile frog is shown on the left. An external photograph [(a) ×12, (b) ×5] and a histological section (×12) are shown at the lower right. Despite the anatomical regulation of the early eye-bud, the retinotectal map is normal.

than directly posterior (Fig. 16). Since the resulting retinotectal map is normal, these cells must have regulated their positional properties slightly in a morpholactic fashion, even though they do not participate directly in the epimorphic surge of the cells at the edge of the fragment.

In summary then, we do not yet have enough data to comment upon regulative mechanisms leading to twinned projections in rounded-up half-eye fragments; and studies are just beginning on the relation between growth dynamics and pattern regulation in more complex fragments. Nevertheless, half-eye fragments which round-up to produce a single normal map clearly undergo a complex regulative process that contains both epimorphic and morpholactic components. The epimorphic component is particularly dramatic: cells near the edge of the half-eye fragment undergo a dramatic overgrowth in the few hours following ablation, ultimately acquiring nearly a quadrant in the mosaic configuration in the healed early larval eye. Yet cells away from the cut edge also show a response, less dramatic but similar in kind, increasing their arc territory on the ciliary marginal ring.

We have also begun to study the relation between clonal patterns and retinotectal patterns in half-eye mosaics and other types of recombinant eyes. In Section II, we described simple half-eye replacements, in which an anterior/posterior mosaic or dorsal/ventral mosaic is produced by replacement of a "half" eye-bud in the 2-day embryo. Thus far, such orthotopic half-eye mosaics have assembled a normal pattern of retinotectal connections with the midbrain. The reconstitution of a single normal pattern, from two fused fragments which reconstitute a whole normal eye, is hardly remarkable. Yet the behavior of recombinant eyes is complicated by what is known of the behavior of single rounded-up fragments; and even in the simple half-eye replacements, both the ambiguities and the potential resolution by mosaic analysis are evident. A single half-eye fragment can round-up to produce a normal retinotectal map. Thus, on the most basic level, a simple half-eye replacement could produce a normal map simply because the graft disappeared or failed to establish a contribution to the configuration leading to subsequent retinal growth. The results of mosaic analysis clearly exclude this possibility. A normal map develops from chimeric eyes in which both fragments have contributed substantial fractions of the final retina.[6]

---

[6] That some form of embryonic regulation is at work is further suggested by the asymmetry of mosaicism and the asymmetries in size of the participating fragments. Individual fragments, as previously noted, may range from 40 to 60% of the cell complement of the intact eye-bud on the opposite side (Berman and Hunt, 1975). Yet the normal maps which develop from recombinant eyes, over a wide range of mosaic patterns in

Rather more dramatic retinotectal patterns occur in more complex recombinants in which a half eye-bud is replaced by a nonmatching half-bud from a donor embryo. For example, when the posterior half of a right eye-bud is replaced by the posterior half of a left bud, the overwhelming majority of cases assembled twinned retinotectal projections that are also of the "double-anterior" archetype. Replacement of a posterior half eye-bud with a *dorsal* half eye-bud from the same side usually gives rise to a single coherent normal map (Ide *et al.*, 1979). All these results are complicated by the fact that *single* anterior fragments can round-up to give a whole normal pattern or a twinned double-anterior pattern. Do the twinned retinotectal maps in the first case (left posterior/right anterior) reflect a failure of the graft to heal into place with subsequent "twinning" by a solitary anterior fragment? Does a right anterior fragment simply muscle its way into control of the healed recombinant, when paired with a dorsal fragment, and produce a normal retinotectal map by the internal regulation process already described for a solitary anterior piece?

Some of these questions have been answered definitively by mosaic analysis in *Xenopus* (Fig. 18). Replacement of a right posterior fragment by a left posterior fragment from a genetically marked donor typically gives rise to an anterior/posterior mosaic, similar to that produced by simple half-eye replacements, with some variation from case to case in the fractional contribution of graft and host tissue. Yet the retinotectal patterns are almost exclusively of the double-nasal twinned variety. The results thus indicate that both fragments participate in the final pattern, and that the anterior fragment definitely changes the patterning behavior in the posterior piece. More than this, they suggest that in some types of recombinants, the interaction leading to twinning involves the recombinant as a whole, and may lead to a rather more symmetrical twinning in the retinotectal map than one

---

which the graft contributes significantly less than half to about half to significantly more than half, are invariably normal. It is a reasonable assumption that some of these recombinants contain two large fragments which contained redundant address values in the region of fusion: for example, two 60% fragments which contained, within each, meridianal eye-bud cells. The fact that ripples and pattern duplications are not evident in the final retinotectal pattern suggests that a regulation event occurs some time shortly after fragment fusion, "smoothing out" any irregularities or redundancies in address value in the healing recombinant. A similar phenomenon may be evident in the more complex recombinants, to be described shortly, in which a twinned retinotectal map is obtained from a frankly mosaic eye. The twinned pattern may be much more symmetrical than the fractional contribution of graft and host tissue to the final retina (Hoskins *et al.*, 1980).

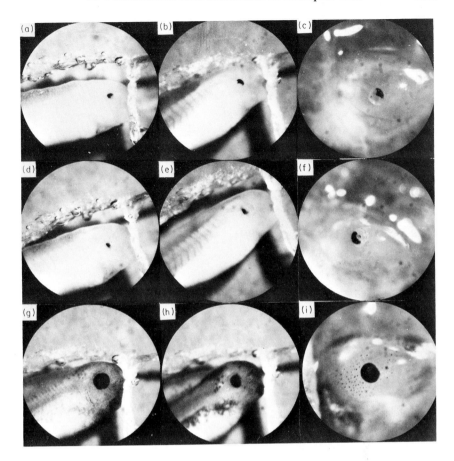

FIG. 17. External photographs of *Xenopus* embryos demonstrating the "marked pole plus delete" experiment (×15). Pole-grafts implanted at stages 24–27 have about 12 hours to heal before stage 35. Marked stage 35 animals are shown on the left (a, d). The anterior half of the eye-bud was deleted. A day later, at stages 40–42, the healed configuration is as shown in the middle (b, e, h). Several days later, the healed configuration is shown on the right (c, f, i). Refer to Fig. 16b for a schematic of the operation shown in the top row. The dorsal pole is marked (a), and after the anterior is deleted, the marked pole "fills in" a large part of the anterior circumference (b, c). Similarly, Fig. 16a has a schematic of the operation shown in the second row. The posterior pole of the eye-bud is marked (d). After the anterior half is deleted, the marked posterior pole moves (e) and later expands (f) as the fragment rounds-up. In the bottom row it is easy to see that control pigmented tadpoles of similar stages round-up after ablation of the anterior half (g, h, i), but it is difficult to assess the contribution from various parts. It appears that the anatomical regulation of a half eye-bud into a whole eye-bud involves both an epimorphic growth near the cut edge, and a morpholactic stretching of parts further away.

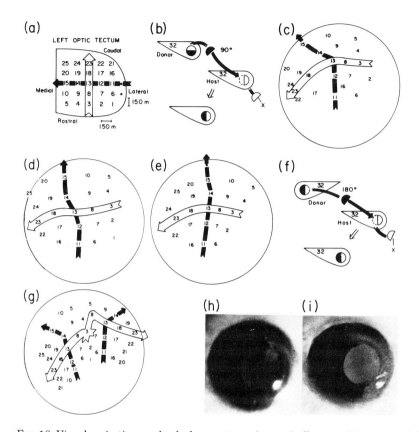

FIG. 18. Visual projections and polyclone patterns in surgically recombinant eyes. (a) Left optic tectum; a standard set of 25 microelectrode recording positions was used in all experiments illustrated, and only one tectum is shown. (b–d) Data from two frogs, with a recombinant eye prepared by fusing a dorsal half-bud with an anterior half-bud at 2 days of development (embryonic stage 32). A third frog, reared after the same transplant maneuver had been performed between a *1-nu* donor and a wild-type host, showed the same retinotectal pattern (e) despite clear nucleolar mosaicism in the neural retina. Operative history (f) and resulting visual projection (g) from a frog with a right anterior/left posterior recombinant eye. A twinned, "double-nasal" visual projection developed. (h, i) External photographs of the eye, at the time of recording, for the two cases in (c, d); the eye shows the clonal organization of the typical half-eye mosaic (×13).

necessarily observes in the clonal contributions of the two pieces (see also Hoskins *et al.,* 1980).

Similarly, when a right anterior/right dorsal recombinant is prepared using mosaic methods, the resulting maps typically show the single coherent normal pattern. This occurs despite the fact that the dorsal fragment gives rise to a large fraction of the eye; and even in nucleolar mosaics, substantial contributions to the *neural* retina are evident from the grafted piece. Thus, another example is provided in which one fragment clearly reorganizes the future address and patterning behavior in a second fragment.[7]

C. RETINOTECTAL PATTERNS FOLLOWING POLE-GRAFTS

The analysis of retinotectal patterns following pole-grafts in the early eye-bud has two antecedent rationales. Simple analysis of the polyclone patterns, as discussed earlier, reveals a retention of position-dependent differences in grafts from different angular positions around the eye-bud. Certain kinds of grafts reliably give rise to larger or smaller clones, reflecting differences in the healing and dynamics by which the recombinant is established and an initial mosaic configuration is created in the healed recombinant. Moreover, certain kinds of pole-grafts show spectacular metamorphic variations, and in many cases these are retained following heterotopic transplantation. It follows, therefore, that local information for retinotectal patterning might be similarly programmed into individual regions and might be retained in heterotopic grafts. The second line of rationale derives from recombination of half-eye fragments of various types. Although very few of these half-eye recombinants have been studied mosaically, earlier data suggest that certain halves possess a more dramatic ability to dominate or reprogram other halves. Anterior half-buds, for example, are particularly effective in dominating other types of fragments. Thus, if we select a small pole-graft from a putative "dominant" region of the

---

[7] In the original electrophysiologic studies of retinotectal patterns from surgically recombinant eyes prepared in *wild-type* embryos, a few frogs in most large experimental series gave atypical retinotectal patterns. For example, twinned "double-anterior" patterns occur as a rare, minority result in anterior/dorsal recombinants and in right anterior/*right* posterior half eye replacements (Ide *et al.*, 1979). The data from mosaic individuals, previously described, leave no doubt that eye-bud fragments can interact to yield a single normal pattern (anterior/dorsal recombinants with both fragments contributing to the final mosaic retina) or a twinned pattern (right anterior/left posterior recombinants with both fragments contributing to the final mosaic retina). In so doing, the mosaic data both establish the general principle that both categories of regulated pattern can occur and confirm the majority result from the original wild-type series. The dilemma concerns the minority results from the original wild-type series. We have not yet obtained the minority result of a twinned retinotectal map from an anterior/dorsal recombinant or half-bud replacement in which the eye was frankly chimeric at the time of recording. Yet, we do not yet have enough cases to infer much from the absence of such a result. In short, it remains a viable hypothesis that the few wild-type recombinants giving atypical patterns do indeed reflect the occasional failure of the graft to heal into place and contribute to the final retina.

eye-bud, and graft it heterotopically into some other position in the eye-bud, will the resultant polyclone show evidence of a *local program* for assigning address values to new ganglion cells?

In fact, pole-grafts do possess local programs for assigning their appropriate subset of address values to the ganglion cells they generate during growth. They can retain the local properties, when grafted heterotopically at day 2 of embryonic life (stage 32). In the most dramatic cases, they can lay down an exquisite mosaic of address values—appropriate to the position of origin of the graft and thus independent of the polyclones new position in the retina. Such results have powerful implications, for they show that the spatial plan for ganglion cell addresses exists as local subroutines at specific angular positions on the 2-day eye-bud, moreover, a mechanism for local, radial elaboration of address values exists within a growing polyclone that is independent of more global controls within the eye as a whole. In these cases, the resulting retinotectal map shows a "pie-slice," in the region of the visual field subtended by the polyclone, wherein the ganglion cells have patterned their tectal connections in accordance with the normal ordering for the position of origin of the graft (Hunt and Ide, 1977; Ide and Hunt, 1978; Hunt *et al.*, 1980a). To avoid confusion in use of the term *mosaic* we will refer to this category of patterns as *pie-slice maps*.

However, not all pole-grafts show pie-slice retinotectal patterns. Indeed, some categories of heterotopic pole-graft give rise, in most cases, to completely *normal* maps. In most other categories, such as anterior grafts into posterior holes, pie-slice maps predominate but some minority patterns (including normal maps) are also seen. In this respect, the retinotectal data are not unlike those described previously for the retention of regional differences, in the size and metamorphic variations of polyclones, when pole-grafts are implanted at heterotopic sites in the 2-day eye-bud. Simply put, some show mosaic development and others show regulative development.

Interpreting such mixed results is aided immeasurably by the uniformity of retinotectal patterns from control experiments. Figure 19a schematizes a range of control procedures we have carried out, without significant perturbation to the retinotectal map. *Excision* controls feature removal of the "host" pole—in a wild-type or albino embryo—with no graft replacement. *Simple replacement* controls feature the excision of the host pole and replacement by an orthotopic graft from a donor embryo. For example, we excise the anterior pole of a right eye-bud and replace it with the anterior pole of the right eye-bud from a donor embryo. The large series of orthotopic pole-graft mosaics, from which the basic polyclone data were taken, has provided ample material for electrophysiologic analysis; and large numbers of orthotopically grafted wild-type individuals have also been analyzed. Thus far, most maps are indistinguishable from those of unoperated animals, and all maps have been very nearly normal. About a dozen frogs have been recorded following introduction of a *0-nu* graft into an anterior or posterior hole in a right albino or wild-type bud. This is the *homozygous* condition of the Oxford marker, and it behaves as a cell-autonomous cell lethal: the graft heals into place and then slowly disintegrates between 1 and 3 days following the operation.

Finally, in previously describing PRE mosaicism, we indicated that a minority of black-into-white mosaics fail to grow out a polyclone. The juvenile eye in these cases showed only a small patch of pigmentation abutting the optic nerve head at the extreme back of the eye; and we suggested that the pole-graft failed to establish any "arc territory" on the germinal ring of the healed recombinant. Thus far, such cases have shown only normal retinotectal maps. These results, then, show that neither the excision, nor simple replacement of pole-grafts, is in itself sufficient to alter retinotectal patterns as a matter of routine. Even the entire process of surgery and healing, of a *heterotopic* graft, when the graft does not go on to contribute a polyclone to the retina is insufficient to produce an ordered aberration in the retinotectal map. Thus, those cases in which a (*wild-type* or *1-nu*) heterotopic pole-graft *does* grow out a polyclone, and the polyclone *does* show "mosaic" mapping to the tectum, must reflect a local program within the graft for assigning address values to ganglion cells within its polyclone.

The uniformity of control data enables us to pose a number of focused questions in analyzing the mixed retinotectal patterns from the experimental series. When a *pie-slice* pattern of retinotectal connections develops between the chimeric eye and the brain, how precise is the ordering within the pie-slice and how invariant is the topography of ordering from one pie-slice to another? Does the pie-slice of autonomous mapping in the visual projection conform closely to the position of the polyclone in the chimeric eye? Is the pattern of retinotectal connections from the surrounding (host-derived) regions of the retina perturbed in any way? In particular, since half-eye chimerae often show symmetrical, "twinned" maps, does the *host*-derived region of the retina ever show topographic distortions of the sort seen in "twinning"? When a *normal* pattern of retinotectal connections develops, is the juvenile eye truely chimeric, with significant contributions from both graft and host tissue to the final retina? Do such eyes show systematic differences in polyclone shape and organization from the eyes which, following an

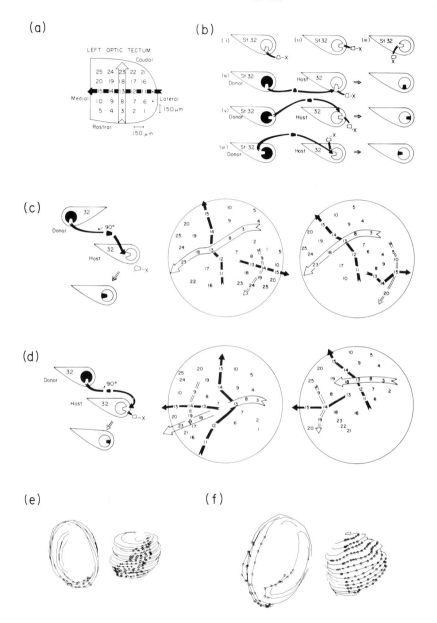

FIG. 19. Visual projections in a young adult *Xenopus* with a chimeric right eye prepared by heterotopic grafting of a ventral pole-graft at 2 days of development (embryonic stage 32). (a) Left optic tectum; a standard set of 25 microelectrode recording positions was sampled in all animals illustrated, and only one tectum is shown. (b) A variety of control surgeries are schematized; all produce normal visual projections. Nor-

ostensibly identical surgical history, assembled a pie-slice map? In particular, does any correlation exist between "mosaicism" in the retinotectal map and retention of regional properties for size and metamorphic variation within the polyclone itself. Finally, do *partially regulated* retinotectal patterns occur—something between completely normal and completely mosaic? If so, what is the form of such patterns and can they provide clues to the way cellular address values are assigned to new ganglion cells within a growing polyclone?

Although we have analyzed retinotectal maps following many types of heterotopic pole-grafts, we will address the above questions in two groups of animals prepared by eye-bud surgery at day 2 of development (embryonic stage 32): frogs in which a ventral pole-graft was implanted into an anterior or posterior hole; and frogs in which an anterior pole-graft was implanted into a posterior hole. In both groups, we possess a large base of retinotectal data from wild-type material, and a sufficient number of genetically marked individuals to begin to relate the retinotectal patterns to patterns of clonal organization in the operated eye.

Figure 19 shows data from several frogs with heterotopic ventral pole-grafts. The data on retinotectal patterns are strictly bimodal: slightly more than half the wild-type cases and the majority of chimerae showed a map of the pie-slice (Fig. 19c and d) class, and the rest showed a radically different class of patterns that ranged from very nearly normal to indistinguishable from the pattern observed in control animals (Fig. 19b).

The pie-slice or sector of aberrant mapping conforms closely, in its position within the visual field, to the sector subtended by the polyclone within the retina. (The exact angular position of this polyclone can of

---

mal visual projections are also obtained when *heterotopic* grafting procedures are performed and the resulting eye fails to grow out a polyclone (not illustrated). (c) Operative history, and resulting visual projections, for two individual chimerae in which a heterotopic ventral pole-graft successfully grew out a polyclone across the posterior retina. The first case shows a clear "pie-slice" pattern while the second "pie-slice" pattern shows more extensive distortions of the entire projection, as occur in twinned visual projections (as in Fig. 15c and d and 18g). (d) Operative history, and resulting visual projections, for two individual chimerae in which a heterotopic transplantation was performed and a ventral pole-graft successfully grew out a polyclone across the anterior adult retina. Heterotopic ventral pole-grafts occasionally lead to normal visual projections despite frank pigment mosaicism in PRE. (e, f) Reconstructions, showing the polyclones in the PRE, for the frogs which gave the visual projections shown in part (c) above. Each pair represents two views of the same eye, one rotated slightly to produce a frontal view ("cornea to cornea" with the observer), the other rotated substantially to provide an optimal view of the polyclone.

course vary slightly from one case to the next.) Sharp "boundaries" exist, within the map itself, between the "normal" surround and the pie-slice or sector of autonomous mapping. Within the sector, more peripheral retinal positions have mapped to more medial positions on the tectum, indicating that the polyclone laid down an increasingly ventral set of address values as it grew. At different angular positions within the polyclone, ganglion cells have ordered their mapping to successive rostrocaudal levels in the tectum in accordance with the behavior of a ventral polyclone when allowed to grow out of its normal orthotopic site. Thus, the polyclone (or at least a region of the retina conforming closely to the polyclone) shared the appropriate patch of tectum with the *endogenous ventral polyclone* descended from host tissue and occupying the ventral quadrant of the same chimeric eye (Fig. 19c and d).

Some variations exist, from case to case within the class of pie-slice maps, in the exact topography of retinotectal ordering within the slice, and in the extent of rostral-to-caudal coverage within the tectum. Especially at the periphery of the slice in the visual field, the metrics of the map may range from entirely normal to slightly compressed, in the direction corresponding to rostrocaudal ordering on the tectum (Fig. 19c, left map). Similarly, distortions in the "normal" surround also vary. At a minimum, there are no *vacated* regions of tectum corresponding to the excised anterior or posterior pole tissue, and the map shows a slightly "bowed" topography in the regions abutting the slice (Fig. 19d). In more extreme cases, a more substantial and topographically *different* distortion is evident in the surround, which is similar (in kind) but less marked (in extent) from that seen in "twinned" visual projections.

Within the group of wild-type recombinants showing *normal* patterns, some individuals undoubtedly reflect a failure of the pole-graft to grow out a polyclone. Yet normal patterns are obtained in a minority of documented chimeric eyes with heterotopic ventral pole-grafts. Earlier we indicated that some but not all polyclones, growing out from heterotopic ventral poles, retain some of the characteristics of orthotopic ventral polyclones. Thus far, the correlation between pie-slice maps and the retention of "ventral" qualities within the polyclone has been strong. Those individuals, in which a pie-slice map was obtained, typically were those in which the polyclone widened on the front face of the eye, occupying a huge angular territory in the iris. Those individuals in which normal maps were obtained were those in which the "ventral" landmarks were less marked in the polyclone, and, in several cases, the polyclone was indistinguishable from those resulting from orthotopic anterior or posterior pole-grafts.

Pie-slice retinotectal maps predominate following introduction of an anterior pole-graft into a posterior hole at embryonic stage 32 (Fig. 20), although occasional normal maps are seen. Pie-slices corresponded in position to the region of visual field subtended by the polyclone, even to the extent that polyclones which *veer toward dorsal* at the extreme front of the eye, are correlated with a veering toward inferior in the slice at the extreme periphery of the visual field (Fig. 20b). The topography of ordering within the slice is different from that seen in the ventral polyclones; here the topography is appropriate to *anterior* polyclones, and more peripheral positions in the polyclone map to more *caudal* positions on the tectum, while different angular positions within the polyclone map to different mediolateral levels in the tectum. When the chimeric eye was prepared by implanting a *left* anterior pole into a right posterior hole, the direction of mediolateral ordering on the tectum (and dorsoventral ordering across the polyclone) was roughly normal (Fig. 20b). When both pole-graft and hole were prepared on the *same* (right) side of the donor and host embryo (Fig. 20c), the direction of mediolateral ordering was usually inverted—in keeping with the dorsoventral inversion of the polyclone at the time of implantation.

Remarkably, however, the latter surgery (right anterior pole into right posterior hole) produced a small minority of individuals in which an "intermediate" retinotectal pattern was obtained. In four cases, including two bona fide chimerae, the polyclone appeared to have assigned an orderly set of increasingly anterior address values to its ganglion cells during growth (Fig. 20d and e). Yet the polyclone failed to retain, across its *angular* dimension, any dorsoventral differences from its position of origin in the donor eye-bud. Although the polyclone showed precise ordering, and internally consistant ordering, in the mediolateral direction over the tectum, the *direction* of ordering was completely appropriate to the implantation site and inappropriate to the position of origin of the pole-graft. Two other cases showed pie-slice maps in which more peripheral positions within the polyclone mapped to successively more caudal positions on the tectum, but different angular positions within the polyclone showed disorganized mapping with little ordering in the mediolateral direction across the tectal surface (Fig. 20f) (Hunt *et al.* 1980).

These cases appear to represent true "informational hybrids" in which some of the polyclone's information, for assigning address values to ganglion cells as it grows, is retained by the pole-graft and expressed intact, while other information is lost or changed. The nature of the information which is spared, and that which is changed, is reminiscent of that inferred in other experiments, in which the retinotectal map was uniformly scrambled in one Cartesian dimension of visual and

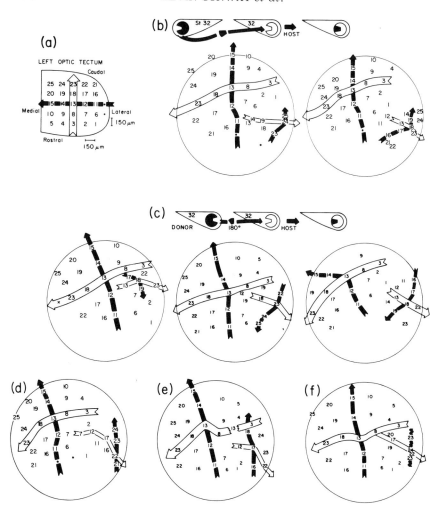

FIG. 20. Visual projections in young adult *Xenopus,* whose chimeric right eye was prepared by heterotopic grafting of an anterior pole at 2 days of development (embryonic stage 32). Data from eight frogs are shown. (a) Left optic tectum; a standard set of 25 microelectrode recording positions was sampled in all animals illustrated and only one tectum is shown. (b) Operative history and resulting visual projections of two frogs prepared by heterotopic grafting of a left eye-bud's anterior pole into a posterior hole in the right eye-bud of a host embryo. (c) Operative history for the remaining six chimerae, whose visual projections are shown in (d–f). An anterior pole-graft, from the right eye-bud of a donor embryo, was heterotopically grafted into a posterior hole in the right eye-bud of the host embryo. (d) Visual projection showing the typical majority result, in which the region of visual field corresponding to the polyclone maps mosaically to the tectum. (e) Visual projection showing a minority result, in which the region of visual field corresponding to the polyclone now orders normally in the mediolateral direction over the

tectal space (Fig. 15g). An important key in the mosaic data derives from the fact that individual polyclones occupy a range of posterior positions in the adult eye. Some occupy a true posterior (9 o'clock) sector, but most are slightly displaced in a dorsal or ventral direction (e.g., 10 o'clock or 8 o'clock). Nevertheless, the "hybrid" patterns with normal mediolateral ordering show *truly* normal mediolateral ordering. The result is a loss of "orthogonality" in the map from the polyclone (Fig. 20). That is, successively more medial levels on the tectum are innervated by successively more *ventral* positions within the polyclone; these sites are shared by optic fibers from the *same* dorsoventral level in the endogenous anterior polyclone, derived from host eye-bud tissue, at the opposite side of the same chimeric retina.[8]

These results provide powerful evidence that (*a*) small bits of tissue at different angular positions on the 2-day eye-bud already contain

___

[8] The notion of "informational hybrids" is a complex one which deserves further comment. If cellular address (in two dimensions) is coded by an ordered pair of two variables, a powerful test for whether these variables are Cartesian or radial is to analyze "nonsense" and "mis-sense" patterns in which the *pairings* of the two variables have been disrupted. The evidence suggests that the positional information for ganglion cell specificity, propagated radially as the polyclone grows, is coded in two *Cartesian* address values. This evidence is of two kinds and derives from the two categories of minority result in which only some of the patterning information is retained within the pole-graft in its new, heterotopic site. The cases in which *complete* regulation occurs, leading to an entirely normal map, are uninformative on the coding question, since *both* putative address variables show regulation—a result compatible with any two-variable coding scheme.

The first line of evidence derives from the cases in which the map from the polyclone is disorganized in one dimension. The *spared* dimension of ordering follows the rostrocaudal axis of the tectum; by inference, one address variable in the eye must reference the dimension that normally corresponds to rostrocaudal level in the tectum, namely *anteroposterior* position in the eye. The second line of evidence is more subtle. When an anterior pole-graft grows out a polyclone from a 10 o'clock or 8 o'clock position, the *angular* dimension across the polyclone is now askew from the true dorsoventral dimension. Yet the four cases in which regulation occurred in this "short dimension" across the polyclone showed *normal dorsoventral ordering* appropriate to the skewed position of the polyclone in the eye. They did not show the "skewed but roughly right-side-up" ordering, seen in some left-into-right heterotopic pole-grafts (Fig. 20b)—a result which (had it occurred as our "informational hybrid" in the *right*-into-right heterotopic pole-grafts) would have been compatible with a radial code and with *internal reversal* of the set of angular values within the polyclone.

___

tectal surface. (f) Visual field projection showing another minority result, in which the region of the visual field corresponding to the polyclone showed disorganized mapping in the mediolateral direction across the tectum. Although heterotopic anterior pole-grafts usually produce chimerae with "pie-slice" visual projections as illustrated here, occasional chimerae show normal or twinned visual projections.

unique information for assigning address information to retinal ganglion cells, and that (*b*) local mechanisms exist for propagation and elaboration of *a specific subset* of address values within a growing polyclone, and thus that (*c*) orderly assignment of address values does not depend upon continuing global orchestration over the eye as a whole. At present, it is impossible to determine whether the local propagation is related to clonal organization by heritable cellular properties or by a system of cell interactions which happen to follow the geometry of the polyclone; but it is clear that the process is local and radial. The information itself—the coded basis of address values—may be Cartesian; for when some of the information is changed, the "hybrid" subset of address values appears to reflect a Cartesian logic. Finally, there is the question of change itself. We do not yet know why some pole-grafts show mosaic patterns, some show regulated patterns, and a few show partially regulated patterns. Yet a key observation is the consistency of ordering within any given polyclone. In all of the experiments described, each polyclone is coherent in its use of information as one proceeds outward, from center to periphery, in the direction that recapitulates its ontogeny. Regulative development, whatever its mechanisms, seems overwhelmingly dependent upon all-or-none decisions in the early recombinant. Like the interacting half-eye buds, in which the plan for ganglion cell patterning can be reorganized within hours, the pole-grafts appear strongly biased toward changing *quickly,* if they change at all, and thereafter to assigning all ganglion cell address values in accordance with a *new* spatial plan. Apparently then, if *continuing* global control is unnecessary for assignment of address values, a mechanism for *early* global control does exist in the eye-bud, which can rapidly reorganize the local information within a misplaced bit of tissue in the larval eye.

V. Some Unanticipated Results

Some very straightforward experiments have produced quite unforeseen results. Many of these experiments involve procedures which are similar, or even strictly analogous, to protocols already described. In most cases, the data are very preliminary and the comments we can make about them are limited. Nevertheless, we have chosen to mention, at least briefly, a few of these observations, in part because they seem to be pointing toward new problems and new areas of research.

For example, dorsal poles grafted into nasal holes often show a "regulated" retinotectal pattern; that is, the map is normal despite clear evidence that a polyclone has grown out of the graft. However, some chimerae, following ostensibly identical surgery, show a much more remarkable result. A widespread perturbation exists in the retinotectal map, that is unlike any described previously for other types of heterotopic pole grafts. Rather than a pie-slice sector of the map, in which retinal ganglion cells have laid down increasingly dorsal address values, such heterotopic dorsal grafts engender an abnormality which extends beyond the boundaries of the polyclone in the PRE. In brief, more anterior points in the retina have receptive fields extending from the front (nasal) to the back (temporal) of the visual field. More posterior retinal points show fairly normal receptive fields, mapping normally to the caudal regions of the tectum. One possible explanation is that dorsal cells on the germinal ring contain special properties which help to organize the local values at other angular positions on the ring. However, until *1-nu* reconstructions of the neural retina are completed, a wealth of other possibilities exists, including extensive and disorganized mixing of graft-derived neurons with their adjacent, host-derived counterparts.

Another surprise occurred when very early pole-grafts were performed replacing the ventral pole of a 1.5-day (stage 24) albino eye-bud with a pigmented ventral graft. In the day following surgery, graft-derived cells moved toward the middle back of the eye-bud and failed to contribute to the juvenile PRE. Thus, premarking of the *ventral* pole, followed by half-eye ablation, was conspicuously absent from our earlier discussions of regulation by individual eye fragments. We currently favor the view that the ventral quadrant of the very early eye-bud may not contribute at all to the later optic cup. Preliminary data, which suggest that anteroventral and posteroventral cells come to occupy the ventral quadrant of the early larval eye, support this view. However, present data are compatible with a number of interpretations and provide a recapitulation of the ambiguities and cautions which accompany results from a single chimeric procedure: the ventral quadrant of the early eye-bud could contribute only to *neural* retina and not PRE; wild-type cells may not autonomously express their ability to synthesize pigments when grafted into the ventral pole of an early eye-bud; the albino genotype may be specificly abnormal in the ventral regions of the emergent eye; or the failure to populate the PRE could reflect a surgical artifact in which ventral cells are unable to heal into place to produce a normal recombinant eye. Until a variety of heterotopic grafts are performed, and this particular experiment is extended with *1-nu* markers, our working view remains only an hypothesis.

Still another unexpected result turned up in certain "batches" of black-into-white mosaics: chimerae prepared concurrently, using the same embryo stock, but representing a variety of orthotopic and heterotopic grafts. Histological examination of the juvenile frogs showed pigment in the ear, nose, and/or skin, in a large fraction of the cases. The pigment in the nose was always incorporated into the nasal epithelium, but pigment in the skin and ear was sometimes encapsulated in a membrane-bound structure. These ectopic melanocytes were not identifiable as either PRE or choroid, and they often showed reduced and variable levels of pigmentation. In a few frogs, pigmented cells were seen on the brain surface. Apparently associated with meningeal tissue, these pigment cells occupied a contiguous patch at the rostrolateral edge of the tectum, ipsilateral to the chimeric eye.

Many of the chimerae which later showed ectopic pigment cells showed a correlated phenomenon in the 2 days immediately following surgery. Following surgical insertion of a pigmented fragment into an albino orbit, pigmented cells appeared to be migrating out of the orbit, sometimes in association with the optic stalk or emergent optic nerve, and, in other cases, in the direction of the ear. Often, the pigmented cells had "disappeared" from external view by early larval stages. Thus, while the correlation is strong, a mechanistic connection remains to be established between the postoperative "migration" of pigmented cells and the occurrence of ectopic melanocytes in juvenile chimerae.

SUPERNUMERARY EYE TISSUE

Perhaps the most dramatic of the unexpected findings, and the one to which we have devoted the most attention to date, is the formation of "supernumerary eyes." Classically, the designation of supernumerary has been reserved for the occurrence of extra tissue parts, organized into a partial or complete organ, which arise in addition to the essentially complete primary organ. In the pioneering studies of Harrison (1918, 1921), for example, certain surgical perturbations on the limb bud produced *two* independently organized limbs in place of one. As far as we know, supernumerary eyes have not been described as a consequence of similar perturbations on the embryonic eye-bud.

In the course of the detailed anatomical reconstruction of chimeric frogs, prepared by orthotopic and heterotopic pole-grafts at 2 days of development, we turned up a significant incidence of ectopic eye tissue that conforms to even the most conservative definition of supernumeraries. In a series of 27 chimerae, in which the experimental eye appeared complete and grossly normal on external view, four cases showed a small additional "eye," external to the main eye (Fig. 21a–f). Certain features appeared to be common to this class of *external* supernumerary eyes, which all showed the characteristic layering seen in the normal vertebrate retina. Three of the four cases were chimeric for pigmented and albino tissue in the retinal epithelium. Three supernumerary eyes showed an inside-out pattern of layering; two of these also showed evidence of nerve fibers exiting from the periphery of the structure (the ganglion cell layer) and coursing caudally (in the direction of the optic tectum); however, these fibers could be followed only for a short distance. One of the eyes showed a coalescence of the fibers, near the point of exit, which resembled the optic nerve head seen in normal eyes. Only one of the four supernumeraries occurred in a nucleolar mosaic (*1-nu*-into-white). The supernumerary was chimeric for both pigmented and albino retinal epithelium and for both *1-nu* and *2-nu* throughout the rest of the retina (Fig. 21d–f).

The external supernumeraries, if unexpected and inexplicable at the level of mechanism, are at least stragithforward as a category for description. The chimera produces one complete main eye and a secondary eye, which conforms to the classic criteria of a supernumerary organ. Other cases—10 from the same series of 27 pole-graft chimerae—showed various kinds of internal abnormalities in which ectopic eye tissue was present within the primary eye. The internal abnormalities are presented with diffidence, against the background of the wide range of ocular abnormalities seen when two whole eyes are simply forced to inhabit the same orbit (Hunt and Jacobson, 1974b). In some respects, given the drastic excisions and insertions used to make chimeric eyes, the occurrence of even grossly abnormal recombinants is hardly remarkable. Yet in their extreme forms, these abnormalities have a peculiar "two-eyes-in-one" quality that is unmistakably reminiscent of the more straightforward external supernumeraries. Some or all of the internal abnormalities may reflect a slightly different output of the same process that gives rise to external supernumeraries, or an altogether different process of aberrant healing and differential growth in individual surgical recombinants.

With the above in mind, the following 10 cases are presented in a simple continuum of abnormality—from the least severe cases of retinal buckling to the case of a bilobate eye. In two cases, retinal buckling was the only abnormality present. In four other cases, the retinal buckling was associated with a small nodule composed of neural tissue, both cell bodies and nerve fibers, which lay internal to the ganglion cell layer and whose fibers appeared to join the fibers of the main ganglion cell layer. A seventh case showed two lenses with no other abnormality present, while another showed two lenses as well as two optic nerve heads.

The final two eyes of our 10 cases with internal abnormalities

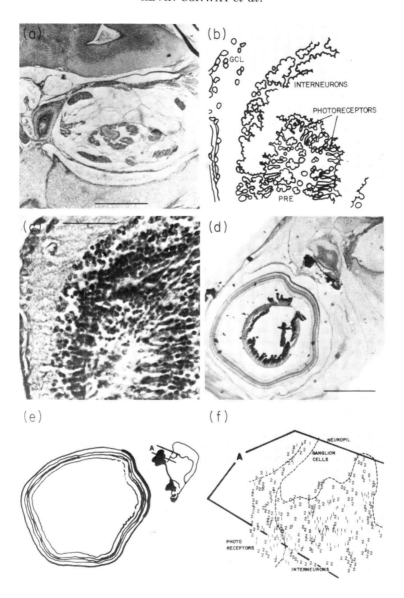

FIG. 21. The occurrence and appearance of supernumerary eye tissue, external to the main eye. The supernumerary eyes were located within the optic orbit, medial to the main eye. In this case, the supernumerary is located medial and posterior to the main eye so that a histologic section through the widest point of the supernumerary eye includes only the optic nerve of the main eye (a). The typical (although inside-out) layering of the vertebrate retina can be recognized at higher magnification (50 μm) (c) and schematized

showed more complex structures. The first was an ectopic but well-organized cul-de-sac of retinal tissue, at the posterior edge of the main eye, sandwiched between the pigment retinal and photoreceptor layers of the main eye. The normal ordering of retinal layers was present within the ectopic structure. The most internal layer was composed of a few clumped ganglion cells; no lens or vitreal space was present. The final eye, derived from a heterotopic graft, was distinctly bilobate on external appearance. Histologic examination revealed two distinct corneas, lenses, and irises. In the front of the eye, the neural retina was organized into two lobes, which merged into one in the back third of the eye. The extreme back of the eye showed a single continuous structure, but two optic nerves were present. Each of the lobes in the front were chimeric for pigmented and albino tissue.

A few easy explanations of this family of phenomena have occurred to us, only to be dismissed on the basis of several isolated findings. The first possible explanation would be the easiest: the graft merely failed to be incorporated and rounded up to produce a separate eye. Of the four cases with frank (external) supernumeraries, only one of the ectopic eyes was nonchimeric for pigmented and albino tissue. Indeed, this eye may be the result of such a failed graft, since the main eye failed to show a clone. In all three other cases, both the primary eye *and* the supernumerary eye were chimeric, for pigmented and albinotic tissue, and one supernumerary was chimeric in all layers for *1-nu* and *2-nu*. In these cases, it seems far-fetched to believe that at the time of the surgery, half of the innoculum "fell out" and was accompanied by some amount of the host tissue. Although less well studied, the internal abnormalities may also defy simplistic mechanical explanations. The bilobate eye, for example, could have resulted from incomplete fusion of two eyes or eye fragments, for two eyes sharing the same orbit can produce a single bilobate structure. Yet this explanation fails to account for the chimerism seen within each lobe.

The other immediate suspect was the mechanical properties specific to ventral pole-grafts or ventral sites created in hosts for receipt of grafts. The ventral part of the eye, during the stages of development used here, contains the choroidal fissure and the optic stalk. It is conceivable that duplicating this region (by inserting a ventral pole in

---

(b). Another of these supernumeraries (d) occurred in the *1-nu/2-nu* mosaic already detailed in Fig. 3 in which the main eye showed a clone of *1-nu* cells in the neural retina (500 μm). Reconstruction at low power (e) and high power (f) of the supernumerary, using scoring procedures detailed earlier, revealed that the supernumerary structure was clearly chimeric for *1-nu* and *2-nu* cells, in roughly a 1:1 ratio.

another location in the host eye) might produce supernumerary nerves if nothing more. Even among the small number of cases presently available, this does not seem to be the case. Heterotopic ventral pole-grafts did produce both of the chimerae with extreme *internal* abnormalities (including the bilobate eye) described, yet some ventral pole-grafts show *no* duplicated structures, and some chimerae with internal abnormalities and external supernumeraries resulted from other types of grafts.

The most exciting explanation is that of intercalary growth, elegantly studied by French *et al.* (1976) in limb systems, but the presence of abnormalities in three eyes resulting from *orthotopic* grafts seems to put the analysis out of the scope of the small numbers we presently have available. It is not clear that analysis of the data for trends will be worthwhile until we can more fully understand which of the abnormalities seen belong in the category of true supernumerary tissues, and which, if any, reflect problems of healing and integration of recombinant tissues. The process by which extra lenses or optic nerves are generated may be entirely different from that creating the external, multilayered supernumeraries. Moreover, if some of the internal abnormalities *are* a form of true supernumerary, our early series contains a sampling error. Our aim was to study clonal patterns in chimeric but otherwise normal eyes; grossly malformed recombinants hardly seemed to serve this aim, and only a few representative cases were reared to maturity.

In short, supernumeraries provided an answer to a question that did not exist; yet, at the same time, they raise a host of questions whose answers remain to be found. Some are approachable by chimeric methods, in conjunction with [³H]thymidine autoradiography. What percentage of the structures are host derived and what percentage are donor derived and how are polyclone territories arranged? At what stage in development do they appear? Do supernumerary eyes grow with the constrained radial geometry of normal eyes? Still other questions invite application of special methods for tracing neural pathways. Do the fibers exiting from external supernumeraries make functional connections with the tectum? Is there any topographic order to the fibers as they leave the supernumerary organ? Still other questions demand a range of experiments and techniques in a second-order analysis of such structures. Why do the highly organized external supernumeraries fail to induce lenses? How is the layering and tissue organization of these structures achieved? Like trying to unravel the Gordian knot, initial examination of supernumeraries has seemed merely to complicate the analysis.

VI. Conclusion

So, it seems that marker analysis is providing a wealth of information even as it is first employed in the *Xenopus* eye. At the most blatant level, it is now clear that the fate of cells in normal and surgically perturbed embryos can be quite surprising. Tissue may be diverted to supernumerary structures, according to rules not yet transparent to us, but presumably reflecting cellular properties and modes of healing. Pigment and perhaps other types of cells can occasionally migrate centrally, and toward the ear, perhaps following pathways used by normally migratory cells such as neural crest. Very early ventral pole-grafts do not contribute to the PRE, perhaps because this region of the early bud does not give rise to eye tissue at all. The "surprise," of course, reflects the crudeness of the available fate maps for vertebrates in general. The classical wisdom—that the front of the early bud makes neural retina and the back makes PRE—is also challenged by the observation that the part of the final eye-bud derives from a blastomere on the opposite side of the embryo (Jacobson and Hirose, 1978). In other systems, such as the fly wing, definitive progress has been possible only after a detailed and accurate fate map has been available (Bryant, 1974).

The fate of cells in a surgically created half eye-bud has been discussed. The results indicate that the rounding up of an eye-bud fragment features both an "epimorphic" addition of cells at the edge, and a "morpholactic" remodeling of the remainder of the eye. Still, the retinotectal maps of these eyes are normal. This result is doubly interesting. First, the half eye may have generated a full set of locus specificities (Hunt and Berman, 1975), analogous to the anatomical regulation that produced a whole eye out of the half eye-bud. The second point is more subtle. That the final eye is not lopsided, despite the very different responses of edge and nonedge cells, indicates that regulation of *form* is an orchestrated process involving the whole eye-bud. Similarly, the retinotectal map is neither compressed from the region added to the cut edge, nor expanded from the rest of the eye. Ignoring for a moment the universe of other regulative possibilities such as plasticity in the neural mapping function, and also ignoring the present lack of *1-nu* cell marking in this experiment, it is necessary to conclude that this regulation involves the whole eye-bud, and not just the new cells added at the wound edge.

This kind of regulation can be seen in surgically recombinant eyes as well, subject to similar qualifications. A pigmented dorsal half eye is changed by an anterior half eye. Cells with new positional values may be added at the graft edge, but we know that some of the existing cells change in some way from "dorsal" to "posterior." Moreover, the new posterior characteristics are maintained throughout development and an orderly succession of posterior address values is laid down, over a geometry that coincides with that of the polyclone. This radial, clonal propagation of information is demonstrated most graphically by "strong" poles grafted into a "weak" region of the eye. An anterior pole-graft will produce neurons with successively more anterior properties as time goes on, whether it is in a nasal or temporal hole. In grafts slightly askew from the Cartesian anterior–posterior axis, the perturbed portion of the retinotectal map is still radial. The coding of the information, on the other hand, is probably Cartesian. Retinotectal maps scrambled in one Cartesian axis at the level of single optic units have been recorded (Hunt, 1976a). Also, pole-grafts sometimes displayed a scrambling or reversal in one Cartesian axis, within a "pie slice" or sector of the map. This indicates not only that the coding is Cartesian, but that each of the axes can be coded, transmitted (clonally or otherwise), and expressed independently. As described earlier, Bodenstein and Hunt (1978, 1980) have proposed a model which features such a radial elaboration of Cartesian positional values.

About pigment lineages in the eye, we can speak directly. The three pigmented cell types in the eye almost certainly exist already as independent lineages prior to our operative protocols at day 2. We cannot say whether or not some pluripotential cells also exist in the 2-day bud which are capable of producing, for instance, both iris and PRE at later dates in development. Clearly, though, *some* precursors for these pigmented cell types, and perhaps all of them, are destined to give rise to only PRE or only iris or only choroid.

Our studies have also begun, in effect, to provide a more refined map of the 2-day (stage 32) eye-bud to the juvenile, for the PRE. In this map, the progeny of cells at the edge of the embryonic eye lie within a circumscribed angular domain in the juvenile. The boundaries of this domain are irregular only over a distance of 10–100 μm in most cases. The annular mode of retinal growth has been previously demonstrated (Straznicky and Gaze, 1971; Jacobson, 1968b, 1976; Beach, 1977), and the persistence of labeled annuli is evidence that mixing in the radial direction is limited or absent. We have further demonstrated that mature regions of retina also have sharp boundaries, but have argued that either the absence of mixing or compensatory sorting (or cell death) could maintain the boundaries. Persistence of forks and tributaries favors the former. Finally, we have shown that occasional mixing or migration events do occur among retinal stem cells in the germinal ring, and that adjustments in local accretion rates may tend to restore progeny of displaced stem cells to their original angular position.

This emerging fate map for PRE also features a smaller contribution from dorsal stage 32 eye than from ventral. This is even more the case in the iris than in the PRE. We have not seen any evidence for or against developmental compartments in the eye, as Garcia-Bellido (1975) and others have seen in insects. Our operative protocols do not include a wide range of times for initiation of clones. Nor do we have a slow growing mutant like *Minute*. After stage 32, when most of our clones are introduced, clones are all oriented radially. Boundaries which meet the formal definition of compartments certainly exist in the eye, between iris and PRE for example, but they are also associated with differences in cell type. Within the PRE, one or more "radial lines" seen in our polyclone boundaries may prove to be compartment boundaries, but we as yet have no evidence for this. The boundary lines we see are variable in position, and even the most orderly radial lines show local irregularities. Nevertheless, because we graft small *groups* of cells (which could contain members of two compartments) and because regulative events may occur during healing, our failure to find lines which polyclones never cross is only suggestive.

The prime conclusion from this work is that clones grow in a radial fashion in the eye of *Xenopus*, and that at least some positional properties are elaborated radially, and thus probably clonally. However, this clonal prepattern can be altered by regulatory events. These events are rapid (12–48 hours) and occur in a variety of experimental situations. This tension between local clonal prepatterns and global regulative events is probably one of the great creative forces in development. One can speculate further that both may predominate, each at its own juncture, at different stages in an emerging tissue. Prepatterns present as early as the unfertilized egg are elaborated clonally, and expressed, in cellular properties such as adhesion and migration only to be modified, supplanted, or overlayed by later global events. These new properties can again be clonally transmitted (Hunt *et al.*, 1980a).

Earlier, we considered morphogenesis as a system of cellular behaviors based on ordinary differentiated traits of the cells involved. Further consideration of the systems nature of pattern formation leads to the question—what is the relation between determination of cell fate by lineage and determination by positional cues? Answers to this come in two categories, phenomenology and mechanism. In some extreme cases, lineage is invariant, and the properties of a particular cell seem most strongly correlated with its particular place in the "family tree."

The phenomenology of insect hair development and the production of ventral cord neurons in worms and leeches have already been described. Nematode worm development as a whole tends to feature highly invariant lineages, starting with the egg. We can speculate on the mechanisms that operate to produce a programmed diversity in the progeny of a single cell. Most diploid cells have given little evidence for unequal apportioning of DNA. However, the associated molecules which we all believe regulate gene expression are not necessarily the same in the two daughters. A small difference in such regulatory molecules could, of course, lead to significantly different cell properties. The mathematics of bifurcation processes is not readily grasped by biologists or easily applied to biological systems. But one conclusion that we can assimilate from afar is that, in a complex system, blatant differences are not required to send two identical subsystems into different trajectories. Merely halving the size of a cell could produce a set of acceptable states, where before there was only one. In addition, there may be real differences in the cytosols of each daughter.

In some other cases, the position of cells seems to have a much greater bearing on their fate than does their lineage. Mechanisms have proved elusive in such cases, but the literature provides a few examples in which progress is being made. In hydra, for example, frequency of head formation can be influenced by an extract that contains mostly small molecules of less than 500 MW (review Gierer, 1978). The idea of a gradient based on diffusion of small molecules is highly attractive in many ways, but finding the exact molecule is intrinsically difficult. Effective concentrations are likely to be quite small, and unambiguous and easy assays do not exist. Also, when confined to some biological geometries, diffusion gradients may not be terribly linear. For instance, the pattern produced by a source and a sink at opposite edges of a circular disk has been computed. Even at long times, there remains a "hill" near the source, and a "valley" at the sink. The same configuration on a sphere produces straight line concentration isobars, but again they are bunched up near the source and sink (Conway, 1978). Bunow (1980) has used more complex activator–inhibitor equations on a wing-disk geometry. He also finds that the patterns produced are not always obviously suitable for generating pattern. However, over small distances, diffusion is viably quick (Crick, 1970), and remains a viable mechanism for producing a graded set of differences in cells.

Cell surface molecules are another obvious candidate for cell–cell communications in pattern formation. In addition, they may play a role in adhesion and migration. Such cell surface interactions may not require physical contact between plasma membranes. In some embryonic induction systems, for example, contact between the extracellular matrix associated with adjacent cells may be sufficient. Recently, a secreted glycoprotein has been implicated in the differentiation of slime molds. Mutants defective in this molecule cannot aggregate, but are rescued by wild-type cells in a 50% mix (Ray *et al.*, 1979). Yet, even in slime molds, diffusible molecules have their role to play (McMahon, 1973). It should perhaps be noted that global changes could be produced by short-range signals, provided that local groups of cells, as they receive the signal, can change in some way that enables the response to be propagated to adjacent groups. Thus a global change could be mediated by cell surface interactions, and a diffusable molecule might produce only a local effect if it were rapidly degradable, or if there was a threshold for detection (Summerbell *et al.*, 1973).

The phenomenology of positional information can be broadly considered to encompass the whole of experimental embryology. Some examples have already been considered. Deletion and transplantation experiments on limb buds, eye-buds, neural crest, presumptive midbrain, and insect imaginal disk all can yield results where final differentiation is position dependent rather than lineage dependent. The normal *Drosophila* wing produced by a wild-type clone in a minute background is a good example. The lineage is clearly different from a normal wing, since the wild-type clone has cells that have divided several extra times as the abnormally large clone develops. Yet hairs and bristles form at the appropriate places, and positional compartment boundaries are respected.

Paradoxically, these position-dependent phenomena do not rule out the presence of a lineage-dependent bias. They only point out that in some cases and at some times in development, position is more important. In fact, in the majority of cases, it is probably the interplay of lineage and position that rules. Heterotopic retinal grafts carry such conceptual complexities. Some grafts reliably regulate into the overall positional pattern, some do not. Further, the geometry of lineage is identical to the geometry of propagation of information. This propagation might be clonal, but then again, it might be mediated by cell surface, small molecule, or matrix interactions which follow the clonal geometry. Experimentally, such situations require neutral environments to assay the lineage properties, and perturbed lineages to assay the positional properties. Furthermore, lineage and positional information may operate by similar mechanisms. Thus, in cases in which lineage appears to be the determinant, the mechanism may involve positional differences *within* a stem cell (polarity). These intracellular differences may be related to, or modulated by, positional cues in the embryo as a whole. In the nematode, for instance, anterior–posterior divisions are often determinant, while left–right ones produce a pair of interchangeable cells (Sulston and Horvitz, 1977).

Obviously, the experimental aspects of clonal analysis and positional information in the *Xenopus* eye have barely been tapped, much less exhausted. The analysis must be pushed to simpler and more mechanistic levels. Systems ideas are deceptively attractive for their generality. "Positional information" explains too much, without detailed experiments. In fact, clonal relationships explain many developmental phenomena without recourse to exotic positional signals. This is true for other biological systems as well. Beyond synaptic specificities, contact guidance and timing of neuronal birthdates explain many aspects of the normal development of neuronal connections. Cells make certain proteins rather than others because they have a peculiar sequence of base pairs in their nucleic acids. However, the vigorous pursuit of mechanisms serves to highlight the interactive and systemic aspects that *remain* unexplained. Cells with identical clonal histories do different *appropriate* things. Neurons can make correct connections following bizarre routes and timetables. And, while the base pair sequence of genes does directly affect the three-dimensional conformation of the resulting proteins, there are other factors at work. Myoglobin, horse hemoglobin, and trout hemoglobin all have three-dimensional structures so similar that difference maps of their X-ray diffraction patterns are used to refine estimates of those structures. Yet, the amino acid sequences vary greatly.

So the focus shifts to more global concerns. What functional or evolutionary pressures put limits on the acceptable variation in the three-dimensional structure of globin molecule? How do positional properties collaborate with contact guidance and developmental schedules to effect orderly neuronal connections? How are cellular properties, related to cell position at one stage of development, conveyed clonally to cells at later stages in development? Why are "normal" and "twinned" patterns the common output of so many different embryological experiments? What kind of cellular interactions constitute positional information?

One final task belongs to the mystic in all of us. The scientific literature of our mechanistic age has little to say about this. However, in the Third Part of his "Principles of Philosophy," Rene Descartes made this comment: "Having now ascertained certain principles of material things which were derived, not from the prejudices of the senses, but from the light of reason, so that we cannot doubt their truth, it is for us to examine whether from these alone we can explain all the phenomena of nature." Like the man searching on the well-lit porch, when the keys are in the garden, we feel the inertia of the mechanistic age. It is an inertia that pushes us toward questions that are answerable, independent of whether they are particularly worth posing. We believe that questions of pattern and form are answerable with the help of clonal analysis—answerable, in fact, in terms of ordinary cellular differentiation. Yet the chasm between what we see and what we can explain is more than mechanistic, and the seduction of clonal analysis goes far beyond our trust in its explanatory power. There is something aesthetic about clonal geometries, an exquisite delicacy to the way boundaries and lines are etched into living forms, that is unmistakable.

ACKNOWLEDGMENTS

It is a pleasure to thank Drs. Charles Ide and Gregory Stock for their important contributions to the development of clonal analysis in *Xenopus* retina, and Drs. Antonio Garcia-Bellido, Jose Campos-Ortega, Howard Holtzer, and Susan Bryant for valuable discussions during the early stages of this work. We also thank Dr. Scott Fraser for suggestions which substantially improved the manuscript. Special thanks are extended to Dr. Marija Duda who prepared the histologic material from which the reconstructions were made, Ms. Diana Ross who prepared the drawings in Figs. 2, 4, and 10, and Ms. Lucinda Hentges and Ms. Suzanne Robinson for their heroic efforts in preparing the manuscript. This work has been supported by grants from the National Science Foundation (BNS-75-18998 and PCM-77-26987), a training grant from the National Institutes of Health (GM-07231), a Biomedical Sciences Research Grant to The Johns Hopkins University, and a fellowship from the Alfred Sloan Foundation. Computing was immensely aided by funds from the Office of the Dean, The Johns Hopkins University.

REFERENCES

Angevine, J. B., Jr., and Sidman, R. L. (1962). *Anat. Rec.* **142**, 210.
Attardi, D. G., and Sperry, R. W. (1963). *Exp. Neurol.* **7**, 46.
Barondes, S. H. (1970). *In* "The Neurosciences: Second Study Program" (F. O. Schmitt, ed.), p. 747. Rockefeller Univ. Press, New York.
Beach, D. H. (1977). Doctoral Thesis, University of Miami.
Beach, D. H., and Jacobson, M. (1979a). *J. Comp. Neurol.* **183**, 603.
Beach, D. H., and Jacobson, M. (1979b). *J. Comp. Neurol.* **183**, 615.
Bergey, G. K., Hunt, R. K., and Holtzer, H. (1973). *Anat. Rec.* **175**, 271.
Berman, N., and Hunt, R. K. (1975). *J. Comp. Neurol.* **162**, 23.
Bodenstein, L. E., and Hunt, R. K. (1978). *Biophys. J.* **25**, 84a.
Bodenstein, L. E., and Hunt, R. K. (1980). In preparation.
Bronner, M. E., and Cohen, A. M. (1979). *Proc. Natl. Acad. Sci. U.S.A.* **76**, 1843.
Brown, D. D., and Gurdon, J. B. (1964). *Proc. Natl. Acad. Sci. U.S.A.* **51**, 139.
Bryant, P. (1974). *Curr. Top. Dev. Biol.* **8**, 41.
Bunow, B. (1980). *J. Theor. Biol.* (in press).
Burnside, B., and Jacobson, A. G. (1968). *Dev. Biol.* **18**, 537.
Chung, S. H. (1974). *Cell* **3**, 201.
Chung, S. H., and Cooke, J. (1975). *Nature (London)* **258**, 126.

Chung, S. H., Keating, M. J., and Bliss, T. V. P. (1974). *Proc. R. Soc. London B* **187**, 449.

Chung, S. H., Stirling, R. V., and Gaze, R. M. (1975). *J. Embryol. Exp. Morphol.* **33**, 915.

Cohen, A. M. (1972). *J. Exp. Zool.* **179**, 167.

Conway, K. (1978). *Biophys. J.* **25**, 159a.

Conway, K., Stock, G. B., Feiock, K., Duda, M., and Hunt, R. K. (1980). In preparation.

Cooke, J. (1977). *In* "Cell Interactions in Differentiation" (M. Karkinen-Jaaskelainen, L. Saxen and L. Weiss, eds.), pp. 111. Academic Press, New York.

Cook, J. E., and Horder, T. J. (1977). *Phil. Trans. R. Soc. B* **278**, 261.

Coulombre, A. J. (1965). *In* "Organogenesis" (R. L. DeHaan, and H. Ursprung, eds.), Holt, New York.

Crick, F. H. C. (1970). *Nature (London)* **225**, 420.

Crossland. W. J., Cowan, W. M., Rogers, L. A., and Kelly, J. P. (1974). *J. Comp. Neurol.* **155**, 127.

Currie, J., and Cowan, W. M. (1974). *Dev. Biol.* **46**, 103.

Dellaney, L. (1978). *Am. Zool.* **18**(2), 289.

Dienstman, S. R., and Holtzer, H. (1975). *Results Prob. Cell Differ.* **7**, 1.

Dixon, J. S., and Cronly-Dillon, J. R. (1974). *Nature (London)* **251**, 505.

Edds, M. V., Gaze, R. M., Schneider, G. E., and Irwin, N. I. (1979). *Neurosci. Res. Prog. Bull.* **17**, 243.

Elsdale, T. R., Fishberg, M., and Smith, S. (1958). *Exp. Cell Res.* **14**, 642.

Feldman, J. D., and Gaze, R. M. (1975). *J. Comp. Neurol.* **162**, 13.

Feldman, J. D., Gaze, R. M., and Keating, M. J. (1971). *Exp. Brain Res.* **14**, 16.

Feiock, K., Conway, C., Stock G. B., Duda, M., Ide, C. F., and Hunt, R. K. (1980). In preparation.

Fraser, S. E. (1978). Doctoral Thesis, The Johns Hopkins University, Baltimore, Maryland.

Fraser, S. E. (1980). *Dev. Biol.* (in press).

Fraser, S. E., and Hunt, R. K. (1980a). *Dev. Biol.* (in press).

Fraser, S. E., and Hunt, R. K. (1980b). *Annu. Rev. Neurosci.* **3**, 319.

Freeman, J. A. (1977). *Nature (London)* **269**, 218.

French, V., Bryant, P. J., and Bryant, S. V. (1976). *Science* **193**, 969.

Garber, B. B., and Moscona, A. A. (1972). *Dev. Biol.* **27**, 217.

Garcia-Bellido, A. (1975). *Ciba Found. Symp.* **29**, 161.

Garcia-Bellido, A. (1976). *Dev. Biol.* **48**, 132.

Gaze, R. M. (1970). "Formation of Nerve Connections." Academic Press, New York.

Gaze, R. M. (1978). *In* "Specificity of Embryological Interactions" (D. Garrod, ed.). Chapman and Hall, London (in press).

Gaze, R. M. (1980). *Curr. Top. Dev. Biol.* (in press).

Gaze, R. M., and Grant, P. (1978). *J. Embryol. Exp. Morphol.* **44**, 201.

Gaze, R. M., and Keating, M. J. (1972). *Nature (London)* **237**, 345.

Gaze, R. M., and Sharma, S. C. (1970). *Exp. Brain Res.* **10**, 771.

Gaze, R. M., Jacobson, M., and Szekely, G. (1963). *J. Physiol. London* **165**, 484.

Gaze, R. M., Keating, M. J., and Chung, S. H. (1974). *Proc. R. Soc. Lond. B* **185**, 301.

Gierer, A. (1974). *Sci. Am.* **231**, 44.

Glucksmann, A. (1940). *Br. J. Ophthalmol.* **153**, 24.

Goldberg, S. (1976). *J. Comp. Neurol.* **168**, 379.

Goodman, C. S., and Spitzer, N. C. (1978). *Soc. Neurosci.* **4**, 113.

Grant, P., and Rubin, J. (1980). *J. Comp. Neurol.* (in press).

Guillery, R., Casagrande, V., and Oberdorfer, M. (1974). *Nature (London)* **252**, 195.

Hall, J., Sidman, R. L., and Benzer, S. (1980). "Prospects for the Study of Neurogenetics." *NRP Bulletin* (in press).

Hamilton, T. (1968). *Science* **161**, 649.

Harris, W. (1980). *Neurosci. Symp.* (in press).

Harrison, R. G. (1918). *J. Exp. Zool.* **25**, 413.

Harrison, R. G. (1921). *J. Exp. Zool.* **32**, 1.

Harrison, R. G. (1935). *Proc. R. Soc. London B* **118**, 155.

Harrison, R. G. (1939). *Proc. R. Soc. London B* **118**, 155.

Harrison, R. G. (1945). *Trans. Conn. Acad. Arts Sci.* **36**, 277.

Hibbard, E. (1967). *Exp. Neurol.* **19**, 350.

Hinds, J. W., and Hinds, P. L. (1974). *Dev. Biol.* **37**, 381.

Hirose, G., and Jacobson, M. (1979). *Dev. Biol.* (in press).

Holtfreter, J. (1939). *Arch. Exp. Zellforsch.* **23**, 169.

Holtzer, H. (1968). *In* "Epithelial-Mesenchymal Interactions" (K. Fleischmajer, ed.), p. 152, Williams & Wilkins, Baltimore, Maryland.

Holtzer, H. (1970). *Symp. Cell Biol.* **9**, 69.

Holtzer, H., Rubenstein N., Fellini, S., Yeoh G., Chi, J., Bernbaum, J., and Okayama, M. (1975). *Q. Rev. Biophys.* **8**(4) 523.

Hope, R. A., Hammond, B. J., and Gaze, R. M. (1976). *Proc. R. Soc. London B* **194**, 447.

Horder, T. J. (1974). *Brain Res.* **72**, 41.

Horder, T. J., and Martin, K. A. C. (1979). *Symp. Soc. Exp. Biol.* **32**, 275.

Horder, T. J., and Spitzer, J. (1973). *J. Physiol.* **233**, 33P.

Hoskins, S., Tosney, K. W., and Hunt, R. K. (1980). In preparation.

Hunt, R. K. (1975a). *Ciba Found. Symp.* **29**, 131.

Hunt, R. K. (1975b). *Results Prob. Cell Differ.* **7**, 43.

Hunt, R. K. (1976a). *In* Developmental Biology" (D. McMahon and C. F. Fox, eds.), p. 227. Benjamin, Menlo Park, California.

Hunt, R. K. (1976b). *In* "Progress in Differentiation Research" (N. Muller-Berat *et al.*, eds.), p. 11. North-Holland Publ., Amsterdam.

Hunt, R. K. (1977). *Biophys. J.* **17**, 128a.

Hunt, R. K., and Berman, N. (1975). *J. Comp. Neurol.* **162**, 43.

Hunt, R. K., and Frank, E. (1975). *Science* **189**, 563.

Hunt, R. K., and Ide, C. F. (1977). *Biol. Bull.* **153**, 430.

Hunt, R. K., and Jacobson, M. (1972). *Proc. Natl. Acad. Sci. U.S.A.* **69**(4), 780.

Hunt, R. K., and Jacobson, M. (1973). *Proc. Natl. Acad. Sci. U.S.A.* **70**(2), 507.

Hunt, R. K., and Jacobson, M. (1974a). *Curr. Top. Dev. Biol.* **8**, 203.

Hunt, R. K., and Jacobson, M. (1974b). *Dev. Biol.* **40**, 1.

Hunt, R. K., and Piatt, J. (1978). *Dev. Biol.* **62**, 44.

Hunt, R. K., Bodenstein, L., Kosofsky, B. E., and Ide, C. F. (1980a). In preparation.

Hunt, R. K., Conway, K., Feiock, K., Ide, C. F., Stock, G. B., and Duda, M. (1980b). In preparation.

Ide, C. F. (1978). *Am. Zool.* **18**, 281.

Ide, C. F., and Hunt, R. K. (1978). *Biophys. J.* **21**, 110a.

Ide, C. F., Kosofsky, B. E., and Hunt, R. K. (1979). *Dev. Biol.* **69**, 337.

Ilmensee, K., and Mintz, B. (1976). *Proc. Natl. Acad. Sci. U.S.A.* **73**(2), 549.

Jacobson, C. O. (1959). *J. Embryol. Exp. Morphol.* **7**, 1.

Jacobson, C. O. (1964). *Zool. Bidr. Upps.* **36**, 73.

Jacobson, M. (1966). *In* "Major Problems in Developmental Biology" (M. Locke, ed.), p. 339. Academic Press, New York.

Jacobson, M. (1968a). *Dev. Biol.* **17**, 202.

Jacobson, M. (1968b). *Dev. Biol.* **17**, 219.

Jacobson, M. (1976). *Brain Res.* **103**, 541.

Jacobson, M. (1977). *Brain Res.* **127**, 55.

Jacobson, M. (1978). *In* "Developmental Neurobiology" 2nd ed. Plenum, New York.

Jacobson, M., and Hirose, G. (1978). *Science* **202**, 637.

Jacobson, M., and Hunt, R. K. (1973). *Sci. Am.* **228**(2), 326.

Jacobson, M., and Levine, R. L. (1975a). *Brain Res.* **88**, 339.

Jacobson, M., and Levine, R. L. (1975b). *Brain Res.* **92**, 468.

Kafatos, F. C. (1972). *Curr. Top. Dev. Biol.* **7**, 1.

Kahn, A. J. (1974). *Dev. Biol.* **38**, 30.

Kankel, D. R., and Hall, J. C. (1976). *Dev. Biol.* **48**, 1.

Keiny, M. (1977). *Wilhelm Roux's Arch.* **183**, 177.

Keller, R. E. (1975). *Dev. Biol.* **42**, 222.

Lawrence, P. A. (1966). *J. Exp. Biol.* **44**, 507.

Lawrence, P. A. (1975). *Res. Prob. Cell Differ.* **7**, 111.

Lawrence, P. A., and Green, S. M. (1979). *Dev. Biol.* **71**, 142.

Lazar, G. (1973). *J. Anat.* **116**, 347.

Le Douarin, N. (1973). *Dev. Biol.* **30**, 217.

LeDouarin, N. (1980). *Curr. Top. Dev. Biol.* **15** (in press).

Le Douarin, N., and Teillet, M. (1974). *Dev. Biol.* **41**, 162.

Levine, R. L., and Jacobson, M. (1974). *Exp. Neurol.* **43**, 527.

Ling, R. T.-K., Ide, C. F., and Hunt, R. K. (1979). *Dev. Biol.* **69**, 361.

Longley, A. (1978). *J. Embryol. Exp. Morphol.* **45**, 249.

McDevitt, D. S., and Brahma, S. K. (1973). *J. Exp. Zool.* **186**, 127.

McDonald, N. (1975). *J. Comp. Neurol.* **162**, 13.

McDonald, N. (1977). *J. Theor. Biol.* **69**, 153.

McMahon, D. (1973). *Proc. Natl. Acad. Sci. U.S.A.* **70**, 2396.

Marchase, R. B., Barbera, A. J., and Roth, S. (1975). *Ciba Found. Symp.* **29**, 315.

Meyer, R. L. (1975). *Anat. Rec.* **181**, 427.

Meyer, R. L. (1978). *Brain Res.* **155**, 213.

Meyer, R. L. (1979a). *Science* (in press).

Meyer, R. L. (1979b). *J. Comp. Neurol.* **183**, 283.

Meyer, R. L. (1980). *J. Comp. Neurol.* (in press).

Meyer, R. L., and Sperry, R. W. (1975). *In* "Studies on the Development of Behavior and the Nervous System" (G. Gottlieb, ed.), Vol. 3 p. 111. Academic Press, New York.

Mintz, B., and Ilmensee, K. (1975). *Proc. Natl. Acad. Sci. U.S.A.* **72**, 3585.

Mullen, R. (1977). *Nature (London)* **270**, 245.

Nieuwkoop, P. D., and Faber, J. (1956). "Normal Table of Xenopus laevis (Daudin)." North-Holland Publ., Amsterdam.

Noden, D. M. (1975). *Dev. Biol.* **42**, 106.

Nordlander, R. H., and Edwards, J. S. (1969). *Arch. Entwicklungsmech. Org.* **162**, 197.

Rakic, P. (1977). *Phil. Trans. R. Soc. London B* **278**, 245.

Ray, J., Shinnick, T., and Lerner, R. (1979). *Nature (London)* **279**, 215.

Ready, D. F., Hanson, T. E., and Benzer, S. (1976). *Dev. Biol.* **53**, 217.

Rho, J. H. (1978). *Biophys. J.* **21**, 137a.

Rho, J. H., and Hunt, R. K. (1980). *Dev. Biol.* (in press).

Runnstrom, J. (1928). *Arch. Entwicklungsmech. Org.* **113**, 556.

Scalia, F. (1977). *In* "Handbook Frog Neurobiology" (R. Llinas and W. Precht, eds.). Springer-Verlag, Berlin and New York.

Schimke, R. T., McKnight, G. S., Tayvar, F., and Tennequin, P. (1976). *In* "Developmental Biology" (D. McMahon and C. F. Fox, eds.), p. 384. Benjamin, Menlo Park, California.

Schmidt, J. T. (1978). *J. Comp. Neurol.* **177**, 279.

Scott, M. Y. (1977). *Exp. Neurol.* **54**, 579.

Sharma, S. C. (1972). *Nature (London) New Biol.* **238**, 286.

Sharma, S. C., and Gaze, R. M. (1971). *Arch. Ital. Biol.* **109**, 357.

Sharma, S. C., and Tung, Y. L. (1979). *J. Physiol.* (in press).

Sidman, R. L. (1961). *In* "The Structure of the Eye" (G. K. Smelser, ed.), p. 487. Academic Press, New York.

Sotello, C., and Changeux, J. P. (1974). *Brain Res.* **77**, 484.

Spemann, H. (1938). *In* "Embryonic Development and Induction." Yale Univ. Press, New Haven, Connecticut.

Sperry, R. W. (1945). *J. Neurophysiol.* **8**, 15.

Sperry, R. W. (1950). *In* "Genetic Neurology" (P. Weiss, ed.), p. 232. Univ. of Chicago Press, Chicago.

Sperry, R. W. (1963). *Proc. Natl. Acad. Sci. U.S.A.* **50**, 703.

Sperry, R. W. (1965). *In* "Organogenesis" (R. L. DeHaan and H. Ursprung, eds.), p. 161. Holt, New York.

Steen, T. P. (1970). *Am. Zool.* **10**, 119.

Steinberg, M. S. (1970). *J. Exp. Zool.* **73**, 395.

Stern, C. (1968). "Genetic Mosaics and Other Essays," Harvard Univ. Press, Boston.

Stohlman, F., Jr., ed. (1970). "Hemopoietic Cellular Proliferation." Grune & Stratton, New York.

Stone, L. S. (1944). *Proc. Soc. Exp. Biol. Med.* **57**, 13.

Stone, L. S. (1960). *J. Exp. Zool.* **154**, 85.

Straznicky, K., and Gaze, R. M. (1971). *J. Embryol. Exp. Morphol.* **28**, 67.

Straznicky, K., and Gaze, R. M. (1972). *J. Embryol. Exp. Morphol.* **28**, 87.

Sturtevant, A. H. (1932). *Proc. VI Int. Congr. Genet.* **1**, 304.

Sulston, J. E., and Horvitz, H. R. (1977). *Dev. Biol.* **56**, 110.

Summerbell, D., Lewis, J., and Wolpert, L. (1973). *Nature (London)* **244**, 492.

Szekely, G. (1954). *Acta Biol. Acad. Sci. Hung.* **5**, 157.

Tompkins, R. (1977). *Dev. Biol.* **57**, 469.

Tosney, K. W., Hoskins, S., and Hunt, R. K. (1978). *Biophys. J.* **21**, 110a.

Trinkaus, J. P. (1969). "Cells into Organs." Prentice-Hall, New York.

Udin, S. B. (1977). *J. Comp. Neurol.* **171**, 561.

Udin, S. B. (1978). *Exp. Neurol.* **58**, 455.

Van Deusen, E. (1973). *Dev. Biol.* **34**, 135.

Wallace, H. (1960). *J. Embryol. Exp. Morphol.* **8**, 405.

Weintraub, H. (1975). *Res. Prob. Cell Differ.* **7**, 27.

Weisblat, D. A., Sawyer, R. T., and Stent, G. S. (1978). *Science* **202**, 1295.

Weston, J. A. (1963). *Dev. Biol.* **6**, 279.

Weston, J. A. (1970). *Adv. Morphogenet.* **8**, 41.

White, K., and Kankel, D. R. (1978). *Dev. Biol.* **65**, 296.

Whittaker, J. R. (1968). *Res. Prob. Cell Differ.* **1**, 25.

Whittaker, J. R. (1973). *Proc. Natl. Acad. Sci. U.S.A.* **70**, 2096.

Wolpert, L. (1969). *J. Theor. Biol.* **25**, 1.

Wolpert, L. (1970). *Curr. Top. Dev. Biol.* **6**, 183.

Yoon, M. G. (1972). *Exp. Neurol.* **37**, 451.

Yoon, M. G. (1975). *Cold Spring Harbor Symp. Quant. Biol.* **40**, 503.

CHAPTER 9

GENETIC APPROACHES TO INVERTEBRATE NEUROGENESIS

E. R. Macagno

DEPARTMENT OF BIOLOGICAL SCIENCES
COLUMBIA UNIVERSITY
NEW YORK, NEW YORK

I. Introduction 319
II. Review of Genetic Approaches 321
    A. Isogenic Organisms 321
    B. Single-Gene Mutations 322
    C. Genetic Mosaics 323
    D. Homeotic Mutants 323
III. Constancy and Variability of Neuronal Phenotype
     in Isogenic Organisms 324
    A. Neuron Number 325
    B. Location of Identified Neurons 327
    C. Neuronal Branching Pattern 328
    D. Synaptic Connectivity 329
IV. Developmental Interactions between the Compound
     Eye and Optic Lobes 332
V. The Formation of Sensory Nerve Projections in
     Homeotic Mutants 336
    A. Centripetal Pathways 336
    B. Central Pathways 337
VI. Summary and Conclusions 342
    References 343

I. Introduction

That individuals of any particular species look alike and function in similar ways is generally accepted to be a consequence of their sharing a common set of genes. Variations between one individual and another are assigned either to the expression of different alleles (or differential expression of the two alleles in diploid organisms) or else to the interplay of genetic and epigenetic factors during development. Elucidation of the respective roles of the genome and of epigenetic factors, broadly conceived to include properties of the local cellular milieu and cellular interactions as well as parameters external to the organism (i.e., the "environment"), is a problem of great interest to both development and genetics.

CURRENT TOPICS IN
DEVELOPMENTAL BIOLOGY, Vol. 15

One approach to the question of the role of the genes in development is to study in detail the abnormalities caused by genetic mutations in model systems. Many such mutations have been identified behaviorally or anatomically, and some of their effects have been studied in great detail in a few organisms, notably *Drosophila, Caenorhabditis elegans,* and highly inbred mice. Yet, we are still far from knowing how genes specify even the gross features of a cell, let alone those of an organism. An alternative approach to this question is to vary environmental parameters during development. In this case, although many factors which are teratogenic have been recognized and studied, we have little understanding of how they affect the developmental process and so produce what are often profound defects.

A number of geneticists and neurobiologists in the past 10 years or so have begun to ask these questions about the nervous system. Since nerve cells can be characterized individually according to size, shape, location, synaptic ultrastructure, neurotransmitter, synaptic inputs and outputs, etc., very specific questions can be proposed about factors that influence their development. All of these anatomic and physiologic parameters can be studied under various genetic or epigenetic conditions. In vertebrate species, which may have many billions of brain cells, neurons generally can be classified into relatively few types. Very few vertebrate neurons are so unique that they can be individually identified (an example is the Mauthner cell in fish). Therefore, the effects of variations in genes or environment must be studied in cells as representatives of classes of cells. Invertebrates have considerably fewer neurons, many of which can be easily and repeatedly identified as individual cells, thereby allowing one to study variations induced in a specific cell.

Genetic approaches to invertebrate neurogenesis have followed the two general directions previously outlined. On the one hand, a few species for which isogenic strains are available (*Daphnia, C. elegans,* locusts) have been studied in order to answer basic questions such as: (*a*) how invariant are certain parameters of the nervous system among isogenic organisms? (*b*) how invariant is the sequence of developmental events in these organisms? and (*c*) how do neurons whose genes are identical respond to altered developmental conditions? On the other hand, a number of mutations affecting nerve structure and function have been isolated in nematodes and insects, and some analyses of their development have been undertaken.

With a few significant exceptions, the observations which have been reported on either isogenic strains or mutants were made on adults. Many of the hypotheses about the development of the nervous system that have been proposed from these observations are therefore inferred from the end result rather than from direct analysis of developmental events. This is a well-recognized and basic shortcoming which is gradually being remedied by extending observations to interesting stages of development. Nevertheless, observations in adults frequently permit us to define the range of probable developmental pathways that could be taken to achieve the end result.

Following a brief discussion of the genetic methods which have been applied to the study of invertebrate nervous systems, we will review some of the exciting developments which are beginning to come out of this rather young field of neurobiology, a field which appropriately has been named "neurogenetics." Despite its relative youth, various aspects of this field have been the subject of a number of recent reviews (Bentley, 1976; Wyman, 1976; Pak and Pinto, 1976; Ward, 1977; Quinn and Gould, 1979; Kankel and Ferrus, 1979). The reader is referred to these reviews for discussions of behavioral and physiological studies. The reader is also referred to other papers in these volumes, in particular to the in-depth discussion by Campos-Ortega of the development of the compound eye of *Drosophila*. Many of the questions addressed by the work on invertebrates reviewed here have also been extensively explored on mouse mutants and chimeras. However, a discussion of the literature on vertebrates is outside the aim of this chapter and the reader is referred to companion reviews in these volumes.

II. Review of Genetic Approaches

A. Isogenic Organisms

Although most would agree, at least in principle, that behavior is determined by the individual properties of each neuron in the nervous system and by the pattern of synaptic connections among them, in fact, we know little about how well-specified these properties are. How much do these attributes vary from individual to individual?

The answer to this question is crucial to the study of neurodevelopment. It is necessay to ascertain what the specifications of the end product are before hypotheses can be made about the set of rules or instructions needed in order to assemble it. One must begin, therefore, by determining how much variation exists in identified neurons under conditions in which the developmental rules, whatever they are, can be presumed to be constant. This is the case in isogenic strains which are reared and maintained in controlled environmental conditions. Much of the work on isogenic organisms has consisted of very fine anatomical mapping of the normal adult nervous system and its development.

However, observations on uniformly raised isogenic animals cannot ultimately tell us which aspects of the resulting phenotype are due to genetic instructions and which to epigenetic factors. This must be ascertained by experimentally modifying development or by comparing different isogenic strains. Both of these approaches have been employed in recent work. In particular, laser and ultraviolet radiation microbeams have been used to produce very fine lesions at specific developmental stages in *Daphnia* (Macagno, 1977, 1978a, 1979) and in *C. elegans* (Sulston and Horvitz, 1977).

B. Single-Gene Mutations

In order to understand the role of the genome in neurogenesis we must identify those genes that affect the structure and function of the nervous system (and of individual neurons), and we must determine in which cells and when in development they are expressed and what parameters they specify. The conceptually straightforward approach to this problem is to examine in detail the nature and genesis of alterations in structure and/or function produced by a large number of single-gene mutations.

Determination of which cells must be of mutant genotype for the organism to be of mutant phenotype is complicated by the fact that normally all somatic cells of the organism carry the mutation. The effects of the mutation can be displaced both spatially and temporally from the primary site of expression of the mutated gene. For example, the normal gene product may be required only in tissue A early in development so that tissue A can later interact with tissue B. If the gene is mutated, this might have no effect on A's phenotype but, by destroying A's ability to interact with B, greatly affect B's phenotype. This difficulty can be dealt with, in part, by making only tissue A or only tissue B carry the mutant genotype, in other words, by making a genetic mosaic. Genetic techniques for generating such mosaics are discussed in Section II,C.

In principle, the time in development when a gene is active can be determined by using temperature sensitive (*ts*) mutants (Suzuki, 1970). In *ts* mutants the wild type phenotype is expressed at certain (permissive) temperatures, and the mutant phenotype at higher or lower (nonpermissive) ones. The effect of shifting to a nonpermissive temperature can be reversed in some cases by shifting back to the permissive range. The time of action of the mutated gene, therefore, can be ascertained by shifting to nonpermissive temperatures for short periods at different times in development. A second way to study the timing of gene expression is with somatic recombination, as discussed in Section II,C.

C. GENETIC MOSAICS

In species for which mutants are available it is possible to obtain single animals in which some cells carry a different genotype from the rest of the animal. Such mosaics can be generated either by means of genetic techniques or by transplantation of tissue of one genotype into a host of a different one.

A number of genetic techniques have been applied to the construction of genetic mosaics in various species of *Drosophila* (Hall *et al.*, 1976; Kankel and Ferrus, 1979). One such technique employs mutants in which spontaneous chromosome loss has a relatively high probability of taking place during mitosis in early embryogenesis. The best-studied of these mutations cause the loss of one X chromosome. When an X chromosome is lost by a cell during early development of a female (XX) embryo, a patch of male (XO) tissue results. The size of the patch depends upon how early in embryogenesis the loss occurs, and is generally quite large. Recessive mutations that are located in the remaining X chromosome are expressed in the male tissue. A second technique uses X-irradiation to induce somatic crossing-over during mitosis, which can result in a cell initially heterozygous at a particular genetic locus giving rise to daughter cells which are homozygous at that locus. A recessive mutation will then be expressed by the progeny of one daughter cell. One advantage of this method over chromosome loss is that it can be applied at specified developmental stages, and hence can also yield information about the timing of gene expression. A second advantage is that much smaller patches of mutant tissue are obtained, and the focus of the mutation is more accurately defined.

Tissue transplantation in principle allows for a much greater control over the pattern of the mosaic (i.e., which tissue will express the mutation), than do the genetic techniques previously described. Since both chromosome loss and induced somatic recombination occur statistically, many specimens must be scanned in order to find the desired mosaic. However, technical difficulties make many developing tissues, especially the central nervous system (CNS), fairly inaccessible to the transplantation approach, and scanning through mosaics obtained genetically remains the method of choice.

D. HOMEOTIC MUTANTS

A number of single-gene mutations in *Drosophila* transform one part of the body into another. For example, the mutations *aristapedia*, *Antennapedia*, and *Nasobemia* transform antennal tissues into leg tissues (Deak, 1976; Stocker *et al.*, 1976). These homeotic mutations, therefore, can be regarded in some ways as the genetic equivalent of the surgical translocation of a leg to the position of an antenna, but without the trauma that is usually entailed by mechanical procedures. Since nerve connections are formed between sensory cells in the homeotic appendages and the CNS, these mutants can be used to determine whether and how nerve fibers which enter the CNS at an incorrect location are capable of finding their normal synaptic targets. However, complications in the interpretation of observations on homeotic mutants can arise from two factors: first, the set of genetic instructions of the mutant fibers could be changed by the mutation, and second, the interaction of growing fibers with other mutant tissues could be affected. The second complication can be dealt with in part by using mosaics in which, for example, the CNS is wild type. But in any case, these factors make the situation in homeotic mutants not exactly equivalent to that in which appendages are surgically translocated, and it is useful to use and compare the results of both experimental paradigms.

Although a large number of homeotic mutants of *Drosophila* have been isolated, careful studies of the effects on the nervous system have been carried out in only a few. These include *Antennapedia, aristapedia,* and *Nasobemia,* which were previously mentioned, as well as a number from the bithorax complex (*bithorax, postbithorax,* and *bithoraxoid*), which transform metathoracic structures into mesothoracic ones.

III. Constancy and Variability of Neuronal Phenotype in Isogenic Organisms

Four specific parameters have been investigated in isogenic invertebrates: (*a*) neuron number, (*b*) neuron location, (*c*) neuronal branching pattern, and (*d*) synaptic connectivity. The observations have been carried out on small groups of identified neurons in the embryonic and adult visual systems of *Daphnia magna,* a small branchiopod crustacean, on the complete adult and embryonic nervous systems of the nematode, *C. elegans,* and on adult ocellar interneurons in two different species of locust, *Schistocerca nitens* and *Schistocerca gregaria.* In *Daphnia* and in locusts the clones used arise by parthenogenetic reproduction, which occurs naturally in *Daphnia* and which can be induced in grasshoppers (Goodman, 1978). [The evidence for the isogenicity of these clones is discussed in detail by Hebert and Ward (1972) for *Daphnia* and by Goodman (1978) for grasshoppers.] Isogenicity in *C. elegans* results from the pressure toward homozygocity of repetitive self-fertilization of the hermaphrodite (Brenner, 1974). We will review some of the results and consider what they tell us about development.

A. NEURON NUMBER

Variability in the number of neurons has been reported in nonisogenic strains of various invertebrate species. Kuffler and Muller (1974) found duplicate sensory and motor neurons in various ganglia of one specimen of the leech, *Hirudo medicinalis,* and determined some of their physiological properties. Duplicates of a single giant neuron (R2) were found and studied physiologically in three specimens of *Aplysia* by Treistman and Schwartz (1976). Goodman (1977) found variations in the number of ocellar interneurons in two breeding populations of the locust *S. nitens.* In one population, duplications of a particular group of two interneurons (ML1-2) were found in eight of 45 specimens examined. In the other population, 13 of 45 animals had duplications in another group of three interneurons (L1-3). Variations of a few percent in the total number (about 400) of neurons and in their distribution in particular leech segmental ganglia have been reported recently for a few species (Macagno, 1980).

Goodman (1977) also examined the occurrence of duplications and deletions of ocellar interneurons in clones of two species of locust, *S. nitens* and *Schistocerca americana.* Among eleven clones he examined, one (clone 2) showed a particularly high incidence of duplications (in 22 of 42 specimens) in one group of interneurons (L1-3). This clone was derived from the breeding population with duplications in the same group of interneurons previously mentioned. Two other groups of interneurons in this clone showed few duplications, indicating that duplications probably did not occur in the nervous system as a whole. Of the other clones, only two showed a significant number of duplications. No parthenogenetic offspring were derived from individuals in these eleven clones, however, and the heritability of this trait was not determined. This is clearly an important aspect that must be checked before statements about genetic control of neuron number in these organisms can be made.

Even if we took these observations on locust clones as suggestive of control of cell number by the genome, they would still not give us a clue as to where or how such effects might be produced. For example, if an excess of ocellar interneurons is routinely made and those that fail to receive enough synaptic input die, genetic effects could be produced by shifting the input threshold for survival, or by changing the number of input fibers, or by many other more or less indirect means.

I have counted the number of axons in the optic nerve of over 100 specimens from a *Daphnia magna* clone in the past few years and found only one with other than the normal number of 176 axons, segregated into 22 bundles of eight. (This animal had one bundle with nine axons.) Nor have I seen a variation from this number in a few specimens of a different clone of *D. magna* or a mixed population of another species, *Daphnia pluex*. The numbers of ommatidia (22) and retinular cells per ommatidium (8) appear to be highly conserved, but again one would be hard put to say how or where control of these numbers is exerted. The number of neurons in the *Daphnia* optic lamina is also constant. This appears to result from constancy in the eye and from the interaction of the eye and lamina during embryogenesis, which is discussed separately in Section IV.

Constancy of cell number has also been observed in the adult nervous system of *C. elegans* (Ward *et al.*, 1975; Ware *et al.*, 1975; Albertson and Thomson, 1976; White *et al.*, 1976). Extensive observations on living postembryonic nematodes, using wholemounts and Nomarskii optics, have revealed that this constant number of cells is a consequence of an invariant pattern of cell divisions and cell deaths (Sulston, 1976; Sulston and Horvitz, 1977). Since cell lineage is unique for each adult neuron, it is possible that lineage determines the specific fate of each cell. However, since cell positions and migrations are also essentially invariant, it is also possible that its position in the body and interactions with its neighbors determine how each neuron will differentiate. Tests of these two possibilities, by means of deletions of precursors at specific locations using either mutations or a laser microbeam (Sulston and Horvitz, 1977), indicate that, in most cases, the fate of a cell is independent of the existence of its near neighbors and that lineage is probably the deciding factor. This is in contrast to what has been found to be the case in the arthropod compound eye, where observations on genetic mosaics in various species, obtained either by induced somatic recombination or by grafting, have shown that cell lineage and cell fate are not uniquely correlated (Shelton and Lawrence, 1974; Ready *et al.*, 1976; Shelton *et al.*, 1977; Campos-Ortega and Hofbauer, 1977; Lawrence and Green, 1979; see also the chapter by Campos-Ortega in this volume).

In summary, it should be apparent that we do not have a broad enough range of data to draw general conclusions about the constancy of neuron number. In a very simple system (*C. elegans*) and in an arthropod eye (*Daphnia*), the numbers are constant. Some clones of an insect (*Schistocerca*) show a somewhat larger and others a somewhat smaller incidence of duplications in a small group of specific interneurons than the breeding populations from which they are derived. Genetically heterogeneous populations show a small level of variability.

It is of interest to note that significant variations in the number of identified neurons have also been documented in vertebrates. Selzer (1979), using wholemount techniques, has reported recently differences of over 30% in the number of large neurons in the lamprey spinal cord. (It should be kept in mind, however, that the animals examined by Selzer were not isogenic.) Such differences are much greater than have been reported for invertebrates, and could indicate a much greater level of redundancy in the vertebrate nervous system.

B. LOCATION OF IDENTIFIED NEURONS

We might expect that where location is functionally significant, neurons or parts of neurons would occupy consistent positions in different animals within a species. The major processes of identified neurons generally follow predictable pathways (see discussion of homeotic mutations below). The cell somata, however, behave differently, in some cases occupying highly invariant locations and in others showing a great deal of positional variability (White *et al.*, 1976; Benjamin, 1976; Goodman, 1978; Macagno, 1980).

For example, the positions of laminar cell somata in the *Daphnia* optic ganglion are very consistent from optic cartridge to optic cartridge in one specimen, and from specimen to specimen of a clone. In only one case, out of 100 optic cartridges examined, was the soma of a laminar neuron in an atypical position (Levinthal *et al.*, 1975), though its main process was correctly located in the neuropil. As a counter example, the positions of the cell bodies of identified neurons, especially in segmental ganglia of various species, vary by relatively large amounts. This is true for genetically mixed populations as well as clones of locusts (Goodman, 1978), where the location of ocellar interneurons can vary by several hundred micrometers. In fact, Goodman (1978) found one clone in which the variability in somata location of one group of interneurons was significantly greater than the average. In *C. elegans* the relative positions of identified neurons are more variable in the retrovesicular ganglion than in the ventral nerve cord (White *et al.*, 1976).

What do these examples tell us about genetic control of soma location or about development? First of all, it is important to realize that somata in many invertebrate ganglia are located within regions of the cortex where they are fairly free to move relative to one another under mechanical stress from, for example, the observer's needle. Normally occurring mechanical stresses (e.g., in molting, squeezing between obstacles, etc.) could be a source of positional variability. It would seem futile, therefore, to look at somata location in adults to determine whether this is a controlled parameter, unless careful controls for such stresses are provided.

In those cases in which there is constancy in the location of cell bodies, as in *Daphnia*, it is probably the result of the extreme orderliness of the development of certain tissues in which soma position is functionally important, such as in the eye. The fact that neurons in the *Daphnia* optic lamina occupy predictable locations tells us that target recruitment by a well-ordered array (the photoreceptors) is also a well-ordered process, as was determined by direct observation (Lo Presti *et al.*, 1973; Macagno, 1979). Variations in the location of cell bodies have also been documented by Selzer (1979) in the sea lamprey spinal cord.

C. NEURONAL BRANCHING PATTERN

Among the features of neurons of a particular type is a characteristic branching pattern. Using dye-marking techniques (Kater and Nicholson, 1973) and computerized three-dimensional reconstruction from serial sections (Macagno *et al.*, 1979), the details of these patterns have been examined in a number of identified invertebrate neurons. The general conclusion, from studies in isogenic strains (*Daphnia*, Macagno *et al.*, 1973; *C. elegans*, Ward *et al.*, 1975, Albertson and Thomson, 1976, White *et al.*, 1976; locusts, Goodman, 1978) as well as many studies on genetically heterogeneous populations (for example, cockroach, Pitman *et al.*, 1973; locust, Burrows, 1973, Goodman, 1974, 1978; lobster, Stretton and Kravitz, 1973), is that, whereas the overall shape of a particular neuron is recognizable, many of the details of the branching pattern are quite variable. In some instances, major abnormalities in primary branching pattern have also been reported (Goodman, 1974, 1978; Burrows, 1975; Altman and Tyrer, 1977). The occurrence of such abnormalities in one ocellar interneuron (L5; see Fig. 1) has been found to be quite variable in different clones of locusts (Goodman, 1978); the range is from none in some clones to about 88% (37 out of 42 individuals) in another (clone 2; this is the same clone showing a high incidence of duplications of L1-3). Interestingly, other ocellar interneurons in this clone do not show a high incidence of abnormal shape.

The observation of interclonal differences in locusts is suggestive of some degree of genetic control over the major features of the branching pattern of neurons, whereas the other observations on isogenic strains indicate that little control is exerted over the finer details. It is impossible, however, to guess where and how such genetic control over the gross features takes place, and what role epigenetic factors play in determining the fine details of the arborizations, without studying

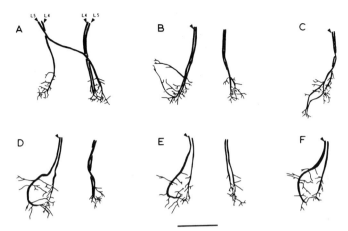

FIG. 1. Camera lucida drawings of cobalt-filled ventral axons of ocellar interneurons L4 and L5 in the posterior region of the brain of six specimens (A–F) from a clone (clone 2) of *Schistocerca*. The axons of L4 and L5 on the right and of L4 on the left are normal, whereas the axon of L5 on the left (indicated by an arrow) is abnormal in all cases. Bar: 200 μm. After Goodman (1978).

more cases and without observations of development. The importance of cell interactions is made clear by observations in experimentally modified systems. For example, genetic deletion (by a single-gene mutation) of mechanoreceptors of the cricket cercus results in the abnormal physiological and structural development of an identified interneuron (Bentley, 1975). Other examples are discussed in subsequent sections.

D. SYNAPTIC CONNECTIVITY

Observations on a variety of invertebrate species, though on a relatively small fraction of all neurons of any one species, have established the predictability of synaptic connections between certain pairs of identified neurons in genetically heterogeneous populations. These observations include physiological measurements of identified sensory–motoneuron, sensory–interneuron, and interneuron–motoneuron pairings, as well as anatomical studies of sensory projections to the CNS and motoneuron projections to muscle. Two notable exceptions to this rule of predictability are the synaptic projection from a population of mechanosensors in the telson of the crayfish onto an identified interneuron, a projection which appears to vary considerably from animal to animal (Kennedy, 1971), and the synaptic connections of an identified interneuron in the locust (Pearson and Goodman, 1979).

Given that synaptic connections between certain neurons are always present in genetically heterogeneous populations, one might ex-

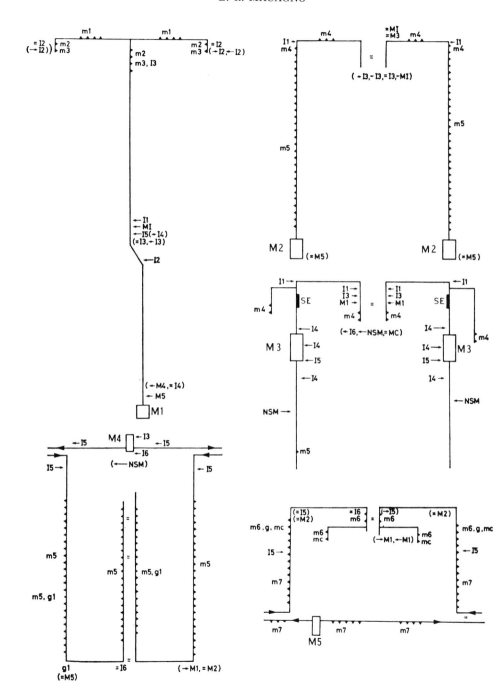

pect to find a similar situation in isogenic groups. Detailed mappings of synaptic connections have been carried out only in isogenic animals from two species, *D. magna* (Macagno *et al.*, 1973) and *C. elegans* (Ward *et al.*, 1975; Albertson and Thomson, 1976; White *et al.*, 1976). These mappings were done morphologically at the electron microscopic level. (The small size of both of these species, which allows such detailed anatomical studies, makes physiological studies of their individual neurons extremely difficult.) In both cases morphological invariance was found in some features, but a certain degree of variability in others.

The study of synaptic projections between photoreceptors and second-order neurons (laminar cells) in *Daphnia* yielded the following results (Macagno *et al.*, 1973; Macagno, unpublished observations). Each photoreceptor terminal arborizes extensively in specific regions of the neuropil. In the same regions, fibers from one or two laminar neurons of the optic cartridge also arborize extensively, but the others do so only weakly, if at all. Fibers and terminals that arborize extensively in the same region form many synapses with each other, but fibers that arborize little form only a few synapses with photoreceptor terminals. The result of this is that two categories of connections exist between specific pairs of cells: strong, with large numbers of synaptic sites (30 or more) and weak, with small numbers of synaptic sites (5 or fewer). If a strong connection was found between a particular pair of neurons in one animal, a strong connection was also found between that pair in every animal studied. The number of synaptic sites between a given, strongly connected pair, however, varied considerably from animal to animal (30–100). Weak connections between identified pairs were unpredictable, occurring in some animals but not others.

Similar observations were reported for neurons in the pharynx (Albertson and Thomson, 1976) and the ventral nerve cord (White *et al.*, 1976) of *C. elegans*. Pharyngeal neurons vary in both number and location of synaptic sites, and some pairs of neurons connect via gap junctions in some animals and via chemical synapses in others (see Fig. 2). In the ventral nerve cord, motoneurons show variable numbers of

---

Fig. 2. Diagrams of the synaptic connectivity of the seven motoneurons (M1 through M5, M2 and M3 paired) in the pharynx of *C. elegans*. Muscle synapses are indicated by filled triangles and the name of the postsynaptic cell. Chemical synapses are indicated by arrows pointing from pre- to postsynaptic cells. Gap junctions are indicated by an equal sign. Cell names: m, muscle cells; g, gland cells; mc, marginal cells; I, interneurons, NSM, neurosecretory-motoneurons; MC, marginal cell neurons; MI, motor-interneuron. Note that synapses shown in parentheses are variable and found only in a single specimen. After Albertson and Thomson (1976).

synaptic sites, and some connections are found in some animals and not in others, although in general synaptic connections between specific pairs are quite predictable. In particular, there appears to be a fairly strict set of restrictions on which classes of cells can make synapses with which other classes.

These two sets of observations generally support the findings from physiological measurements in genetically heterogeneous organisms, but they also indicate that some variation in connectivity occurs even in these two relatively simple nervous systems. Whether this noise level of connectivity is functionally significant is not known, and, unfortunately, any attempt at a complete mapping of the synaptic connectivity of neurons in larger animals (which are more accessible physiologically) would require a truly heroic undertaking. Purves and McMahan (1972) reconstructed one motoneuron in leech and estimated the number of synaptic sites as being probably in the thousands. They did not identify other partners at these synapses. King (1976) found similarly large numbers in his reconstructions of a few lobster stomatogastric ganglion neurons, and determined that there were multiple sites of synaptic interaction between specific pairs of neurons. Other attempts to map synaptic sites between particular pairs are currently in progress (Macagno, 1978b; Thompson *et al.*, 1976).

IV. Developmental Interactions between the Compound Eye and Optic Lobes

The arthropod visual system has been the subject of numerous anatomical and experimental studies (reviewed by Meinertzhagen, 1973, 1976). The pattern of connections, at least between photoreceptors and second-order (laminar) neurons, is extremely reproducible (Horridge and Meinertzhagen, 1970). Of particular interest in the context of this chapter are the recent studies of the developmental interactions of the compound eye and optic centers carried out in *Daphnia* (Macagno, 1977, 1978a, 1979) and *Drosophila* (Meyerowitz and Kankel, 1978). These experiments were designed to determine the role of interactions between developing photoreceptors and their targets, the laminar neurons, in the formation of the pattern of synaptic projections found in the adult. The experimental approaches were quite different: modification of development within an isogenic background for *Daphnia,* and generation of genetic mosaics for *Drosophila.*

The *Daphnia* compound eye contains a constant number of photoreceptors (176) segregated into 22 eight-cell clusters known as ommatidia. The eight optic fibers from one ommatidium travel together to the optic lamina, where they make synaptic connections onto five laminar neurons forming an optic cartridge. The number of neurons in the lamina (110) is also constant. Laminar neurons synapse onto medullary neurons, of which there are about 320. During embryogenesis, a first or "lead" fiber from each ommatidium grows into the lamina, followed by the other seven fibers. The growing bundle sequentially contacts five immature laminar cells forming transient gap junctions with them (Lo Presti *et al.*, 1974). Contacted laminar neurons then begin to grow their own fibers and mature to form the optic cartridge. These events are repeated for each ommatidium and cartridge in a specific spatiotemporal order (Lo Presti *et al.*, 1973).

In a series of experiments (Macagno, 1977, 1978a, 1979), photoreceptors in the *Daphnia* compound eye were deleted at specified developmental stages and in the adults to test the hypotheses that growing retinular fibers trigger and affect the differentiation of laminar neurons, thereby recruiting them as synaptic targets. Deletion of retinular neurons was accomplished by producing small lesions with either UV or laser microbeams. The effects of the lesions on the eye and optic ganglion were assayed quantitatively using computerized techniques for the three-dimensional reconstruction of biological structures from serial light or electron micrographs (Macagno *et al.*, 1979).

Retinular cells were deleted at three developmental stages: stage A, embryos before any contact occurs between growing retinular fibers and immature laminar cells; stage B, embryos some hours after the initial contact, when nascent synapses are already seen between fibers and their laminar targets, and stage C, adults. The results of these experiments can be summarized as follows:

1. In animals with lesions produced at either embryonic stage an increase in cell death was seen in the laminar anlage at late embryonic stages. The number of laminar neurons that survive in these experimental animals was found to be roughly proportional to the number of remaining retinular neurons which sent fibers into the optic ganglion. When retinular neurons were deleted in adults, however, no evidence of degeneration of laminar neurons was found for some weeks. Hence embryonic, but not adult, laminar neurons require an interaction with retinular fibers to survive.

2. When an ommatidium was partially deleted at embryonic stage A, the number of laminar neurons that were found in its optic cartridge was less than five only if more than three retinular cells were deleted. Hence, a smaller than normal ommatidium can maintain a full set of five laminar neurons.

3. A few optic cartridges with six instead of five laminar neurons

were found in two experimental adults in which large lesions had been made at embryonic stage A. No cartridge with more than five laminar neurons was found in any of the controls or in adults with small lesions. In these two adults many extra immature laminar cells would have been available for recruitment by the remaining retinular cells. It is possible, therefore, that the recruitment of targets is at least in part a function of the availability of target cells.

4. Immature laminar cells deprived of initial contact with retinular fibers failed to differentiate morphologically, though they survived for some hours before degenerating. It appears, therefore, that the initial contact is a necessary trigger of laminar cell differentiation and serves to recruit laminar cells for a particular cartridge.

5. It is not clear whether all laminar cells are born or are available for recruitment by retinular fibers in embryos with large retinular deletions. Some evidence indicates that in these animals the laminar anlage is smaller than normal prior to the beginning of degeneration, probably because there are fewer cells.

6. Higher order cells in the medulla of the optic ganglion also degenerate when retinular cells are deleted, but only if the number deleted is 80% or more. This threshold effect, seen in the medulla but not in the lamina, may result from the fact that a medullary neuron receives multiple connections whereas a laminar neuron receives most synaptic inputs from only a few retinular neurons of a single ommatidium.

7. Particularly interesting was the observation that in a few cartridges in which the ratio of optic fibers to laminar neurons was higher than normal (Macagno, 1977), laminar neurons from adjacent cartridges grew additional branches (not found normally) into the abnormal cartridges (see Fig. 3). These branches formed morphologically normal synapses with the optic fibers of the abnormal cartridges. It appears, therefore, that optic fibers can modify the pattern of differentiation of laminar neurons.

In their experiments, Meyerowitz and Kankel (1978) used genetic mosaics to test whether the genetic instructions required to achieve the ordered patterns of optic fiber projections to the *Drosophila* optic lamina, and of other fiber pathways in the optic lobes, originate in the eye tissue or in the optic lobes. They first found three mutations which produced abnormal ommatidial and optic lobe patterns as well as clearly disorganized fiber projections. Genetically mosaic flies were then obtained in which either the eye or the optic lobes were of mutant genotype and the other wild type. Mosaics were generated either by

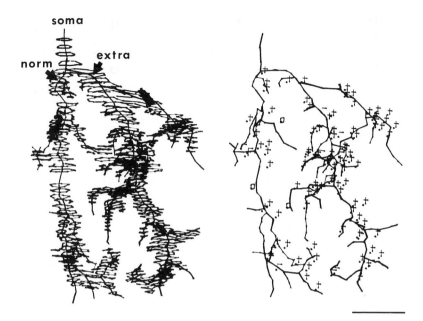

FIG. 3. Computer reconstruction of a portion of a *Daphnia* laminar neuron from serial electron micrographs. Normally this cell has only a single major branch, corresponding to the branch labeled normal (norm), on which it receives synaptic inputs, mainly from one optic axon. In the case illustrated, a lesion in the eye, produced with a UV microbeam early in development, has resulted in the existence of a group of optic axons without their normal target laminar neurons. In response, adjacent laminar neurons, including the one shown here, have sprouted additional major branches (labeled extra) to receive synaptic inputs from these optic fibers. The computer drawing on the left illustrates the surface morphology; the one on the right shows the branching pattern and the location of synapses (shown as a dot and a + sign) from optic axons. On its normal branch this cell receives 37 synaptic sites from the usual optic axon; on the extra branch it forms 59 synaptic sites with one optic axon from the adjacent bundle of axons without normal targets. Bar: 5 μm. After Macagno (1977).

inducing somatic recombination with X-rays or by transferring the visual system mutation to flies carrying mitotic chromosome-loss mutations. The genotype of the eye was marked with autonomous eye color mutations linked to the array mutations; the genotype of the optic lobes was marked histochemically by means of a mutation in which normal acid phosphatase activity is absent from nervous tissue (Kankel and Hall, 1976).

The mosaic analysis of the three mutants studied demonstrates that these array mutations are expressed autonomously in the *Drosophila* eye, but are expressed in the optic lobes only as a result of an interaction with a mutant eye. No effects on the pattern of the eye were found when mosaics carrying these mutant genotypes in the optic lobes were examined. As pointed out by Meyerowitz and Kankel (1978), this does not prove that no developmental instructions are transmitted from the optic lobes to the eyes, but only that the mutations that were studied do not affect instructions, if they exist. The authors also point out that these mutations could either modify signals that are normally transmitted from eye to brain or generate new ones which alter the normal development of the optic lobes.

The results discussed demonstrate that in both *Daphnia* and *Drosophila* the eye and optic lobes interact in development. Substantially similar results have been obtained by means of mechanical ablation or cauterization in a number of other invertebrates (e.g., Mouze, 1974, 1978; Anderson, 1978). In addition, the experiments on *Daphnia* indicate that this interaction occurs at a particular time in development and that it is mediated by the optic fibers. It is possible that in *Daphnia* the mechanism for signaling from optic fiber to laminar neuron is in part through the transient gap junctions and the nascent synapses that appear at this time in development (Lo Presti *et al.*, 1973, 1974). Further work is necessary to demonstrate this point.

V. The Formation of Sensory Nerve Projections in Homeotic Mutants

Homeotic mutants have been used to determine which pathways are followed by sensory fibers when they cannot follow their normal projections into the *Drosophila* CNS and whether sensory fibers that enter the CNS at ectopic sites find their normal synaptic targets.

A. CENTRIPETAL PATHWAYS

Observations of normal development in many different invertebrates indicate that nerve fibers grow along preexisting substrates toward the CNS. That a substrate is necessary was first clearly demonstrated by Wigglesworth (1953) in the bug *Rhodnius*. He observed that axons of newly formed sensillae grew along sensillar axons that had grown previously into the CNS. When this pathway was destroyed, the newly formed axons grew in loops without ever achieving a connection to the CNS. Subsequent observations in other species have always identified a substrate which serves as a guide for centripetal growth of sensory fibers. For example, the "lead" optic axon from each *Daphnia* ommatidium grows along a glial sheet which connects the eye and laminar primordia, and the rest of the optic fibers (the "followers") grow along the lead fiber (Lo Presti *et al.*, 1973). Imaginal optic axons in

Drosophila grow along a larval stalk that connects the eye disc to the brain (Melamed and Trujillo-Cenoz, 1975) and imaginal antennal axons in *Manduca* follow a preexisting pupal nerve (Sanes and Hildebrand, 1975). Bate (1976) observed that in *Locusta* two "pioneer" neurons from each limb bud establish a pathway which is later followed by other sensory fibers. Bate suggests that these pioneer fibers themselves follow preexisting sheathing (glial) cells into the CNS.

Ghysen and Deak (1978) investigated the question of which pathway different *Drosophila* sensory nerves would follow in experimental conditions which would force the fibers to use pathways other than their normal ones. Sensory pathways were studied in three experimental situations: (*a*) in flies in which gross abnormalities of the mesothorax were produced by X-irradiation of the larvae, (*b*) in flies in which the larval connections between imaginal discs and the CNS were destroyed surgically, and (*c*) in homeotic mutants (*Antennapedia, bithorax, postbithorax,* and *bithoraxoid*).

In flies with gross abnormalities caused by X-rays, Ghysen and Deak found that wing nerves entered the CNS either at their normal location or at sites appropriate for other nerves. In animals perturbed surgically, wing and haltere nerves were found to join a normal nerve at some distance from the CNS and to follow it there. In homeotic mutants, the homeotic nerve followed a pathway to the ganglion appropriate to the position of the homeotic appendage, irrespective of the nature of the mutation.

All the results obtained by Ghysen and Deak are consistent with the hypothesis that imaginal sensory fibers follow the nearest larval nerve during their growth toward the CNS. However, none of their observations were carried out in developing animals, so it is not possible to make a statement about how the final pathways are actually established.

B. CENTRAL PATHWAYS

Nerve fibers generally follow well-defined and predictable pathways to their targets within invertebrate ganglia, though some variations have been documented (see Section III,C). What happens to sensory fibers which enter the CNS at ectopic locations? Do they find their usual routes and their normal synaptic targets? Investigations of these questions in *Drosophila* homeotic mutants during the past few years have produced some interesting results which, although obtained in adults, shed some light on development.

The mutation *spineless-aristapedia* (*ss*) transforms the antennal arista to tarsal segments; the mutations *Antennapedia* (*Antp*) and

Nasobemia (*Ns*) produce similar but more extreme transformations, with most of the antenna and even part of the head cuticle becoming leg cuticle. Deak (1976) tested behaviorally whether sensory neurons in the homeotic appendage of these mutants respond to stimuli appropriate to an antenna or to a leg. He found that a sugar solution, which normally results in proboscis extension when applied to normally located tarsi, could evoke a similar (though somewhat weaker) response when applied to the homeotic tarsi. No such response is produced if a sugar solution is applied to normal antennae. Application of a sugar solution containing sodium chloride to the legs of wild type flies produces no proboscis extension, the sodium chloride inhibiting the response to sugar. In *ss* flies, however, the response was not inhibited when the double solution was applied to either the normal or homeotic tarsi. Proboscis extension could not be elicited by applying sugar solution to the homeotic legs of *Antp* or *Ns,* though the normal legs in these mutants produced the normal response. This was expected since the stocks of *Antp* and *Ns* used did not show in the antennal legs the tarsal structures which contain the chemosensors. Deak concluded that in *ss* flies the homeotic chemosensors acted according to their origin (leg) as opposed to their location (antenna) and that, clearly, the sensory fibers had made functional connections somewhere in the nervous system.

The anatomy of the central projections of homeotic sensory fibers was determined by Stocker *et al.* (1976) in *Antp* flies using degeneration and cobalt backfilling methods. They found that these homeotic fibers enter the head ganglion along the antennal nerve and distribute themselves in a manner which closely parallels that of the normal antennal sensory fibers. Furthermore, they found no homeotic fibers in the neck connectives, which shows that none of these fibers reach their usual targets in the thoracicoabdominal ganglion. Since no wild type leg sensory fibers reach the head ganglion, it is apparent that homeotic leg fibers in *Antp* do not make connections onto their normal targets, but behave anatomically as if they were antennal fibers.

The results of Deak (1976) on *ss* flies and those of Stocker *et al.* (1976) on *Antp* flies are puzzling when taken together. Behavior in the first case indicates that homeotic fibers can produce responses normally elicited by leg sensors, but anatomy in the second shows that these fibers never get to their normal targets. It is possible, of course, that no response to sugar can be elicited in the antennal legs of the *Antp* stock studied by Stocker *et al.* (which is different from the stock studied by Deak; *Antp*[73b] as opposed to *Antp*[B]). However, in a subsequent paper, Stocker (1977) reported that in *Antp*[73b] flies, which have tarsi in the homeotic appendages, a sugar stimulus applied to either thoracic or homeotic tarsi evokes a proboscis extension response. No such response is elicited by a sugar stimulus to the wild type antenna. Hence, homeotic fibers in $Antp^{73b}$ look like antennal sensory fibers but act like those of a leg (see Fig. 4). We must presume that these fibers can find, if not induce, interneurons in the head ganglion which can complete the signaling pathway to the motoneurons that extend the proboscis. What in fact happens is unknown, and will remain so until more detailed knowledge of the pathways of interneuronal processes is obtained. A further complication stems from the fact that CNS neurons also carry the $Antp$ genotype, which could affect their properties, a point that could be resolved by using mosaic techniques.

Somewhat different results have been obtained in the analysis of

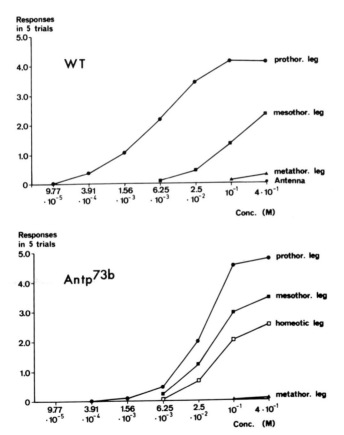

FIG. 4. Plot of the arithmetic means of proboscis extensions in wild type (WT) and mutant (Antp^{73b}) flies elicited by five successive stimuli with fructose solutions of various concentrations. Each point is based on a minimum of 40 flies. After Stoker (1977).

bithorax mutations. Using horseradish peroxidase backfilling to visualize normal and homeotic sensory fibers in the double mutant *bithorax postbithorax* (*bx pbx*), Ghysen (1978) determined that sensory fibers achieved nearly normal central projections even if they entered the CNS at unusual places. In this mutant the metathorax, which normally consists of a narrow strip of cuticle bearing the halteres, is transformed into a second mesothorax carrying a second pair of wings with a full set of sensory structures. The thoracicoabdominal ganglion, however, is of normal size and has a normal set of nerve roots. Sensory fibers from the homeotic wings enter the ganglion through more posterior roots than do the normal fibers, but their positions within the ganglion are quite similar. A particularly interesting example is that of the axon of the anterior scutellar bristle of the notum. The normal axon enters the ganglion near the boundary of the prothoracic and mesothoracic segments, travels first toward the midline and then turns and travels in a posterior direction, terminating in the metathoracic segment (Fig. 2a of Ghysen, 1978). The homeotic axon, however, enters the ganglion between the mesothoracic and metathoracic segments, also travels medially, but then bifurcates, sending one branch posteriorly into the metathoracic segment and the other anteriorly to the prothoracic segment along a path that closely parallels the normal one (Fig. 2b in Ghysen, 1978). Hence, at least part of the homeotic axon travels along the usual path but in the opposite direction to the normal axon. Similar observations are reported by Ghysen on fibers that were misrouted using surgical techniques. He concludes from his observations on both homeotic and surgically modified flies that a sensory axon can establish appropriate central projections independently of where it enters the ganglion, and suggests that the growing axon is capable of recognizing a specific trail which it must follow to arrive at the correct target neurons. It must be kept in mind, however, that these observations were carried out in the fully formed system and that little is known about the intermediate steps. It is entirely possible that the growing axon sends branches down many highways and retains only those which reach synaptic targets, these targets being located along a particular route. This hypothesis would require only the recognition of targets, but not the following of a specific trail.

Palka and collaborators (Palka, 1977; Palka *et al.*, 1979) arrived at somewhat different conclusions than Ghysen (1978) from similar but more extensive experiments on flies carrying either the *bithorax* (*bx*) or *postbithorax* (*pbx*) genotypes, or the double mutation *bx pbx*. The central projections of sensory fibers from the wing and haltere were determined in wild type flies using methylene blue staining and cobalt back-

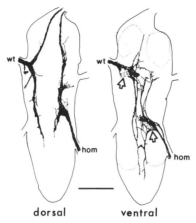

dorsal   ventral

FIG. 5. Camera lucida drawings of the dorsal and ventral components of cobalt-filled wing sensory fibers projecting into the thoracicoabdominal ganglion of a double homeotic mutant, bx^3pbx/Ubx^{130}, of *Drosophila*. Fibers from a normal wing (wt) were filled on the left side, those from the homeotic appendage (hom) on the right. The pattern of the dorsal component of the homeotic fibers, although not completely unlike that of the wt fibers, in fact more closely resembles the normal pattern of sensory fibers from the haltere. The ventral components from the wt and homeotic appendages show generally similar branching patterns, but the short fine fibers branch in a more posterior position in the homeotic case than in the wt (arrows). Bar: 100 μm. After Palka *et al.* (1979).

filling. The wing sensillae were grouped into three classes according to the structure of the sensory organs and the anatomy of their central projections, which were different from those of the sensory fibers of the haltere. Central projections of each of the three classes of sensilla from the homeotic wings (which replace the halteres in these mutants) were found to behave differently from one another (see Fig. 5).

Class 1 fibers from the normal wing form a large ipsilateral ventral projection in the mesothoracic segment of the ganglion, near the point where they enter the ganglion. In the mutants the homologous fibers from the homeotic wing enter the metathoracic segment and form a ventral projection in this more posterior segment which resembles the normal one except in its location. Class 2 fibers project ventrally to all three segments of the ganglion in the wild type. They show a very similar distribution in the mutants, in agreement with the observations of Ghysen (1978). Class 3 fibers normally form a dorsal projection which bifurcates, sending one group of fibers in an anterior direction and the other in a posterior direction. In the mutants, however, Class 3 fibers form a projection whose distribution in the ganglion closely parallels that of the normal haltere sensory fibers.

Palka and collaborators hypothesize from these observations the existence of a different developmental program for each class of sensilla. Class 1, for example, would be programmed to send fibers ventrally and locally, wherever they enter the ganglion, but always expressing a wing phenotype. Class 2 fibers would be programmed similarly, except for extending to all segments of the ganglion, but still expressing a wing phenotype, independent of location of origin. Class 3 fibers, however, would be programmed to respond phenotypically to their location, becoming haltere-like when they originate in the metathorax.

Palka and co-workers also carried out a genetic mosaic analysis to determine whether the mutant genotype of the CNS affects the phenotypic expression of the homeotic fibers. Their analysis of sensory projections from wing clones into wild type ganglia in mosaics generally reproduced the above results on mutants but revealed some significant differences in the morphology of the ganglion and of the sensory projections between mosaics and mutants. The evidence that changes are introduced by *bithorax* mutations in the CNS points out the importance of using mosaics in the analysis of the effects of homeotic mutations on central sensory projections. A difficulty in the interpretation of the effects of a mutant CNS remains, however, since differences in the mosaic projections could be due to interactions between the mosaic and adjacent wild type tissue in the appendage, rather than to the influence of a mutant versus wild type ganglion.

VI. Summary and Conclusions

The formulation of a coherent model for the roles of genes and epigenetic factors in the development of the invertebrate nervous system is at present premature. Although the experiments discussed in this article yield some interesting and important results, they are neither complete nor broad enough to form the basis for such a model. The work is now at a stage where the results, rather than providing definitive answers, provide the background from which we can ask further and more sppecific questions. This is in great part due to our lack of knowledge about the details of what actually happens in development, and many straightforward but tedious and time-consuming phenomenological observations still must be made.

The following is a summary of the preliminary conclusions that can be drawn from the observations reviewed in this article:

1. Specific neurons are not morphologically identical from individual to individual, even under conditions where we might reasonably expect that the set of instructions which are followed in their develop-

ment are the same. In other words, some features of neurons are not strictly controlled.

2. For a particular group of neurons, variations in morphology and in number from individual to individual can be as great within a clone as they are within a genetically heterogeneous population. However, whether variability of certain properties is inherited remains to be shown conclusively. The significance of variability to models for the development of the nervous system has yet to be explored.

3. The genotype and phenotype of sensory neurons can profoundly affect the differentiation of target neurons in the CNS. This has been shown directly in the visual system but only circumstantially for peripheral chemosensors. The developmental mechanisms that mediate these interactions are still to be identified.

4. Sensory fibers which grow into the CNS at ectopic sites can reproduce apparently normal branching patterns and branch locations. This conclusion can be reached from experiments with both homeotic mutations and mechanical translocation. However, the attainment of a normal branching pattern must be considered only one of several possibilities, since some fibers in homeotic mutants have been seen to behave in other ways. In some cases they reproduce their normal branching pattern but at incorrect positions in the ganglion, and in other cases they reproduce the branching pattern of sensory fibers which normally grow in at the ectopic site. How much these complications are due to the mutation itself, or to what extent these variations tell us that there are different mechanisms of growth for different populations of sensory fibers remains to be determined by further experimentation.

ACKNOWLEDGMENTS

I thank Robert Wyman, Murray Flaster, and Robert Schehr for critical readings of the manuscript and Linda Sproviero for typing it. Preparation of this chapter was partially supported by NIH grant NS14946.

REFERENCES

Albertson, Donna G., and Thomson, J. N. (1976). *Phil. Trans. R. Soc. London B* **275**, 299–325.

Altman, J. S., and Tyrer, N. M. (1977). *J. Comp. Neurol.* **172**, 431–440.

Anderson, H. (1978). *J. Embryol. Exp. Morphol.* **45**, 55–83.

Bate, C. M. (1976). *Nature (London)* **260**, 54–56.

Benjamin, P. R. (1976). *Nature (London)* **260**, 338–340.

Bentley, D. (1975). *Science* **187**, 760–764.

Bentley, D. (1976). *In* "Simpler Networks and Behavior" (J. C. Fentress, ed.), pp. 126–139. Sinauer, Sunderland, Massachusetts.

Brenner, S. (1974). *Genetics* **77**, 71–94.

Burrows, M. (1973). *J. Comp. Physiol.* **83**, 165–178.
Burrows, M. (1975). *J. Exp. Biol.* **62**, 189–219.
Campos-Ortega, J. A., and Hofbauer, A. (1977). *Wilhelm Roux Arch.* **181**, 227–245.
Deak, I. I. (1976). *Nature (London)* **260**, 252–254.
Ghysen, A. (1978). *Nature (London)* **274**, 869–872.
Ghysen, A., and Deak, I. I. (1978). *Wilhelm Roux Arch.* **184**, 273–283.
Goodman, C. S. (1974). *J. Comp. Physiol.* **95**, 185–201.
Goodman, C. S. (1977). *Science* **193**, 1384–1386.
Goodman, C. S. (1978). *J. Comp. Neurol.* **182**, 681–706.
Hall, J. C., Gelbart, W. M., and Kankel, D. R. (1976). *In* "Genetics and Biology of *Drosophila*" (M. Ashburner and E. Novitsky, eds.), Vol. 1a, pp. 265–314. Academic Press, New York.
Hebert, P. D. N., and Ward, R. D. (1972). *Genetics* **71**, 639–642.
Horridge, H. A., and Meinertzhagen, I. A. (1970). *Proc. R. Soc. London B* **175**, 69–82.
Kankel, D. R., and Ferrus, A. (1979). *In* "Neurogenetics: Genetic Approaches to the Nervous System" (X. Breakefield, ed.) pp. 27–66. Elsevier, New York.
Kankel, D. R., and Hall, J. C. (1976). *Dev. Biol.* **48**, 1–24.
Kater, S. B., and Nicholson, C. (1973). "Intracellular Staining in Neurobiology." Springer-Verlag, Berlin and New York.
Kennedy, D. (1971). *The Physiol.* **14**, 5–30.
King, D. G. (1976). *J. Neurocytol.* **5**, 239–266.
Kuffler, D. P., and Muller, K. J. (1974). *J. Neurobiol.* **5**, 331–348.
Lawrence, P. A., and Green, S. M. (1979). *Dev. Biol.* **71**, 142–152.
Levinthal, F., Macagno, E. R., and Levinthal, C. (1975). *Cold Spring Harbor Symp. Quant. Biol.* **40**, 321–331.
Lo Presti, V., Macagno, E. R., and Levinthal, C. (1973). *Proc. Natl. Acad. Sci. U.S.A.* **70**, 433–437.
Lo Presti, V., Macagno, E. R., and Levinthal, C. (1974). *Proc. Natl. Acad. Sci. U.S.A.* **71**, 1098–1102.
Macagno, E. R. (1977). *In* "Cell and Tissue Interactions" (J. W. Lash and M. M. Burger, eds.), pp. 293–309. Raven, New York.
Macagno, E. R. (1978a). *Nature (London)* **275**, 318–320.
Macagno, E. R. (1978b). *Brain Theory Newsl.* **3**, 186–189.
Macagno, E. R. (1979). *Dev. Biol.* **73**, 206–238.
Macagno, E. R. (1980). *J. Comp. Neurol.* **190**, 283–302.
Macagno, E. R., Lo Presti, V., and Levinthal, C. (1973). *Proc. Natl. Acad. Sci. U.S.A.* **70**, 57–61.
Macagno, E. R., Levinthal, C., and Sobel, I. (1979). *Annu. Rev. Biophys. Bioeng.* **8**, 323–351.
Meinertzhagen, I. A. (1973). *In* "Developmental Neurobiology of Arthropods" (D. Young, ed.), pp. 51–104. Cambridge Univ. Press, London.
Meinertzhagen, I. A. (1976). *Phil. Trans. R. Soc. B* **274**, 555–596.
Melamed, J., and Trujillo-Cenoz, O. (1975). *J. Ultrastruct. Res.* **5**, 79–93.
Meyerowitz, E. M., and Kankel, D. R. (1978). *Dev. Biol.* **62**, 112–142.
Mouze, M. (1974). *J. Embryol. Exp. Morphol.* **31**, 377–407.
Mouze, M. (1978). *Wilhelm Roux Arch.* **184**, 325–350.
Pak, W. L., and Pinto, L. H. (1976). *Annu. Rev. Biophys. Bioeng.* **5**, 397–448.
Palka, J. (1977). *Soc. Neurosci. Abstr.* **3**, 187.
Palka, J., Lawrence, P. A., and Hart, H. S. (1979). *Dev. Biol.* **69**, 549–575.
Pearson, K. G., and Goodman, C. S. (1979). *J. Comp. Neurol.* **184**, 141–166.

Pitman, R. M., Tweedle, C. D., and Cohen, M. J. (1973). *In* "Intracellular Staining in Neurobiology" (S. B. Kater and C. Nicholson, eds.). Springer-Verlag, Berlin and New York.
Purves, D., and McMahan, U. J. (1972). *J. Cell. Biol.* **55**, 205–220.
Quinn, W. G., and Gould, J. L. (1979). *Nature (London)* **278**, 19–23.
Ready, F. D., Hanson, T. E., and Benzer, S. (1976). *Dev. Biol.* **53**, 217–240.
Sanes, J. R., and Hildebrand, J. G. (1975). *Wilhelm Roux Arch.* **178**, 71–78.
Selzer, M. E. (1979). *Brain Res.* **163**, 181–193.
Shelton, P. M. J., and Lawrence, P. A. (1974). *J. Embryol. Exp. Morphol.* **32**, 337–353.
Shelton, P. M. J., Anderson, H. J., and Eley, S. (1977). *J. Embryol. Exp. Morphol.* **39**, 235–252.
Stocker, R. F. (1977). *J. Comp. Physiol.* **115**, 351–361.
Stocker, R. F., Edwards, J. S., Palka, J., and Schubiger, G. (1976). *Dev. Biol.* **52**, 210–220.
Stretton, A. O. W., and Kravitz, E. A. (1973). *In* "Intracellular Staining in Neurobiology" (S. Kater and C. Nicholson, eds.), pp. 21–40. Springer-Verlag, Berlin and New York.
Sulston, J. E. (1976). *Phil. Trans. R. Soc. London B* **275**, 287–297.
Sulston, J. E., and Horvitz, H. R. (1977). *Dev. Biol.* **56**, 110–156.
Suzuki, D. T. (1970). *Science* **170**, 695–706.
Thompson, E. B., Bailey, C. H., Castellucci, V. F., and Kandel, E. R. (1976). *Soc. Neurosci. Abstr.* **2**, 337.
Treistman, S. N., and Schwartz, J. H. (1976). *Brain Res.* **109**, 607–614.
Ward, S. (1977). *Annu. Rev. Genet.* **11**, 415–450.
Ward, S., Thomson, N., White, J. G., and Brenner, S. (1975). *J. Comp. Neurol.* **160**, 313–338.
Ware, R. W., Clark, D., Crossland, K., and Russell, R. L. (1975). *J. Comp. Neurol.* **162**, 71–110.
White, J. G., Southgate, E., Thomson, J. N., and Brenner, S. (1976). *Phil. Trans. R. Soc. London B* **275**, 327–348.
Wigglesworth, V. B. (1953). *Q. J. Microsc. Sci.* **94**, 93–112.
Wyman, R. J. (1976). *In* "Simpler Networks and Behavior" (J. C. Fentress, ed.), pp. 153–166. Sinauer, Sunderland, Massachusetts.

CHAPTER 10

ON COMPOUND EYE DEVELOPMENT IN

Drosophila melanogaster

J. A. Campos-Ortega

INSTITUT FÜR BIOLOGIE III
ALBERT LUDWIGS-UNIVERSITÄT
FREIBURG IM BREISGAU
FEDERAL REPUBLIC OF GERMANY

I. Introduction	347
II. The Morphology of the Compound Eye	349
III. The Embryonic and Larval Development of the Compound Eye	350
IV. Pattern of Mitosis in Compound Eye Development	353
V. Early Cell Lineages	358
VI. Late Cell Lineages	360
VII. Genetic Analysis of Compound Eye Morphogenesis	363
VIII. Concluding Remarks	369
References	370

I. Introduction

Two different aspects can be distinguished in any morphological pattern: the elements of the pattern and their spatial arrangement. In multicellular organisms many structural patterns are composed of distinct cells, or of cell products, integrated in a characteristic texture. Both pattern elements and their arrangement are the consequence of developmental processes, the sum of which constitutes what is called morphogenesis. I would like to suggest the hypothesis that the developmental processes producing the elements of the pattern are different from those processes leading to the formation of the pattern: whereas differential gene activity within cells is responsible for the origin of cellular diversity, the pattern arises from manifold, unknown properties of morphogenetic fields acting upon the cells. I am obviously considering these two classes of events in purely operational terms, irrespective of any causal relationship that might exist between them.

In the sections to follow I shall discuss some experiments on the origin of both the ommatidial cell types and the structural pattern they form in the compound eye of *Drosophila melanogaster*. The compound eye of the fruit fly is an extremely regular, repetitive array of one elementary pattern, the ommatidium, consisting of a few cell types

347

represented by some 20 pattern elements (see Benzer, 1973). The huge number of mutants isolated and genetically characterized in *Drosophila* by previous workers (see Lindsley and Grell, 1968), the important inventory of genetic techniques which they have developed, and, finally the ease in producing new mutants render the compound eye of the fruit fly one of the most promising model systems to study morphogenesis.

Morphogenesis in *Drosophila* is currently envisaged as the product of interactions between genetic signals and morphogenetic field properties (see Garcia-Bellido and Ripoll, 1978). There is scanty evidence concerning the nature of these interactions or the genetic signals involved in the process. Most of the existing experimental evidence is derived from studies on morphogenesis of thoracic segments in *Drosophila,* where the morphological pattern is simpler (Garcia-Bellido, 1975). Much less is known about the compound eye. Minimal requirements for understanding morphogenesis in the compound eye consist of the following: (1) a complete description of events normally going on during eye development; (2) the knowledge of functions relevant for morphogenesis; and (3) the knowledge of the genes that code for those functions. The aim of this chapter is to review the work done on these problems during the past few years.

Three different approaches have been used in these studies. The first consists of histological analysis of wild-type eye imaginal discs of increasing ages, by means of serial section light and electron microscopy. [^{3}H]Thymidine autoradiography of discs or compound eyes has been used to investigate the pattern of divisions and the "birth days" of ommatidial cells during the terminal phases of proliferation. The second approach consists of the transplantation of complete discs or of disc fragments of different ages into larvae ready to pupate according to the paradigm devised by Ephrussi and Beadle (1936). Metamorphosis of host larvae forces immature test implants to start cytodifferentiation, thus bypassing variable periods of the normal time for development. This approach permits analysis of the temporal sequence in the acquisition of differentiation abilities by disc cells. Most of the work presented here has been done using the third approach, that of clonal analysis, in which genes are brought to phenotypic expression through X-ray-induced mitotic recombination (Stern, 1936). Clonal analysis can be successfully applied for cell lineage studies, where dividing cells are labeled with marker genes made homozygous by irradiation (Becker, 1957). Marker genes generally affect cytodifferentiation processes or functions of adult cells, without interfering with the proliferative phase of development, expressing themselves, therefore, when all mitoses have been performed. A clone of labeled cells can be easily distinguished from the remaining, nonlabeled cells of the adult eye using histological techniques to show their marker phenotype. Thus clone members can be traced back to a common precursor cell and questions about genealogical relationships of eye cells can be approached. Another application of clonal analysis is the study of mutant gene functions affecting development. In this experimental paradigm mutant gene expression can be studied at the cellular level interacting with wild-type tissue in a morphogenetic mosaic, and questions about the autonomy of phenotypic expression or phenocritical periods can be posed. The reader is referred to the reviews of Nöthiger (1972, 1975), Becker (1976), Garcia-Bellido and Ripoll (1978), and Wieschaus (1978) for further details on clonal analysis.

II. The Morphology of the Compound Eye

The compound eye of *Drosophila melanogaster* consists of about 700 ommatidia precisely arranged in an hexagonal pattern. Each ommatidium contains about 20 singly identifiable pattern elements which belong to four different cell types. There are four cone cells, two primary pigment cells, four or five secondary pigment (SP) cells, and eight photoreceptor (R) cells in each ommatidium. In addition one bristle apparatus, comprised of four cells (Waddington and Perry, 1960; see, however, Perry, 1968), can be assigned to each ommatidium. Other authors (Ready *et al.,* 1976) distinguish as tertiary pigment cell one pigmented cell situated at the posterior edge of each horizontal ommatidiae face. Since the pigment in this cell does not differ from that in the remaining, secondary, pigment cells, and is affected by the same mutant genes, we do not make this distinction and therefore consider secondary pigment cells as all cells which surround the R cell assemblies in their proximodistal extent.

Three characteristic features of the *Drosophila* compound eye are worth mentioning: its astonishing architectural precision, the asymmetrical pattern of the rhabdomeres of R cells, and the mirror-image inversion of this pattern that can be observed at the level of the topographical equator of the eye. The structural precision of the ommatidia allows us to unequivocally distinguish both cell types, e.g., cone versus R cells, and cell classes, e.g., R3 from R4 cells, for we can assign a number to practically each cell of the ommatidium (Dietrich, 1909). The pattern of rhabdomeres is formed by the eight R cells and is strictly trapezoid, with an additional, central rhabdomere. Two different cells,

R7 distally and R8 proximally, contribute microvilli to this central rhabdomere. In each ommatidium the row formed by R1, R2, and R3 cells is located anteriorly, R5 and R6 posteriorly; R3 points to the poles of the eye and R1 and R6 are oriented toward the equator. There are no exceptions to this general pattern, nor are incomplete R cell sets found in a wild-type eye. Nevertheless, R cells are different in their anatomical and physiological properties (see Pak and Grabowski, 1978). Furthermore, those from one ommatidium originate at different times during development. Thus, qualifying R cells only by their position in the ommatidial assembly might be insufficient (see below, and Campos-Ortega et al., 1979). The polarity of the ommatidial pattern undergoes a mirror-image inversion at the middle of the eye along a line (line of pattern inversion, LPI) that horizontally traverses the eye in a zig-zag course, occasionally jumping one or two ommatidial rows (Franceschini and Kirschfeld, 1971).

Ommatidial pattern elements possess other characteristics apart from those imposed by their positions within the pattern itself; evidence indicates that they maintain those characteristics even in abnormal patterns. For example, irradiation of wild-type third instar larvae produces characteristic zones of roughening in the eye (Becker, 1957) manifesting incompleteness of ommatidia due to X-ray-induced cell death. However, elements within such abnormal patterns can still be distinguished because of their anatomical characteristics. The analysis of the mutant sev (Campos-Ortega et al., 1979) has shown that cells with the properties of R8 can sometimes develop in the position of R7. In one mutant of Musca, R.A.C., kindly provided by Christian Wehrhahn (Tübingen), one of the R1–6 cells is missing; in some cases R8 adopts the position of the missing element at the R4 site, but without losing the R8 properties (unpublished observations). Thus the developmental operations that contribute to the production of the pattern elements might be different from those giving rise to the pattern.

III. The Embryonic and Larval Development of the Compound Eye

Most of the cuticular structures that form the head of an adult fly derive from the so-called eye-antennal imaginal discs (Bodenstein, 1938; Vogt, 1946; Gehring, 1966; Ouweneel, 1970). These are epithelial specializations which are set apart in the embryo as invaginations of the ectoderm (see Poulson, 1950). They are already visible in the 16-hour embryo and in the mid-first instar they seem to establish contact with the larval brain by means of the eye stalk (the eye stalk contains the axons of the stemmatal nerve during the first and second instar, increasing in volume as R cell axons are forming during the third instar and the first hours after pupariation; (Hofbauer, unpublished; see Trujillo-Cénoz and Melamed, 1973, for a similar observation in *Phoenicia sericata*). At the time when clearly visible contact with the brain is established, the eye-antennal disc is a flattened epithelial sac lying on the brain surface, with an inner face from which the compound eye will form and an outer face, the peripodial membrane, which will give rise to some cuticular structures (Spreij and Oldenhave, 1974). Cell proliferation in the eye disc starts after some 40 hours of development (Madhavan and Schneiderman, 1978) and is completed about 10 hours after pupariation (Campos-Ortega and Hofbauer, 1977). Becker (1957) inferred from the size of mosaic patches induced during early development (see the following) that the compound eye begins development with at least two cells; similar estimations from the size of clones initiated at the end of the first instar gave a total of about 20 cells populating the ommatidial field anlage at this time. Cell counts of squashed second instar eye-antennal discs (Becker, 1957) demonstrated an 8- to 12-fold increase in cell number, from 131 to 1300–1600, during this stage. Since eye-antennal disc cells undergo three or more consecutive mitoses during the second instar, the number of presumptive eye cells increases to 100–150 by the end of the second instar. These cells must then produce the final number of about 15,000 ommatidial cells during the third instar, until 10 hours after pupariation mitotic activity is extinguished in the imaginal disc.

At the end of the second instar, eye and antennal parts are individualized. Cells in the posterior, presumptive eye part of the disc do not show any sign of cytodifferentiation until some 10 hours after the beginning of the third instar. At this time, groups of clustered cells are visible posteriorly in the anlage, their number increasing as time progresses (Waddington and Perry, 1960). The appearance of cell clusters roughly coincides with the formation of a deep longitudinal furrow that extends across the disc in a mediolateral direction, corresponding to the dorsoventral one of the adult eye, called morphogenetic furrow (Ready *et al.*, 1976) (see Fig. 1A). Its position varies with time, paralleling the increase in surface of the patterned area. Thus, a relationship of the furrow with the patterning of ommatidial cells has been assumed. Electron microscopy of mid-third instar eye discs shows that the more anterior cell clusters, immediately contiguous to the morphogenetic furrow, usually contain five cells surrounded by other nonpatterned cells. More posteriorly, dividing cells are visible and behind these, ommatidial clusters have increased in cell number by the addition of new elements to the previous clusters of five (Ready *et al.*, 1976). Three different cell types can be identified in each posterior cluster: a distal

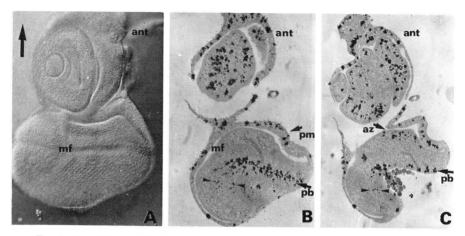

Fıɢ. 1. The wild-type third instar eye-antennal imaginal disc. (A) A Nomarski-optics picture of a late third instar disc, illustrating the general disposition of eye and antennal (ant) parts, the morphogenetic furrow (mf) and the patterned disc area within the presumptive ommatidial field (micrograph kindly provided by R. Ransom). The arrow points to anterior. (B) and (C) Autoradiographs from a series of a disc of about the same age as the one in (A), fixed immediately after *in vitro* incubation in [³H]thymidine. The sections (Durcupan embedding, 2 μm thick, methylene blue staining) are predominantly tangential, slightly oblique, and show distinctly antennal (ant) and eye parts. Within the eye part two different zones of labeling are visible (pb and az) separated by the morphogenetic furrow (mf). Labeling within the anterior zone (az) is diffusely distributed; within the posterior (pb), on the contrary, it is sharply defined. Clusters with five cells are found between the posterior band and the mf and complete clusters with eight presumptive R cells appear behind the pb. Two arrowheads point to a group of pycnotic nuclei situated behind the pb. Pycnotic nuclei move in their position rostralward, in register to the posteroanterior displacement of mf, pb, and clustering. See text for further discussion on this topic. Labeling in the peripodial membrane (pm) seems to be in register to that in the ommatidial field.

group of four presumptive cone cells, a middle group of eight presumptive R cells, and a proximal group, not obviously patterned and therefore providing difficulty in counting its elements, which will give rise to primary and secondary pigment cells. Behind the first complete R cell clusters, i.e., with eight R cells, a band of pycnotic nuclei is visible in the proximal half of the disc (see Fig. 1B and C). Since their position varies in register with the posteroanterior displacement of the morphogenetic furrow, it seems plausible that they might be related to the clustering and cytodifferentiation processes of ommatidial cells.

In whole mounts of third instar discs, an equatorial groove is visible at right angle to the morphogenetic furrow. Electron microscopic observation of the pattern of presumptive R cell clusters reveals their mirror-image inversion along this groove. Thus it may play a role in the formation of the LPI (Ready *et al.,* 1976).

Eye imaginal disc cells can be brought to cytodifferentiation following implantation into late third instar larvae. During metamorphosis of the host, the implant concomitantly undergoes cytodifferentiation and, after eclosion of the host fly, exhibits recognizable adult structures. By increasing the age of test implants it is possible to ascertain a sequence for the developmental abilities of disc cells (Mindek and Nöthiger, 1973; Gateff and Schneiderman, 1975; Campos-Ortega and Gateff, 1976). This sequence begins with the acquisition of competence to produce pigment at the mid-second instar and ends with the formation of an ommatidial field that, disregarding its smaller size, does not differ from an adult compound eye. Electron microscopy of differentiated test implants (Campos-Ortega and Gateff, 1976) demonstrated that the youngest test implants forming pigment already contained two different types of cells, one of them identifiable as R cells and the other as one of the primary or secondary pigment cells. These studies further showed that implanted cells must have performed a minimum of mitoses before acquiring cytodifferentiation abilities (Mindek and Nöthiger, 1973; see, however, Bodenstein and Schweizer, 1975), probably as many as they would have done under normal conditions (Campos-Ortega and Gateff, 1976).

IV. Pattern of Mitosis in Compound Eye Development

Early studies by Becker (1957), who determined the mitotic indices of the second instar head anlage, showed three different temporal maxima in this stage which he interpreted as mitotic waves. Since Becker studied squashed discs, in which the normal geometry is lost, there is no information on any spatial distribution of those waves. In the third instar disc, Ready *et al.* (1976), using [³H]thymidine autoradiography, found isotope incorporation in two different regions of the eye anlage separated by the morphogenetic furrow. Whereas labeled cells positioned anteriorly to the furrow are diffusely distributed, posterior labeling occurs in a well-defined, narrow, longitudinally arranged zone (see Fig. 1B and C). Further, single labeled cells are seen well behind the posterior band of labeling. The intradisc distribution of labeling changes in parallel to both the displacement of the morphogenetic furrow and to the increase of patterned disc regions, mentioned previously. Thus, these three phenomena might be interrelated. Two similar mitotic waves have been found by Egelhaaf *et al.* (1975) in the eye anlage of *Ephestia kühniella*.

"Birth days" (Sidman, 1970) of ommatidial cells can be assessed by

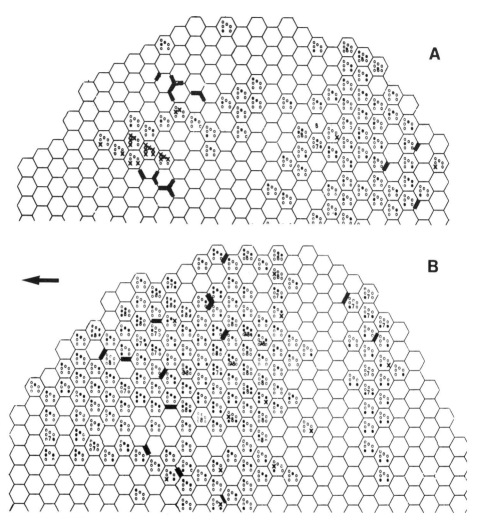

Fig. 2. The proliferation pattern of the eye disc during the third instar. (A) and (B) are partial reconstructions of two different w $+/+$ $rdgB^{EE170}$ eyes. The animals were injected with about 0.2 μl of [^{3}H]thymidine (spec act 50 Ci/mM; conc 1 Ci/ml) at approximately 74 hours (A) and 100 hours (B) after egg laying; immediately afterward they were irradiated with 1000 rad (100 kV, 15 mA, 20 cm distance, 0.7 mm Al filtering) to induce genetic labeling with w and with $rdgB$. After eclosion the flies were processed for light microscope autoradiography, following standard techniques, and on the same slides w and $rdgB$ phenotypes of secondary pigment cells (bars) and R1-7 cells (hasps), respectively, were scored (w R cells could not be scored at this level of resolution of 2-μm-thick sections, which is imposed by the autoradiography). [^{3}H]Thymidine labeling in (A) is confined to the posterior of the eye and corresponds to the beginning of anterior labeling of older discs (see text, and Campos-Ortega and Hofbauer, 1977). Labeling spreads throughout the disc and injections into larvae a few hours older result in continuous posteroanterior

injecting [³H]thymidine into third instar larvae and allowing them to complete development (see Fig. 2A and B). Serial section autoradiography of compound eyes (Ready *et al.*, 1976; Campos-Ortega and Gateff, 1976; Campos-Ortega and Hofbauer, 1977) confirms the existence of the two main zones of labeling found in autoradiograms of discs. The density of cell labeling varies from case to case, being dependent on the amount of the isotope and on the time span during which it was available for uptake. Within the anterior zone, distribution of labeling is strikingly patchy after short incubation periods (see Fig. 1 in Campos-Ortega and Hofbauer, 1977) showing groups of contiguous ommatidia containing labeled cells, separated by others devoid of radioactivity, indicating the existence of local synchrony in the cell cycle of anlage cells. This appearance does not become more obvious in longer pulses (see Fig. 10 in Campos-Ortega and Gateff, 1976).

A distinct labeling behavior can be assessed in ommatidial cells within the different regions of labeling (see Figs. 2 and 3). Whereas in the anterior zone ommatidia contain labeled representatives of all cell types and classes, the ommatidia of the posterior band do not show any labeled R2, R3, R4, R5, and R8 cells. Therefore, these cell classes must go through their terminal divisions earlier than the remaining cells. Furthermore, in cases in which longer pulses are given there is generally no gap in the labeling of R1, R6, and R7 cells in posterior ommatidia; thus these three classes of cells must originate from mitoses in the posterior band. As far as non-R cells are concerned, it becomes evident when studying heavily labeled eyes that all cone cells and primary and secondary pigment cells must originate from the mitotic activity within the posterior band (Fig. 3), or from the remaining mitoses behind it, which still produce a few cells. Non-R cells, or R1, R6, and R7 found labeled in the anterior zone (Fig. 2) must then be derivatives of cells which took up the isotope during the incubation

---

labeling. About 20 hours after the beginning of the third instar a gap is found in the labeling at the rearmost region. Injections shortly afterward (B) already make evident the posterior band of labeling. Whereas representatives of all R1–8 cells might be labeled anteriorly, only R1, R6, and R7 cells are found labeled posteriorly (see also Fig. 3). Genetic labeling in (A) and (B) is localized within the area of [³H]thymidine labeling. The topographical distribution of isotope uptake in eye discs indicates that cells both anteriorly positioned and within the posterior band might be in either phase of their cell cycle, while those in the gap between both labeling zones are either in G1 or in cytodifferentiation. Therefore, genetic labeling seems to correlate with anlage cells being somewhere between DNA synthesis and mitosis. Two relatively large twin-spots are present within the anterior half of the eye depicted in (A). Spots of these characteristics appear anteriorly in the eye after irradiations during the first 10 hours of the third instar. The arrow in (B) points to anterior.

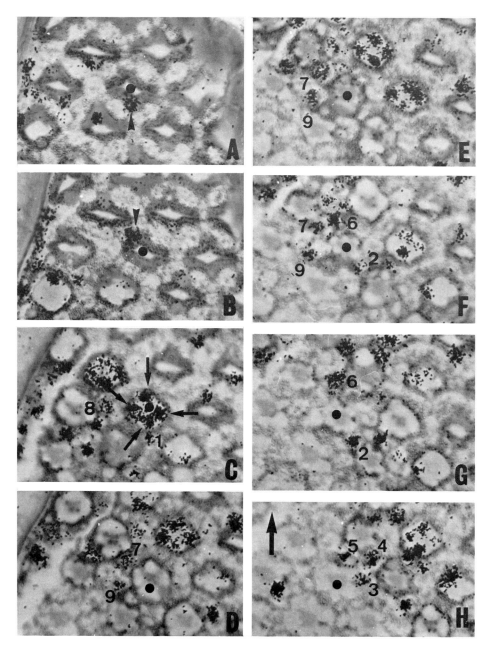

FIG. 3. The proliferation pattern of eye disc cells during the third instar. [³H]Thymidine labeling of non-R cells within the posterior band. Serial sections from the posterior band of labeling of one late third instar injection showing the same om-

period but went through their terminal mitoses when the second mitotic wave passed them later on.

These results taken together indicate that the ommatidial cells originate in two main steps, the first one giving rise to receptor cells R2, R3, R4, R5, and R8, and the second one to receptor cells R1, R6, and R7, all cone cells and primary pigment cells, and almost all secondary pigment cells. The few remaining secondary pigment cells arise from isolated mitoses taking place afterward. The grouping of cells to constitute the ommatidium seems to follow immediately after their production. However, histological observations do not distinguish whether postmitotic cells already meet in front of the morphogenetic furrow or whether their clustering is triggered by the furrow itself.

There is evidence that the presumptive ommatidial anlage corresponds to a morphogenetic field and that its spatial integrity is relevant to the formation of the normal imaginal pattern. Therefore, the pattern can be modified by altering the characteristics of the field. For example, flies of the genotype $M(1)o^{sp}/ywf^{36a};ey^2/+$ have normal eyes. However, if they are irradiated as first instar larvae there is increased cell death during the third instar localized horizontally within the ventral third of the disc and the anlage becomes divided into two or more parts. As a consequence, adult flies have two or more ommatidial fields with a LPI each, instead of a complete compound eye (Fig. 4A and B). Thus, grouping cells must be able to register interruptions of the field coordinates and to change the final polarity of the ommatidium according to their new position, so that ommatidia within the ventral half of the head have the dorsal pattern (Campos-Ortega and Waitz, 1978). The situation is different when the cell grouping which forms the ommatidium has been completed in a given eye position, since there is no possibility of reversing its polarity despite variations in the configuration of the anlage. For example, when imaginal disc fragments from late third instar larvae are brought to cytodifferentiation by means of implanting them into larvae ready to pupate, no pattern regulation occurs, i.e., only those fragments derived from the presumptive LPI disc region form a LPI whereas dorsal or ventral eye disc fragments express, respectively, only the dorsal or the ventral eye pattern

matidium (marked with a dot) at eight different levels. All non-R cells in or around this ommatidium are labeled. (A) and (B) show both primary pigment cells (arrowheads); (C) shows the four cone cells (arrows); labeled secondary pigment cell nuclei, marked 1–9, are visible from (C) to (H). The same ommatidium has R1, R6, and R7 cells labeled at deeper levels of sectioning (not shown). The arrow in (H) points to anterior; dorsal is at the left-hand side of each picture. See text.

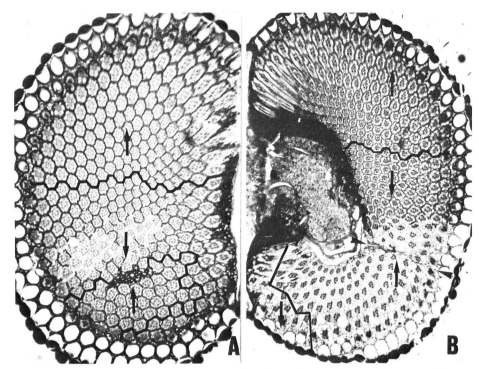

Fig. 4. Cell death localized ventrally within the eye disc produces modifications of the ommatidal pattern. (A) A compound eye with a normally positioned LPI (solid line at the middle of the eye). A small scar is visible ventrally; ommatidia beneath the scar have inverted polarity, i.e., they show the pattern of dorsal ommatidia (delineated by a solid line). In addition, a small *w* cell clone is present in the ventral eye half. Anterior is at the left-hand side of the figure. (B) Another eye in which the scar (arrowheads) divides the compound eye into two independent ommatidial fields, each one of them showing a LPI. A large *w* clone extends throughout both ommatidial fields and stops at the level of one developmental restriction line. Anterior is at the right-hand side of the figure. The arrows in (A) and (B) indicate the ommatidial polarity. See text for further discussion.

(Campos-Ortega and Gateff, 1976). Similar findings have been reported by Trujillo-Cénoz and Melamed (1978) in *P. sericata*.

V. Early Cell Lineages

The majority of the largest clones studied by Becker (1957, 1966), 17 among 23, had a boundary at the middle of the eye with a strikingly rectilinear course; he further found that the progeny of eye anlage cells at the end of the first instar preferentially populate determined sectors within the ventral half of the eye. Becker (1966) therefore concluded that "the cell lineages of the upper and the lower halves of the eye seem to be separated" (p. 158) and that "at the end of the first larval instar each cell of the eye seems to have been assigned to formation of a definite section of the eye" (pp. 159–160). Becker's observations are important for they were the first suggesting the existence of both developmental restrictions during the growth of imaginal disc cells and of a cell lineage relationship in the formation of the compound eye. Similar observations led Garcia-Bellido *et al.* (1973) to postulate the concept of developmental compartments. These later authors used Minute flies for their work in the mesothorax, thereby expanding the size of labeled clones (see Morata and Ripoll, 1975; Ferrus, 1975), which allowed them to uncover developmental restrictions. Further experimental elaboration of the compartment hypothesis followed, and today it is generally accepted among *Drosophila* workers that the development of cells within a compartment, with all their properties, is under the control of a few genes called selector genes (Garcia-Bellido, 1975). Their activation in a group of founder cells (Crick and Lawrence, 1975) is operative in determining a definite developmental pathway (Garcia-Bellido and Capdevilla, 1978).

Campos-Ortega and Waitz (1978) performed a clonal analysis of eye disc development during the first and second instars using Minute flies and histological techniques (see also Baker, 1977). One of the primary aims of that study was to ascertain the restrictive efficacy of both mid-eye and sectorial clone boundaries discovered by Becker (1957, 1966), when allowing Minute $^+$ cells to perform additional mitoses in a background of slowly dividing Minute cells. Five lines were found to be preferential boundaries of labeled clones in the compound eye of Minute flies, delineating together with the eye margin six different regions. After a given developmental stage cell clones growing within each of those regions generally do not overgrow their boundaries. The positions of three out of five restriction lines found in Minute eyes correspond quite accurately to that of the dorsal and anterior sectorial boundaries I, II, and VII described by Becker; none of the remaining sectorial boundaries could be confirmed when working with Minute flies. The results of both studies further agree in the sequential modality in establishing regional restrictions.

Histological observations of Minute$^+$ cell clones demonstrated that the mid-eye clonal boundary follows quite precisely the LPI, although they are not identical: electron microscopic study of the interrelationships between LPI and equatorial restriction line shows that they may deviate from each other by one or two ommatidial rows. Thus, the dorsal and the ventral eye *patterns* do not have clonal origin (Ready *et al.*, 1976) although the *cells* of the ventral and the dorsal eye halves may have clonal origin (Becker, 1957; Baker, 1977; Campos-Ortega and Waitz, 1978). Independence of LPI and ocular restriction lines could be further substantiated by experiments in which labeled cell clones were induced in eyes with dislocated or multiple LPIs (Campos-Ortega and Waitz, 1978). LPI abnormalities occur when the coordinates of the developing eye anlage are interrupted during the third instar by local cell death (see previously). In those eyes with abnormal LPI, clones have boundaries at the same positions, with respect to the head coordinates, as in normal eyes (see Fig. 4B). Therefore the LPI is not identical to any restriction line, as seen before, and does not seem to be causally related to restriction boundaries.

A developmental restriction line found within an organ is *a priori* a candidate for the border of a developmental compartment. However, definitive evidence can be obtained only from the analysis of mutants demonstrating the genetic control of compartments (Morata and Lawrence, 1975; Garcia-Bellido, 1977). In the compound eye any genetic evidence for compartments is lacking. Thus, the question as to whether eye restriction lines correspond to true compartment boundaries remains open.

VI. Late Cell Lineages

Benzer (1971) demonstrated that any ommatidium in *Drosophila* does not necessarily correspond to a clone of cells. He studied the boundaries of phenotypes in mosaic eyes and discovered the existence of ommatidia mosaically composed of mutant and wild-type cells, thus of derivatives of more than one cell. Consequently, cells must be recruited into ommatidia following rules that are not based on their linkage by ancestry. This finding has been subsequently confirmed by others (see Hofbauer and Campos-Ortega, 1976). The question now arises as to when disc cells are committed to form the various cell types of the ommatidium. This question is directly concerned with the developmental operations that give rise to the pattern elements.

There are two alternative hypothetical possibilities: (1) anlage cells, sharing segment and compartment specificities, are equipotent with respect to tissue and cell specificities throughout development, commitment of individual cells occurring at the moment of clustering; (2) anlage cells become segregated during the proliferative phase of development into the precursors of the different cell types, giving rise to fixed cell lineages. In other words, differential gene activity might be initiated either in postmitotic, grouping cells or in those cells which still have to divide a few times. These two possibilities are obviously extremes in a series of other possible mechanisms which cover transi-

tional forms between them. We have, like others, tried to decide between the determinative mechanisms. Due to technical reasons (discussed in Hofbauer and Campos-Ortega, 1976; Campos-Ortega and
Hofbauer, 1977; Campos-Ortega *et al.*, 1978) we confined our analysis
to the R1–7 and the secondary pigment cells (SP), neglecting R8 and
the remaining ommatidial cells. R1–7 cells and SP cells lie together in
the ommatidium and are morphologically and functionally distinguishable from each other. There is conclusive evidence for differential
gene activity in both cell types, since several genes are known to express themselves in one but not in the other type of cells. We asked the
following question: do R and SP cells at the latest developmental stage
belong to the same or to different lineages? Clonal analysis with genetic labeling of dividing cells should, in principle, be an appropriate
approach to this question. One marker gene is used which expresses
itself in both cell types. Whether segregation of lineages occurs can be
deduced from the analysis of spot composition.

The results show that, whereas spots induced during the first and
second instar invariably contain cells of both types, only 10–15% of
those from the third instar have a mixed composition. These crucial
mixed spots were subject to further analysis (see Campos-Ortega *et al.*,
1978), the results of which made plausible the possibility that they arise
from independent simultaneous labeling events in contiguous precursors of R and SP cells. Thus, dividing cells during the third instar
might well be segregated in different lineages. The data from clonal
analysis do not indicate further segregation among R1–6 cells; their
final commitment as any one of the R cell classes seems to be exclusively dependent on the position they adopt in a forming ommatidial
cluster, i.e., on the time at which they meet the other cells (Hofbauer
and Campos-Ortega, 1976; Campos-Ortega and Hofbauer, 1977). Nevertheless, there are some indications from those studies that R7 cells
might be segregated from other R cells by means of a differential
mitosis (see also Campos-Ortega *et al.*, 1979).

Finally, it must be emphasized that the interpretation of results
from clonal analysis at the level of resolution of single cells is extremely difficult. On the one hand these conclusions are exclusively
based on statistical considerations, based on the calculation of the
probability of certain events occurring; on the other hand the approach
is naturally vitiated by the fact that we do not have any insight into
the cellular substrate during the time span between irradiation and
histology. Important sources of error, such as X-ray-induced cell death,
modifications of the divisional cycle of anlage cells conditioned by the
irradiation, etc., cannot be satisfactorily controlled (see Nöthiger,

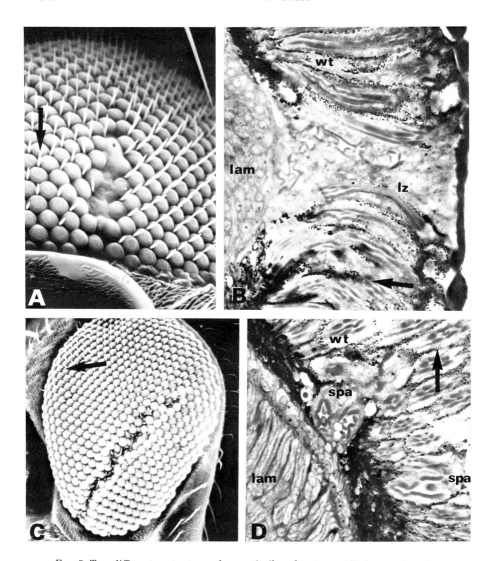

F ɪɢ. 5. Two different mutants produce a similar phenotype. (A) A scanning electron micrograph of a *w lz*^50e homozygous cell clone in a *M(1)o*^Sp/*y w lz*^50e compound eye. In the clone territory bristles are not visible and lenses have been replaced by smooth cuticle. However, cone cells can be distinguished in transmission electron micrographs (not shown). (B) A 2-μm-thick methylene blue-stained section through another *w lz*^50e clone (lz). It shows the pattern abnormalities of R cell assemblies, which have grown beneath the basement membrane of the retina. (C) A scanning electron micrograph of an elongated *w; spa*^pol cell clone in *ywf*^36a/*T(1;4) sc*^H/*spa*^pol compound eye. As in *lz*, lenses are affected in *spa*^pol tissue but, contrary to the previous mutant, bristles are present in the territory of the clone. (D) Two small *w; spa*^pol clones (spa), induced during the second

1972). Thus, an alternative approach to clonal analysis becomes indispensable in order to decide when the ommatidial cells are committed.

VII. Genetic Analysis of Compound Eye Morphogenesis

A genetic analysis of development has the major aim of discovering the functions involved in this process and the way in which these functions interact with each other during development. The strategy followed consists of introducing genetic variations which act during either proliferation or cytodifferentiation and to study their effect upon the developing organ. When mutagenizing wild-type flies we isolate mutant phenotypes and identify simultaneously loci in the genome that are necessary for normal morphogenesis. Further study of the development of those mutants allows inferences about genetically controlled functions relevant for morphogenesis; for instance, recognition properties of grouping cells, spatial polarity, cell growth, etc. In *Drosophila* many mutant functions have been found to have deleterious or lethal effects on the entire animal but also to be capable of cellular expression when the mutant genes are homozygous only in a cell clone (Ripoll and Garcia-Bellido, 1973). Most of those genes, which are lethal for the animal but viable in clones, give rise to morphological abnormalities during the development of homozygous cells. For this reason, in order to make lethal genes accessible to analysis, we study mutant gene expression in cell clones by inducing mitotic recombination in heterozygous animals at different developmental stages (see Ferrus and Garcia-Bellido, 1976).

The greatest difficulty in the analysis of mutants is the assessment of the cellular focus of mutant gene functions, i.e., of the cell autonomy of phenotypic expression, since primary defects in any one of the cell types may secondarily affect the normal morphogenesis of the remaining cells. For example, a mutant phenotype which is commonly encountered in the eye is distortion of the hexagonal arrangement of lenses, which gives a rough appearance to the outer surface of the eye. Histologically, roughening always reflects irregularities of the ommatidial assembly. These irregularities can be manifold, for example, when the ommatidia lack some cells, or when the assemblage or the growth of the cells is impaired in any way. Among the mutant alleles affecting the cell assembly, several (lz^{50e}, spa^{pol}, $l(2)ff10$) have peculiar effects on R cells, such as forming rhabdomeres beneath the basement membrane of

---

instar of larvae of the same gentoype as in (C). The effect of spa^{pol} upon R cells is comparable to that of lz. See text for further discussion. The arrows point to anterior. wt, wild-type tissue in mosaic eyes; lam, lamina ganglionaris.

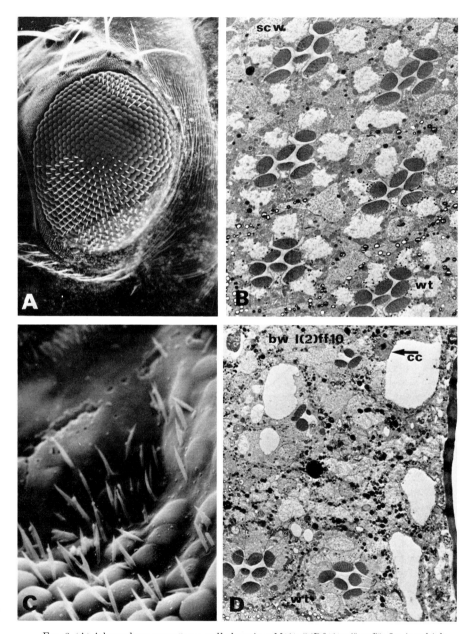

F<small>IG</small>. 6. (A) A large homozygous *sc* cell clone in a *M(1)o^{Sp}/Df(1)sc¹⁹, wf^{36a}* fly, in which bristles are missing. The remaining cells, however, are not affected. (B) An example of another mosaic eye from the boundary between wild-type (wt) and *sc w* tissue, demonstrating the normality of R and secondary pigment cells. (C) A scanning electron micro-

the retina, within the territory of the lamina; thus, either growth or stretching of R cells may be affected in those mutants (see Fig. 5). However, this phenotype is attained in a different manner in each mutant (unpublished observations). lz^{50e} seems to act during the proliferative phase of eye cells since the mutant phenotype cannot be uncovered anymore when homozygosis is induced in cells during the third instar. This phenomenon, called perdurance of wild-type function (Garcia-Bellido and Merriam, 1971), indicates that sufficient amounts of the gene product of lz^{50e+} may be present in heterozygous $w\ lz^{50e}/ +\ +$ cells to last for two or three mitoses. Despite the homozygous lz^{50e} genotype of clone cells after recombination, they differentiate as wildtype cells. spa^{pol}, on the other hand, seems to affect ommatidial growth. The phenotype of spa^{pol} apparently has a nonautonomous component which is not yet understood; clones of spa^{pol} cells in $y\ w\ f^{36a}/T(1;4)sc^H/$ spa^{pol} animals show mutant cells with a wild-type phenotype at the clone margins. Finally the R cell phenotype of $l(2)ff10$ is apparently secondary to the impairment of cone cells by the mutant gene (see the following): at the boundary of $l(2)ff10\ bw$ homozygous cells there is a correlation between the absence of cone cells in mosaic ommatidia and the abnormalities of R cells (Fig. 6D). The most plausible explanation for the R cell phenotype of $l(2)ff10$ clones is that R cells need cone cells for normal morphogenesis, being affected when the cone cells are absent. Therefore, three different genes produce a similar phenotype acting at different times during development, and affecting different functions.

One possible function which may be affected by mutation is the one responsible for differential gene activity. Irrespective of the time at which this process is initiated in the cell history, either in cells still able to divide or in postmitotic cells, mutation in one of those genes should affect one of the different cell types. One expected phenotype should be the nonformation of a given cell type, for example, of R cells or of cone cells. The phenocritical period of gene expression is important in deciding between those functions which are required during the proliferative phase of development and those which act on the grouping

---

graph from the boundary between wild-type tissue and a $bwl(2)ff10$ homozygous cell clone in a $cn\ bw\ l(2)ff10/Df(2R)33aM(2)c$ (location of $l(2)ff10$ within the right arm of the second chromosome is not yet definitively established). The clone territory lacks lenses, whereas bristles are present. (D) From the boundary between wild-type (wt) and $bw\ l(2)ff10$ tissue showing the smooth cuticle at the right-hand side, the distortion of R cells, which are chiefly beneath the basement membrane (not seen), and the lack of cone cells. R cells present within the clone territory are from the clone margins and can be correlated with existing cone cells in mosaic ommatidia (cc). See text.

process or on cytodifferentiation. We are currently analyzing four mutant genes which specifically eliminate different cell types.

Developing bristles have fixed cell lineages (Lees and Waddington, 1942; Peters, 1965). Precursor cells undergo two differential mitoses giving rise to the four bristle cells, i.e., trichogen, tormogen, neuronal, and glial cells. One gene complex, achaete-scute, has been shown to be necessary for the normal development of bristles in head, thorax, and abdomen (Garcia-Bellido and Santamaria, 1978). Consequently the phenotype of the amorphic condition, that of the deficiency of the *sc* locus, is the elimination of all bristles within the mutant tissue. Furthermore, the *sc*⁺ function is apparently required by dividing precursor cells, since there is perdurance of wild-type function lasting for a few mitoses during the third instar. sc^+ has been found to be required by developing eye cells as well, where *sc* exclusively affects bristle formation (Jürgens and Campos-Ortega, unpublished; Fig. 6A and B). Thus sc^+ might be involved, among others, in the process of differential gene activity which, in the bristle cells, seems to be accomplished before they have finished dividing.

Benzer and co-workers (Harris *et al.*, 1976) recovered a mutant called sevenless that has ommatidia with only seven R cells. We have recently studied the development of the *sev* compound eye and found that the gene expresses itself only in R7 cells (Campos-Ortega *et al.*, 1979; see Fig. 7). There is no evidence from our analysis that the *sev* function affects any cytodifferentiation process; it seems rather that presumptive R7 cells either do not form or do not take part in developing R cell clusters. A perdurance analysis of sev^+ function indicated that this function may be required by dividing precursor cells to produce the pattern element R7.

Two further mutants, *l(2)ff225* and *l(2)ff10,* have been isolated in my laboratory by Robert Ransom, and Gerd Jürgens is currently studying their effect upon compound eye development. Both are recessive lethals, or are closely associated with a lethal, but survive in clones of homozygous cells. Two alleles at the same locus, *l(2)ff40* and *l(2)ff225,* producing a similar phenotype although with somewhat different expressivity, have been recovered by Robert Ransom. The majority of ommatidia in *l(2)ff225* cells clones are lacking three R cells which, according to the characteristics of the other R cells, should be the equatorial cells R1, R6, and R7. The remaining ommatidia in *l(2)ff225* (see Fig. 8), or those from *l(2)ff40* clones, lack only one or two cells, which might be any of the R1, R6, and R7 cells. Thus, we have tentatively named this locus *equatorialless (eql)*. The mutants were initially recovered after mutagenesis with EMS (Lewis and Bacher, 1968) of *cn*

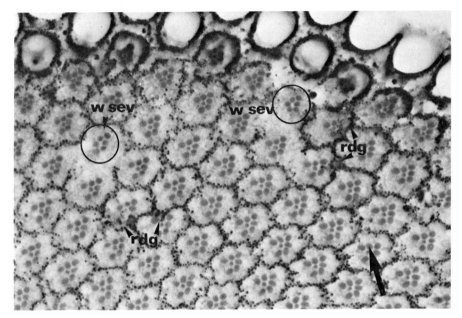

FIG. 7. Two small *w sev* =*rdgB* twin-spots induced during the second instar in *w sev* +/+ + *rdgB*^{EE170} larvae. *sev* ommatidia are encircled in each *w* twin. Irradiations during the third instar failed to uncover the *sev* phenotype in R7 cells. Arrow points to anterior.

bw chromosomes. Preliminary results, using $\widehat{XX}$, *y w f*^{36a}; *Dp(1;2)w*$^{76f5+}$/*cn bw l(2)ff225* flies, show that the mutant phenotype cannot be uncovered when homozygosis is initiated between 0 and 48 hours before puparium formation. Thus, it might be that the *l(2)ff225*$^+$ gene function is being required by dividing cells to produce the pattern elements R1, R6, and R7.

The phenotype of *l(2)ff10* is more complex. As mentioned, it may primarily affect cone cells, which are absent from the clone territory; consequent to this lack of cone cells the lenses do not form and their place is occupied by smooth cuticle containing bristles. All remaining ommatidial constituents are present although strongly modified, probably secondarily to the absence of cone cells (see Fig. 6D). However, the ascertainment of the primary focus of phenotypic expression in *l(2)ff10* cell clones, either in cone cells or in cone and R cells, is not yet possible since there is no reliable marker for cone cells at the present time. Nevertheless, the mutant phenotype cannot be made evident in R cells, labeled with *w* in $\widehat{XX}$, *ywf*^{36a}; *Dp(1;2)w*$^{51b7+}$/*cn bw l(2)ff10* flies, when mitotic recombination is induced 0–48 hours before pupariation.

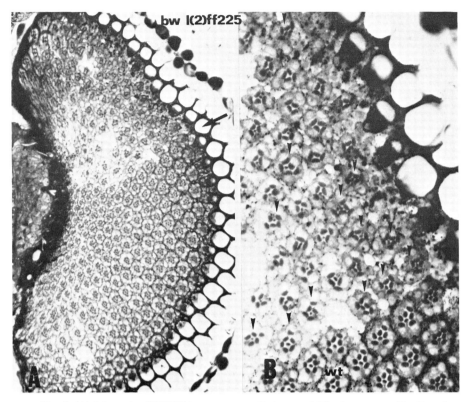

Fig. 8. (A) A large *bw l(2)ff225* homozygous cell clone and (B) a large magnification of the clone area. The arrow in (A) points to clone boundary. The phenotype of this mutant consists of the absence of some R cells in mutant ommatidia. According to the pattern formed by the remaining R cells, the missing elements are equatorial cells R1, R6, and R7 (B). However, the expression of the mutant phenotype varies slightly from one ommatidium to another. Arrowheads in (B) point to ommatidia maximally lacking two cells while the remaining are strictly *equatorialless,* i.e., lacking R1, R6, and R7. Clones of *l(2)ff225* labeled with *w* in $\widehat{XX}$, *ywf; Dp(1;2)w$^{76/5+}$ /cn bw l(2)ff225* (not shown) demonstrate that these phenotypic differences are, in fact, due to incomplete expression rather than to migration of wild-type cells into the clone territory. wt, wild-type tissue. Anterior is at the right-hand side.

Therefore, the gene product of $l(2)ff10^+$ seems to be present in sufficient amounts in homozygous mutant cells to allow their normal development.

These four genes, *sc, sev, l(2)ff225,* and *l(2)ff10,* have been found to specifically affect particular cell types in the compound eye and to act during the proliferative phase of development rather than at cytodifferentiation. Further analysis will show whether they are involved in the process of cell determination.

VIII. Concluding Remarks

This chapter has necessarily turned out to be an inventory of what we know about compound eye development. I have actually tried to present results rather than—obviously premature—speculations and, since the results are still insufficient, there is no way of venturing a model on compound eye morphogenesis in *Drosophila* at this time.

Clonal analysis, combined with histology and [³H]thymidine autoradiography of discs and eyes, has demonstrated its efficiency as an experimental method for the investigation at the cellular level of compound eye morphogenesis. However, we do not yet have a complete description of events normally occurring during eye development, i.e., of the first of the three requirements considered in Section I to be prerequisites for understanding morphogenesis. In fact, cell lineage analysis has been brought in some cases above its level of resolution and many questions have remained either unsatisfactorily answered or not answered at all. Problems still to be solved involve the correspondence of developmental restriction lines in the eye and boundaries of developmental compartments in the thorax, and, still requiring further confirmation with a different technique, late cell lineages, i.e., when determination of ommatidial cells takes place during development. I am convinced that the analysis of the development of appropriate mutants will be helpful in clarifying these two points. This work is already in progress, and some preliminary results have been presented here.

Concerning knowledge of both morphogenetically relevant functions and the genes that code for those functions, we are still at the very beginning of a long process. Fortunately the subject seems to have become straightforward, with an apparently clear strategy: more mutagenesis work is necessary, with the aim of cataloguing morphogenetic mutants on the basis of their cell phenotype, eventually followed by analysis of the development of those mutants.

ACKNOWLEDGMENTS

I would like to thank Sigried Krien for continuous assistance during the realization of the work presented here. Most of the experiments related in this article arose from discussions with Alois Hofbauer and Gerd Jürgens, who also gave me permission to quote some of their unpublished results and critically read previous versions of the paper. The research of my group has been supported by grants of the Deutsche Forschungsgemeinschaft (SFB 46).

NOTE ADDED IN PROOF

Experiments recently reported by Lawrence and Green (1979) appear to rule out fixed cell lineages as the mechanism responsible for ommatidial cell diversity in *Drosophila*. These authors have used mitotic recombination within the white locus of larvae trans-heterozygous for two different *w* alleles to label clone cells with pigment grains. This method considerably facilitates the identification of genealogically linked cells and eliminates some of the technical difficulties encountered when using the conventional method of clonal analysis described in this chapter. Therefore, the best existing experimental evidence emphasizes the importance of spatial mechanisms in the determination of ommatidial cells and does not support the hypothesis of segregating mitoses within the developing eye imaginal disc. (See Lawrence, P. A., and Green, S. M. (1979). *Dev. Biol.* **71**, 142–152.)

REFERENCES

Baker, W. K. (1977). *Dev. Biol.* **62**, 447–463.

Becker, H. J. (1957). *Z. Indukt. Abstamm. Vererbungs l.* **88**, 333–373.

Becker, H. J. (1966). *In* "Current Topics in Developmental Biology" (A. A. Moscona and A. Monroy, eds.), Vol. 1, pp. 155–171. Academic Press, New York.

Becker, H. J. (1976). *In* "The Genetics and Biology in *Drosophila*" (M. Ashburner and E. Novitski, eds.), Vol. 1c, pp. 1019–1087. Academic Press, New York.

Benzer, S. (1971). *J. Am. Med. Assoc.* **218**, 1015–1022.

Benzer, S. (1973). *Sci. Am.* **229**, (12), 24–37.

Bodenstein, D. (1938). *Wilhelm Roux Arch. Entwicklungs. Org.* **137**, 475–505.

Bodenstein, D., and Schweizer, P. (1975). *Proc. Natl. Acad. Sci. U.S.A.* **72**, 4674–4678.

Campos-Ortega, J. A., and Gateff, E. A. (1976). *Wilhelm Roux Arch.* **179**, 373–392.

Campos-Ortega, J. A., and Hofbauer, A. (1977). *Wilhelm Roux Arch.* **181**, 227–245.

Campos-Ortega, J. A., and Waitz, M. (1978). *Wilhelm Roux Arch.* **184**, 155–170.

Campos-Ortega, J. A., Jürgens, G., and Hofbauer, A. (1978a). *Nature (London)* **274**, 584–586.

Campos-Ortega, J. A., Jürgens, G., and Hofbauer, A. (1979). *Wilhelm Roux Arch.* **186**, 27–50.

Crick, F. H. C., and Lawrence, P. A. (1975). *Science* **189**, 340–347.

Dietrich, W. (1909) *Z. Wiss. Zool.* **92**, 465–539.

Egelhaaf, A., Berndt, P., and Küthe, H. -W. (1975). *Wilhelm Roux Arch.* **178**, 185–202.

Ephrussi, B., and Beadle, G. W. (1936). *Am. Nat.* **70**, 218–225.

Ferrus, A. (1975). *Genetics* **79**, 589–599.

Ferrus, A., and Garcia-Bellido, A. (1976). *Nature (London)* **260**, 425–426.

Franceschini, N., and Kirschfeld, K. (1971). *Kybernetik* **8**, 1–13.

Garcia-Bellido, A. (1975). *In* "Cell Patterning," 29th Ciba Symposium, pp. 161–178. Elsevier, Amsterdam.

Garcia-Bellido, A. (1977). *Am. Zool.* **17**, 613–629.

Garcia-Bellido, A., and Capdevila, M. P. (1978). *In* "The Clonal Basis of Development" (S. Subtelny and I. M. Sussex, eds.), pp. 3–21. Academic Press, New York.

Garcia-Bellido, A., and Merriam, J. R. (1971). *Proc. Natl. Acad. Sci. U.S.A.* **68**, 2222–2226.

Garcia-Bellido, A., and Ripoll, P. (1978). *In* "Results and Problems in Cell Differentiation" (W. Gehring, ed.). Springer-Verlag, Berlin and New York.

Garcia-Bellido, A., and Santamaria, P. (1978). *Genetics* **88**, 469–486.

Garica-Bellido, A., Ripoll, P., and Morata, G. (1973). *Nature (London) New Biol.* **245**, 251–253.

Gateff, E. A., and Schneiderman, H. A. (1975). *Wilhelm Roux Arch.* **176**, 171–189.

Gehring, W. (1966). *J. Embryol. Exp. Morphol.* **15**, 77–111.

Harris, W. A., Stark, W. S., and Walker, J. A. (1976). *J. Physiol. (London)* **256**, 415–439.

Hofbauer, A., and Campos-Ortega, J. A. (1976). *Wilhelm Roux Arch.* **179**, 275–289.

Lees, A. D., and Waddington, C. H. (1942). *Proc. R. Soc. B* **131**, 87–110.

Lewis, E. B., and Bacher, F. (1968). *Drosophila Inf. Serv.* **43**, 193.

Lindsley, D. L., and Grell, E. H. (1968). "Genetic Variations of *Drosophila melanogaster*." Carnegie Institution of Washington, Washington, D.C.

Madhavan, M. M., and Schneiderman, H. A. (1978). *Wilhelm Roux Arch.* **183**, 269–305.

Mindek, G., and Nöthiger, R. (1973). *J. Insect. Physiol.* **19**, 1711–1720.

Morata, G., and Lawrence, P. A. (1975). *Nature (London)* **255**, 614–617.

Morata, G., and Ripoll, P. (1975). *Dev. Biol.* **42**, 211–216.

Nöthiger, R. (1972). *In* "Results and Problems in Cell Differentiation" (H. Ursprung and R. Nöthiger, eds.), Vol. 5, pp. 1–34. Springer-Verlag, Berlin and New York.

Nöthiger, R. (1976). *In* "Insect Development" (P. A. Lawrence, ed.), pp. 109–117. Blackwell, London.

Ouweneel, W. J. (1970). *Wilhelm Roux Arch. Entwicklungsm. Org.* **166**, 76–88.

Pak, W. L., and Grabowski, S. R. (1978). *In* "The Genetics and Biology of *Drosophila*" (M. Ashburner and T. R. F. Wright, eds.), Vol. 2a, pp. 553–604. Academic Press, New York.

Perry, M. M. (1968). *J. Morphol.* **124**, 249–262.

Peters, W. (1965). *Z. Morphol. Ökol. Tiere* **55**, 259–320.

Poulson, D. F. (1950). *In* "Biology of *Drosophila*" (M. Demerec, ed.), pp. 168–274. Wiley, New York.

Ready, D. F., Hanson, T. E., and Benzer, S. (1976). *Dev. Biol.* **53**, 217–240.

Ripoll, P., and Garcia-Bellido, A. (1973). *Nature (London) New Biol.* **241**, 15–16.

Sidman, R. L. (1970) *In* "Contemporary Research Methods in Neuranatomy" (W. J. H. Nauta and S. O. E. Ebbesson, eds.), pp. 252–274. Springer-Verlag, Berlin and New York.

Spreij, T. E., and Oldenhave, M., (1974). *Neth. J. Zool.* **24**, 291–310.

Stern, C. (1936). *Genetics* **21**, 625–730.

Trujillo-Cénoz, O., and Melamed, J. (1973). *J. Ultrastruct. Res.* **42**, 554–581.

Trujillo-Cénoz, O., and Melamed, J. (1978). *J. Ultrastruct. Res.* **64**, 46–62.

Vogt, M. (1946). *Biol. Zbl.* **65**, 223–238.

Waddington, C. H., and Perry, M. M. (1960). *Phil. Trans. R. Soc. London B* **153**, 155–178.

Wieschaus, E. (1978). *In* "Results and Problems in Cell Differentiation" (W. Gehring, ed.), Vol. 9, pp- 97–118. Springer-Verlag, Berlin and New York.

CHAPTER 11

EARLY ORGANIZATION OF THE CENTRAL NERVOUS SYSTEM: FORM AND PATTERN

Jonathan Cooke

DIVISION OF DEVELOPMENTAL BIOLOGY
NATIONAL INSTITUTE FOR MEDICAL RESEARCH
MILL HILL, LONDON, ENGLAND

I. Introduction 373
II. The Spatial Pattern of Brain Parts: Field Properties in the
    Plane of the Primitive Neuroepithelium/Inducing Mesoderm 376
    A. Cell Layer of Origin and Early Decline of Field Properties 376
    B. Field Phenomena in the Neural Plate 378
    C. Forces for Morphogenesis: Shape Change in Plate and Tube 380
    D. Theories for Field Organization 385
III. The Radial (Ependymal→Pial) Structure within Brain Parts: Cell
    Birthday and Organization over the Primitive Epithelium 392
    A. Organization of the Cell Cycle and Cell Birthdays 392
    B. Contrasting Models for the Origin of Neuron Types 397
    C. The Causes of Radial Position and Local Synaptic Relationships
       among Neuron Classes 398
IV. Fiber Tracts: The Plan of Connectivity between Centers 399
    A. Tissue Polarity as a Local Guidance Factor, versus Specific
       Chemotropisms, in Axon and Tract Development 399
    B. The Need to Consider Growth, Morphogenesis, and Timing
       in Evaluating Models 401
    C. Tracts and the Organized Projections between Centers:
       Remarks on the Retinotectal Pathway as a Model System 402
    References 404

I. Introduction

Immediately following primary embryonic induction (see Saxén, this volume), the future central nervous system (CNS) is a pear-shaped area of columnar or pseudostratified epithelium committed to neural development (Spemann and Mangold, 1924), although some further spatial organization may be achieved almost immediately (Waddington and Deuchar, 1952; Nieuwkoop, 1967a,b; Leussink, 1970). Subsequently developed features of the gross architectural organization of the CNS, whose study can be said strictly to be part of developmental biology, are the following: anatomical regions with well-defined shapes, arranged in a particular spatial sequence, and defined by the

373

CURRENT TOPICS IN
DEVELOPMENTAL BIOLOGY, Vol. 15

histological and connectivity arrangements of classes of neurons within them; a system of fiber tracts whereby the axonal output from particular populations of neurons within each center makes functional connections only with certain neuron populations in certain other such centers; and, finally, an organization whereby, independently of mature neuronal function, sensory experience, or behavior, a certain mapping relationship (i.e., "topicity") has been achieved between the positions of output cells within their population in one center and the positions of the cells in the corresponding input population, elsewhere, which specifically receive their axonal terminals.

The aim of this article is to survey the classes of processes which must occur to bring the newly induced neural plate to this final organization, leaving aside the further shaping influence of function-dependent maturation and plasticity.

The last-mentioned aspect of brain development is achieved via the phenomenon usually known as neuronal specificity (Sperry, 1965) or neuronal locus specificity (Hunt and Jacobson, 1974) although these could be misleading terms in relation to ultimate biological mechanisms. In a sense, it forms a bridge between truly embryological inquiry and inquiry into plasticity and functional maturation because, while many systems of neuronal mappings between brain centers give evidence of being able to develop in the absence of neural activity patterned by experience and behavior (e.g., Chung et al., 1973), other systems displaying comparable spatial selectivity of connections are indeed dependent on function for their completion (e.g., Keating, 1976; Blakemore and Mitchell, 1973). This spectrum may represent two ends of a continuum, sharing mechanisms, but on the other hand may involve two separate levels of nervous system development altogether (see Jacobson, 1970). Embryological aspects of topicity, or formation of nerve projections between centers, are fully reviewed elsewhere (cf. Gaze, Volume 17, this series) and will be dealt with here only as necessary for my overall aim.

As will be seen, the earlier the spatial interactions underlying pattern that we are enquiring into, the less we understand. Brain development considered as a basic problem in biological pattern formation is an exciting field of inquiry indeed, but the fact is that as yet we know little or nothing of the most fundamental modes of intercellular communication, whose existence it is necessary to postulate in order to explain the facts about biogenesis of spatial patterns (Waddington, 1956; Wolpert, 1971; Cooke, 1975).

This is not a comprehensive review. In instances in which several experimental studies have concurred in supporting a generalization, the references cited are samples of the consensus, even if apparent counterexamples exist. I have tried to make clear any areas of substantial controversy that affect the tenability of a model being discussed.

The object of the exercise has been to compile, from an experimental embryologist's point of view, a list of the phenomena that ultimately will have to be accounted for in any adequate understanding of each aspect of neurogenesis discussed. The aspects being considered are each depicted in a schematic way, keyed to relevant text sections, as parts of the composite diagram of nervous system organization that forms Fig. 1.

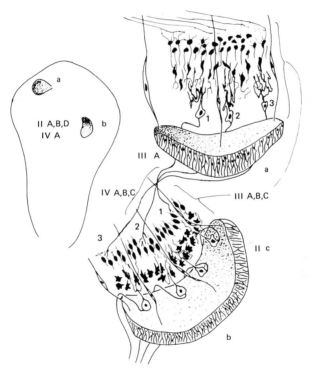

Fig. 1. Positions of territories becoming determined as two brain centers (a and b) within the pattern of the primary epithelium are marked with the outline of the neural plate (Section II). Form-building movements (Section II, C) continue from this time into the period of neuron birth, when the two ependymal areas are shown with the radial structure that is subsequently built up over them (Section III). Large cells in (a) send axons via a tract to (b), the organization of the tract including topicity of representation (selective connections, e.g., 1, 2, 3) of (a) upon (b) as part of the developmental program (Section IV). Density of stippling, parallel to the epithelial plane, represents the typical feature of gradation in timing of the events (Section III) across centers. The ependymal epithelium is shown as if in a primitive condition, though the radial neuronal structure is shown as completed.

II. The Spatial Pattern of Brain Parts: Field Properties in the Plane of the Primitive Neuroepithelium/Inducing Mesoderm

A. CELL LAYER OF ORIGIN AND EARLY DECLINE OF FIELD PROPERTIES

Saxén (this volume), Toivonen *et al.* (1978), and Nieuwkoop (1967a,b) have reviewed current ideas concerning inductive signals, passing from dorsal embryonic mesoderm into overlying ectoderm during the latter part of the cell movements known as gastrulation, which cause the definitive switch in the latter cell layer from the developmental pathway leading to epidermis into those giving rise to various parts of the central nervous system. Most work has been done on amphibians, since the classic work of Spemann and Mangold (1924, reviewed in Spemann, 1938) and of Holtfreter (1933), which established that in whole embryos the neural plate came into existence within the primitive ectodermal layer only as a result of its becoming underlain by the immigrating mesoderm, the pattern for development of other axial structures of the body meanwhile becoming autonomously determined and stabilized within the latter. The fundamental organization of development at this time has not been found to differ greatly in other vertebrate groups. More recently, there have been suggestions that a prepatterned bias toward development of various nervous system structures may already exist across early gastrula ectoderm (Barth, 1941); however, these may reflect more the hair-trigger nature of the ectodermal competence to be switched into neural development, which can be activated by a variety of changes in balance of the cellular milieu, other than those whose reliable presence and spatial patterning evokes the CNS during normal development (e.g., Barth and Barth, 1959, 1962, 1969).

Reference to the above-cited reviews from the Finnish and Dutch schools reveals that, despite great advances, the cellular organelles and actual molecules involved in normal passage of the inductive signal(s) from dorsal axial mesoderm to ectoderm are still largely unknown. But most important for the questions we are considering is the knowledge that at a very early stage these signals are spatially patterned, roughly along the plane of the two opposed cell layers (see also Waddington and Deuchar, 1952). Only induction caused by anteriormost and first-invaginating mesoderm causes a simple switch toward development of the pseudostratified, generative neural epithelium known subsequently as primitive ependyma in its role throughout the nervous system (see Section III). Without further influence, such ependymal organization seems to lead to development of forebrain derivatives only (archencephalic development, see Kallen, 1965), but very soon, possibly immediately at different mesodermal locations, the relative intensity of one or more modulating signals acts to change the developmental tendencies, locally, within the recently induced ependyma (Leussink, 1970; Toivonen and Saxén, 1968; Nieuwkoop, 1967a,b). Thus as a final result of the movements of gastrulation, and of the expression of an emerging pattern of determinations for various body parts (thus inductive specificities) within itself, the mesoderm may be said to emit a pattern of modulations on the inductive stimulus which goes a long way toward *determining* that each locality within the primitive ependyma shall subsequently give rise to neural organization appropriate to its position within the body.

Now the mesodermal layer is itself a developmental field of a classic type before and during gastrulation, exhibiting, on a massive scale, properties similar to those ascribed to more local regions of the neural plate in Section II, B, whose explanation demands consideration of the types of theories discussed in Section II, D. It is just losing these properties, i.e., the spatial pattern for its own differentiations is becoming determined, during the critical phase of induction and the pattern determination within the plane of the epithelium of the neural plate. The pattern of inductive signals that brings the latter about is presumably a parallel expression of the determined pattern within the mesoderm, since in all observed body patterns both normal and experimentally abnormal, there is close coordination between the CNS pattern and the other (mesodermal) aspects of body pattern (Nieuwkoop, 1967a,b). Thus it is very difficult to assess the extent to which, in its own right, the neural plate ever possesses the dynamic field properties to be discussed in the following section (Böterenbrood, 1970; Källen, 1953, 1956, 1965). Many of the graft translocation experiments followed by "regulation" may also be interpreted on the assumption that the primitive nervous system progresses from a defined area of simply neural epithelium to a mosaic of specific locally induced territories, without ever possessing the ability to restore pattern to wholeness or correct for reversals and rearrangements of material. In other words, large scale pattern development, down to the determination of regions within the anatomical pattern of brain parts, may be a passive response and not a dynamic property within the primitive epithelium. Whichever is the case, in the best studied embryos the transition to a largely determined set of territories within the plate follows quite precociously after the latter's initial demarcation from the other ectoderm. Field events progress toward the determination of pattern quite rapidly after the close of gastrulation, whether the site of the field is in dorsal mesoderm, in induced neurectoderm, or in both.

B. Field Phenomena in the Neural Plate

A stimulating review of the kinds of classic finding relevant to this topic can be found in Chapters X and XX of Waddington (1956). An embryonic field is usually said to exist as long as, within a domain whose normal fate is to give rise to a particular part of the final body pattern of an organism (including as a limiting instance the whole body), ablations and rearrangements of the cellular material can lead to certain unknown interactions such that a whole, normally proportioned example of the pattern of differentiated parts subsequently develops. At early stages of development, fields tend to occupy sheets of cells that are fundamentally forming patterns of cellular determinations in the plane of their surfaces, and both neural epithelium and the dorsal-inducing field conform with this. Normal strategy in plotting the decline of field properties has been to determine the *presumptive fate map* of the structure concerned, i.e., to gain knowledge of which cells finally contribute to which part of it in normal undisturbed development, and then to discover to what degree cells can be made to depart from their presumptive fates by translocation within the field, removal into isolation, etc., at various times in early development.

As should be apparent from Section II, A., only translocations and isolations of strictly neural plate or tube material can go toward looking for field dynamics within the primitive CNS itself. Many experiments have rearranged the mesodermal archenteron roof along with the plate, but only those that have left the former *in situ* will be considered. Even so, for all experiments except isolation the appearance of regulation is also consistent with passive acceptance of subsequent signals by a neutral neural epithelium; in addition, matters are complicated by inconsistencies of operating salines and thus of meaningful times for reestablishment of "communication" between rearranged cells, by variations in the speed of development after operations as between different species used, and by fuzzy knowledge of the real contours of fate maps for normal development.

This rather negative assessment of results does not imply that I consider field phenomena in the plane of the primitive epithelium to be only of secondary importance in the genesis of CNS form and pattern. On the contrary they are of fundamental importance (see Section II, D) to a degree insufficiently realized by many of those in pursuit of cellular and molecular models for pattern development. The period over which field properties operate may be brief, and such properties in their dynamic form may exist mainly between mesodermal cells rather than the responding neural ones. But the very brevity of the period of dynamic cell interactions in forming pattern, in relation to certain contemporaneous events in the responding tissue, is of importance in eliminating some candidate models concerning how the spatial pattern is generated (Section II, D, 1).

1. Regulation after Polarity Reversals in Situ

Even when operations rotating mesoderm along with plate itself are excluded (e.g., Sládecek, 1952, 1955) the timing of regional determination within the amphibian neural plate remains unclear. C. -O. Jacobson (1964) reviews previous work in introducing his own extended study in the Axolotl, which indicates that the plate is becoming mosaic with respect to developmental programs just around raised neural fold stages (i.e., well before tube formation). Roach (1945) had reported irreversible regionalization for brain parts at times well before this, however, while Model (1978) found extensive regulatory ability still at fold stages. Differences may be due to varying times taken for significant restoration of cells' capacities to communicate between rotated and surrounding tissue, in view of the varied salines and temperatures used throughout this work. Positive finding of regulatory capacity at any stage must always outweigh negative findings, since it is the more meaningful result. Thus, the best estimate is of progressive regionalization over the middle part of neurulation, the maximum-sized reversal compatible with adaptation diminishing with embryonic stage under any one set of conditions (e.g., Alderman, 1935). There is a pronounced tendency for loss of plasticity in the craniocaudal dimension of pattern to precede that in the mediolateral dimension, and for inclusion of the marginal neural fold material to prejudice regulation as if this were an autonomous, boundary-signaling region. There are some suggestions that mediolateral (i.e., now dorsoventral) organization in the long closed neural tube at spinal cord levels may still regulate to adapt to the surrounding axial tissues (Watterson, 1965; Martin, 1977), though it is questionable whether this involves shape only, and not the functional capacities (motor vs sensory plate) of the neurons produced.

In the writer's hands, cutting and splicing operations on frog CNS from late plate stages on invariably show autonomous development of material according to presumptive fate, on a fine-grained level (Chung and Cooke, 1978; see also Watterson, 1965; Narayanan, 1970). But there is a level of functional specialization within the CNS pattern, beyond that involved in the development of neurons of certain broad connectivity classes, in particular histogenetic arrays. This is the specific modification of the ependymal program involved in the various spinal cord levels of the body plan (brachial, flank, lumbar, etc.). These modifications involve the numbers of neurons produced, perhaps their peripheral connectivity properties, and certainly their capacity to mediate the complex reflex activity involved in locomotion. There is some evidence that such specializations may set in, slowly and progressively, only at morphological stages long after the interactions discussed (Straznicky, 1963, 1967; Straznicky and Székely, 1967; Székely, 1963, 1968).

2. Regulation in Isolated Parts

Waddington (1956) reviewed older data pertinent to this, the most positive test for field character within the early CNS rudiment. It is fair to state that production of a whole CNS pattern by only a part of the early neural plate has never been observed. Whole secondary CNSs after dorsal lip grafting operations must be due to the more complete regulatory interactions possible within the inducing mesodermal layer itself, but before CNS induction ever occurs (Spemann, 1938, see Section II, A). However, there is much evidence from explantation of plate regions into culture or into ectopic, neutral (noninducing) sites on hosts that considerably more of the CNS pattern than that deriving from presumptive fate can be produced [see also Böterenbrood (1970) for work with cell reaggregates].

3. Late Regulation by Cell Division

Until advanced neural tube stages, or later in some amphibians, there is evidence of a certain capacity for the initiation of a prolonged regenerative form of regulation, whereby loss of pattern parts triggers an extra division program in the ependyma, restoring the pattern at a late stage by completion from neighboring territories. Such interactions and replacement are seen between mediolateral levels of the pattern rather than adjacent parts in the rostrocaudal dimension. For simple mechanical reasons it is difficult to test for the more usual, rapid type of regulative interaction after simple ablations; the tissue faces cannot be placed together afterward, so that slow migration (or the special growth mentioned) is the only means of restoring continuity and communication.

C. FORCES FOR MORPHOGENESIS: SHAPE CHANGE IN PLATE AND TUBE

Overall shape and extent of the territory of neurally induced cells forming the plate are presumably derived from a combination of the effective boundaries of the underlying inducing territory, together with the diffusion or other transmission properties of the primary neuralizing signal *within* the responding epithelium. The extent of the

role played by homoiogenetic induction (e.g., Deuchar, 1970—
neuralization of ectoderm in culture, solely by contact with already
neuralized ectoderm) is unknown in delimiting the normal nervous
system. Determination of neural crest cells, occurring distinctively at
the plate margins, presumably represents a particular grade of inductive stimulus, marginal to that causing CNS determination. The subsequent fate of these cells, programmed to wander individually in
search of secondary inductive instructions, is reviewed elsewhere (Le
Douarin, Volume 16, this series).

    We have no reason to assume that the initially determined plate
boundary is of more complex shape than a hemisphere or broad segment of a sphere (C.-O Jacobson, 1962; A. Jacobson and Gordon, 1976).
Its subsequent modification to a keyhole or pear shape in many species,
before its inrolling to form a tube, may be accounted for by relatively
simple combinations of the forces engendered by a tight adhesion with
the median, notochordal strip of mesoderm extending cranially only to
the mid-brain area, plus the generalized dorsal convergence movements of the more lateral strips of mesoderm and columnarization of
their cells (see following) preparatory to somite formation. There is
generally also a great craniocaudal stretching endogenous to the
mesoderm at this time, which has been thought to play a role in ensuring that the autonomous inrolling of the neural plate converts the
latter to a tube rather than to a more highly symmetrical vesicle (e.g.,
C.-O. Jacobson, 1962). Yet while isolated parts of the plate, transferred
to neutral embryonic sites devoid of vigorous stretching movements,
may develop only into vesicles, they equally often develop into tubes.
Such tubes show much specificity and regionalization in their subsequent shape changes. Sometimes, exposure to inappropriate stretch in
isolated early neural plate turned through 90° in the epidermis will
cause it to roll up, tubewise, along its original mediolateral dimension.

    In past decades, models which tended to ascribe much of the early
form-building in the plate to organized forces from the underlying tissues have been replaced by models ascribing more of such form-
building, from earlier stages after induction of the neural territory, to
programmed forces developed within plate and tube itself (see, e.g.,
C.-O. Jacobson, 1962; A. Jacobson, 1976; A. Jacobson and Gordon,
1976; Burnside, 1971; Baker and Schroeder, 1967). The spatially patterned expansions, contractions, and foldings, which are the first ex-
pressions of the pattern of future brain parts not long after the plate
has rolled into a tube, rapidly become too complex for execution by any
but endogenously developed programs of forces. Thus it is safe to conclude that extrinsically generated forces and patterns of adhesion to

other cell layers are important in the earliest phases of form-building. But these are supplemented by programming intrinsic to the plate, as evidenced by the complex sculpted shapes of early neural plates in many frog species and are rapidly replaced altogether by schedules, for development of patterned tensile forces, endogenous to the CNS rudiment itself. It is now being recognized, at an ultrastructural level, that there is a fairly universal repertoire for the development of shape change by individual cells in creating the physical forces that shape the embryo, whether these are then transferred from one cell layer to another or are effective *in situ*.

1. Cellular Activities and Models for Shape Change

During that era in developmental biology in which schedules of cell division were thought to be prime movers of morphogenesis generally, it was once suggested that relative mitotic rate shapes the neural plate and early tube. We now know that this is not so. The normal rate of cell generation, across the time scale over which complex and localized deformations occur, is in any case totally inadequate. Broadly normal early tube and brain shaping (including optic vesicles, etc.) occurs in *Xenopus* when, due to long-term mitotic inhibition since gastrula stages, there has been no increase of cell number since a time preceding neural induction itself (Cooke, 1973). Form-building, which then occurs among a greatly reduced number of abnormally large neural plate cells, is limited only by the restricted capacity for vesicle formation among very few, very large cells. In early vertebrate morphogenesis, experiments indicate that it is less a matter of the cells as individuals, their activities, and what each is performing, than of what is taking place within each region of the total cellular material, considered as a continuum. At the stages dealt with in this section, as opposed to much later "neuronal" stages (Section III), selective cell death would appear to play as small a role in the development of the nervous system as does selective cell division.

The idea of programmed patterns for development of tensile and bending forces within the cell sheet is now supported by investigations of shape change and force generation at the ultrastructural level (Burnside, 1971; Schroeder, 1970; A. Jacobson, 1976; Karfunkel, 1971, 1972). Programs available for production of forces by cells in the plane of an epithelium they compose seem to be as follows. Columnarization, an increase in the ratio of height-to-cross-sectional area adopted by the cells, may occur by increase in the cells' adhesiveness for one another relative to that for the basement membrane. This may initially involve special functions near apical and basal ends of cells, and perhaps a general increase in lateral adhesive forces, but it later appears to be stablized by embodiment in the cytoskeleton as an axial arrangement of microtubules. By such means a "height program," as a specific cellular response to being part of a pattern, can be instituted (A. Jacobson and Gordon, 1976). Another type of response, made by cells at particular key locations in patterns of shape change, is the pursestring-like constriction of their terminal surfaces that are to face a cavity, or lumen, which may be brought into being by the bending forces thus caused (Karfunkel, 1971, 1972; Baker and Schroeder, 1967). This "bottling" of cells seems to be accomplished and stabilized by development of a terminal, tangential microfilamentous apparatus, and there is evidence that such cells maintain their anisodiametric shapes autonomously upon dissociation (e.g., Holtfreter, 1946). Cells that perform "bottling" activity are often very restricted in number and location during any one episode of morphogenesis, as in the longitudinal zones of cells that accompany *Xenopus* tube closure (Schroeder, 1970).

There is little actual displacement of cells' neighborhood relationships within the epithelium throughout the series of deformations that accompany basic shaping of the tube from the plate and the brain from the tube. It is likely that the cell–cell slippage that *is* necessary for the more extreme movements is accompanied by this "bottling" or extreme constriction of the juxtaluminal surfaces of cells. This would fit this mode of cellular activity, as seen early in neurogenesis, together with what is understood of it in the even earlier movements of gastrulation itself. The only other relative cell displacement involved, in ependyma formation from the initial state of neuralized ectoderm, derives from the fact that in many lower vertebrates the ectoderm is a two-layered epithelium, whereas ependyma is in reality a single-layered, columnar epithelium. Observations on *Xenopus* (Schroeder, 1970) suggest that most of the forces are generated within the deep neurectoderm, and that during tube closure cells of the superficial layer literally slide, laterally, over the deep one to be squeezed out from participation in its structure. Some, however, may be incorporated.

Most workers feel that all the bendings, thickenings, and vesicle formation involved in formation of the outline of the brain are explicable in principle by patterned alterations to tensile forces within the plane of the epithelium, and between its two faces, by means of the variegated occurrence of the two cell activities mentioned— columnarization and bottling. It is unclear to what extent the stabilization of altered shapes in individual cells by microtubule arrangement is necessary to the normal, mass movements. Changes of relative cell adhesion, plus tangential contraction involving microfilaments, could be sufficient. Thus concentrations of colcemid that prohibit mitosis sometimes allow almost normal form-building for some time, whereas drugs disrupting the microfilamentous apparatus of cells characteristically stop or even reverse it. However, this could reflect a compartmentalization of microtubulin units—those destined for cytoskeletal roles being less susceptible to colcemid disruption than those for the mitotic apparatus.

Deformations (grooves and bulges in the ependymal wall) that first divide the primitive CNS into forebrain, midbrain, hindbrain, optic vesicles, etc., which occur within periods on the order of 24 hours after neural tube formation, are probably controlled by the patterned forces discussed. Some of these variations in size of the primitive CNS cavity, almost spatially periodic in appearance, have been thought to correspond to an obscure, archetypal segmentation of the nervous system, reflecting the mesodermal metamerism (the neuromeres, see Kallen, 1956, 1965), and to reflect a patterned mitotic rate. However, generation of cells seems highly unlikely to be involved, because of the reported rate of appearance and disappearance of the more transient of these features in relation to mitotic rate in the tube as a whole, and the rate of formation of those (the primitive brain divisions) that are permanent. On the other hand their existence, once brought about by mechanisms akin to those already discussed, might be basic to the establishment of defined regions subsequently coming to be characterized, as part of their individuality, by particular schedules of mitotic rate and neural birthdate (see Kallen, 1965; Kallen and Bergquist, 1954; Watterson, 1965; and Section III, A).

2. Organization of the Spatial Pattern of Form-Building Forces as an Aspect of the Field

It has been assumed that, in the very early nervous system, the balance of forces causing shape change is itself an expression of the spatial pattern whereby cells also become determined as giving rise to defined future structures (Section II, D), and that form-building is organized by the same intercommunication system that is organizing the pattern of cellular differentiations, both being, as the embryologist Waddington would have stated, aspects of one "individuation" field. This is still the simplest view, and is implicit in some of the models cited previously. However, it will be a fascinating exercise to test the soundness of the assumption that the field is indivisible in its effects, as we approach a more molecular understanding of force production among cells on the one hand, and of developmental restriction toward differentiated states on the other. At the cellular level within the neural plate, is determination as to possible fate in pattern formation tantamount to being programmed to undergo a set temporal sequence of the motor/adhesive behaviors discussed in this section? Or are these two aspects of cell cooperation independently controlled (albeit normally in a coordinated way)?

While contributed to by individual cells, the early shaping forces are necessarily transmitted and balanced mechanically, via the effects of many cells. The final outcome of an episode in normal morphogenesis must be an adaptive resultant, from the configuration of programmed tensile forces developed over wide regions. We should thus expect abnormal geometrical configurations to develop in isolates of restricted size even where the latter embodied, at the time of isolation, completely determined but as yet unexpressed cellular programs. Conversely, after *in situ* transpositions of determined neural plate material causing development of defined cells and histological arrangements in abnormal spatial sequence, we might sometimes expect the more global architecture of the CNS developed to be normal. There are observations of both types in the literature (e.g., Böterenbrood, 1970; see C.-O. Jacobson, 1964).

The CNS of some teleost fishes (Miyayama and Fujimoto, 1977) provides an instance in which, during evolution, structures which are obviously homologous may come to be created through programs of cell motor/adhesive activity which on the face of it are different. We are somehow reminded of the capacity for systems of early but determined cells to reconstruct, after dissociation and culture, the histogenetic array that they would have developed *in situ* (Adler, 1970). The teleost CNS is induced as a solid cord derived from deep ectodermal cells, among which cavitation then occurs by a secondary process to give the normal tube lumen.

D. THEORIES FOR FIELD ORGANIZATION

The findings surveyed in Sections II, A and B show that a brief consideration of theories for the control of patterns within cell sheets (i.e., theories concerning the spatial variables and the mode of cellular interpretation of these) is essential for a complete survey of early neural development. Organization for the pattern of CNS regions in the plane of the epithelium occurs across a brief interval in comparison with the prolonged period of neuron generation that follows (Section III), but the determination of a reliable and typical pattern in this plane is fundamental to neurogenesis, whether the cell interactions occur in the neural epithelium itself or in the underlying mesoderm. We have seen that such determination on a broad scale seems to be derived in response to modulated inductive signals from mesoderm which are an expression of the pattern being determined there during the brief period ending gastrulation. We have also seen that the neural plate itself does appear to exhibit classic field properties similar to the preceding ones in pregastrular mesoderm, but over more restricted domains of regulation and for a briefer interval following its induction from the ectoderm.

Embryonic fields are characterized as populations of interacting cells (usually in the form of a sheet) such that, over periods of a few hours before progression to the determined, mosaic state, rearrangements within them can be compensated for to give a normal pattern by adjustments of the cells' fates. Key articles discussing theories and models for genesis of this type of spatial organization include Wolpert (1971)—the concept of positional information; Lewis and Wolpert (1976)—the principle of nonequivalence for cells in different regions of patterns; Zeeman (1974) and Kauffman *et al.* (1978)—who introduce a theory concerning cell-switching and determination into a distinctive theory of spatial organization; and Cooke (1975)—for a general description of field phenomena and a critique of models for fields. Any of these models may prove relevant to our future understanding of the dynamics underlying organization within the plane of the primitive epithelium in neurogenesis. But one aspect of this problem about which even now there is something positive and observational to say concerns not the unknown spatial variables, but the biology of the cellular response in determination.

1. Inappropriateness of Cell Lineage Theory

One frequently encounters the idea that, in early development, a relatively highly determined cell (in terms of possible contribution to the final body structure) may be derived from a relatively less determined one only *via* one or more cell divisions; that the restrictive, switching event whereby the possible pathways open to a cell's progeny become fewer is always a correlate of cell division or at least of genome replication. It leads to the idea that pattern formation might be the consequence solely of organized cell lineage. This notion is distinct from the experimentally well-substantiated notion that particular states of developmental restriction are rather stably heritable. Such cell lineage theory may have validity for development of certain systems at certain phases, e.g., the blood-forming tissues or even the aspect of CNS organization to be discussed in Section III, but for the type of early pattern formation being considered here it can probably be discounted. This can be illustrated by reference to the neural plate.

Although regional differences in the incidence of mitosis set in soon after primary induction (Cooke, unpublished data) and cell cycle time may decrease in comparison with surrounding ectoderm (Maleyvar and Lowery, 1973), the cells are randomly phased with respect to the cycle. Mean cell cycle time, though roughly tuned to the developmental rate as a whole across a variety of amphibian species, is long enough to span the entire development of the plate from the first inductive signal establishing a neural pathway of development, to the onset of a highly mosaic condition in the raised neural fold stage. The situation is at its most extreme in urodeles (Gillette, 1944) with their slow cell cycle. Even if the multiple subdivision (according to position) of the developmental possibilities for primitive neural cells occurred in one round of restriction events, this gives two such events in series, ectoderm → neural and neural → brain region, to fit into a period during which not all cells will have divided even once. If as is more likely (see, e.g., Kauffman *et al.*, 1978) successive restriction events in pattern formation are binary choices only, correspondingly more such events must be accommodated during the stated period to account for the complexity of mosaicism observed (e.g., Chung and Cooke, 1978; C.-O. Jacobson, 1964). The lack of significant cell death, or generation of postmitotic cells, or translational movement of individual cells within the plate, leaves no room for theories of selective cell death and selective geographical aggregation, etc., in genesis of the pattern of determinations. Whatever the nature of the spatial variables "read" by cells at each location, we are faced with the fact that cells effectively become highly restricted, with time, in a way that bears little relation to the passage of cell generations.

A striking instance of the slow tempo of the cell cycle in relation to developmental events occurs in the work of Vargas-Lizardi and Lyer (1974), though their own conclusions from their data seem oddly drawn. After ^{3}H labeling of *Xenopus* embryos, to establish the timing of final DNA replication among precursors of neurons examined in the larval CNS, they find that the mother cell destined to give rise to the unique Mauthner's neuron has always ceased DNA synthesis permanently by stage $11\frac{1}{2}$ during gastrulation. At this stage, few if any cells have been switched into neural development, and the CNS has not yet been defined within the primitive ectoderm. Neural plate grafting experiments (C.-O. Jacobson, 1964; Model, 1978) in comparable organisms make it very unlikely that a cell is picked out as *the* Mauthner's neuron before mid-neural plate stages, more than 4 hours after stage $11\frac{1}{2}$ in this species. Thus although the authors' interpretation would have the Mauthner's cell "determined" before determination of the nervous system's location within the organism, what has been discovered is that the chromosomes of the cell finally chosen for determination have never been in DNA synthesis within less than 4 hours of that determination event. Since we have no reason to assume that it is an atypical cell before determination, neural plate cell cycles of 6, 8, or more hours are indicated as normal (in line with some other data). Over such a time, the CNS in *Xenopus* certainly proceeds from initial induction to a state of quite fine-grained determination. We must assume that, as one particular event in that process, a G_1 cell is set aside and prohibited from reentering the cycle, to form Mauthner's cell.

The criterion for mosaicism at neural fold stages is autonomy of pattern development by (small) transposed groups of cells. We are unable to assert that single cells, repositioned, would never alter fate in adaptation to new neighbors. But small groups, of 100 cells or less, can by these stages maintain permanently either the microenvironments or the intracellular states which have determined their fates. It is many hours, or days in some embryos, before these fates are further expressed in development. What has just been asserted about lack of correspondence between effective *determination* and the cell cycle is quite separate from the proposition that many determined precursor cells go on to *express* their programs through cell divisions, often quite a long series of them. That the latter proposition is very plausible for neural development will be emphasized, it is hoped, in Section III.

2. *Positional Information, Threshold, and Wave Theory*

In the absence of any molecular knowledge that ties in with what is known of other aspects of cell organization, discussion of highly formalized and speculative theories for fundamental pattern formation may seem fatuous. But such a theoretical enterprise has helped to dissect the logical possibilities for organization of this aspect of development and to focus attention on the types of experimental approaches which should most quickly lead to some real knowledge. It is worth charting this territory, unfamiliar to most students of neurobiology, for two reasons. We have already seen that true embryonic fields, which positional information and allied theories were developed to describe, are central to early neurogenesis. Moreover, a basic advance in understanding of pattern formation might as likely come from work on the CNS rudiment as from any of the other complex systems currently being studied. According to positional information theory the problem is analyzable into two aspects, sharply distinguished from one another in the most straightforward models, and again allowed to interact subtly in later theories. These aspects are, respectively, the system of graded variables that signal a cell's relative position in the array (or field), and an intracellular interpretation mechanism whereby perceived values of these variables cause determination of the cell as contributing to a particular part of the pattern (expressing a given program of divisions, differentiated types of progeny, timing of activities, etc.).

The signal variables are sometimes believed to be literal gradients, in some simple parameter such as concentrations of particular substances, with cells at "reference" positions specified to maintain distinct boundary concentrations while the remaining cells participate in a communication system that maintains the gradation of signal value by processes akin to averaging (e.g., a diffusion gradient). This model does emerge naturally from known phenomena; of "organizer" regions in fields (prespecified "boundary" source or sink cells), the capacity to adjust and form normal pattern sequence and proportions after deletion or internal rearrangement of cells (diffusional flow or averaging interactions), and the "rule of continuity" whereby after operations rearranging material, pattern parts always become determined in normal spatial order, without *omissions,* across the site of operation. However, there are alternative models for spatially graded variables that the cells interpret, which would give much the same phenomenology. Examples are oscillatory, propagated signals with progressive phase shift away from pacemaker (organizer) regions, sets of labile surface markers coding for cell position with respect to which cells interact dynamically, and diffusion–reaction systems involving interactive cross-activation and cross-inhibition of synthesis of signal substances. What all these have in common is that prior to any interpretative commitment by cells, geometrical disturbance is always followed by restoration of a normal profile of spatial variables, scaled to the available extent of the field. At this point it is worth noting that the vertebrate mesoderm and overlying CNS will form normal whole patterns from experimentally small initial cell populations, as well as perform the types of regulation described in Section II, B.

There are various models for the intracellular interpretative mechanisms, whereby variables in simple spatial configurations might be used in the formation of a mosaic of differentiated states. They are of interest in that refinements of the kinds of rearrangement experiments discussed in Section II, B, especially in conjunction with chimerism for genetic markers (see Section II, D, 3), may help unravel the structure of cellular decision making. Are restriction decisions in pattern formation within the plate sequential binary ones, multichoice all at once, or something less definite than either of these? Originally, positional information models assumed that various threshold levels of the signal variables might activate a succession of switches, or unstable feedback loops, to bring about a series of finally stable cell states which coded the "remembered" position in the gradient system. Such states either involved, or in turn were interpreted in terms of, differential genetic read-out to produce a pattern such as is seen to emerge biologically. More recent modeling such as that by Zeeman (1975) and Kauffman *et al.* (1978) tends to assume that switching within cells to produce the final array of determined states is sequential in nature and of essentially binary form, giving a combinatorial tree structure to individual cell restrictions. This allows the spatial dynamic (gradient) to be very simple, and set up again within each "compartment" (see Section II, D, 3) to produce one new threshold, thus two new "compartments" after switching. Alternatively, according to "wave theory," the spatial dynamic still spreads across the entire field throughout pattern formation, but sequential cell switching occurs as a series of propagated waves of sudden state change, each sweeping across the system but being halted to form a boundary or frontier at a characteristic position determined by the positional variables.

When we look at the anatomy of the neural plate we see little that encourages us to prefer any particular one of the candidate models for cell interactions in the plane of its surface. The cells are columnar, and no anatomically polarized structural asymmetries have been reported in the relevant dimensions. If an anthropormorphism may be permitted, the cells look to be too busy at the motor/adhesive activities described in Section II, C to be simultaneously doing much positional interacting, though we know they must be doing so. One interesting clue however may come from the work of Warner and her colleagues (Warner, 1973; Blackshaw and Warner, 1976), who find a spatially organized electropotential structure among the cells of the early plate, as yet hard to understand, which could be part of a basis for its progressive regionalization at this time.

3. A Note on Polyclonal Compartments

The rich potential, in insects, for genetic manipulation of individual embryonic cells so that their descendants are specifically marked in the adult structure, has revealed the phenomenon known as polyclonal compartmentation during early stages of their pattern formation (Garcia-Bellido, 1975; Crick and Lawrence, 1975). Its generality in animal development, and its significance for mechanisms, cannot yet be assessed. Briefly, ectodermal patterns in insects appear to be preorganized, among the expanding cell population early in development, by relatively sudden restriction events that assign small groups of cells (the compartments) to be sole builders of particular areas within the final pattern—areas which are consistent between individuals. These geographical restrictions occur in hierarchical series, long before overt differentiation of the cells, and establish a system of boundaries that survives, through the great and uneven cell multiplication that follows, by selective cell surface recognition and cohesion. If such boundaries corresponded only to those between adjacent pattern parts, or structures, the phenomena would be merely a trivial documentation of positional information plus interpretation, or wavefronts plus switching, etc., in action. They are fascinating, in fact, because the events are so early, the initial numbers of cells set aside per compartment so few, and the boundaries between compartments often arbitrary in relation to the final pattern constructed, though constant as between individuals.

It is supposed that positional information must be used to control differentiation within these, yet there is little doubt that where they have been detected by genetic means, compartments are important contributors to genesis of spatial organization and may offer clues to the way in which cellular developmental restriction takes place. The constant cell–cell relationships within neural plate and tube, during critical phases of pattern formation, certainly make plausible the suggestion that such serial erection of restriction boundaries may occur with time. Indeed it would almost be expected on some theories for control of pattern, including the ideas of thresholds and serial switches mentioned in Section II, D, 2, and there has been considerable excitement at the possibility of such an experimental analysis. Paucity of genetic tools and techniques might be compensated for, e.g., in amphibians, by injecting fertilized eggs with long-lasting substances that do not cross intercellular functions and can be made visible by subsequent histochemistry, for use as donors of small cell groups in neural plate grafting experiments. There is one great difficulty however. The schedule of cell divisions need not have anything to do with an organized succession of restrictions (see Section II, D, 1); but a considerable expansion of cell number, across the period of determination, is technically necessary in order to show any succession of compartmentations that may in reality be taking place by an analysis of clone shapes in "chimeric" nervous systems. The vertebrate neural plate appears to contrast sharply with the insect epidermis. In the insert epidermis, much sequential pattern determination takes place very early, during a period of vigorous cell multiplication and long before the visible expression of pattern as form-building movements. In the vertebrate neural plate, pattern formation (possibly sequential) occurs over a period in which cell number increases only by a modest factor, immediately prior to the form-building which expresses the determined pattern as the shape of the primitive brain.

III. The Radial (Ependymal → Pial) Structure within Brain Parts: Cell Birthday and Organization over the Primitive Epithelium

There must be a lower limit to the number of cells, composing the newly induced neural plate, that would allow normal expression of its pattern-forming capacities. Nevertheless, as I have tried to emphasize, the increase of spatial complexity and determination involved in laying down the basic plan of the CNS is brought about by processes which are not closely tied to cell replication as such. By contrast, during the following extended period over which that plan is expressed on a local level, encompassing the highly organized sequences of births of the neurons themselves (permanently postmitotic cells), there is agreement that organization depends quite heavily on schedules of cell division. The question of just how intimate this dependence is, is currently open to argument and experiment (see Section III, B). Analysis of this period of neurogenesis is best begun by a brief description of what is seen in the various brain regions, that is, what behavior has been programmed into the precursor cells determined as different parts of the CNS rudiment by their response to the positional variables discussed in Sections II, A and D.

A. Organization of the Cell Cycle and Cell Birthdays

The primitive epithelium (becoming the ependymal layer) was once believed to be a multilayered structure, since cell nuclei appear at various levels relative to the ventricular surface, and in many regions continuity of a cell between inner and outer faces can rarely be seen. Sauer (1935) published an early report arguing for what is now agreed to be its real, pseudostratified monolayer structure. Its behavior as its cell population multiplies early on, and as it later becomes the inner ependymal layer giving rise to the radially disposed populations of postmitotic cells, is described in detail by Sidman et al. (1959) and reviewed by Watterson (1965). The mitotic cycle appears randomly phased among neighboring cells (the impression of synchrony given by Sidman et al. is surely not a real implication of the data they present). It is difficult strictly to check the assertions (Watterson, 1965; Källen and Bergquist, 1954; Narayanan, 1970) that local geographical differences of cycle time exist within the ependyma at various stages of neurohistogenesis, owing to differences of cell-packing, plane of sectioning, etc., but such heterogeneity would not be surprising since the epithelial cell cycle can respond to patterning influences even as early as beginning neural plate stages, when the *Xenopus* neural rudiment is regionalized with respect to mitotic index (Cooke, unpublished observations). Källen and his associates (Källen, 1953, 1956, 1965; Källen and Bergquist, 1954) have championed the view that the earliest compartmentation of the rudiment into regions having their own schedules of cell production is due to spatial periodicities in craniocaudal and ventrodorsal dimensions.

Each ependymal cell pursues a cycle whereby DNA is replicated at positions far from the ventricle and mitosis occurs near the ventricular surface, the nuclei thus migrating in and out along the flexible, columnar cell bodies to give the pseudostratified appearance. Cells leaving this cycle to become neurons are usually retained in the DNA-replicative (G_0) state, although tetraploid (G_2) neurons are known. A cell's destiny as neuronal is probably determined at or soon after the mitosis that gives birth to it, though it is difficult in principle to distinguish an intracellular (nuclear?) asymmetry, causing one daughter to be set aside at mitosis, from a mechanism whereby cells respond at random to microenvironmental factors, during their G_1 phase, in choosing whether to enter the cycle again or to leave the ependyma. The newborn cells leaving the epithelium remain in its vicinity for some time before ascending (migrating) to particular levels within the radial structure that is being established over the ependyma, at some time during this process commencing overt differentiation as neurons of the appropriate anatomical class, without further mitosis. Notable exceptions to this usual pattern are seen in cerebellar development, where populations of migrated cells take up a superficial (outer) position to become a secondary generative layer, delivering newly postmitotic cells inward to contribute to particular layers of the radial structure beneath, and in parts of the hippocampus (Angevine, 1965) in which cells seem to divide to form neuroblasts *in situ*.

During the period of neuronal birth a radially arranged filamentous (glial cell) framework seems to be erected within the CNS, extending from ependyma to an outer basement membrane at the developing pial surface. The strong impression is that neuroblast migration is almost always along the radial guidelines of this framework, though the fact may be obscured by thickening, folding, and bending of the wall in various CNS regions during growth. Topographic relationships between the birthplaces of neurons within the primitive epithelium are thus strongly preserved during development of the CNS despite migration, the various classes of cell arriving at each locality coming to vary principally in their final positions along the radial dimension. Exceptional populations of neuroblasts, however, do migrate in a highly specific manner within the primary CNS pattern between their sites of birth and final function (Harkmark, 1954—rhombic lip of hindbrain; Sidman and Rákic, 1968, 1974—human forebrain). The problem of such migration by cell bodies is probably more akin to that of developing axonal tract guidance (Section IV).

The basis of morphogenesis within this new, radial dimension of CNS structure must be the generation of postmitotic cells of determined classes (as to anatomical neuron type) in the proper absolute numbers, which then take up their proper relationships after migration within the ependymal–pial scaffolding to give rise to the laminated cortical structures (Angevine and Sidman, 1961; La Vail and Cowan, 1971a,b) or "nuclei" (Angevine, 1970; Clarke et al., 1976), characterizing the pattern in each place. Even at this stage it seems safe to conclude that final acquisition of their radial relationships reflects mutual recognition properties intrinsic to the cell classes themselves, at least in association with possible clues on the glial scaffolding (Sidman and Rákic, 1974). There is also overwhelming evidence from the study of a variety of developing brain centers, under conditions of deprivation of normal output targets or normal input axons from other centers, that the absolute numbers, classes, birthdays, and even basic radial positions of the neurons to be born are intrinsic to the program of the ependyma. Final surviving numbers, and detailed architecture of synaptic relationships of cells in a center, are modified only by later trophic types of interaction via axons between centers or between CNS and periphery (Clarke et al., 1976; Clarke and Cowan, 1976; Currie and Cowan, 1974; De Long and Sidman, 1962; Kelly and Cowan, 1972).

Instances of such secondary interactive adjustment of neuron numbers by differential survival probably include passage of information in both anterograde and retrograde directions through the CNS (relative to the final flow of electrophysiological stimulation) (Clarke et al., 1976; Clarke and Cowan, 1976; Caviness and Rákic, 1978). Detailed architecture and orientation of dendritic trees seem also to be subject to epigenetic interactions between contacting cell classes in some cases (see Caviness and Rákic, 1978). The basic morphology of neurons, however, is almost certainly an expression of their births at particular times and positions in what might now be termed the ependymal program for cell production.

If the foregoing is a valid conclusion from the literature, the problem becomes one of a program for specific cell births, in the right relative numbers, imbued in the stem cell population of the primitive epithelium at each location by virtue of the latter's original determination as part of the primary CNS pattern (Section II). Grafting experiments, from later neural plate stages through neural tube stage (C.-O. Jacobson, 1964; Roach, 1945; Chung and Cooke, 1978), show that across this time the program is becoming endogenous in more and more of its details within ependymal regions, not only with respect to neuron types generated and their relative numbers, but most strikingly with respect to the spatially patterned timing according to which the births of the neurons take place (see following). Note that many of the cell classes (neuron types) are indistinguishable, at least anatomically, as generated in one brain region or another. Yet their birth schedules, as well as ultimate connectivity preferences and physiology, are distinctive to each such region of the original pattern. This is a prime example of the principle of nonequivalence between parts of patterns, in developmental biology, set out by Lewis and Wolpert (1976). Karten (1969), Sidman et al. (1959), and Sidman and Angevine (1962) have given interesting discussions of evolutionary considerations, including the nature of homology between brain structures among different vertebrate groups and of the increase in complexity within a structure during evolution. It is suggested that the natures and extents of the neuronal birth schedules, implemented by stem cell determinations within a primary CNS pattern, are much more subject to evolutionary change than is that pattern itself.

Certain features of the schedules of neuronal birthdays are exciting in causing the feeling that one is nearer an understanding of this, relatively late aspect of neurogenesis than of earlier phases, where global interactions must be postulated but are currently quite obscure. The principal method for their study has been the labeling of cells going through their final rounds of DNA synthesis with a quickly cleared systemic injection of [³H]thymidine (e.g., Sidman et al., 1959). Spatiotemporal patterns of neuron birthdays which are thus revealed by the last S phase of the precursor cells have two aspects: there are systematic relationships between birthday and cell position (after migration) within the radial structure, and between the whole spread of birthdays and position of the stem cells within the pattern of the CNS.

In the radial structure at each location, neurons of particular anatomical classes, due to occupy specific layer positions and synaptic relationships, tend to be born within particular restricted periods of the brain's development. Cells of large, pyramidal types tend to be born early and those of smaller internuncial (locally connecting) type tend to be born later. Thus successively later administration of [³H]thymidine tends to label successive strata of cells in an inside-out or outside-in sequence, depending upon the brain region studied (see Section III, C).

This relationship of cell birthday to cell type and position is by no means clear-cut in most regions, however. The births of the component cell populations within a region's structure form broad, overlapping distributions.

The second aspect of birthday patterning is that in which the whole birthday sequence characterizing development of the cortical layered structure, or that of a "nucleus," shifts with progression through the brain along dimensions parallel to the original generative epithelium (i.e., ventrodorsally and/or craniocaudally). It is difficult to describe these patterns adequately in a short discussion, and the reader is referred to the following representative studies: Angevine (1965) and Angevine and Sidman (1961)—mammalian cortex; Angevine (1970) and De Long and Sidman (1962)—parts of mouse midbrain; La Vail and Cowan (1971a,b)—bird optic tectum; Clarke et al. (1976)—parts of bird midbrain tegmentum; Straznicky and Gaze (1972) and Currie and Cowan (1974)—amphibian optic tectum. The last-named structure is exceptional in that the timing gradient in histogenetic schedule, in the plane of the epithelium, is so extended (weeks long) that a sharp zone of newly postmitotic cells is present at each developmental stage. Much more commonly, the spread of cell birthdays occupies an appreciable fraction of the spread within the brain as a whole when studied within each brain region (i.e., many days or weeks), whereas the shift in actual onset and cessation of neuron production occurs as a shallow timing gradient across whole areas of the pattern parallel to epithelium, traversing say, the diencephalon, or a future cortical region, or the midbrain tectum in some 48 hours. These early timing gradients are few and sweeping within the brain pattern; the future individuality of particular thalamic nuclei, say, or anatomically defined regions of cortex, is swamped at early stages within the timing gradient along forebrain or hindbrain as a whole. The forebrain–midbrain junction is a notable center in early development, from which caudorostral and rostrocaudal cell birthday gradients tend to spread, respectively, into forebrain and midbrain as development proceeds (see Section IV, C).

In Sections III, B and C, I suggest that the first aspect of cell birthday timing, related to anatomical type and normal position within the radial structure, could be a most important clue to the generation of this aspect of pattern. The functional importance of the second aspect of timing, the waves of birth schedule running through the pattern, is however problematic. It could sometimes be of importance in the generation of the "topic" organization within fiber tracts (Sections IV, B and C), since axon development from sheets of output neurons usually proceeds according to an organized sequence, in line with the original sequence of cell birth. But it may simply reflect a side-effect of the early determination of pattern and nonequivalence within cell sheets (Section II, D) (see Cooke, 1975; Lewis and Wolpert, 1976). In at least one important case, the well-marked gradient of target-cell birthdate, programmed early on into embryonic tissue, bears no necessary relationship to overall orientation of the set of selective nerve connections, whereby axon terminals from one center form a "map" of it across another via a tract. This is revealed in the abnormally orientated projections that may finally be formed under experimental conditions (Chung and Cooke, 1978).

B. CONTRASTING MODELS FOR THE ORIGIN OF NEURON TYPES

The local relationship between cell birthdate and fate in formation of the radial CNS structure is currently susceptible to two sorts of interpretation, implying different mechanisms for generation of neuron types. The correlation between birthday and final position within this dimension really does reflect self-organizing capacities among the set of determined cells that has been generated (Section III, C, see Caviness and Rákic, 1978). The birthday–layer position correlation thus reflects a birthday–anatomical class relationship, and the crucial question becomes one of how highly organized and exact that relationship is at the cellular level.

Because of overlapping birthdates among adjacent cell classes from each local ependymal region, compounded by overall shift in the schedule with progress through the brain pattern parallel to ependyma, the picture does not look impressive superficially. One class of model would be based on the proposition that, among the asymmetrical cell divisions each giving rise to a further stem cell and one outward-migrating neuroblast, there is a probabilistic, sequential change with time in the class of neuroblast likely to be generated. Such a series of changes in the conditions of birth of successively later generations of cells might result from changes in the milieu, not programmed within any one cell lineage but caused in some way by the cell population as a whole—an expression of the physiological age of the developing nervous system. Overall timing gradients along the primitive ependyma would then represent systematic shifts, across the CNS pattern, of the rate or time of onset of such "aging" progressions, developing systems having known capacities for exhibiting preprogrammed wavefronts of cell change during development (Zeeman, 1974).

An alternative class of model proposes that, starting at an unknown time before the first birth of definitive neuroblasts, individiual cells within the ependyma become quite strictly programmed as to future, asymmetrical series of cell divisions that they will undergo, each time producing one new stem cell (of greater developmental restriction than before) and one neuroblast of a particular anatomical class determination. In certain animals remote from the vertebrates, such strict lineages between the cells in patterns are recognized as part of development from early stages. In earlier vertebrate development, lineage mechanisms are certainly overshadowed by the sorts of dynamic intercellular communication systems, leading to regulative "field" development, discussed earlier. But recent studies of adult vertebrate tissues supported by cell replacement from a small "stem" population have produced evidence for an asymmetrical assortment of genome material, at the molecular level, during the initial cell division whereby the mortal, functional cell lineage branches off from the stem cell one. Such capacities for controlled partitioning of genome copies (with attendant apparatus of specific derepression, switches, etc.) would be a favorite candidate for the molecular substrate of specific cell lineages.

The apparent sloppy nature of the cell-class/position/birthdate linkages is not strong evidence against a particulate lineage mechanism for cell class generation within the brain. Known variability of cycle times, possible variation in time of onset of lineage programming, and slight wandering of neuroblasts parallel to the ependyma during radial migration allow little to be deduced of lineage events from appearances at histological levels of analysis. I believe that, from a certain time point in CNS development, lineage programs become an exciting possibility for the generation of pattern.

C. The Causes of Radial Position and Local Synaptic Relationships among Neuron Classes

Broadly speaking there are two types of developmental sequences found in the brain. In highly laminated structures such as cortex, successively generated classes of neuroblasts migrate past the previous ones during development to assume their positions, leading to a basically inside-out sequence with the youngest class of neurons occupying superficial (subpial) positions. In other regions characterized more by development of "nuclei"—definitive cell populations with boundaries within the pattern—such as thalamus or medulla, the histogenetic sequence may be the reverse of this. Later-generated cell classes remain at the inside of the structure, displacing their older relatives toward more superficial positions. Certain structures, e.g., bird optic tectum (La Vail and Cowan, 1971b), have more complex radial histogenetic sequences.

Studies on a series of mouse mutants with primary expression in

CNS, such as reeler, weaver, staggerer, etc., have provided the beginnings of understanding of the behavior whereby cells achieve normal positionings in the radial structure. In one or more of the brain parts in the reeler mouse the order of histogenesis, as judged by cell birthday and by visible anatomical class of the cells concerned, proceeds from outside-in instead of from inside-out. Caviness and Rákic (1978) have instructively reviewed what can be learned from these mutants. Note that the association of cell class with birthday remains normal, supporting their causal relationship. Systematic malpositioning of classes must be due to disturbance of an instruction system whereby the cells self-assemble, rather than instructions received from other cells during histological assembly causing determination of each cell class (see also Sidman and Rákic, 1974). This positional instruction system might reside only in the neuroblasts themselves, in spatial or temporal sequences of surface markers on the glial scaffolding which the migrating blasts certainly contact intimately, or in both components. There is evidence for primary glial cell abnormality in one of these mutants. Electrophysiology reveals that cells can also respond to the abnormal geometrical relationships to establish roughly normal connectivity sequences (though not sufficiently to give normal behavior), and there also seem to be very local trophic relationships whereby incoming axons seek target dendrites and vice versa.

IV. Fiber Tracts: The Plan of Connectivity between Centers

A. Tissue Polarity as a Local Guidance Factor, versus Specific Chemotropisms, in Axon and Tract Development

Axons from many types of neurons in central and peripheral (Burnstock, 1972) nervous system have a proven capacity to "test out" potential classes of target cell that they contact, rejecting inappropriate classes, particularly if faced with a choice. But it is very doubtful whether such observations could form the basis for any theory whereby, through many specific chemoattractant or neurotrophic substances acting at distance, the complex plan of intercenter connectivity via axonal tracts could be built up during development. There is much evidence that developing nervous tissue offers local clues to growing axons, to which the term tissue polarity might be applied; that is to say, clues which orient the direction of growth of specific fibers in relation, not to their prospective target structures as in chemotaxis, but in relation to some local expression of the original embryonic axes of the brain. Such a system, although its molecular basis is unknown as with so many others in developmental biology, is inherently more plausible and more in accord with what is known already than is the idea of multiple, brain center-specific chemoattractant signals. Three examples will be given.

After rotation *in situ* of pieces of neural plate material after pattern determination in the Axolotl (Section II, A), C.-O. Jacobson (1964) studied the behavior of Mauthner's cell axons and of fiber tracts, both of which of course grow out at much later stages. The early Mauthner's axon, in the vicinity of its cell body, had its direction of growth determined by the *original* embryonic polarity of tissue through which it was actively growing. Only later, after such axons had associated with a developing tract involving many fibers, did such fibers as a group seem able to penetrate through the region of reversal, often to proceed to normal destinations. It is as if the fiber-following, that accompanies nearly synchronous outgrowth from many cells, can overcome adverse orientation of certain intimate substrate clues that dominate the single fiber.

There are controversial observations concerning fiber development from ectopically implanted eye rudiments (Constantine-Paton and Capranica, 1976; Sharma, 1972; Giorgi and van der Loos, 1978). According to some studies, fibers can ascend from the spinal level of input to innervate their normal target the tectum, in frogs, thus traversing much tissue in a contrapolar manner. Other studies find that fibers traverse the brainstem, from entry at hindbrain levels, in a specifically dorsocaudal trajectory beneath the pia resembling that of normally situated optic tracts in development and regeneration (Gaze and Grant, 1978), although this now has no adaptive relation to target structures. Finally, observations on amphibian brains after rotations *in situ* of dorsal diencephalic and/or midbrain regions at neural tube stages (Chung and Cooke, 1978) suggest that normal ongrowth of the optic tract is intimately dependent on what might be termed the embryonic polarity of the structure through which it is developing. Tracts in which the fibers, on entering at the basal chiasm and coursing dorsocaudally up the walls of the diencephalon, meet a point at which there is a reversal of the original embryonic polarity, are characteristically subject to blockade at this sharply defined position. This apparently remains for much of larval life, until a few fibers escape by following a still caudal but much more ventral path through unrotated levels of brain structure, where they gain entry to the tectum by what is *now* its caudal end in the brain. The bulk of fibers can then follow to form substantial innervation from the rear of the tectum, which is now of course its earliest developing end (see Chung and Cooke, 1978 and Section III, A). There is no scar tissue or discontinuity of cellular structure after such operations, but to pursue a normally shaped pathway to maturing tectal tissue, optic fibers would have to grow through still embryonic, preneuronal tissue that would *originally* have formed the late-developing caudal tectum. The tract in this system seems to form by preserving a particular polarity relation between its route and the developing tissue, a relation which prohibits the crossing of territory less advanced in development in order to reach more advanced target cells (Stirling and Cooke, unpublished observations).

It should be clear that intercenter connectivity in the developed CNS is so multiple and complex that, if such an intimate set of embryonic polarity cues are actually involved in tract guidance, there is no question of simple substrate guidance of a mechanical sort orienting fibers per se in constant relationship with polarity. Fibers from each center would need to be programmed for traversal of tissue in their own unique direction in relation to a polarity grid, as it were "on a set compass bearing" within the nervous system, in order to encounter their prearranged target area.

B. The Need to Consider Growth, Morphogenesis, and Timing in Evaluating Models

The problem of complex intercenter connectivity becomes less daunting if, in thinking about it, one is not overseduced by the complex form attained late in CNS development. Two features of earlier neurogenesis need to be remembered. Because of the gradation of timing in the cessation of growth divisions (i.e., onset of neuroblast birth) across the pattern, pairs of future centers whose first axonal connections were formed as between closely adjacent, small populations of neurons, may finally be situated in rather more distant relative positions, with most of the projection from one to the other involving very long axons. This is more so since bending and rotating movements of whole areas of pattern in the plane of the original epithelium may occur quite late on, and since connected centers often form parts of adjacent pattern areas characterized by maturation gradients that are mirror-imaged across their junction (e.g., Angevine, 1970). Second, the span of time across which neuron maturation occurs is such that although axons composing each tract usually grow out in a smooth coherent time sequence related to that of cell birthdays, the times of onset of outgrowth are widely disparate as *between* tracts. If the pioneering fibers of each tract exert particularly powerful influences upon their successors, the possibility of mutual interference among successively developing tracts within the same structure is thereby minimized.

In spite of the above encouraging remarks, it would be very implausible to derive a model for the entire mature interconnectivity pattern (including, e.g., that between equivalent cerebral cortical areas via the callosum) from maturation timing and growth movements alone. There is evidence (see Caviness and Rákic, 1978) from mutant mice that the same set of clues that assists the radial ordering of cell bodies may be instrumental in the choice of stratum for passage of fiber tracts within the structure, when near their targets. The whole problem of setting up the tract structure within the developing CNS will become less mysterious in principle if recent ideas of M. Singer and his collaborators (Singer *et al.*, 1979) receive biochemical ratification. It is proposed that a primitive "blueprint" for the tract system, by implication one having the requisite specificities of labeling, is a direct property of the ependymal program as expressed in the nonneuronal cellular scaffolding of the brain.

C. Tracts and the Organized Projections between Centers: Remarks on the Retinotectal Pathway as a Model System

Preservation of order in connections between successive laminae *within* the structure of brain centers would seem to follow from local guidance in the neighborhood of the parallel cell populations, plus coordinated schedules of neuron maturation between them. Something similar seems to play a considerable role in ensuring ordered connections at successive synaptic levels in arthropod systems (Anderson, 1978). Preservation of global ordering in connections between different brain centers, known as neuronal projection systems, cannot be explained as easily, however. It is certainly widespread in the genetic plan (independent of functional experience) of the vertebrate nervous system, though the mapping is not always a simple representation of output on input target arrays as in the retinotectal system which has been widely adopted as an experimental model. Progress in our understanding of this system in development and regeneration, since the work of Sperry and his collaborators and the initial hypothesis of neuronal specificity (see Sperry, 1965), is reviewed by Gaze (Volume 17, this series). In conclusion, I shall draw attention to certain aspects of the problem, since it is a final feature of gross CNS architecture.

The literature on regeneration of connections after ablation or transposition within retina or tectum now suggests that, by times remote from initial destruction of the nerve, adaptive forces may succeed in reestablishing a simple, coherent mapping of remaining input onto remaining target under some conditions (Sharma and Romeskie, 1977; Schmidt *et al.,* 1978; Schmidt, 1978; Udin, 1977). But initially a mosaic type of specificity, matching up regenerating axons to their original target cells, may dominate the picture, and current hypotheses are that this represents fiber recognition of specific cues within the debris of the previous innervation, or that specific labels are somehow "induced" on postsynaptic cells by previous occupancy of the input (e.g., von der Malsburg and Willshaw, 1977).

In initial development of the map, there is much more room for models of structural guidance, timing of fiber growth, fiber–fiber population interactions, etc., whereby only minimal information is required to be represented on cells as individuals, for an ordered set of connections to result (Hope et al., 1976; Willshaw and von der Malsburg, 1976, 1979; Bunt and Horder, 1977; Schwartz, 1977). Despite this, theories assuming embryological specificity in the form of matching sets of cytochemical markers have held sway in the imaginations of most biologists interested in these systems ever since Sperry's original hypothesis and the attendant tag of "neuronal specificity" or "locus specificity" (Hunt and Jacobson, 1974). Developmental observations which require that the array of input terminals slides bodily with respect to the target cell array as development proceeds, implying the making and breaking of connections until the end of growth, challenge strongly the chemospecificity hypothesis in its simplest form (see Gaze, 1980; Longley, 1978; M. Jacobson, 1977). The term "specificity" is perhaps too often used at present to imply the a priori necessity of a certain class of underlying mechanism, when what is observed is after all only a selectivity, for relative positions of termination in the target structure among incoming fibers.

Neuronal projection systems such as the retinotectal have two crucial properties: preservation of neighbor relationships between cells of origin among their axonal terminations, and the representation of the output surface with a certain characteristic orientation on the input surface. These properties can often survive development of a projection via an (experimentally) abnormal pathway of the optic tract as a whole through the brain. Thus structural models postulating little individual information in either retinal or tectal cells will remain relevant only if a high degree of preservation of neighbor relations between fibers in the optic tract, currently known to accompany undisturbed development in lower vertebrates, is found also in such grossly ectopic tracts. Such fiber guidance cannot account, in principle, for control of overall orientation of the map. For this feature, something appropriately termed biological specification, for development of reference points in the retinal cell array and corresponding "anchor" or receptor channels in or near the developing tectum, seems inescapable. Rotation of the eye rudiment in the head, before fiber connection to the brain has started, really does result in development of a rotated map from the visual world to the tectum and in correspondingly mismatched behavior.

Recent work (Scholes, 1979) shows that in a fish retinotectal system local fiber ordering (as if by contact following) is highly preserved within the tract throughout, but that at a certain position near the tectum the whole array becomes violently rearranged within its cross-section (in a way surely mediated by extrinsic cues) so as to form naturally the map that is observed as it invades the tectum.

There have been suggestions that the polarity according to which maturation is graded with time in brain centers (Section III, A) is itself a correlate of neuronal specificity, so that position within the schedule of cell birthday parallel to the ependyma is effectively synonymous with the assumed cytochemical specificity in map construction. At least in the retinotectal system, an experimental counterexample has been the finding (Chung and Cooke, 1978) of maps normally organized in relation to the rostrocaudal axis of the brain as a whole, following initial development across tectal tissue of reversed embryonic polarity which was thus maturing in abnormally reversed caudorostral sequence. Programmed cell birthday, a basic expression of nonequivalence within target tissue as the latter forms part of the primitive pattern (see Sections II, D and III, A), has no necessary role in the selective connections achieved by the input array. Some might take this as evidence against any specificity among the target cells, though other interpretations remain. In the same work, a reference point capable of orienting the projection as a whole within the brain seemed to reside in the tissue determined to form diencephalon, through which the optic tract gains entry to the tectum.

REFERENCES

Adler, R. (1970). *Dev. Biol.* **21**, 403–423.
Alderman, A. L. (1935). *J. Exp. Zool.* **70**, 205–232.
Anderson, H. (1978). *J. Embryol. Exp. Morphol.* **45**, 55–83.
Angevine, J. B., Jr. (1965). *Exp. Neurol. Suppl.* **2**, 1–70.
Angevine, J. B., Jr. (1970). *J. Comp. Neurol.* **139**, 129–188.
Angevine, J. B., Jr., and Sidman, R. L. (1961). *Nature (London)* **192**, 766–768.
Baker, P., and Schroeder, T. E. (1967). *Dev. Biol.* **15**, 432–450.
Barth, L. G. (1941). *J. Exp. Zool.* **87**, 371–383.
Barth, L. G., and Barth, L. J. (1959). *J. Embryol. Exp. Morphol.* **7**, 210–222.
Barth, L. G., and Barth, L. J. (1962). *J. Morphol.* **110**, 347–373.
Barth, L. G., and Barth, L. J. (1969). *Dev. Biol.* **20**, 236–262.
Blackshaw, S. E., and Warner, A. E. (1976). *J. Physiol. (London)* **255**, 231–247.
Blakemore, C., and Mitchell, D. E. (1973). *Nature (London)* **241**, 467–469.
Boterenbrood, E. C. (1970). *J. Embryol. Exp. Morphol.* **23**, 751–760.

Bunt, S. M., and Horder, T. J. (1977). *J. Physiol. (London)* **272**, 10P–11P.
Burnside, B. (1971). *Dev. Biol.* **26**, 416–441.
Burnstock, G. D. (1972). *Pharmacol. Rev.* **24**, 509–581.
Caveney, S. (1974). *Dev. Biol.* **40**, 311–322.
Caviness, V. S., and Rakic, P. (1978). *Annu. Rev. Neurosci.* **1**, 297–317.
Chung, S. H., and Cooke, J. (1978). *Proc. R. Soc. (London).* B **201**, 335–373.
Chung, S. H., Gaze, R. M., and Stirling, R. V. (1973). *Nature (London)* **246**, 186–189.
Clarke, P. G., and Cowan, W. M. (1976). *J. Comp. Neurol.* **167**(2), 143–164.
Clarke, P. G., Rogers, L. A., and Cowan, W. M. (1976). *J. Comp. Neurol.* **167**(2), 125–142.
Constantine-Paton, M., and Capranica, R. R. (1976). *J. Comp. Neurol.* **170**(1), 33–51.
Cooke, J. (1973). *J. Embryol. Exp. Morphol.* **30**, 49–62.
Cooke, J. (1975). *Annu. Rev. Biophys. Bioeng.* **4**, 185–218.
Crick, F. H. C., and Lawrence, P. (1975). *Science* **189**, 340–347.
Currie, J., and Cowan, W. M. (1974). *J. Comp. Neurol.* **156**, 123–142.
De Long, G. R., and Sidman, R. L. (1962). *J. Comp. Neurol.* **118**, 205–223.
Deuchar, E. M. (1970). *Dev. Biol.* **22**, 185–199.
Garcia-Bellido, A. (1975). *In* "Cell Patterning" CIBA Symposium (K. Elliot and M. O'Connor, eds.), Vol 29, pp 161–183. Associated Scientific Publ., London.
Gaze, R. M., and Grant, P. (1978). *J. Embryol. Exp. Morphol.* **44**, 201–216.
Gillette, R. (1944). *J. Exp. Zool.* **96**, 201–222.
Giorgi, P. P., and van der Loos, H. (1978). *Nature (London)* **275**, 746–748.
Harkmark, W. (1954). *J. Comp. Neurol.* **100**, 115–209.
Holtfreter, J. (1933). *Wilhelm Roux' Arch. Entwicklungsmech. Org.* **129**, 670–793.
Holtfreter, J. (1946). *J. Morphol.* **79**, 27–62.
Hope, R. A., Hammond, B. J., and Gaze, R. M. (1976). *Proc. R. Soc. (London)* B **194**, 447–466.
Hunt, R. K., and Jacobson, M. (1974). *Curr. Top. Dev. Biol.* **8**, 203–259.
Jacobson, A. G. (1976). *J. Supramol. Struct.* **5**(3), 371–380.
Jacobson, A. G., and Gordon, R. (1976). *J. Exp. Zool.* **197**(2), 191–246.
Jacobson, C.-O. (1962). *Zool. Bidrag. Uppsala.* **35**, 434–449.
Jacobson, C.-O. (1964). *Zool. Bidrag. Uppsala* **36**, 73–157.
Jacobson, M. (1970). *In* "The Neurosciences: Second Study Programme" (F. O. Schmidt, ed.), pp. 116–128. Rockefeller Univ. Press, New York.
Jacobosn, M. (1977). *Brain Res.* **127**, 55–67.
Källen, B. (1953). *J. Embryol. Exp. Morphol.* **1**, 387–392.
Källen, B. (1956). *Acta Anat.* **27**, 351–360.
Källen, B. (1965). *In* "Organogenesis" (R. D. De Haan and H. Ursprung, eds.). Holt, New York.
Källen, B., and Bergquist, H. (1954). *Acta Anat.* **17**, 353–378.
Karfunkel, P. (1971). *Dev. Biol.* **25**, 35–56.
Karfunkel, P. (1972). *J. Exp. Zool.* **181**, 289–302.
Karten, H. (1969). *Ann. N.Y. Acad. Sci.* **167**, 164–179.
Kauffman, S. A., Shymko, R. M., and Trabert, K. (1978). *Science* **199**, 259–269.
Keating, M. J. (1976). *In* "Studies on the Development of Behavior and the Nervous System" (G. Gottlieb, ed.), Vol. 3, pp. 59–110. Academic Press, New York.
Kelly, J. P., and Cowan, W. M. (1972). *Brain Res.* **42**, 263–288.
La Vail, J. H., and Cowan, W. M. (1971a). *Brain Res.* **28**, 391–419.
La Vail, J. H., and Cowan, W. M. (1971b). *Brain Res.* **28**, 421–441.
Leussink, J. A. (1970). *Neth. J. Zool.* **20**(1), 1–79.
Lewis, J. H., and Wolpert, L. (1976). *J. Theor. Biol.* **62**, 479–490.

Longley, A. (1978). *J. Embryol. Exp. Morphol.* **45**, 249–270.

Maleyvar, R. P., and Lowery, R. (1973). *In* "The Cell Cycle in Development and Differentiation" (M. Balls and F. S. Billet, eds.). Symposium of the Society for Development in Biology.

Martin, A. H. (1977). *Acta Embryol. Exp.* **3**, 305–313.

Miyayama, Y., and Fujimoto, T. (1977). *Okijamas Folia Anat. Jpn.* **54**, 97–120.

Model, P. G. (1978). *Brain Res.* **153**, 135–143.

Narayanan, C. H. (1970). *J. Comp. Neurol.* **139**, 189–198.

Nieuwkoop, P. D. (1967a). *Acta Biotheoretica.* **17**, 151–177.

Nieuwkoop, P. D. (1967b). *Acta Biotheor.* **17**, 178–198.

Roach, F. C. (1945). *J. Exp. Zool.* **99**, 53–77.

Sauer, F. C. (1935). *J. Comp. Neurol.* **63**, 13–23.

Schmidt, J. T. (1978). *J. Comp. Neurol.* **177**, 279–299.

Schmidt, J. T., Cicerone, C. M., and Easter, S. S. (1978). *J. Comp. Neurol.* **177**, 257–277.

Scholes, J. H. (1979). *Nature (London)* **278**, 620–624.

Schroeder, T. E. (1970). *J. Embryol. Exp. Morphol.* **23**, 427–462.

Schwartz, E. L. (1977). *J. Theor. Biol.* **69**, 665–683.

Sharma, S. C. (1972). *Nature (London)* **238**, 286–287.

Sharma, S. C., and Romeskie, M. (1977). *Brain Res.* **133**, 367–370.

Sidman, R. L., and Angevine, J. B., Jr. (1962). *Anat. Rec.* **142**, 326–327.

Sidman, R. L., and Rakic, P. (1968). *Anat. Rec.* **160**, 428 (Abstr).

Sidman, R. L., and Rakic, P. (1974). *In* "Pre- and Post-Natal Development of the Human Brain. Modern Problems in Paediatrics," Vol. 13, pp 13–43. S Karger, Basel.

Sidman, R. L., Miale, I. L., and Feder, N. (1959). *Exp. Neurol.* **1**, 322–333.

Singer, M., Nordlander, R. H., and Egar, M. (1979). *J. Comp. Neurol.* **185**, 1–21.

Sládecek, F. (1952). *Vest. Cs. Zool. Spol.* **16**, 322–333.

Sládecek, F. (1955). *Vest. Cs. Zool. Spol.* **19**, 138–151.

Spemann, H. (1938). "Embryonic Development and Induction," Ch. VIII. Yale Univ. Press. New Haven, Connecticut.

Spemann, H., and Mangold, H. (1924). *Arch. Mikrosk. Anat. Entwicklungsmech.* **100**, 599–638.

Sperry, R. W. (1965). *In* "Organogenesis" (R. D. De Haan and H. Ursprung, eds), pp. 161–186. Holt, New York.

Straznicky, K. (1963). *Acta Biol. Hung.* **14**(2), 145–155.

Straznicky, K. (1967). *Acta. Biol. Hung.* **18**(4), 437–448.

Straznicky, K., and Gaze, R. M. (1972). *J. Embryol. Exp. Morphol.* **28**, 28–115.

Straznicky, K., and Székely, G. (1967). *Acta Biol. Hung.* **18**(4), 449–456.

Székely, G. (1963). *J. Embryol. Exp. Morphol.* **11**, 431–444.

Székely, G. (1968). *In* "Growth of the Nervous System". CIBA Symposium (D. Wolstenholme and M. O'Connor, eds.), pp. 77–93. Little, Brown, Boston, Massachusetts.

Toivonen, S. (1978). *In* "Organizer" (O. Nakamura and S. Toivonen, eds.), pp. 119–156. Elsevier, Amsterdam.

Toivonen, S., and Saxén, L. (1968). *Science* **159**, 539–540.

Udin, S. B. (1977). *J. Comp. Neurol.* **173**(3), 561–582.

Vargas-Lizardi, P., and Lyer, K. M. (1974). *Dev. Biol.* **38**, 220–228.

von der Malsburg, C. H., and Willshaw, D. J. (1977). *Proc. Natl. Acad. Sci. U.S.A.* **74**(11), 5176–5178.

Waddington, C. H. (1956). "Principles of Embryology." George, Allen & Unwin, London; Macmillan, New York.

Waddington, C. H., and Deuchar, E. M. (1952). *J. Exp. Biol.* **29**(3), 496–510.

Warner, A. E. (1973). *J. Physiol. (London)* **235**, 267–286.

Warner, A. E., and Lawrence, P. A. (1973). *Nature (London)* **245,** 47.

Watterson, R. L. (1965). *In* "Organogenesis" (R. L. De Haan and H. Ursprung, eds.), pp. 129–159. Holt, New York.

Willshaw, D. J., and von der Malsburg, C. H. (1976). *Proc. R. Soc. B* **194**, 431–445.

Wolpert, L. (1971). *Curr. Top. Dev.* **6,** 183–223.

Zeeman, E. C. (1974). *In* "Lectures on Maths in the Life Sciences," Vol. 7, pp 69–161. Amer. Math. Soc., Providence, Rhode Island.

CHAPTER 12

NEURAL INDUCTION: PAST, PRESENT, AND FUTURE

Lauri Saxén

DEPARTMENT OF PATHOLOGY
UNIVERSITY OF HELSINKI
HELSINKI, FINLAND

I. Past: Biological Framework for Induction 409
II. Present: Chemical Nature and Mode of Transmission
of the Signal Substances 413
III. Future: Toward Molecular Mechanisms 415
References 417

Since the early days of the classical German school of developmental biologists, amphibian embryos have been the main focus for experimental work on early determination and differentiation. These embryos are easily available and convenient to handle operatively, and their subsequent development can be followed up in simple, reproducible conditions. Methods to study developmental events in avian embryos are also available, and there are results related to the induction problem (e.g., Hara, 1961; Deuchar, 1969; Eyal-Giladi, 1969; Gallera and Nicolet, 1969). Finally, early mammalian embryos have become available for experimentation, and the British school, especially, has used them in their pioneering studies. The first results suggesting inductive interactions between the different germ layers in mammalian embryos have also been published (Škreb *et al.*, 1976).

Despite the recent studies on avian and mammalian embryos, much of our knowledge on neural induction is still based on experimentation with amphibian embryos. Hence, this chapter will be restricted to that area.

I. Past: Biological Framework for Induction

The first determinative events in an amphibian embryo take place very early: at the eight-cell stage, separation and subcultivation of the four animal and the four vegetal blastomeres result in different types of cytodifferentiation (Grunz, 1977). The presumptive mesodermal and endodermal zones are determined as early as the morula stage (Nakamura 1969). The presumptive neuroectoderm becomes determined relatively late, and even during early gastrulation it retains

CURRENT TOPICS IN
DEVELOPMENTAL BIOLOGY, Vol. 15

several developmental alternatives. This was shown by Spemann
(1916, 1918) and is illustrated in Fig. 1. When a fragment of the presumptive neuroectoderm is transplanted into the ventral region of
another gastrula at the same stage of development, the transplant differentiates in accordance with its new site and not according to its presumptive value (Fig. 1A). When the same experiment is performed at a
late gastrula stage, a secondary neural plate develops on the site of the
transplant, indicating that the neuroectoderm had been irreversibly
determined between the two stages (Fig. 1B). The source of the determinative stimulus for this commitment was found by Spemann and
Mangold in 1924. They transplanted a piece of the blastoporal lip on
the ventral side of another gastrula and observed a secondary neuraxis
there. Using interspecies transplantations, they were able to demonstrate that only a small fraction of the secondary structures originated
from the transplant. The majority had been "induced" by the dorsal lip
transplant. The next step was to discover the age-dependent and regional specificity of the inductor tissue: the blastoporal lip of an early
gastrula differed in its action from the same tissue of an advanced
gastrula, and the anterior part of the latter induced predominantly
head structures whereas the posterior part led to the formation of secondary trunk and tail structures (Spemann, 1927). Soon thereafter, the
same group reported results suggesting that these inductions were
transmitted by chemical compounds (Bautzmann *et al.*, 1932); and with
this hypothesis, the basic framework for subsequent speculation and
design of experiments was formed.

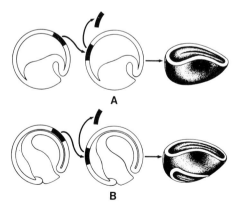

FIG. 1. The transplantation experiment of Spemann (1918) demonstrating the determination of the presumptive neuroectoderm.

In developmental biology the main problem of the 1930s was: How does the inductor tissue create a template for the neuroectoderm leading to its spatially restricted determination and regional specialization? In an attempt to answer this question two, seemingly opposite, theories developed toward the end of the 1930s: the "quantitative" hypothesis of the Belgian school and the "qualitative" theory of Chuang (1938, 1939) and Toivonen (1938, 1940).

The quantitative theory suggested two initial hypothetical gradients within the embryo, one dorsoventral and one caudocranial. It was suggested that the gradients determined the synthesis of "organicine," a third hypothetical factor carrying the actual inductive message. The organicine was unevenly distributed in the embryo and it formed a third gradient. This concentration gradient and the different threshold values of the target tissues determined the ultimate fate of the latter (Dalcq and Pasteels, 1937, 1938). Meanwhile, Chuang (1938) and Toivonen (1938, 1940) independently acquired an opposing view suggesting several inductive factors with different actions. The responses to the three still hypothetical inductors were later defined by Lehmann (1945) as "archencephalic," "deuterencephalic," and "spinocaudal."

Experiments employing various heterotypic tissues and their fractions as inductors seemed to favor the hypothesis of qualitatively different inductors. In 1950, Lehmann formulated a slightly modified theory with elements from the gradient hypothesis. Accordingly, regionalization of the central nervous system (CNS) was determined by two inductive principles (archencephalic and spinal) acting either separately or jointly in different ratios. Subsequent fractionation experiments suggested that the *primary* action of the two active principles were *neuralization* and *mesodermalization,* respectively. In 1953, Toivonen managed to find an almost pure mesodermalizing heterotypic inductor, the guinea pig bone marrow.

The first direct demonstration of an interaction between two inductive principles came from experiments in which two heterotypic inductors with different actions were combined and tested on gastrula ectoderm. The result from the combination of a pure neuralizing inductor and an almost pure mesodermalizing inductor was a new type of induction rather than a simple summation of their individual effects. The new induction corresponded to the classical "deuterencephalic" type resulting in the development of hindbrain structures and their derivatives not obtainable with the two inductors when tested separately (Toivonen and Saxén, 1955). Further evidence was found to support the conclusion of a combined action from a "reverse" experiment by

Tiedemann *et al.* (1963). They showed that a deuterencephalic-inducing fraction from chick embryos could be chromatographically separated into two components, an archencephalic (neuralizing) fraction and a spinocaudal fraction from which a purely mesodermalizing component could further be purified.

The demonstration of a combined action of the two inductors led Toivonen and Saxén in 1955 to formulate a "two-gradient" hypothesis (Toivonen and Saxén, 1955). The hypothesis suggested two concentration gradients, a mediolateral gradient of the neuralizing factor and a caudocranial gradient of the mesodermalizing principle. The Lehmann hypothesis could now be rephrased as follows:

Neuralizing factor   → forebrain
Neuralizing factor + weak mesodermalizing effect → hindbrain
Neuralizing factor + strong mesodermalizing effect → spinal cord
Mesodermalizing factor   → mesodermal derivatives

To test the two-gradient hypothesis a series of experiments was performed in the period 1960–1967. Since the two inductors were not available in pure form, all experiments had to be done with heterotypic tissues expressing different inductive actions that closely mimicked the "neuralizing" and "mesodermalizing" effects. In the first series of experiments HeLa cells were used as inductors. They are strong spinocaudal-mesodermalizing inductors and lose their mesodermalizing action after short-term heat treatment showing thereafter only a neuralizing effect. Treated and untreated cells were mixed in different ratios and tested on isolated gastrula ectoderm (Saxén and Toivonen, 1961). The results (Fig. 2A) show that the whole array of CNS regions could be induced with the different mixtures. When increasing amounts of untreated cells were added to the heated ones, a gradual caudalization of the secondary CNS structures was observed. The action of these mixtures closely resembled the inductive action of the natural inductor in its various territories (Fig. 2B).

Subsequent experiments showed that the primary neuralization of the presumptive neuroectoderm and its segregation into various regions of the CNS are sequential events. An ectoderm first exposed to a pure neuralizing inductor could still be converted into hindbrain and spinal cord structures after 24 hours when combined with mesodermalized cells (Saxén *et al.*, 1964). Hence, the ultimate test to prove the two-gradient hypothesis was to expose cells from the presumptive forebrain region of the neural plate to varying quantities of mesodermal cells obtained from the axial mesoderm of the same neurulae. The results (Fig. 2C) show that the presumptive forebrain cells can be con-

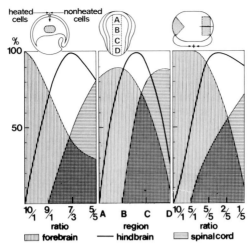

Fig. 2. Differentiation of the various regions of the CNS in three types of experiments. (A) Untreated, mesodermalizing HeLa cells and heat-treated, neuralizing cells were used as inductors after combining them in different ratios (Saxén and Toivonen, 1961). (B) Various territories of the natural inductor were used as inductors (Sala, 1955). (C) Cells from the presumptive forebrain region of the anterior neural plate were disaggregated and varying amounts of mesodermal cells from the axial mesoderm were added (Toivonen and Saxén, 1968).

verted into elements of the hindbrain and spinal cord when exposed to increased quantities of mesodermal cells (Toivonen and Saxén, 1968). The resemblance of the results to those obtained by mixed HeLa cells and by different regions of the natural inductor is striking.

In conclusion, the presumptive neuroectoderm of an early amphibian gastrula is multipotent, and it can be converted into neural, mesodermal, and endodermal derivatives. During normal development it first becomes neuralized by a stimulus from the dorsal lip mesoderm. In the second step, the neuralized cell population becomes segregated into the different parts of the CNS. This is due to an interaction with the axial mesoderm, and the action is quantitative in nature.

II. Present: Chemical Nature and Mode of Transmission of the Signal Substances

In accordance with the biological data reviewed, the first fractionation experiments on heterotypic inductors had already revealed results which clearly suggested the existence of two chemically different signal substances with different inductive actions, one neuralizing factor and another factor with a spinocaudal inductive action (Toivonen and Kuusi, 1948; Kuusi, 1951). Subsequently, a fraction with a predominantly deuterencephalic action was separated by Tiedemann (1959). Later experiments showed, however, that this action was most probably due to an interaction of a neuralizing and a mesodermalizing inductor (Tiedemann *et al.*, 1963).

Whereas most investigators seem to agree on the existence of a neuralizing factor(s), the "spinocaudal" inductor has evoked some confusion and even the terminology has not been fixed yet. Its effect on the preneuralized ectoderm resulting in the segregation of the CNS has been referred to as "transformation" by Nieuwkoop (1973); but, as this is apparently due to a secondary interaction with the mesodermalized cells, the term does not as such apply to the direct effect of the inductor. According to Yamada (1961) and the previously presented results, the primary action of the inductor would be mesodermalization of the target cells, and, hence, the term "mesodermalizing" has been widely used. However, Tiedemann (1976) prefers the term "vegetalizing" because not only mesodermal structures but also endodermal derivatives can be induced with his purified substance. High concentrations of this fraction lead to endodermal induction whereas lower concentrations or short-term exposure to the factor results in mesodermal differentiation of the target cells (Kocher-Becker and Tiedemann, 1971). Tiedemann (1976) has pointed out the possibility that his fraction may in fact consist of two chemically closely related compounds responsible for the two types of induction. Hence, we again face the classical problem of "quantitative" versus "qualitative."

A neuralizing activity has been found in practically all heterotypic tissues tested, but the signal substance is still unknown and no purified fractions with this activity have been reported. The activity remains in tissues after short-term heat treatment, but it is lost after treatment with proteolytic enzymes (cf. Saxén and Toivonen, 1962; Tiedemann, 1976, 1978). The neuralizing effect also resists digestion with RNAse (Hayashi, 1959). The vegetalizing factor has been obtained in relatively pure form from 11- to 13-day chick embryos, and in a crude form from amphibian gastrulae (Tiedemann *et al.*, 1969; Faulhaber, 1970). The final purification of the former fraction was made by isoelectric focusing and sodium dodecyl sulfate (SDS)–acrylamide electrophoresis (Geithe *et al.*, 1975). The active compound has a molecular weight of 30,000 and is inactivated by proteolytic enzymes and by heat (Tiedemann, 1976).

The localization of the factors in (or on) the cells is not known, but there is some information about their intercellular transmission. The neuralizing effect can be carried out over considerable extracellular distances in transfilter experiments where actual cell contacts are excluded by 12- to 25-μm-thick filters (Saxén, 1961; Toivonen *et al.*, 1975). Data from similar experiments with mesodermalizing (vegetalizing) inductors are still inconclusive. Minuth (1978) has reported mesodermalization of the presumptive neuroectoderm exposed to the blastoporal lip in transfilter position. However, he has not definitely excluded cell contacts mediated by cell processes in the filters. After prolonged culture, such processes have, in fact, been reported by Toivonen and Wartiovaara (1976) who used similar filters. Close apposition of the ectodermal and mesodermal cells has also been noted *in vivo* (H. Grunz, personal communication). Hence, there is the interesting possibility to be considered that the neuralizing and the mesodermalizing signal substances also differ in their mode of transmission as the former is clearly diffusible and the latter is perhaps transmitted only through cell contacts. These two transmission types have been reported in other interactive systems (Saxén *et al.*, 1976; Karkinen-Jääskeläinen, 1978).

Recent work by Tiedemann and Born (1978) suggests a third difference between the two factors. When a fraction with both neuralizing and vegetalizing actions is covalently bound to CNBr-Sepharose beads, the vegetalizing activity is lost, but the neuralizing one remains. After an enzymatic cleavage of the Sepharose matrix, the vegetalizing activity will be fully restored. A plausible explanation would be that the action of the vegetalizing factor requires its incorporation into the target cells whereas the neuralizing factor acts upon receptors of the plasma membrane.

In conclusion, primary neuralization of the competent, presumptive neuroectoderm and its subsequent regional determination are brought about by two different factors (or groups of factors). In addition to their different effects, they differ in their chemical composition, in their mode of transmission, and most probably also in their site of action. Their mode of action is still unknown.

III. Future: Toward Molecular Mechanisms

The crucial question related to neural induction still unanswered is: How does an external trigger act upon a cell with several developmental options so as to channel it into one of them? Several interesting hypotheses have been put forward in recent years, but the experimental evidence is still meager and inconclusive.

At the *tissue level*, a simple explanation would be a selection of one predetermined cell population by a permissive stimulus (Ave *et al.*, 1968). The presumptive neuroectoderm has traditionally been considered a homogeneous, uncommitted, and undifferentiated cell population with many developmental options. However, the possibility cannot be excluded that determination may already have taken place to some degree. In fact, ectoderm represents a heterogeneic cell population. Results from electrophoretic analysis (Ave et al., 1968) and direct cultivation experiments (Grunz, 1975) support this view. The former study showed several cell populations with different electrophoretic mobility, and the latter observed two types of well-differentiated epidermal cells when "uninduced" gastrula ectoderm was isolated and subcultured. For the "selection" theory, more evidence is, however, needed.

At the *cell level,* two primary sites should be considered, the intracellular compartment and the plasma membrane. In both instances, the two active factors should be examined separately. The Sepharose-binding experiments referred to already suggest that the vegetalizing factor may act in the intracellular compartment, and observations on labeled fractions of the vegetalized factor show that it becomes incorporated into the target cells (Grunz, 1975). An action directly on the cell genome has been suggested by Tiedemann et al. (1972) who showed that the action of the vegetalizing fraction on the presumptive neuroectoderm is inhibited when combined to chick or *Xenopus* DNA. The neuralizing action is not affected. The authors mention the interesting possibility that the extra DNA might compete with the DNA of the target cells, but they conclude that the hypothesis needs further evidence.

The experiment showing that the neuralizing factor was not inactivated while bound to a Sepharose matrix suggests that it may act primarily on the plasma membrane. The diffusibility of this factor is compatible with the theory suggesting an action on the membrane receptors, but experiments applying "second messengers" have yielded somewhat contradictory results. While Grunz and Tiedemann (1977) failed to find an effect when cyclic nucleotides were added to the culture media of isolated amphibian ectoderms, Wahn et al. (1976) reported neural differentiation of small ectodermal explants exposed *in vitro* to dibutyryl cAMP. Larger explants did not respond by neuralization. To explain this paradox, the authors have elaborated a rather complicated theory suggesting that restricted cell movements in the large explants prevented neural differentiation.

An action on or via the plasma membrane has also been suggested by authors working on the paradoxic effect of inorganic ions on cells from the presumptive neuroectoderm (Masui, 1961; Barth and Barth, 1968, 1972; Johnen, 1970). Both monovalent cations (Li, Na, K) and several divalent cations (Mn, Ca, Mg) act on isolated ectoderm by inducing differentiation of neural and mesodermal structures. The ultimate result is determined by the constitution of the culture medium.

The mode of action of these ions is not known, but Barth and Barth (1968, 1972) suggest that they may primarily affect the permeability of the plasma membrane, and consequently alter the intracellular ion pool. They also consider the possibility that natural induction operates through similar mechanisms.

In conclusion, the molecular mechanism of neural induction is not known. Future work must consider molecular interactions both in the intracellular compartment of the target and on its plasma membrane. Ultimately, the whole chain of events starting from the synthesis and transmission of the signal substances and ending in the initiation of differentiation should be clarified.

REFERENCES

Ave. K., Kawakami, I., and Sameshima, M. (1968). *Dev. Biol.* **17**, 617.

Barth, L. G., and Barth, L. J. (1968). *J. Embryol. Exp. Morphol.* **19**, 387.

Barth, L. G., and Barth, L. J. (1972). *Dev. Biol.* **28**, 18.

Bautzmann, H., Holtfreter, J., Spemann, H., and Mangold, O. (1932). *Naturwissenschaften* **20**, 971.

Chuang, H.-H. (1938). *Biol. Zbl.* **58**, 472.

Chuang, H.-H. (1939). *Wilhelm Roux Arch. Entwicklungsmech. Org.* **139**, 556.

Dalcq, A., and Pasteels, J. (1937). *Arch. Biol.* **48**, 669.

Dalcq, A., and Pasteels, J. (1938). *Bull. Acad. Med. Belg.* **3**, 261.

Deuchar, E. M. (1969). *J. Embryol. Exp. Morphol.* **22**, 295.

Eyal-Giladi, H. (1969). *J. Embryol. Exp. Morphol.* **21**, 177.

Faulhaber, I. (1970) *Z. Physiol. Chem.* **351**, 588.

Gallera, J., and Nicolet, G. (1969). *J. Embryol. Exp. Morphol.* **21**, 105.

Geithe, H. P., Asashima, M., Born, J., Tiedemann, H., and Tiedemann, H. (1975). *Exp. Cell. Res.* **94**, 447.

Grunz, H. (1975). *In* "New Approaches to the Evaluation of Abnormal Embryonal Development" (D. Neubert and H. Merker, eds.), pp. 792–803. George Thieme Publ., Stuttgart.

Grunz, H. (1977). *Wilhelm Roux Arch. Entwicklungsmech. Org.* **181**, 267.

Grunz, H., and Tiedemann, H. (1977). *Wilhelm Roux Arch. Entwicklungsmech. Org.* **181**, 261.

Hara, K. (1961). "Regional neural differentiation induced by prechordal and presumptive chordal mesoderm in the chick embryo." Drukkrij Libertas N.V., Utrecht.

Hayashi, Y. (1959). *Dev. Biol.* **1**, 343.

Johnen, A. G. (1970). *Wilhelm Roux Arch. Entwicklungsmech. Org.* **165**, 150.

Karkinen-Jääskeläinen, M. (1978). *Differentiation* **12**, 31.

Kocher-Becker, U., and Tiedemann, H. (1971). *Nature (London)* **233**, 65.

Kuusi, T. (1951). *Experientia* **7**, 299.

Lehmann, F. E. (1945). "Einführung in die physiologische Embryologie." Birkhäuser, Basel.

Lehmann, F. E. (1950). *Rev. Suisse Zool. Suppl.* **1**, 141.

Masui, Y. (1961). *Experientia* **17**, 458.

Minuth, W. (1978). *Med. Biol.* **56**, 349.

Nakamura, O. (1969). *Ann. Embryol. Morphog. Suppl.* **1**, 261.

Nieuwkoop, P. (1973). *Adv. Morphog.* **10**, 1.

Sala, M. (1955). *Proc. Acad. Sci. Amst. C* **55**, 635.

Saxén, L. (1961). *Dev. Biol.* **3**, 140.

Saxén, L., and Toivonen, S. (1961). *J. Embryol. Exp. Morphol.* **9**, 514.

Saxén, L., and Toivonen, S. (1962). "Primary Embryonic Induction." Academic Press, New York.

Saxén, L., Toivonen, S., and Vainio, T. (1964). *J. Embryol. Exp. Morphol.* **12**, 333.

Saxén, L., Lehtonen, E., Karkinen-Jääskeläinen, M., Nordling, S., and Wartiovaara, J. (1976). *Nature (London)* **259**, 662.

Škreb, N., Švajger, A., and Levak-Švajger, B. (1976). *In* "Embryogenesis in Mammals," Ciba Foundation Symposium 40, pp. 27–38. Elsevier, Amsterdam.

Spemann, H. (1916). *S. B. Ges Naturf. Fr. Berlin* (9) p. 306.

Spemann, H. (1918). *Wilhelm Roux Arch. Entwicklungsmech. Org.* **43**, 448.

Spemann, H. (1927). *Naturwissenschaften* **15**, 946.

Spemann, H., and Mangold, H. (1924). *Wilhelm Roux Arch. Entwicklungsmech. Org.* **100**, 599.

Tiedemann, H. (1959). *Naturwissenschaften* **46**, 616.

Tiedemann, H. (1976). *J. Embryol. Exp. Morphol.* **35**, 437.

Tiedemann, H. (1978). *In* "Organizer" (O. Nakamura and S. Toivonen, eds.), pp. 91–117. North Holland Publ., Amsterdam.

Tiedemann, H., and Born, J. (1978). *Wilhelm Roux Arch. Entwicklungsmech. Org.* **184**, 285.

Tiedemann, H., Becker, U., and Tiedemann, H. (1963). *Biochim. Biophys. Acta* **74**, 557.

Tiedemann, H., Tiedemann, H., Born, J., and Kocher-Becker, U. (1969). *Wilhelm Roux Arch. Entwicklungsmech. Org.* **163**, 316.

Tiedemann, H., Born, J., and Tiedemann, H. (1972). *Wilhelm Roux Arch. Entwicklungsmech. Org.* **163**, 316.

Toivonen, S. (1938). *Ann. Soc. Zool. Bot. Fenn. Vanamo* **6**(5), 1.

Toivonen, S. (1940). *Ann. Acad. Sci. Fenn., Ser A IV,* **55**(6), 1.

Toivonen, S. (1953). *J. Embryol. Exp. Morphol.* **1**, 97.

Toivonen, S., and Kuusi, T. (1948). *Ann. Soc. Zool. Bot. Fenn. Vanamo* **13**(3), 1.

Toivonen, S., and Saxén, L. (1955). *Exp. Cell Res. Suppl.* **3**, 346.

Toivonen, S., and Saxén, L. (1968). *Science* **159**, 539.

Toivonen, S., and Wartiovaara, J. (1976). *Differentiation* **5**, 49.

Toivonen, S., Tarin, D., Saxén, L., Tarin, P. J., and Wartiovaara, J. (1975). *Differentiation* **4**, 1.

Wahn, H., Lightbody, L. T., Tchen, T. T., and Taylor, J. D. (1976). *J. Exp. Zool.* **196**, 125.

Yamada, T. (1961). *Adv. Morphog.* **1**, 1.

INDEX

A

Adrenergic neurons
  differentiation from neural crest, 15–21
  neurotransmitter modulation in, 31, 36
β-Adrenoreceptors, in cerebellum, 47–48
Afferent fibers
  of dentate gyrus, 109–114
    development, 130–139
    distribution, 160–169
  in Purkinje dendrite growth, 85–91
Associational afferents, of dentate gyrus, 135–136
Axons
  of dentate gyrus, development, 163
  dendritic growth and, 71–74
  development of, in brain, 399–404

B

Benzodiazepine receptors, in cerebellum, 49–80
Brain
  early organization of, 373–407
  fiber tract development in, 399–404
  radial structure in parts of, 392–399
  spatial pattern of parts of, 376–392

C

Carbohydrates, of neuron surface, 52–54
Cell migration, neural crest and, 1–25
Central nervous system, early organization of, 373–407
Cerebellum
  development of, in rat, 79–85
    partially agranular, 87–89
  mutants involving, 42–45
Choroid, of Xenopus eye, 264–273
Climbing fibers, in Purkinje dendrite growth, 89–90
Clonal analysis
  cell tracking and, 223–229
  in Xenopus eye studies, 220–223

Clonal culture, of neural crest cells, 7–8
Commissural afferents, to dentate gyrus, 131–135
Compound eye, of Drosophila, see Drosophila compound eye
Cones, of dendrites, 68–71
Cyclic nucleotides, in cerebellum, 50–52

D

Daphnia, developing visual system of, 324–334
Dendrites
  axon interaction with, 71–74
  cones and filopodia of, 68–71
  growth of factors controlling, 85–94
    metrical analysis, 75
    neuronal form and, 67–101
    in Purkinje cells, 77–91
    topological analysis, 75–76
  mature, remodeling of, 93–95
Dentate gyrus
  afferent connections of, 102–114
    cellular mechanisms for, 167–169
    development, 130–139
    distribution, 160–169
  cell migration in, 121–123
  cell numbers of, 104–109
  development of, 103–157
  efferent fibers of, 114–115
  granule cells of, 115–130
  morphology of, 104–115
  synaptogenesis in, 139–145
    regulation, 169–171
Drosophila
  genetic mosaics of, 323
  homeotic mutations in, 336–343
Drosophila compound eye
  cell lineages of, 358–363
  development of, 347–371
  embryonic and larval development of, 350–353
  mitosis in, 353–358

419

morphology of, 349–350
mutant analysis of, 334–336, 363–369
optic lobe interaction with, 332–336

E

Efferent fibers, of dentate gyrus, 114
Embryos
limb innervation in, 197–200
retinotectal patterning in, 278–285
Embryonic regulation
in neural primordia, 378–391
in retina, 279–291, 297–300
Entorhinal afferents
to dentate gyrus, 109
development, 135–136
Eye, of *Xenopus,* growth patterns and
polyclones in, 217–317

F

Fiber tracts, in developing brain, 399–404
Filopodia, of dendrites, 68–71

G

GABA receptors, in cerebellum, 48–49
Genetics, of invertebrate neurogenesis,
319–345
Genetic mosaics
in *Drosophila,* 323, 332–335, 356–369
strategies of, 220–239, 323
in *Xenopus* visual system, 245–273
Granule cells
of dentate gyrus, 115–130
development, 145–152
migration, 121–123
origin, 115–121
process growth, 123–130

H

Hippocampal afferents, to dentate gyrus,
109–110
Hippocampus
maturation of, 159–180
inhibitory factors, 173–175
later stages, 171–178
self-recognition processes, 175–177

"stop" signals, 177–178
synaptogenesis in, 159–180
timing and fiber composition, 145–
152, 161–163
Homeotic mutants
of *Drosophila,* 336–343
sensory nerve projections in, 336–342
Hypothalamic afferents, to dentate gyrus,
111–112

I

Innervation, of developing limbs, 181–
215
Iris, of *Xenopus* eye, 264–273
Isogenic organisms
neurogenesis in, 321–322
phenotype constancy, 324–332
strategies for use of, 321

L

Lateral motor column, development of,
189–194
Lectins, as probes in developing cerebellum, 52–54
Limbs
innervation of
development, 194–200
experimental manipulation, 200–
209
mechanisms, 209–212
motoneuron histogenesis and, 181–
215
supernumerary, experimental innervation studies on, 203–207

M

Melanocytes
differentiation of
in frog eye, 245–269
from neural crest, 12–21
Monoaminergic fibers
to dentate gyrus, 113
in Purkinje dendrite growth, 90–91
Motoneurons
cell death in, 192–194
histogenesis in, 181–215

production of, 190
of spine, 182–189
Mouse, neurological mutants in, 41–65
Mutants
    homeotic, neurogenesis studies on,
        323–324
    neurological, in mouse, 41–65
    single-gene, in neurogenesis studies,
        322

N

Neural crest, 1–25
    clonal culture of, 7–8
    differentiation of, 15–21, 29–31
    migration of, 1–25, 29–31
        control, 4–15
        normal routes, 3
    phenotype of, 28–29
Neural induction, 409–418
    molecular mechanisms in, 413–417
    neuralizing and mesodermalizing prin-
        ciples in, 411–413
Neural plate
    field phenomena in, 378–380
        theories, 385–392
    regional organization of, 376–385
    shape change in, 380–385
Neural retina, of Xenopus eye, 264–273
Neurogenesis
    branching patterns in, 328–329
    invertebrate, genetic approaches to,
        319–345
    neuron variability in, 325–328
    synaptic connectivity in, 329–332
    sensory nerve projections in, 336–342
Neuromuscular connections
    development of, 194–199
    mechanisms underlying, 200–208
Neurons
    components of types of, 53–61
    form of, control, 67–101
Neurotransmitters
    specificity of
        in cerebellum, 45–52
        developmental changes, 33–36
        in neural crest, 31–36
        regulation, 36–38
Nervous recessive autosomal mutation, of
    cerebellum, 43

O

Optic lobes, interaction with Drosophila
    eye, 332–336
Oxford nucleolar marker, use in eye
    growth studies, 230

P

P$_{400}$ protein, in Purkinje cell, 59–61
Parallel fibers, role in Purkinje dendrite
    growth, 85
Periodic albinism mutation, use in eye
    growth studies, 230
Pigment retinal epithelium
    of Xenopus
        as clone organization model, 262–264
        polyclone patterns in, 245–265
Pole-grafts, retinotectal patterns after,
    291–300
Polyclones
    compartments and, 225–227, 347–363,
        390–392
    in half-eye mosaics, 246–251
    irregularities in boundaries of, 259–262
    retinotectal patterns and, 285–291
    in Xenopus eye, 245–265
Purkinje cells
    dendritic growth in, 77–91
        control, 85–91
    immunological studies on, 54–59
    mutation involving degeneration of, 43

R

Reeler mutation, effects on cerebellum,
    44–45
Retinotectal patterns
    of Xenopus eye, 273–300
        development, 244–245, 285–299,
            402–404
        neuronal specificity, 274, 277–278,
            281–285, 402–404
        after pole-grafts, 291–300
        regeneration, 273–278

S

Sensory nerves, projection formation in
    homeotic mutants, 336–342

Septal afferents, to dentate gyrus, 113
Spine
  motoneurons of, 182–189
  segments
    experimental deletion, 207–209
    regional differentiation, 189–190
Sprouting, as a residual developmental
    process, 177–178
Staggerer mutation
  effects on cerebellum, 43–44
    dendrite growth, 85–86
Stratum granulosum, formation of, 121–
    123
Synaptogenesis
  in dentate gyrus, 139–145
  in hippocampus, 159–180
  in invertebrates, 329–332

W

Weaver mutation
  effects on cerebellum, 43
    dendrite growth, 85

X

Xenopus eye
  cell marking in, 229–239
  development of, 239–245
  growth of, 217–317
  iris, choroid, and neural retina of, 264–
    273
  pole-grafts of, 251–259
  polyclone patterns in, 245–265
  supernumerary tissue in, 302–306

CONTENTS OF PREVIOUS VOLUMES

Volume 1

Remarks
Joshua Lederberg
On "Masked" Forms of Messenger RNA in Early Embryogenesis and in Other Differentiating Systems
A. S. Spirin
The Transcription of Genetic Information in the Spiralian Embryo
J. R. Collier
Some Genetic and Biochemical Aspects of the Regulatory Program for Slime Mold Development
Maurice Sussman
The Molecular Basis of Differentiation in Early Development of Amphibian Embryos
H. Tiedemann
The Culture of Free Plant Cells and Its Significance for Embryology and Morphogenesis
F. C. Steward, Ann E. Kent, and Marion O. Mapes
Genetic and Variegation Mosaics in the Eye of *Drosophila*
Hans Joachim Becker
Biochemical Control of Erythroid Cell Development
Eugene Goldwasser
Development of Mammalian Erythroid Cells
Paul A. Marks and John S. Kovach

Genetic Aspects of Skin and Limb Development
P. F. Goetinck
Author Index—Subject Index

Volume 2

The Control of Protein Synthesis in Embryonic Development and Differentiation
Paul R. Gross
The Genes for Ribosomal RNA and Their Transaction during Amphibian Development
Donald D. Brown
Ribosome and Enzyme Changes during Maturation and Germination of Castor Bean Seed
Erasmo Marrè
Contact and Short-Range Interaction Affecting Growth of Animal Cells in Culture
Michael Stoker
An Analysis of the Mechanism of Neoplastic Cell Transformation by Polyoma Virus, Hydrocarbons, and X-Irradiation
Leo Sachs
Differentiation of Connective Tissues
Frank K. Thorp and Albert Dorfman
The IgA Antibody System
Mary Ann South, Max D. Cooper, Richard Hong, and Robert A. Good
Teratocarcinoma: Model for a Developmental Concept of Cancer
G. Barry Pierce

Cellular and Subcellular Events in Wolffian Lens Regeneration
  Tuneo Yamada
Author Index—Subject Index

Volume 3

Synthesis of Macromolecules and Morphogenesis in *Acetabularia*
  J. Brachet
Biochemical Studies of Male Gametogenesis in Liliaceous Plants
  Herbert Stern and Yasuo Hotta
Specific Interactions between Tissues during Organogenesis
  Etienne Wolff
Low-Resistance Junctions between Cells in Embryos and Tissue Culture
  Edwin J. Furshpan and David D. Potter
Computer Analysis of Cellular Interactions
  F. Heinmets
Cell Aggregation and Differentiation in *Dictyostelium*
  Günther Gerisch
Hormone-Dependent Differentiation of Mammary Gland *in Vitro*
  Roger W. Turkington
Author Index—Subject Index

Volume 4

Genetics and Genesis
  Clifford Grobstein
The Outgrowing Bacterial Endospore
  Alex Keynan
Cellular Aspects of Muscle Differentiation *in Vitro*
  David Yaffe
Macromolecular Biosynthesis in Animal Cells Infected with Cytolytic Viruses
  Bernard Roizman and Patricia G. Spear
The Role of Thyroid and Growth Hormones in Neurogenesis
  Max Hamburgh
Interrelationships of Nuclear and Cytoplasmic Estrogen Receptors
  Jack Gorski, G. Shyamala, and D. Toft

The Biological Significance of Turnover of the Surface Membrane of Animal Cells
  Leonard Warren
Author Index—Subject Index

Volume 5

Developmental Biology and Genetics: A Plea for Cooperation
  Alberto Monroy
Regulatory Processes in the Maturation and Early Cleavage of Amphibian Eggs
  L. D. Smith and R. E. Ecker
On the Long-Term Control of Nuclear Activity during Cell Differentiation
  J. B. Gurdon and H. R. Woodland
The Integrity of the Reproductive Cell Line in the Amphibia
  Antonie W. Blackler
Regulation of Pollen Tube Growth
  Hansferdinand Linskens and Marianne Kroh
Problems of Differentiation in the Vertebrate Lens
  Ruth M. Clayton
Reconstruction of Muscle Development as a Sequence of Macro-Molecular Synthesis
  Heinz Herrmann, Stuart M. Heywood, and Ann C. Marchok
The Synthesis and Assembly of Myofibrils in Embryogenic Muscle
  Donald A. Fischman
The T-Locus of the Mouse: Implications for Mechanisms of Development
  Salome Gluecksohn-Waelsch and Robert P. Erickson
DNA Masking in Mammalian Chromatin: A Molecular Mechanism for Determination of Cell Type
  J. Paul
Author Index—Subject Index

Volume 6

The Induction and Early Events of Germination in the Zoospore of *Blastocladiella emersonii*
  Louis C. Truesdell and Edward C. Cantino

Steps of Realization of Genetic Information in Early Development
  A. A. Neyjakh
Protein Synthesis during Amphibian Metamorphosis
  J. R. Tata
Hormonal Control of a Secretory Tissue
  H. Yomo and J. E. Varner
Gene Regulation Networks: A Theory for Their Global Structure and Behaviors
  Stuart Kauffman
Positional Information and Pattern Formation
  Lewis Wolpert
Author Index—Subject Index

Volume 7

The Structure of Transcriptional Units in Eukaryotic Cells
  G. P. Georgiev
Regulation of Sporulation in Yeast
  James E. Haber and Harlyn O. Halvorson
Sporulation of Bacilli, a Model of Cellular Differentiation
  Ernst Freese
The Cocoonase Zymogen Cells of Silk Moths: A Model of Terminal Cell Differentiation for Specific Protein Synthesis
  Fotis C. Kafatos
Cell Coupling in Developing Systems: The Heart-Cell Paradigm
  Robert L. DeHaan and Howard G. Sachs
The Cell Cycle, Cell Lineages, and Cell Differentiation
  H. Holtzer, H. Weintraub, R. Mayne, and B. Mochan
Studies on the Development of Immunity: The Response to Sheep Red Blood Cells
  Robert Auerbach
Author Index—Subject Index

Volume 8: Gene Activity and Communication in Differentiating Cell Populations

Reception of Immunogenic Signals by Lymphocytes
  Michael Feldman and Amiela Globerson

Determination and Pattern Formation in the Imaginal Discs of *Drosophila*
  Peter J. Bryant
Studies on the Control of Differentiation of Murine Virus-Induced Erythroleukemic Cells
  Charlotte Friend, Harvey D. Preisler, and William Scher
Concepts and Mechanisms of Cartilage Differentiation
  Daniel Levitt and Albert Dorfman
Cell Determination and Biochemical Differentiation of the Early Mammalian Embryo
  M. C. Herbert and C. F. Graham
Differential Gene Activity in the Pre- and Postimplantation Mammalian Embryo
  Robert B. Church and Gilbert A. Schultz
Neuronal Specificity Revisited
  R. K. Hunt and Marcus Jacobson
Subject Index

Volume 9: Experimental Systems for Analysis of Multicellular Organization

Histones, Chromatin Structure, and Control of Cell Division
  E. M. Bradbury
Control of Gene Expression during the Terminal Differentiation of Erythroid Cells
  A. Fantoni, M. Lunadei, and E. Ullu
Changing Populations of Reiterated DNA Transcripts during Early Echinoderm Development
  H. R. Whiteley and A. H. Whiteley
Regulation of Messenger RNA Translation during Insect Development
  Joseph Ilan and Judith Ilan
Chemical and Structural Changes within Chick Erythrocyte Nuclei Introduced into Mammalian Cells by Cell Fusion
  R. Appels and Nils R. Ringertz
Drosophila Antigens: Their Spatial and Temporal Distribution, Their Function and Control
  David B. Roberts
Subject Index

Volume 10: Experimental Systems for Analysis of Multicellular Organization

Experiments with Junctions of the Adhaerens Type
Jane Overton
The Extracellular Matrix: A Dynamic Component of the Developing Embryo
Francis J. Manasek
The Role of the Golgi Complex during Spermiogenesis
Baccio Baccetti
Phenomena of Cellular Recognition in Sponges
G. Van de Vyver
Freshwater Sponges as a Material for the Study of Cell Differentiation
R. Rasmont
Differentiation of the Golgi Apparatus in the Genetic Control of Development
W. G. Whaley, Marianne Dauwalder, and T. P. Leffingwell
Subject Index

Volume 11: Pattern Development

Interactions of Lectins with Embryonic Cell Surfaces
Steven B. Oppenheimer
Biological Features and Physical Concepts of Pattern Formation Exemplified by Hydra
Alfred Gierer
Molecular Aspects of Myogenesis
John Paul Merlie, Margaret E. Buckingham, and Robert G. Whalen
Origin and Establishment of Embryonic Polar Axes in Amphibian Development
P. D. Nieuwkoop
An Old Engine: The Gray Crescent of Amphibian Eggs
J. Brachet
Control of Plant Cell Enlargement by Hydrogen Ions
David L. Rayle and Robert Cleland
Subject Index

Volume 12: Fertilization

Patterns in Metazoan Fertilization
C. R. Austin
Biochemistry of Male Germ Cell Differentiation in Mammals: RNA Synthesis in Meiotic and Postmeiotic Cells
V. Monesi, R. Geremia, A. D'Agostino, and C. Boitani
Cell Communication, Cell Union, and Initiation of Meiosis in Ciliate Conjugation
Akio Miyake
Sperm–Egg Association in Mammals
R. Yanagimachi
Sperm and Egg Receptors Involved in Fertilization
Charles B. Metz
Transformations of Sperm Nuclei upon Insemination
Frank J. Longo and Mel Kunkle
Mechanisms of Activation of Sperm and Egg during Fertilization of Sea Urchin Gametes
David Epel
Subject Index

Volume 13: Immunological Approaches to Embryonic Development and Differentiation, Part I

Cell Surface Antigens during Mammalian Spermatogenesis
Clarke F. Millette
Immunoperoxidase Localization of Bindin during the Adhesion of Sperm to Sea Urchin Eggs
Gary W. Moy and Victor D. Vacquier
Cell Surface Differentiations during Early Embryonic Development
Alberto Monroy and Floriana Rosati
Immunofluorescent Analysis of Chromatin Structure in Relation to Gene Activity: A Speculative Essay
Lee M. Silver and Sarah C. R. Elgin
Immunogenetics of Mammalian Cell Surface Macromolecules
Carol Jones and Theodore T. Puck

Cell Surface and Early Stages of Mouse Embryogenesis
François Jacob
Developmental Stage-Specific Antigens during Mouse Embryogenesis
Davor Solter and Barbara B. Knowles
Early Embryonic Cell Surface Antigens as Developmental Probes
Lynn M. Wiley
Surface Antigens Involved in Interactions of Embryonic Sea Urchin Cells
David R. McClay
Cell Surface Antigens of Cultured Neuronal Cells
Richard Akeson
Cell Type-Specific Antigens of Cells of the Central and Peripheral Nervous System
Kay L. Fields
Cell Surface Antigens of the Nervous System
Melitta Schachner
Antibody Effects on Membrane Antigen Expression
Edward P. Cohen and Weitze Liang
Topographic Display of Cell Surface Components and Their Role in Transmembrane Signaling
Garth L. Nicolson
Subject Index

Volume 14: Immunological Approaches to Embryonic Development and Differentiation, Part II

The Use of Monoclonal Antibody Techniques in the Study of Developing Cell Surfaces
C. Milstein and E. Lennox
Early Stages of Lymphocyte Development
Irving Goldschneider
Somatic Cell Genetics and the Development of the Immune System
Peter D'Eustachio and Frank H. Ruddle
Complete Primary Structure of Human Histocompatibility Antigen HLA-B7: Evolutionary and Functional Implications
Jack L. Strominger, Victor H. Engelhard, Braydon C. Guild, Thomas G. Kostyk, Doron Lancet, Jose A. Lopez de Castro, Harry T. Orr, Peter Parham, Hidde L. Ploegh, and Jordan S. Pober
Aspects of Surface Membrane Differentiation during Maturation of Human Hematopoietic and Tumor Cells: The Ia System
R. J. Winchester
The ABH Blood Groups and Development
Aron E. Szulman
Cell-Mediated Immune Responses to Mouse Embryonic Cells: Detection and Characterization of Embryonic Antigens
Suzanne Ostrand-Rosenberg
Immunological Methods in the Study of Chondroitin Sulfate Proteoglycans
Albert Dorfman, Barbara M. Vertel, and Nancy B. Schwartz
Immunological Studies on Collagen Type Transition in Chondrogenesis
Klaus von der Mark
The Application of Labeled Lectins and Antibodies to SDS Gels and Their Use in Studying Glycoproteins and Cell Surface Antigens during Development
Keith Burridge and Lois Jordan
Univalent Antibody Fragments as Tools for the Analysis of Cell Interactions in *Dictyostelium*
Günther Gerisch
Techniques for Localizing Contractile Proteins with Fluorescent Antibodies
Keigi Fujiwara and Thomas D. Pollard
Antiserum to Myosin and Its Use in Studying Myosin Synthesis and Accumulation during Myogenesis
Richard C. Strohman, Paul S. Moss, and Julie Micou-Eastwood
Immunological Approaches to the Study of Myogenesis and Lens Fiber Junction Formation
Martin Friedlander
Immunology and Developmental Biology: Summary and Concluding Remarks
Elizabeth D. Hay
Subject Index